My Country

AUSTRALIAN

Poetry & Short Stories

TWO HUNDRED YEARS

Volume 2
1930s – 1980s

Leonie Kramer

My Country

AUSTRALIAN

Poetry & Short Stories

TWO HUNDRED YEARS

Volume 2
1930s – 1980s

Selected and with an Introduction by
Leonie Kramer

URE SMITH PRESS

Front cover:

Russell Drysdale *Moody's Pub* 1941
Oil on wood panel 50.8 x 61.6 cm
National Gallery of Victoria

Back cover:

Roland Wakelin *Black Mountain, Canberra* 1944
Oil on cardboard panel 59.5 x 68.5 cm
National Gallery of Victoria

Published by Ure Smith Press
an imprint of Weldon International
372 Eastern Valley Way, Willoughby, NSW 2068, Australia

First published by Lansdowne Press 1985
Reprinted by Ure Smith Press 1991

© Copyright introduction and this collection: Leonie Kramer 1985
© Copyright design: Kevin Weldon & Associates Pty Limited

Typeset in Australia by Savage Type Pty Ltd, Brisbane
Printed in Australia by Griffin Press

National Library of Australia Cataloguing-in-Publication data

My country: Australian poetry and short stories:
  two hundred years.

  Includes indexes.
  ISBN 0 7254 0857 X (set).
  ISBN 0 7254 0858 8 (v. 1).
  ISBN 0 7254 0859 6 (v. 2).

  1. Australian poetry. 2. Short stories, Australian.
  I. Kramer, Leonie, 1924-   .

A821.008

Contents

CONTENTS

Introduction

This volume begins with the poetry of Kenneth Slessor, who firmly establishes the voice of the city in Australian writing. Blamire Young's painting of the same period dramatically portrays the old world of bush life, and the rising new city. Earlier, Victor Daley had written of the convivial pleasures of city life, while Shaw Neilson saw the city as Stony Town, inimical and joyless. Slessor celebrates the liveliness and beauty of the landscape of Sydney and its harbour in a way which makes one see them in a new light. Yet beneath the sharpness and dazzle of his imagery is a persistent sense of isolation. For him windows do not provide access to the world outside, but prevent it. He looks out but feels nothing for the figures he sees; or inwards at the warmth and enjoyment of others from which he is excluded. Slessor's is a modern voice expressing a strong sense of personal loneliness, and a search for the meaning of life which is unrewarded by any positive revelation. His voyage of discovery ends in a resigned acceptance of the limits to human understanding.

Writers and painters are like explorers, in that they bring to light observations, new impressions, and ideas, and produce individual maps of the terrain they traverse. Their perceptions are shaped by the places and times in which they live, and by their knowledge of the tracks their predecessors have travelled. So they look to the past, as well as at the world around them, when they create works of imagination.

Through much of the writing and painting of the last fifty years the past continues to speak. Writers and painters look back to earlier years, sometimes with nostalgia, sometimes critically, and frequently in an attempt to explain and interpret their attitudes to and feelings about their country. Some acknowledge quite directly a debt to their predecessors. James McAuley offers a tribute to Shaw Neilson; in *Two Gums* John Perceval pays homage to Buvelot; David Campbell revives the bush ballad, and Les Murray the Aboriginal song-cycle. Brennan's influence can be detected in poets as different as A. D. Hope, R. D. FitzGerald and Judith Wright; and Lawson continues to be a point of reference for short story writers.

It is curious, in a way, that while in the first one hundred and fifty years one has a sense of an energetic drive towards the future, a desire to consolidate the gains and to build a vigorous and progressive nation, in the modern period there seems to be an attempt to recover the past and to reflect on its meaning for the Australia of the present. History is the impulse behind much of the writing of the period. Judith Wright and Roland Robinson recall the vanished life of the Aborigines, as did Mary Gilmore earlier in the century. Wright also reflects on her family history, as do David Malouf, Vincent Buckley and David Campbell. But perhaps most significant is the attempt to find in one's own personal history a way of defining what it is to be Australian.

In many works of the last fifty years, such as Frank Dalby Davison's *The Road to Yesterday*, John Manifold's poems, Vincent Buckley's autobiographical poems, Dorothy Hewett's revival of the ballad tradition, R. D. FitzGerald's voyages of discovery and the convict past, and Les Murray's reference to the Aboriginal song-cycle in "The Buladelah-Taree Holiday Song Cycle", the past becomes a way of explaining the present. Hal Porter's immensely detailed recollection of the places, habits, customs and domestic life of the first half of the century epitomises the modern writer's passion for the past, which is not "mere history", or a museum full of inert objects of by-gone days. It is an active memory, shaping attitudes and opinions, and providing elusive clues as to how Australian experience might be defined.

Slessor expresses some of the attitudes and sensations that characterise modern life. Porter, on the other hand, recovers the distant, but not lost world of childhood, youth and maturity, in order to elucidate his own experience as a modern Australian travelling the world and meeting a whole variety of people. But more often than not, his subject is himself. Who is he? What elements of his parents have been handed on to him? What did life in an Australian country town in the 1920s give to him? Even when he writes about characters such as Brett, or Mrs Brewer, his own personality can be sensed through his pointed, rich and ornamental style. Yet though one catches glimpses of his opinions, of his likes and dislikes, he remains an elusive observer, ever-present, yet always ready to slip away.

In this last fifty years the novel has been much more important than it was in the 19th century. Some writers, such as Martin Boyd, Patrick White, and Randolph Stow may therefore appear in this anthology slighter than in fact they are; and some, such as Thomas Keneally, cannot be represented at all. But the anthology does not exaggerate the great importance of poetry. There are at least six or seven poets of the period whose careers span forty years or more, and who have mapped the features of Australian landscape and experience as fully and accurately as any geographer could map its physical contours.

Here, as in the first one hundred and fifty years, readers will notice some strong resemblances between writers and painters. Sidney Nolan and Randolph Stow share a vision of "the land's meaning". John Perceval's close-ups of the detail of the bush are akin to Douglas Stewart's small lyrics about native plants, or to James McAuley's "Bush Scene". Painting in the period reflects modernist movements much more strongly than does the poetry; abstract, expressionist and surrealist forms comment more cryptically and obliquely on Australian life than do the representational or impressionist paintings of the early period. Robert Dickerson's stark geometrical portraits and Brett Whiteley's surprising juxtapositions of images, challenge traditional ways of seeing people and landscape. But throughout the paintings there is a sense of a tradition acknowledged, even while it is being refreshed and extended in the light of contemporary experience.

It would be wrong to give the impression that Australian writers have turned their back on the modern world. They might not have been as daringly experimental as their European and American contemporaries, but they have been sensitive to the changes in ideas and style which characterise modern movements. Writers' interest in the illumination of the present by the past, and of the indigenous by the foreign, creates an Australian species of modernism. Observations and perceptions which build up a rich store of experience in the first one hundred and fifty years, are, in the modern period, reinterpreted and evolve into legend. Ned Kelly becomes something of a national hero, and he and the human figures of explorers are larger than life in the paintings of Sidney Nolan. Fact turns into fiction, and observation into metaphor. Thus, for the modern writer, the actual exploration of the country can be a metaphor for an imaginative exploration of personal identity.

There is no way of summarising the diversity and richness of the last fifty years without distortion. But certain preoccupations recur, and the landscape continues to dominate the imagination of painters and writers. What, in the 19th century, were mixed feelings of wonder at the new country and nostalgia for the old, increasingly become curiously ambivalent feelings towards Australia. Its unique beauties are compelling even when it appears either indifferent or hostile to man's endeavour. It seems to offer a distinctive experience, yet relies heavily on its traditional affiliations. Most of all, perhaps, it appears to shape the mind and imagination in ways which can be sensed, but not analysed. Hence, many of the poets express a feeling of communion with the land which goes beyond a simple appreciation of nature.

In the last thirty years the composition of the Australian population has changed radically. It is more difficult than ever to try to identify the qualities that define what it is to be Australian, and there continues to be debate about this question. But one cannot read nearly two hundred years of literature and view the paintings of the period without discovering that there is continuity of experience, mysterious though its character might be.

Some writers and artists of the modern period clearly identify themselves strongly with an older Australian tradition, and Aborigines, in particular, use modern techniques to recover their old traditions; some have assimilated foreign experience into their work. All have profited, whether they acknowledge it or not, from the work of the painters, poets and storytellers of the perilous early years. The vitality of literature and painting in Australia today promises a rich future. Just as the physical labour and stamina of the pioneers made this country habitable, so the creative imagination of their counterparts in the arts gave, and continues to give, human experience "a local habitation and a name".

Leonie Kramer
Sydney, 1985

Note on the Editing

The material in the anthology is arranged chronologically, but no strict progression is implied. Sometimes, within the selection of an individual author, minor chronological adjustments have been made for aesthetic reasons, and there is obviously some overlap between individual authors. Where the author is known to have revised work, the text of the latest revision has been used. In the texts from the early period older forms of spelling have been retained where these preserve the flavour of the original. Typographical errors have been corrected.

The works have been selected to show how writers and painters have responded to a variety of experiences and how well they have expressed their observations and impressions for a very diverse audience, here and abroad.

Kenneth
Slessor

Five Visions of Captain Cook

I

Cook was a captain of the Admiralty
When sea-captains had the evil eye,
Or should have, what with beating krakens off
And casting nativities of ships;
Cook was a captain of the powder-days
When captains, you might have said, if you had been
Fixed by their glittering stare, half-down the side,
Or gaping at them up companionways,
Were more like warlocks than a humble man —
And men were humble then who gazed at them,
Poor horn-eyed sailors, bullied by devils' fists
Of wind or water, or the want of both,
Childlike and trusting, filled with eager trust —
Cook was a captain of the sailing days
When sea-captains were kings like this,
Not cold executives of company-rules
Cracking their boilers for a dividend
Or bidding their engineers go wink
At bells and telegraphs, so plates would hold
Another pound. Those captains drove their ships
By their own blood, no laws of schoolbook steam,
Till yards were sprung, and masts went overboard —
Daemons in periwigs, doling magic out,
Who read fair alphabets in stars
Where humbler men found but a mess of sparks,
Who steered their crews by mysteries
And strange, half-dreadful sortilege with books,
Used medicines that only gods could know
The sense of, but sailors drank
In simple faith. That was the captain
Cook was when he came to the Coral Sea
And chose a passage into the dark.

1

How many mariners had made that choice
Paused on the brink of mystery! "Choose now!"
The winds roared, blowing home, blowing home,
Over the Coral Sea. "Choose now!" the trades
Cried once to Tasman, throwing him for choice
Their teeth or shoulders, and the Dutchman chose
The wind's way, turning north. "Choose, Bougainville!"
The wind cried once, and Bougainville had heard
The voice of God, calling him prudently
Out of a dead lee shore, and chose the north.
The wind's way. So, too, Cook made choice,
Over the brink, into the devil's mouth,
With four months' food, and sailors wild with dreams
Of English beer, the smoking barns of home.
So Cook made choice, so Cook sailed westabout,
So men write poems in Australia.

II

Flowers turned to stone! Not all the botany
Of Joseph Banks, hung pensive in a porthole,
Could find the Latin for this loveliness,
Could put the Barrier Reef in a glass box
Tagged by the horrid Gorgon squint
Of horticulture. Stone turned to flowers
It seemed — you'd snap a crystal twig,
One petal even of the water-garden,
And have it dying like a cherry-bough.

They'd sailed all day outside a coral hedge,
And half the night. Cook sailed at night,
Let there be reefs a fathom from the keel
And empty charts. The sailors didn't ask,
Nor Joseph Banks. Who cared? It was the spell
Of Cook that lulled them, bade them turn below,
Kick off their sea-boots, puff themselves to sleep,
Though there were more shoals outside
Than teeth in a shark's head. Cook snored loudest himself.

One day, a morning of light airs and calms,
They slid towards a reef that would have knifed
Their boards to mash, and murdered every man.
So close it sucked them, one wave shook their keel,
The next blew past the coral. Three officers,
In gilt and buttons, languidly on deck
Pointed their sextants at the sun. One yawned,
One held a pencil, one put eye to lens:
Three very peaceful English mariners
Taking their sights for longitude.
I've never heard
Of sailors aching for the longitude
Of shipwrecks before or since. It was the spell
Of Cook did this, the phylacteries of Cook.
Men who ride broomsticks with a mesmerist
Mock the typhoon. So, too, it was with Cook.

III

Two chronometers the captain had,
One by Arnold that ran like mad,
One by Kendal in a walnut case,
Poor devoted creature with a hangdog face.

3

Arnold always hurried with a crazed click-click
Dancing over Greenwich like a lunatic,
Kendal panted faithfully his watch-dog beat,
Climbing out of Yesterday with sticky little feet.

Arnold choked with appetite to wolf up time,
Madly round the numerals his hands would climb,
His cogs rushed over and his wheels ran miles,
Dragging Captain Cook to the Sandwich Isles.

But Kendal dawdled in the tombstoned past,
With a sentimental prejudice to going fast,
And he thought very often of a haberdasher's door
And a yellow-haired boy who would knock no more.

All through the night-time, clock talked to clock,
In the captain's cabin, tock-tock-tock,
One ticked fast and one ticked slow,
And Time went over them a hundred years ago.

IV

Sometimes the god would fold his wings
And, stone of Caesars turned to flesh,
Talk of the most important things
That serious-minded midshipmen could wish,

Of plantains, and the lack of rum
Or spearing sea-cows — things like this
That hungry schoolboys, five days dumb,
In jolly-boats are wonted to discuss.

What midshipman would pause to mourn
The sun that beat about his ears,
Or curse the tide, if he could horn
His fists by tugging on those lumbering oars?

Let rum-tanned mariners prefer
To hug the weather-side of yards;
"Cats to catch mice" before they purr,
Those were the captain's enigmatic words.

Here, in this jolly-boat they graced,
Were food and freedom, wind and storm,
While, fowling-piece across his waist,
Cook mapped the coast, with one eye cocked for game.

V

After the candles had gone out, and those
Who listened had gone out, and a last wave
Of chimney-haloes caked their smoky rings
Like fish-scales on the ceiling, a Yellow Sea
Of swimming circles, the old man,
Old Captain-in-the-Corner, drank his rum
With friendly gestures to four chairs. They stood
Empty, still warm from haunches, with rubbed nails
And leather glazed, like agéd serving-men
Feeding a king's delight, the sticky, drugged
Sweet agony of habitual anecdotes.
But these, his chairs, could bear an old man's tongue,
Sleep when he slept, be flattering when he woke,
And wink to hear the same eternal name
From lips new-dipped in rum.

"Then Captain Cook,
I heard him, told them they could go
If so they chose, but he would get them back,
Dead or alive, he'd have them,"
The old man screeched, half-thinking to hear "Cook!
Cook again! Cook! It's other cooks he'll need,
Cooks who can bake a dinner out of pence,
That's what he lives on, talks on, half-a-crown
A day, and sits there full of Cook.
Who'd do your cooking now, I'd like to ask,
If someone didn't grind her bones away?
But that's the truth, six children and half-a-crown
A day, and a man gone daft with Cook."

That was his wife,
Elizabeth, a noble wife but brisk,
Who lived in a present full of kitchen-fumes
And had no past. He had not seen her
For seven years, being blind, and that of course
Was why he'd had to strike a deal with chairs,
Not knowing when those who chafed them had gone to sleep
Or stolen away. Darkness and empty chairs,
This was the port that Alexander Home
Had come to with his useless cutlass-wounds
And tales of Cook, and half-a-crown a day —
This was the creek he'd run his timbers to,
Where grateful countrymen repaid his wounds

At half-a-crown a day. Too good, too good,
This eloquent offering of birdcages
To gulls, and Greenwich Hospital to Cook,
Britannia's mission to the sea-fowl.

It was not blindness picked his flesh away,
Nor want of sight made penny-blank the eyes
Of Captain Home, but that he lived like this
In one place, and gazed elsewhere. His body moved
In Scotland, but his eyes were dazzle-full
Of skies and water farther round the world —
Air soaked with blue, so thick it dripped like snow
On spice-tree boughs, and water diamond-green,
Beaches wind-glittering with crumbs of gilt,
And birds more scarlet than a duchy's seal
That had come whistling long ago, and far
Away. His body had gone back,
Here it sat drinking rum in Berwickshire,
But not his eyes — they were left floating there
Half-round the earth, blinking at beaches milked
By suck-mouth tides, foaming with ropes of bubbles
And huge half-moons of surf. Thus it had been
When Cook was carried on a sailor's back,
Vengeance in a cocked hat, to claim his price,
A prince in barter for a longboat.
And then the trumpery springs of fate — a stone,
A musket-shot, a round of gunpowder,
And puzzled animals, killing they knew not what
Or why, but killing . . . the surge of goatish flanks
Armoured in feathers, like cruel birds:
Wild, childish faces, killing; a moment seen,
Marines with crimson coats and puffs of smoke
Toppling face-down; and a knife of English iron,
Forged aboard ship, that had been changed for pigs,
Given back to Cook between the shoulder-blades.
There he had dropped, and the old floundering sea,
The old, fumbling, witless lover-enemy,
Had taken his breath, last office of salt water.

Cook died. The body of Alexander Home
Flowed round the world and back again, with eyes
Marooned already, and came to English coasts,
The vague ancestral darknesses of home,
Seeing them faintly through a glass of gold,
Dim fog-shapes, ghosted like the ribs of trees
Against his blazing waters and blue air.
But soon they faded, and there was nothing left,
Only the sugar-cane and the wild granaries
Of sand, and palm-trees and the flying blood
Of cardinal-birds; and putting out one hand
Tremulously in the direction of the beach,
He felt a chair in Scotland. And sat down.

Nuremberg

So quiet it was in that high, sun-steeped room,
So warm and still, that sometimes with the light
Through the great windows, bright with bottle-panes,
There'd float a chime from clock-jacks out of sight,
    Clapping iron mallets on green copper gongs.

But only in blown music from the town's
Quaint horologe could Time intrude . . . you'd say
Clocks had been bolted out, the flux of years
Defied, and that high chamber sealed away
    From earthly change by some old alchemist.

And, oh, those thousand towers of Nuremberg
Flowering like leaden trees outside the panes:
Those gabled roofs with smoking cowls, and those
Encrusted spires of stone, those golden vanes
    On shining housetops paved with scarlet tiles!

And all day nine wrought-pewter manticores
Blinked from their spouting faucets, not five steps
Across the cobbled street, or, peering through
The rounds of glass, espied that sun-flushed room
    With Dürer graving at intaglios.

O happy nine, spouting your dew all day
In green-scaled rows of metal, whilst the town
Moves peacefully below in quiet joy. . . .
O happy gargoyles to be gazing down
    On Albrecht Dürer and his plates of iron!

Waters

This Water, like a sky that no one uses,
Air turned to stone, ridden by stars and birds
No longer, but with clouds of crystal swimming,
I'll not forget, nor men can lose, though words
Dissolve with music, gradually dimming.
So let them die; whatever the mind loses,
Water remains, cables and bells remain,
Night comes, the sailors burn their riding-lamps,
And strangers, pitching on our graves their camps,
Will break through branches to the surf again.

Darkness comes down. The Harbour shakes its mane,
Glazed with a leaf of amber; lights appear
Like thieves too early, dropping their swag by night,
Red, gold and green, down trap-doors glassy-clear,
And lanterns over Pinchgut float with light
Where they so long have lain.
All this will last, but I who gaze must go
On water stranger and less clear, and melt
With flesh away; and stars that I have felt,
And loved, shall shine for eyes I do not know.

Crow Country

Gutted of station, noise alone,
The crow's voice trembles down the sky
As if this nitrous flange of stone
Wept suddenly with such a cry;
As if the rock found lips to sigh,
The riven earth a mouth to moan;
But we that hear them, stumbling by,
Confuse their torments with our own.

Over the huge abraded rind,
Crow-countries graped with dung, we go,
Past gullies that no longer flow
And wells that nobody can find,
Lashed by the screaming of the crow,
Stabbed by the needles of the mind.

Talbingo

"Talbingo River" — as one says of bones:
"Captain" or "Commodore" that smelt gunpowder
In old engagements no one quite believes
Or understands. Talbingo had its blood
As they did, ran with waters huge and clear
Lopping down mountains,
Turning crags to banks.

Now it's a sort of aching valley,
Basalt shaggy with scales,
A funnel of tobacco-coloured clay,
Smoulders of puffed earth
And pebbles and shell-bodied flies
And water thickening to stone in pocks.

That's what we're like out here,
Beds of dried-up passions.

Wild Grapes

The old orchard, full of smoking air,
Full of sour marsh and broken boughs, is there,
But kept no more by vanished Mulligans,
Or Hartigans, long drowned in earth themselves,
Who gave this bitter fruit their care.

Here's where the cherries grew that birds forgot,
And apples bright as dogstars; now there is not
An apple or a cherry; only grapes,
But wild ones, Isabella grapes they're called,
Small, pointed, black, like boughs of musket-shot.

Eating their flesh, half-savage with black fur,
Acid and gipsy-sweet, I thought of her,
Isabella, the dead girl, who has lingered on
Defiantly when all have gone away,
In an old orchard where swallows never stir.

Isabella grapes, outlaws of a strange bough,
That in their harsh sweetness remind me somehow
Of dark hair swinging and silver pins,
A girl half-fierce, half-melting, as these grapes,
Kissed here — or killed here — but who remembers now?

Country Towns

Country towns, with your willows and squares,
And farmers bouncing on barrel mares
To public-houses of yellow wood
With "1860" over their doors,
And that mysterious race of Hogans
Which always keeps General Stores. . . .

At the School of Arts, a broadsheet lies
Sprayed with the sarcasm of flies:
"The Great Golightly Family
Of Entertainers Here To-night" —
Dated a year and a half ago,
But left there, less from carelessness
Than from a wish to seem polite.

Verandas baked with musky sleep,
Mulberry faces dozing deep,
And dogs that lick the sunlight up
Like paste of gold — or, roused in vain
By far, mysterious buggy-wheels,
Lower their ears, and drowse again. . . .

Country towns with your schooner bees,
And locusts burnt in the pepper-trees,
Drown me with syrups, arch your boughs,
Find me a bench, and let me snore,
Till, charged with ale and unconcern,
I'll think it's noon at half-past four!

Winter Dawn

At five I wake, rise, rub on the smoking pane
A port to see — water breathing in the air,
Boughs broken. The sun comes up in a golden stain,
Floats like a glassy sea-fruit. There is mist everywhere,
White and humid, and the Harbour is like plated stone,
Dull flakes of ice. One light drips out alone,
One bead of winter-red, smouldering in the steam,
Quietly over the roof-tops — another window
Touched with a crystal fire in the sun's gullies,
One lonely star of the morning, where no stars gleam.

Far away on the rim of this great misty cup,
The sun gilds the dead suburbs as he rises up,
Diamonds the wind-cocks, makes glitter the crusted spikes
On moss-drowned gables. Now the tiles drip scarlet-wet,
Swim like birds' paving-stones, and sunlight strikes
Their watery mirrors with a moister rivulet,
Acid and cold. Here lie those mummied Kings,
Men sleeping in houses, embalmed in stony coffins,
Till the Last Trumpet calls their galleries up,
And the suburbs rise with distant murmurings.

O buried dolls, O men sleeping invisible there,
I stare above your mounds of stone, lean down,
Marooned and lonely in this bitter air,
And in one moment deny your frozen town,
Renounce your bodies — earth falls in clouds away,
Stones lose their meaning, substance is lost in clay,
Roofs fade, and that small smoking forgotten heap,
The city, dissolves to a shell of bricks and paper,
Empty, without purpose, a thing not comprehended,
A broken tomb, where ghosts unknown sleep.

And the least crystal weed, shaken with frost,
The furred herbs of silver, the daisies round-eyed and tart,
Painted in antic china, the smallest night-flower tossed
Like a bright penny on the lawn, stirs more my heart,
Strikes deeper this morning air, than mortal towers
Dried to a common blindness, fainter than flowers,
Fordone, extinguished, as the vapours break,
And dead in the dawn. O Sun that kills with life,
And brings to breath all silent things — O Dawn,
Waken me with old earth, keep me awake!

City Nightfall

Smoke upon smoke; over the stone lips
Of chimneys bleeding, a darker fume descends.
Night, the old nun, in voiceless pity bends
   To kiss corruption, so fabulous her pity.

All drowns in night. Even the lazar drowns
In earth at last, and rises up afresh,
Married to dust with an Infanta's flesh —
   So night, like earth, receives this poisoned city,

Charging its air with beauty, coasting its lanterns
With mains of darkness, till the leprous clay
Dissolves, and pavements drift away,
   And there is only the quiet noise of planets feeding.

And those who chafe here, limed on the iron twigs,
No greater seem than sparrows, all their cries,
Their clockwork and their merchandise,
   Frolic of painted dolls. I pass unheeding.

The Night-ride

Gas flaring on the yellow platform; voices running up and down;
Milk-tins in cold dented silver; half-awake I stare,
Pull up the blind, blink out — all sounds are drugged;
The slow blowing of passengers asleep;
Engines yawning; water in heavy drips;
Black, sinister travellers, lumbering up the station,
One moment in the window, hooked over bags;
Hurrying, unknown faces — boxes with strange labels —
All groping clumsily to mysterious ends,
Out of the gaslight, dragged by private Fates.
Their echoes die. The dark train shakes and plunges;
Bells cry out; the night-ride starts again.
Soon I shall look out into nothing but blackness,
Pale, windy fields. The old roar and knock of the rails
Melts in dull fury. Pull down the blind. Sleep. Sleep.
Nothing but grey, rushing rivers of bush outside.
Gaslight and milk-cans. Of Rapptown I recall nothing else.

from *The Old Play*

A bird sang in the jaws of night,
Like a star lost in space —
O, dauntless molecule to smite
With joy that giant face!

I heard you mock the lonely air,
The bitter dark, with song,
Waking again the old Despair
That had been dead so long,

That had been covered up with clay
And never talked about,
So none with bony claws could say
They'd dig my coffin out.

But you, with music clear and brave,
Have shamed the buried thing;
It rises dripping from the grave
And tries in vain to sing.

O, could the bleeding mouth reply,
The broken flesh but moan,
The tongues of skeletons would cry,
And Death push back his stone!

The Knife

The plough that marks on Harley's field
  In flying earth its print
Throws up, like death itself concealed,
  A fang of rosy flint,

A flake of stone, by fingers hewed
  Whose buried bones are gone,
All gone, with fingers, hunters, food,
  But still the knife lives on.

And well I know, when bones are nought,
  The blade of stone survives —
I, too, from clods of aching thought,
  Have turned up sharper knives.

North Country

North Country, filled with gesturing wood,
With trees that fence, like archers' volleys,
The flanks of hidden valleys
Where nothing's left to hide

But verticals and perpendiculars,
Like rain gone wooden, fixed in falling,
Or fingers blindly feeling
For what nobody cares;

Or trunks of pewter, bangled by greedy death,
Stuck with black staghorns, quietly sucking,
And trees whose boughs go seeking,
And trees like broken teeth

With smoky antlers broken in the sky;
Or trunks that lie grotesquely rigid,
Like bodies blank and wretched
After a fool's battue,

As if they've secret ways of dying here
And secret places for their anguish
When boughs at last relinquish
Their clench of blowing air —

But this gaunt country, filled with mills and saws,
With butter-works and railway-stations
And public institutions,
And scornful rumps of cows,

North Country, filled with gesturing wood —
Timber's the end it gives to branches,
Cut off in cubic inches,
Dripping red with blood.

South Country

After the whey-faced anonymity
Of river-gums and scribbly-gums and bush,
After the rubbing and the hit of brush,
You come to the South Country

As if the argument of trees were done,
The doubts and quarrelling, the plots and pains,
All ended by these clear and gliding planes
Like an abrupt solution.

And over the flat earth of empty farms
The monstrous continent of air floats back
Coloured with rotting sunlight and the black,
Bruised flesh of thunderstorms:

Air arched, enormous, pounding the bony ridge,
Ditches and hutches, with a drench of light,
So huge, from such infinities of height,
You walk on the sky's beach

While even the dwindled hills are small and bare,
As if, rebellious, buried, pitiful,
Something below pushed up a knob of skull,
Feeling its way to air.

Last Trams

I

That street washed with violet
Writes like a tablet
Of living here; that pavement
Is the metal embodiment
Of living here; those terraces
Filled with dumb presences
Lobbed over mattresses,
Lusts and repentances,
Ardours and solaces,
Passions and hatreds
And love in brass bedsteads . . .
Lost now in emptiness
Deep now in darkness
Nothing but nakedness,
Rails like a ribbon
And sickness of carbon
Dying in distances.

II

Then, from the skeletons of trams,
Gazing at lighted rooms, you'll find
The black and Röntgen diagrams
Of window-plants across the blind

That print their knuckleduster sticks,
Their buds of gum, against the light
Like negatives of candlesticks
Whose wicks are lit by fluorite;

And shapes look out, or bodies pass,
Between the darkness and the flare,
Between the curtain and the glass,
Of men and women moving there.

So through the moment's needle-eye,
Like phantoms in the window-chink,
Their faces brush you as they fly,
Fixed in the shutters of a blink;

But whose they are, intent on what,
Who knows? They rattle into void,
Stars of a film without a plot,
Snippings of idiot celluloid.

William Street

The red globes of light, the liquor-green,
The pulsing arrows and the running fire
Spilt on the stones, go deeper than a stream;
You find this ugly, I find it lovely.

Ghosts' trousers, like the dangle of hung men,
In pawnshop-windows, bumping knee by knee,
But none inside to suffer or condemn;
You find this ugly, I find it lovely.

Smells rich and rasping, smoke and fat and fish
And puffs of paraffin that crimp the nose,
Or grease that blesses onions with a hiss;
You find it ugly, I find it lovely.

The dips and molls, with flip and shiny gaze
(Death at their elbows, hunger at their heels)
Ranging the pavements of their pasturage;
You find it ugly, I find it lovely.

Five Bells

Time that is moved by little fidget wheels
Is not my Time, the flood that does not flow.
Between the double and the single bell
Of a ship's hour, between a round of bells
From the dark warship riding there below,
I have lived many lives, and this one life
Of Joe, long dead, who lives between five bells.

Deep and dissolving verticals of light
Ferry the falls of moonshine down. Five bells
Coldly rung out in a machine's voice. Night and water
Pour to one rip of darkness, the Harbour floats
In air, the Cross hangs upside-down in water.

Why do I think of you, dead man, why thieve
These profitless lodgings from the flukes of thought
Anchored in Time? You have gone from earth,
Gone even from the meaning of a name;
Yet something's there, yet something forms its lips
And hits and cries against the ports of space,
Beating their sides to make its fury heard.

Are you shouting at me, dead man, squeezing your face
In agonies of speech on speechless panes?
Cry louder, beat the windows, bawl your name!

But I hear nothing, nothing . . . only bells,
Five bells, the bumpkin calculus of Time.
Your echoes die, your voice is dowsed by Life,
There's not a mouth can fly the pygmy strait —
Nothing except the memory of some bones
Long shoved away, and sucked away, in mud;
And unimportant things you might have done,
Or once I thought you did; but you forgot,
And all have now forgotten — looks and words
And slops of beer; your coat with buttons off,
Your gaunt chin and pricked eye, and raging tales
Of Irish kings and English perfidy,
And dirtier perfidy of publicans
Groaning to God from Darlinghurst.

Five bells.

Then I saw the road, I heard the thunder
Tumble, and felt the talons of the rain
The night we came to Moorebank in slab-dark,
So dark you bore no body, had no face,
But a sheer voice that rattled out of air
(As now you'd cry if I could break the glass),
A voice that spoke beside me in the bush,
Loud for a breath or bitten off by wind,
Of Milton, melons, and the Rights of Man,
And blowing flutes, and how Tahitian girls
Are brown and angry-tongued, and Sydney girls
Are white and angry-tongued, or so you'd found.
But all I heard was words that didn't join
So Milton became melons, melons girls,
And fifty mouths, it seemed, were out that night,
And in each tree an Ear was bending down,
Or something had just run, gone behind grass,
When, blank and bone-white, like a maniac's thought,
The naphtha-flash of lightning slit the sky,
Knifing the dark with deathly photographs.
There's not so many with so poor a purse
Or fierce a need, must fare by night like that,
Five miles in darkness on a country track,
But when you do, that's what you think.

Five bells.

In Melbourne, your appetite had gone,
Your angers too; they had been leeched away
By the soft archery of summer rains
And the sponge-paws of wetness, the slow damp
That stuck the leaves of living, snailed the mind,
And showed your bones, that had been sharp with rage,
The sodden ecstasies of rectitude.
I thought of what you'd written in faint ink,
Your journal with the sawn-off lock, that stayed behind
With other things you left, all without use,
All without meaning now, except a sign
That someone had been living who now was dead:
"At Labassa. Room 6 × 8
On top of the tower; because of this, very dark
And cold in winter. Everything has been stowed
Into this room — 500 books all shapes
And colours, dealt across the floor
And over sills and on the laps of chairs;
Guns, photoes of many differant things
And differant curioes that I obtained. . . ."

In Sydney, by the spent aquarium-flare
Of penny gaslight on pink wallpaper,
We argued about blowing up the world,
But you were living backward, so each night
You crept a moment closer to the breast,
And they were living, all of them, those frames
And shapes of flesh that had perplexed your youth,
And most your father, the old man gone blind,
With fingers always round a fiddle's neck,
That graveyard mason whose fair monuments
And tablets cut with dreams of piety
Rest on the bosoms of a thousand men
Staked bone by bone, in quiet astonishment
At cargoes they had never thought to bear,
These funeral-cakes of sweet and sculptured stone.

Where have you gone? The tide is over you,
The turn of midnight water's over you,
As Time is over you, and mystery,
And memory, the flood that does not flow.
You have no suburb, like those easier dead
In private berths of dissolution laid —
The tide goes over, the waves ride over you
And let their shadows down like shining hair,

But they are Water; and the sea-pinks bend
Like lilies in your teeth, but they are Weed;
And you are only part of an Idea.
I felt the wet push its black thumb-balls in,
The night you died, I felt your eardrums crack,
And the short agony, the longer dream,
The Nothing that was neither long nor short;
But I was bound, and could not go that way,
But I was blind, and could not feel your hand.
If I could find an answer, could only find
Your meaning, or could say why you were here
Who now are gone, what purpose gave you breath
Or seized it back, might I not hear your voice?

I looked out of my window in the dark
At waves with diamond quills and combs of light
That arched their mackerel-backs and smacked the sand
In the moon's drench, that straight enormous glaze,
And ships far off asleep, and Harbour-buoys
Tossing their fireballs wearily each to each,
And tried to hear your voice, but all I heard
Was a boat's whistle, and the scraping squeal
Of seabirds' voices far away, and bells,
Five bells. Five bells coldly ringing out.

Five bells.

Beach Burial

Softly and humbly to the Gulf of Arabs
The convoys of dead sailors come;
At night they sway and wander in the waters far under,
But morning rolls them in the foam.

Between the sob and clubbing of the gunfire
Someone, it seems, has time for this,
To pluck them from the shallows and bury them in burrows
And tread the sand upon their nakedness;

And each cross, the driven stake of tidewood,
Bears the last signature of men,
Written with such perplexity, with such bewildered pity,
The words choke as they begin —

''*Unknown seaman*'' — the ghostly pencil
Wavers and fades, the purple drips,
The breath of the wet season has washed their inscriptions
As blue as drowned men's lips,

Dead seamen, gone in search of the same landfall,
Whether as enemies they fought,
Or fought with us, or neither; the sand joins them together,
Enlisted on the other front.

El Alamein.

Frank Dalby
Davison

The Road to Yesterday

ENGINEERS HAVE built a new road up the Plenty Ranges to Westgate — or Tommy's Hut, as we used to call it when I was a lad.

The new road is a modern mountain highway, a black stream of bitumen that loops and sidles along the flank of the range, with pointed bends in the shadowed gullies, and scenic sweeps round the sunny shoulders of the spurs. There are neat white hand-rails to the little bridges and white posts marking the outer edges of the curves. Each cutting and embankment is like a brown cicatrice on the aboriginal body of the mountain, but the road passing between these earthy scars is smoothly purposeful in its upward course. Above and below the road the bush is impressively tall, dense and flourishing, with high undergrowth, bright wheels of tree-ferns; and the trunks of the mountain-gums are like long white stitches in the green. The air is cool, moist, and fragrant with leafage. The ascent of the range is so gradual you'd scarcely notice it.

The old road was different — unsurfaced earth, a pioneer track, broadened and graded within the limited resources of a rural shire. Its course had been determined by that axiom of simple bushmanship: "To get through the ranges, stick to the tops of the ridges." The settlers had had no road-building gear — and you can't take a cart along the side of a mountain gully — so they had taken the foremost spur by frontal assault. It was a long stiff pull, and raised the sweat on a horse. You might have to spell him on the way up by chocking the wheels. You must needs walk beside him to help lighten the load, and you had to give him a spell at the top, where he would stand with quivering chest and dripping belly. If you were heavily loaded someone would have to meet you at the foot of the range with a spare horse to hook on in front.

The roadside timber was different from that which shades the new road. The thin soil of the ridges ran to no opulence of leafage, only to slender, grey messmate saplings, with bare gravel and rocky outcrops between, and a few tufts of grey wire-grass. Here was no bird-song, no undergrowth, no ground life. It was a lean, spare bush; life clung to these bony heights only by drawing in on itself; you imagined that the putting forth of a new leaf would be a matter affecting deep issues, and notable in an uneventful calendar.

At long distances — and for brief seasons — the roadside would be adorned with miraculous clumps of wattle and sarsaparilla, but the old road — though it occasionally commanded noble vistas of valley and range, was wholly a working road. In places it broke into a broad web of tracks — detours made among the trees by the settlers over boggy hollows in wet weather. On the high places the wheels ground over protruding boulders, or lurched over the exposed roots of trees.

By the kindness of friends I was on my way to revisit Tommy's Hut for a day, after many years and much wandering. We had motored from Melbourne, gliding across the plain in less than half an hour, along a highway horses had needed a day to cover in more laborious years. From the last township before you come to the foot of the range I had been welcoming old landmarks, resenting new ones, noting the disappearance of others; becoming, bit by bit, a little uncertain of myself.

The general contours of the landscape were much as I remembered them, although there was a timbered hill which I seemed to have forgotten, and the willowed creek was closer to the township than I thought. A grey homestead drowsing on the lower slope of a green knoll was reassuringly familiar — even to its rust-mottled roof — and the sheep grazing on the flat below might have been those that memory recalled, rather than their probable descendants of many generations. But a sprawling roadside barn had vanished, the grass quite unmarked where it had once stood; and bleached and broken skeletons were all that remained of a once notable clump of old red-gums. Split-rail fences had largely given way to wire, and some rows of tall pines that had no place in recollection affirmed the slow passing of the years. A red tractor with plough in tow — modernity in the long-remembered place — was a small shock to the heart, even while reason hastened to bring feeling to heel.

"The old road up the range should begin about a half a mile further on," I said, almost anxiously, as we came under the foothills, and, "Yes, there it is," as it came into sight.

John must have caught the note in my voice. "We'll have a look-see," he said, and shortly after turned onto the gravel. A hundred yards farther on he slipped into second gear and we purred steadily up the spur where the mountain settlers' horses had once won their way toilsomely.

As we ascended, the sides of the spur fell away like the sides of a roof-gable, revealing valley and lowland on either side. Down in the valley to the left there was a patch of brown tillage where I remembered a peach orchard in a mist of pink bloom. Near the top of the rise we passed the spot where a loaded cart had once gone hurtling backward down the right-hand declivity.

It was eleven o'clock at night, and we were trying to get up the range with a horse weary from the day's journey from the city. A chock thrown under the wheel must have been a clod of clay and not a rock as was intended, for the cart ran back.

"Chock! For God's sake, chock!" The driver's voice had panic in it. There was a frantic scraping of hooves as the horse struggled to regain control. Then the horse and cart disappeared into the night. Out of the dark came the thump of something overturning, and a bang clatter as the dislodged load shot off and avalanched down the hill. Then the groan of a horse, followed by sounds of ineffectual plunging. Then silence again.

It was chill dawn before we had extricated the horse from under the cart, man-handled the cart back onto the road, collected our scattered goods, reloaded, and — shaken and hollow-eyed — were again on our way. A shaft of the cart, lodging against a stump, had stood prop against complete disaster.

From the top of the first rise the ascent of the range is more gradual, but steep enough; a heavy pull and a bit of level going; a dip down along a saddle between two ridges, and then ascent of another spur; always with that lean bush on either side, perspectives of slender grey trunks, with a scattering of trees of larger growth as you penetrated the hills.

It was not good travelling for a car. John would have had an easier time on the new road. His interest in the old road — and that of Hilda and Hugh — was only through me. I appreciated his setting himself to tool a sedan carefully up six miles of rough going; and I appreciated the willingness of the other two, consenting to be thrown about in the back seat as we lurched slowly across deep-wash-outs dug by the rains of past winters, and accepting in faith our gingerly passage over rotting culverts.

Up the first spur, and for half a mile afterwards, we saw a couple of recent cartwheel marks on the road before us — firewood cutters', most likely — then these disappeared among the trees, and we realized that the old road was quite abandoned. It was natural to wonder if we could reach our destination; but the road went on as if in the forlorn keeping of a faith no longer required of it; and John, with no exchange of words, accepted the challenge.

As well as being deeply channelled by past rains, the road was littered with fallen timber — a lace of twigs, leaves, great branches, an occasional whole tree — brought down by the winds in the years since it was last used by the settlers. The side-tracks that had led to the settlers' homes were abandoned, the moss deep in the old wheel-ruts. Haulage was by motor-truck now, and passed along the new road. The dray, the spring-cart, the jinker, the occasional bullock-wagon that had once comprised the old road's trickle of slow traffic were at one now, presumably, with the split-rail fences, the vanished barn and the splintered red-gums.

Only the old road itself endured, a weathered line scrawled roughly through the ranges. Its loneliness and emptiness grew upon us as we topped each rise and turned each bend and came upon further untravelled stretches; a highway advanced in disrepair, still passable, but unmarked in years by wheel or hoof or foot. It had something of the quality of an old garment that has given good wear, and something of the eeriness of a deserted dwelling.

As we passed the old side-tracks I named them from memory — "Glendenning's Turn-off", "Cummins's Turn-off", "Jamieson's Turn-off".

I explained how each of these turn-offs had once led to the homes of two or three selectors, and took its name from the family that had been first to settle. Each track's point of departure from the road had once been the scene of small twice-weekly meetings. Mr Bailey, who owned the store at Tommy's Hut, used to journey on Tuesdays and Fridays of each week to the railway below the ranges, with his wagon and horses. He carried mail for the settlers, sold them newspapers, picked up packages for them at the rail, bought butter and eggs from them, and did a small wayside business in groceries, haberdashery, lamp-wicks and other kinds of country-store stock. He also did a gratis trade in local gossip.

His times of passing were known, and a little before he was due there would be a small gathering of people at each turn-off; a woman or two — perhaps with a piece of crochet or other current needlework to fill the time of waiting — a few small children, a boy or girl past school age, and perhaps a man or youth with sprouting beard, if there was a sack of flour to be shouldered. These little gatherings of an hour were a pleasant break in the isolation of selection life, and notable in a restricted social round.

Mr Bailey could always be heard before his wagon came into sight around the nearest bend of the road. Years on the road had accustomed him to driving with his thoughts on other things. His cry of command to the horses had become clipped to a shrill bark uttered loudly and repeated unthinkingly every fifty yards. "Yah-yep! Yah-yep!" He might have had a lively terrier for passenger.

He often approached his stopping-places bottom first as he groped behind the seat for packages. The horses drew up thankfully of their own accord. As he shuffled the mail he peered at each envelope as if he were seeking the answer to a difficult riddle, and he shouted the names as if he were announcing the result to an expectant multitude instead of the little knot of humans close about his wheel. He was the only man of business in the community. In his dealings with us he was very obliging and scrupulously just, and yet, as he gathered up his reins, he always looked as if he were counting up how many pennies we had been worth to him; and there always seemed to be a note of triumph in the terrier bark that came back to us as he trundled off with the dust rolling up behind his wagon.

It was White's Turn-off I was looking for, and Sims's selection, where I first put down roots in the earth. Arthur Sims was from the Old Country, a man of Kent who had spent the better part of a lifetime in Australia — or the Colonies, to use the term he employed with a slight air of patronage — bringing up a large family by dint of heavy toil until, in his late fifties, he had found himself with enough money to make a small start for himself on the land; a dream that had stalked his thoughts for years, growing more insistent as the time before him shortened. I was the boy about the place, wide-eyed, and with a mind as receptive as the soil to water.

The family, in addition to Mr and Mrs Sims, comprised two daughters and three sons; there was Jessie, aged about fourteen, in her last year at school, strong-limbed, blue-eyed and as blonde as new rope; imbued with something more than a tomboy interest in every aspect of the outdoor life of the selection. We were friends, even acknowledged sweethearts, following the day when we exchanged, in the twilight of the barn, the first startling kiss of adolescence. Annie, aged sixteen, a buxom girl with smooth honey-coloured hair parted in a white line up the centre of her head, was one to whom the four walls of a dwelling were in the nature of a cocoon. She was the protectress and student observer of our virtuous attachment.

The sons — Ernie who was before my time, Harry who came after my arrival, and whose going overlapped Charlie's arrival and preceded my own departure — were a special feature of the place. They came in their turn from their wanderings far and wide to toil awhile shoulder to shoulder with the old man. Here was a home-life and mum and dad. Here was a son's duty. Here was effort with which they could identify themselves, until the calls that young men answer drew them off. Harry, the one I came to know best, was twenty-four, sober to the point of dourness, hard-working, and with a pride in past feats of labour on the ballast trucks of railway construction camps.

Mrs Sims I remembered only as a smallish dark figure ever hurrying about some household task, someone whose kindness I took as much for granted as I had taken my own mother's. Mr Sims was a man of medium physique and courageous countenance. Under a bald head fringed with greying curls he had fine blue-grey eyes in a bronzed face, a straight nose, and a good mouth showing between moustache and grizzled beard. Hard work had affected him. His gait was stiff-kneed and he walked with drooping shoulders and dangling hands. He had a habit — perhaps it was the Kentish accent — of drawling and distorting certain vowels. In his mouth "yes" became "yuurce" and "year" "yurr". He had a melodious voice and in his lighter moments would pause in his work to troll a line of song, most often, "I'll Be a Jolly Pedlar and Around the World I'll Roam".

In bed he wore a nightgown and nightcap. I saw him in them once when he returned to the living-room, after going to bed, for something he had forgotten.

I had never seen such garments and, in combination with whiskers, the sight overwhelmed me. I think my astonished stare embarrassed him a little, an embarrassment he sought to turn to humorous account with a large wink before darting from view.

He was not one to take part in evening activities. After tea he would scratch his beard a little while the washing-up was in progress, then remove his boots, and, carrying them, depart stocking-footed to his room at the opposite end of the small dwelling. Sometimes he would take with him a large seedsman's catalogue, the only book I ever saw in his hands, to read for a few minutes in bed before putting out the light. On these occasions — much to the annoyance of us young ones — he would interrupt the elementary card game or snakes-and-ladders that followed washing-up by communicating the results of his study in a voice that carried clearly through the hessian partitions.

"Jessie! Annie! Are you thuure?"

"Yes, dad."

"I think I'll plant 'taters between the Jonathans, where we had the beans last yuur."

Silence from the players absorbed with their game.

"Jessie! Annie! Do you huur me?"

"Yes, dad."

Another silence.

"Jessie! Annie! Are you thuure?"

A resigned voice: "Yes, dad."

"It says here, that Yates's Mammoth Maincrop is the thing for cool climates and heavy soils, but I don't care for 'em. I think I'll plant Bates's Early Wonder, same as I did yuur afore last."

Silence, accompanied by glances of exasperation between the players.

"Jessie! Annie! Do you huur me?"

"Y-e-e-s! Of course we can hear you!" And mumblingly, "Worse luck!"

Mr Sims had little time for reading even his seedsman's catalogue. In his reckoning, when it was too dark for work it was time for sleep. In this he was something of a household tyrant. Soon after we heard the catalogue flop on the floor we would hear his voice inquiring whether we were ever going to bed, and expressing surprise that we still had the lamp burning. These words, addressed ostensibly to the younger members of his household, were perhaps also by way of tactful intimation to his spouse, Lucy, that it was time she laid aside her darning and joined him in sleep.

He would wear us down in the end, and we would break up reluctantly, the girls to their room adjoining the living-room and I to my bunk in a little room at the end of the barn, there to be companioned before falling asleep by the munching of the horse in his stable at the other end of the building, the occasional rattle of the watchdog's chain, the spooky call of a mopoke, or the complaining bark of a fox in the nearby bush.

Mr Sims had selected a hundred acres on the edge of the big timber country; heavily forested land, some of the trees as thick through at the butt as the length of a couple of axe-handles. My arrival was in the fourth year when, a little at a time, ten acres had been cleared, ploughed, and planted with fruit-trees, and a house and barn had been built. But clearing was still going on at the edge of the bush in the intervals between caring for the young orchard, so I came to know what it meant to uproot the living forest with a few small tools and make it vanish back to the elements.

It took upwards of half a week of sweat and hard breathing with mattock, shovel, and axe to grub and fell one of those trees. It went over at last like grandeur undone, its leaves wailing, and crashed to earth with terrible and dusty impact. Its trunk lay dramatically inert, and the yellow ends of its shattered tangle of branches seemed to protest dumbly against our triumph. The severed roots of the stumps were cocked up as high as a man's head; you could have buried a dray in the hole you had dug; and two men could see each other only from the chest up across its prone trunk. The trunk had to be sawn through in several places, the branches lopped and cut into manageable lengths, the stump end rolled clear of the hole, and the sawn logs of the trunk swung round and piled for burning — human strength and the craft of pole and lifting-jack pitted against earth's tenacious clutch of her own.

The fires had to be stoked for weeks on end, as well as being shaken down each night — spark fountains leaping in the dark — before you went to bed. Every chip from the axe, stick and fragment of wood, had to be stooped for and fed in armfuls to the fires. While the burning went on — and that was just one tree — the buttress roots remaining in the ground had to be traced and uncovered to below plough-depth, cut through in several places, torn from their moorings in the subsoil, and lifted and cast on the fires, then the heavy clay returned, shovelful by shovelful, to the holes from which stump and root had come. From all this you got some idea of how much had been done since the day Mr Sims and Ernie had pitched their tent in the forest and made a start.

When we paused for a breather or a strengthening snack it was Mr Sims's habit to sit facing the young orchard, fondling his beard and heartening himself in present labour with the thought of labour done. At such moments he was prone to live past struggles over so fully as to forget that another son now toiled beside him.

"Ernie, d'you mind that whopping big gum that stood right where the end of that row of Ribston Pippins is now?" he would say, turning round. "Oh, it's you, Harry! Well, Ernie looked up at that tree and he said to me, 'Dad,' he said, 'we won't get the best of this bugger inside a twelvemonth!' Man, he was a big 'un!'' Here Mr Sims paused to dwell in thought on the size of the branching giant that had been vanquished, and to give us time to imagine its proportions. ''But we got rid of him!'' he added in triumphant recollection. ''By frawst, we did!''

In addition to the living trees there were the stumps of the dead, like great half-decayed teeth, to be dug and wrenched piecemeal from the earth and piled for burning, and the striving horde of saplings to be worried loose with mattock and axe one by one and gathered up to the fires, and the ground raked clean of everything that might foul the tillage. It was Mr Sims's pride that there should be no by-passed stumps in the cultivation, no forest litter to sour the soil, no hidden root to snub the flow of the plough. When at last the acre marked was cleared it looked strangely tidy, like a school-yard on a Saturday morning, only that the earth was criss-crossed with red and white bars where the log fires had been.

There were only light cultivation tools on the selection, so a man had to be brought from a distant place with a heavy plough and three big horses to break up the ground; and the heavy earth gave to his mould-board with unwilling groans and the explosive snapping of small roots; and the yellow-grey furrows lay over against each other as hard and unyielding as paving slabs. It was left to lie like that, to weather, while we shifted the fence to include the new cultivation. Then the sods were ready to break down and must be ploughed and harrowed and rolled and ploughed and harrowed again and made up into banked lands before the little fruit-trees were set out in their sedate rows.

It was Mr Sims's ambition to recreate on his selection the Kentish garden of his youthful recollections, and his orchard was a picture of careful tillage. Just as the company of well-bred people gives you the feeling, ''Here is gentleness'', or a library, ''Here is learning'', so when you came to Mr Sims's place you had the feeling, ''Here is husbandry''. I felt it myself when first I entered the gate, though I had no word for it.

The grown apple-trees to the right as you went down the lane leading to the house were as straight in their latticed rows as if they had been set out by some exact machine; and there were no ragged headlands or weedy corners; ground that couldn't be reached with the plough was turned by the spade, right up to the fence-posts. Between the apple-trees, in their rows, gooseberry-bushes were growing, two at equal distances between each tree, and between the lines of apple-trees there were rows of vegetables. On the left-hand side there were two acres of raspberry-plants, the canes supported, not, as was the local custom, by stakes driven through the crown of the plants, but by being trained on wire fencing stretched taut along the rows. The fork-dug ground was free from so much as a single leaf of weed or sorrel. The lane itself was fenced from the cultivation and the strip on each side of the cart-track sown with grass — a bit of Saturday afternoon grazing for the horse.

The house comprised three rooms in a row, light and cheap in construction, but comfortable, with a raised wooden floor, papered walls, a fireplace, a slabbed veranda with a garden strip in front of it, and a grass plot adjoining for bleaching clothes.

The barn was built of slabs, split from vanished trees, adzed smooth and fitted close. It had an iron roof, and its supporting timbers were the straightest and soundest to be won from the bush. There was a tool-room at one end of the barn, with, behind it, a small bunk-room, which was my sleeping-quarters; adjoining both these was the wagon shelter. Through a door from that was a store-room for the products of the soil; beyond that was a stable where the horse could be warm on winter nights, and, adjoining his stall, the bail where the two cows were milked. It was a model barn and the subject of approving comment from all callers.

To the right, below the barn, was the second year planting of young trees, standing in a catch-crop of red clover; and to the left, below the lane that led across the bottom of the raspberry patch to the bush paddock, was the third year planting of fruit-trees — pronged sticks, merely — standing in a catch-crop of rye, just greening the ground.

Mr Sims lived in two worlds, that of his present labour and that of his early recollections, and they wove in and out of his thoughts as he worked, each the inspiration of the other. He would pause sometimes in the midst of work — when a breathing spell was reasonably indicated — to speak of the past; or would be very easily stimulated by question or comment to point the differences between Old Country and local methods, even to his own disparagement.

I commented once on the straightness of a furrow he had just turned in starting the winter ploughing-out in the four-year-old orchard.

"Straight!" said he. "Oh, no, boy! That's as crooked as a dog's hind-leg!"

He paused to give time for this correction to sink in, staring at me the while from wide blue eyes which dared me to point out that his furrow really was straight except for a very small wobble half-way along. Then followed an explanation of how ploughing was done in Kent; and not, mind you, just in a two-acre patch, but a furrow drawn the length of a twenty-acre field. The ploughman would be expected to cut his furrow as straight as a taut string and with the turned earth lying over as smooth as if it had been trowelled from end to end! He was no ploughman if he couldn't!

It was the same with almost everything about the place that I found reason to admire. It might be good enough in its way — and he was grateful in so far as he might accept my words as a compliment to a man who was doing his best under adverse conditions — but it was always about three jumps behind Kent. "Yuurce! Yuurce!" he would say after telling me about the thatching, the stabling, the hop-picking, or the milking byres of Kent, and stare into the distance awhile from his blue-grey eyes before turning back to his task.

I came to regard Kent as a sort of fabled country, something to look back on much as the people of the Dark Ages must have looked back on the fabled days of Roman order, so that I was a little surprised and disconcerted to note that Harry was not always at one with his father in reverential regard for Kentish ways. I noticed it first when the winter pruning of the four-year-old apple-trees was under way. Mr Sims had not changed his ideas of pruning during his years away from Kent, while Harry had absorbed some of the ideas of his own country. In most things about the farm he honoured his father's superior knowledge, but in the matter of pruning he felt that Mr Sims had something new to learn and that he must take a stand. They argued the matter while they worked, and the sound of their dispute came down from among the twiggy trees. Neither would yield, and, as they worked facing each other, one side of each row of trees was pruned in Kent, so to speak, and the other at Tommy's Hut.

Notwithstanding this significant clash, I continued to accept the fable — it was a happy one — and my acceptance stimulated Mr Sims in his own belief in it, even sentimentalizing it to a point that led him into a rather shattering encounter with his son. One day, following a recent talk by him on the splendid spectacle of huntsmen riding to hounds, and of the generosity of the Kentish gentry at Yuletide, he came to me with a very happy glint in his eyes — the glint of one who has inadvertently stumbled upon evidence substantiating a theme. He was carrying a folded sheet of paper, which I happened to have seen before, and which I knew had reached the farmstead wrapped round some groceries. He unfolded it and held it before me. It was from an English illustrated journal, and on the page facing me were rows of photographs of rural gentlemen in hunting garb, shooting rig-outs, and velveteen jackets.

"Now, boy!" exclaimed Mr Sims, beaming at me over the top of the page like a benign but expectant schoolmaster, and quite evidently expecting me to recall our earlier conversation. "Now, boy! If I were to ask you which of these men was a typical dee-ar old English country gentleman, which would you say?"

He had overlooked the nearby presence of Harry. Harry snorted as if his tonsils had exploded. "Dee-ar old English country gentleman!" he repeated in drawling mimicry.

Mr Sims bent on him a look of mingled embarrassment and reproach, before thrusting the sheet into my hands and darting off.

It was not in the mind of Mr Sims alone that thoughts of the fabled land of Kent wove in and out of the realities of the moment. His stories set up the same habit with me, and one day I asked him a question which I had been pondering for some time, and which drew an enlightening answer. We were fork-digging the raspberry plantation. You bent your back for long periods at a stretch and nothing could be heard but the sound of heavy breathing, the shifting of feet on the soil, and the occasional ring of a fork prong on a pebble. You worked like this because as soon as the raspberries were forked there would be the potatoes to hill-up in the top orchard, or the young fruit-trees to spray; or if nothing was calling for immediate attention in the orchard there were some fence-posts to be split.

Half-way down a raspberry row Mr Sims signalled a rest by standing up and looking about him, while rubbing his loins with the back of his hand. It was then that I put the question that had been troubling my mind.

"Mr Sims, why did you leave Kent?"

My question fetched from Harry a deep belly-chuckle which ended in a ringing laugh and, although it had been asked in all innocence, drew upon me a shrewd look from both men. Mr Sims seemed to feel that I had challenged him, so, while Harry listened, grinning, he explained.

"Well, boy, seeing that you've asked me, I'll tell you!" And then followed an explanation from which I learnt that while Kent was a very beautiful and wonderful place — "the finest county in all England, I've heard say" — it was a place in which everything was owned by someone, pretty well down to the last minnow in the brook, and the people who owned it, and had owned it "for hundreds and hundreds of yuurs", were very jealous of their rights. If the farm steward saw me eating as much as one raspberry unbidden by him he might lay his whip about my legs; and if my father took some faggots from the woods for firing and the steward came to know of it he might be brought before the "magistr'te" and be turned off the place — the "magistr'te" being a friend of his master and a neighbouring squire.

There slowly faded from Mr Sims's face the somewhat dramatic expression with which he made me this explanation, and he looked long into the distance, while Harry lit a pipe and looked at me with an ironic smile about his mouth. Mr Sims said, "Yuurce, yuurce," and we bent again to our digging; and to our several trains of thought.

I was deeply shocked by this talk of whipping, entrenched proprietorship, and dear old country gentlemen who were also stern magistrates. I assumed, as an article of faith, that my own country was free from comparable harshness, and I went over to Harry's equivocal view of the fabled land of Kent. I saw that Kent, as Mr Sims most kindly remembered it, was mainly an ideal of thorough farming which he kept in mind to help him, and, for the rest, something which had its lovable side and which he was trying to reconstruct with its worse parts left out. The more I thought about it all the more I liked him for what he was trying to do.

From then on he spoke to me of Kent in the tone of one speaking to another who is in the know; but I think he was anxious lest I should think too badly of his home country, because a few days later, when we were hilling-up the potatoes in the top orchard, he interrupted work to tell a few yarns of the great larks they used to get up to in the Old Dart. When we reached the headland he put his hoe on his shoulder and to Harry's amusement and my vast delight did a few steps of a village break-down.

My mirth seemed to gratify him. "Yuurce, yuurce," he said. "The living was hard, I suppose; but we were cheery lads!" Presently he lowered his hoe: "Well," he said, "I 'spose we'd better be getting on with looking after these 'taters." And then our backs were bent to it again, our bright blades stabbing the earth and drawing it up around the growing plants.

It was about this time that I began to understand something of the chances governing Mr Sims's hopes of success in his enterprise. I came from the house one raw winter evening to get some wood for the stove just as he — last home from the field of toil — was stumping up from the barn. I heard his footsteps cease at the gate, and glanced up. He stood there for a while looking back through the murk at the lower cultivation, and then he spoke, half to himself and half as if he had become aware of a listener, "Yuurce, yuurce," he said, "we'll have the living comin' in in a couple more yuurs." Then he turned and stumped on towards the lighted kitchen.

It was the first time I really became aware that the living was not yet coming in. The way he spoke, as if reassuring himself, made me wonder whether — despite the fact that it would be impossible for him, of his nature, to slum any kind of work — there was not a measure of desperation behind the fine state of cultivation in which his orchard was kept.

People round about were not doing very well. The cold clayey soil just didn't seem sufficiently responsive to cultivation; crops seemed, as a rule, rather uncertain, and orchard-trees seemed to run more to wood than to fruit. I had come to understand, from the tenor of Mr Sims's observations, that the indifferent success of his neighbours was due in some part to slack methods, and that good methods would prevail over disadvantages of soil and climate. That was the farmer's justification!

But then there was the afternoon when I was returning by a short-cut through the bush from meeting the storekeeper's wagon on the road, and saw Mr Sims standing on the headland below the barn, facing the crop of red clover. I climbed through the fence and joined him.

"That clover's not doing very well," he said.

The clover looked well enough from a distance, but when you came to look at it closely it was very sparse, with a lot of bare ground between the plants.

He left me and walked into the middle of it and looked about him, and stood a long while in thought. I saw that he had forgotten me and was deep in a problem. When he came back he looked at me with a slight widening of the eyes that showed he had just recalled my presence. We stood together for a moment or two, looking at the clover, then he said quietly, "We'll start to plough that in in the morning. I'll try something else — swedes, probably." And you could tell from his tones that in the minutes when I had watched him standing alone in the middle of his unsuccessful crop of clover one hope had been courageously abandoned and another, with equal courage, taken up in its place.

It was about this time that I began to understand that in the affairs of the selection too much depended on too little for comfort of mind. The failure or success of this or that small cropping venture made a difference in immediate living prospects. Hard work had anxiety for its invisible team-mate. No jollity accompanied the ploughing-in of the clover and sowing of the swedes.

Nor was there any margin to cover loss by disaster. There was the time when we were driving down the range in the wagon to the railway and Billy, the creaky old horse-of-all-work, slipped and fell and knocked the wind out of himself and couldn't get up. Mr Sims was the first to scramble from the wagon and rush to kneel at his head. It seemed for a minute that the horse had broken his leg and would have to be destroyed. Mr Sims had great difficulty in controlling his feelings. He made a funny noise. He seemed for a moment to shrink in bodily size, and the hand that rested on Billy's head was shaking. When we had got Billy up and were driving on again I sat very quiet, not saying anything to Mr Sims for fear talk might be unwelcome at the moment. I just sat there watching the trees move past, rather frightened at discovering that accident could rip away the surface of things and show the works underneath. It seemed to be my first glimpse of works.

It was all right on the drive home from the railway. Mr Sims had enjoyed the glass of beer he always drank on his rare visits to the township, and he had had some pleasant conversation with people he met in the store — as well as a day sitting in the wagon instead of working himself to death. While we were jogging back over the level road between the rail and the foot of the range he talked about things on the selection, what good growth the young apple-trees had made since the day they were planted, how healthy the raspberry-canes looked and about the fowls coming on to lay very soon. He sang a bit of "I'll Be a Jolly Pedlar and Around the World I'll Roam"; and when we came to the place on the mountain road where Billy had fallen down he didn't seem to notice; he just slapped Billy's back with the reins in a friendly way.

Things went up and down like that, and it was not always a matter of whether they were up or down in themselves, but to some extent a matter of how you were feeling in yourself. There was the day Mr Sims came along just when I had finished cleaning out Billy's stable and stacking the manure neatly on the heap outside the stable door. He stopped very kindly to give me a word of praise for the thorough way I did the job; which really wasn't deserved because to me old

Billy was all the grand horses in the world and I just enjoyed fixing things up comfortably for him. I was even pleased with what he left on the stable floor for me to clean up, and I said to Mr Sims, "That's a fine lot of manure we've got now!"

Mr Sims said, "Boy, that's only a spoonful! That'll go nowhere!" And then followed a tale of the manuring of Kentish fields. How, in addition to the manure of byre and stable, cartloads of fish would be brought from the nearby markets in time of glut and ploughed in; and how, after a storm at sea, the wagons would go down to the beaches and come back loaded with seaweed to be spread on the fields.

Mr Sims stood looking out over his own acres, and I saw that hope was at a low ebb. Perhaps he was tired and perhaps he was thinking of the clover that had failed. "That land 'ad been tilled and manured for hundreds and hundreds of yuurs," he said. "And that's just the difference!" He kicked a nearby clod and watched it burst into dust.

It occurred to me to wonder if Kentish fields had not been better soil to begin with; to wonder, in fact, if he had not selected unwisely. The same thought must have been running through his own head — and possibly was no newcomer — for he said, as if in answer to my speculation, "Perhaps I did wrong in coming to this part of the country." He asked me then why I didn't work in the city and grow up to sit at a desk and wear a coat and be a gentleman; and I had difficulty in making my preference for cleaning out stables and splitting fence-posts sound very sensible.

The good sense of my preferences was linked in a certain way with his moods and I was reassured to notice that the moments when he seemed to wonder if his hopes were hollow didn't last. He went on working just the same, and presently the beginning of some new job would indicate that he had forgotten his doubts. It was only a couple of days after our talk that we started digging the well he had been planning for some time. I noticed later that the successful completion of one job seemed always to set his mind busy with plans for the future. When we were finishing off the well — shovelling away the spoil from around the top — he fell to talking of the nice pastures, in place of the rough grazing of the bush paddock, he hoped to have for his livestock "by and by".

The swedes came up nicely, but a few months later the weather dealt Mr Sims a heavy blow. It was the only occasion on which I heard him driven by excess of feeling to lay his troubles at the door of a malignant fate.

The part of the range where the selection lay jutted to the south and was sometimes swept by unseasonable hail. One of these storms came over in early spring, just when the raspberry-blossoms were setting to fruit. I was bringing the two milking cows home from the bush one afternoon when the sky darkened, and by the time we were in the lane leading from the bush paddock to the barn the hail was dancing off the cows' backs and was getting heavier. I made a bolt for the house with face screwed up against the stinging pellets, and arrived at the gate just in time to run into Annie and Jessie, who had been across the road to visit a neighbour. We raced pell-mell for the shelter of the veranda and reached there breathless, laughing and shouting.

It was a wonderful hailstorm; the iron roof roared under it. You couldn't see fifty yards from the veranda. The ground whitened with hail while you watched. We stood admiring the transformation, pointing out the big fellows — like pigeons' eggs — and exclaiming over the way the hail danced back from the veranda ledge. We hadn't thought of it knocking every blossom from the raspberry-canes.

Just then we saw Mr Sims coming towards the house from the lower cultivation. He wasn't running. Indifferent to the pelting hail, he was walking more heavily than usual, and his shoulders were more drooped. We remembered the raspberry-canes then. Our voices were hushed and our eyes fixed on him.

Within a few yards of the veranda he stopped and lifted a haggard face and a clenched fist to the sky, and shouted, "Send it down! Send it down, Hughie!"

His wife gasped in the doorway. "Oh, Arthur," she cried, "you shouldn't speak like that!" And she drew back into the shadows of the kitchen.

Mr Sims shouldered past us to the end of the veranda, and stood looking out, his hands clutching the rail. His face was no longer tan, but grey. He turned and spoke as if his outburst demanded justification. "That's a yuur's work gone in less than two minutes!" he said, and turned grimly to watch the hail again.

We were silent. His arms, from shoulder to the hands gripping the veranda rail, were shaking. He spoke again. "And half the next yuur's livin' gone with it!" he added. Soon afterwards he slumped down on the slab wash-bench and was lost to us in unhopeful reckonings and bleak meditation.

The storm passed shortly after. The air cleared and all the earth was white. The trunks of the trees in the bush paddock looked like charcoal marks on paper. Then the sun shone forth, and all the world sparkled like fairyland. But we could take no delight in it. The farmer's loss was heavy on us. It seemed as if all his hope lay under a shroud of bright ice.

You'd have thought that a blow like that would have sunk Mr Sims for ever but he came right side up again. Perhaps despondency was a luxury beyond his means. At any rate, within a few days we had begun work — "to take advantage of the cool weather" — on a new bit of clearing. It was in the following weeks that I learnt what it meant to uproot and destroy the forest. It was during the later part of those weeks, too, that I heard Mr Sims, as if misfortune and disaster were unheard of things, recalling with satisfaction the epic days when he and Ernie began in the virgin bush.

The tide was on the turn while we grubbed and burnt the trees, and there came a Sunday morning in middle spring when it seemed as if soil and season were conspiring to encourage the farmer in his best hopes. Sunday morning on the selection was a time when you had the world in repose and therefore in condition for stock-taking. You couldn't work on Sunday, but you could walk about at ease and see how things were getting on. You could look back over the work you had been doing, and plan what you were going to do next week. You might end up raking the fowlyard, but that wasn't really work; that was just making the fowls comfortable and putting in a half-hour while waiting for dinner.

My own Sunday morning was generally taken up with a prowl down the fern gully that led off from near the back of the house, there to commune with the boles of the aloof gums, with running waters, and to disturb the peace of a wombat whose burrow I had discovered; afterwards, perhaps, to return to wait about the kitchen in hope of a kiss from Jessie when her mother was out of the room.

On some Sundays, however, Mr Sims would indicate a liking for my company on his tour of the farm, and we would go off something like page and Good King Wenceslas. This occasion in mid-spring proved a very hopeful morning. The pods of the early peas had swelled nicely and would soon be ready for picking, while there was a good show of blossom on the later sowing. This was only the kitchen garden, of course, but success here indicated something that might be done in a bigger way for market. There had been plentiful rain followed by tempered warmth — good growing weather — and wherever you looked, tomatoes, carrots, cabbages, seemed to be visibly racing towards maturity.

In the larger world of the market crops the swedes that had replaced the red clover were making good headway. "If the blight don't get at them," said Mr Sims, and stooped and turned up a few leaves, only to find them comfortingly clean and healthy-looking.

In the top orchard the gooseberry-bushes were thick with little goosegogs. There weren't many gooseberry-bushes of course. They had just been planted between the apple-trees as an afterthought, and their promise didn't compensate for the loss of the raspberry crop; but still, it was cheering to see them thriving and the jam made from them would cut down the grocery bill. There were some apples, too, on the young four-year-old trees; not a great number; the upper branches were rather bare; but half-way up from the fork there was quite a showing. With careful brown hands Mr Sims turned back the leaves to reveal the delicate green fruit marked with faint bars of pink.

He mentioned that there had been some apples last year, a few bucketfuls — all that could be expected from three-year-old trees. "And excellent apples, boy!" he exclaimed, looking up at me.

I had thought that apples were just apples.

"Oh, excellent apples!" he repeated, seeing that I had failed to be properly impressed. "I've never seen better in my life!"

No mention of Kent! The omission seemed almost deliberate. Those last-year apples instantly loomed in my mind as large as coconuts, and I stooped to look at those his hands were revealing, convinced that they were fruit of very notable promise.

Mr Sims stopped at the top of the orchard and looked back at the trees. "Yuurce," he said, in confident and happy anticipation, "we'll have some cases of apples to sell this yuur!"

The raspberry plantation didn't interest us much that morning. We viewed it briefly from over the fence that separated it from the lane. Mr Sims remarked, "We might have better luck next yuur," but there was some doubt in his voice, and some distaste in the glance he bent on the flourishing but fruitless canes. Hope had received a cruel blow and it was clear from the way he spoke that the future of the raspberries rested with themselves.

The rye, below the raspberries, was more inviting to look at. We could see it from where we stood, now going on for two feet high, a fine dark green, and dense, like a soft pile. Here waved the true banner of hope.

That rye was a great source of pride and satisfaction to Mr Sims during the last weeks of its growth. It was a hay crop, for the comfort and sustenance of the horse and cows during the winter when the picking would be lean in the bush paddock and the nights frosty. It stood for the future of animal husbandry on the selection, and was of a piece with the projected pasture paddocks.

When we passed along the lane at noon or evening, during the warming weather when we were at the grubbing and burning off, Mr Sims would often lag behind on the headland to enjoy the sight of his prospering crop, dark — like wheat — and full of a sappy fragrance. The wind blowing across it made catspaws of silver-grey, and the leaves rustled as if they were talking together. The crop sprang from the first sowing of grain on the selection, and Mr Sims — who could look so far back through the years — was looking forward for the first time to garnering for himself where he had tilled and seeded.

At table, he discoursed on the technique of successful harvesting. Knowledge and good luck would both be necessary. The right time to cut would be when the lowest part of the stalks turned yellow — showing that the roots had done their work for the year — but before the grain fully ripened, while it was yet soft and milky and there was nourishment all through the upper stalk and leaves. Good weather would be looked for then, so that the crop could be cut without delay, and brought to cover without damage from rain.

On a Sunday morning when there was a twinkle of warmth in the air, and the seedheads were beginning to make their appearance in the rye, Mr Sims took down his scythe from its peg on the wall of the tool-shed and wiped the dust and protective grease from the blade. He referred back to Kent, of course, saying that he supposed they had reapers and binders now, at any rate on the larger farms; but in his day the grain was cut by scythe-men, working as many as ten and twelve in line. Then he went out in front of the barn and had a few practice swings to make sure that hand and eye were still in trim.

When clearing was finished the next developmental job was the splitting of posts in the bush for the new fencing. But the season was advancing and the rye harvest was in close prospect. It now loomed as the big event of the year, and we were caught up in the feeling with which the farmer watched crop and sky. We knew that even while he pulled on his end of the cross-cut saw, or barked logs ready for splitting, his thoughts often strayed to the cultivation. His view of the rye was no longer confined to the headlands. He ventured a few feet into the green, here and there, crumbling a seedhead, parting the flag with his hands to examine the stalk. If he was late for meals we knew where he had been lingering.

There came days when the rye was almost in full head, and the world seemed working up to burst with light and warmth. We were some while into the time of year when meals were eaten in shirt-sleeves, and with door and windows wide open. You could tell how Mr Sims's thoughts were running by the way he harked back at meals and at work to little stories of harvests long past, the lucky and the unlucky.

In the bush, work moved at a steadied pace, and we often rolled a log into the shade before beginning on it with maul and wedges. Every green thing in forest and clearing was moving to a climax of growth. Cicadas made the still noonday loud and Billy drowsed under the trees on three legs. Something in the air told you that the season was at the turn. The weather held; and there came an evening when Mr Sims was more than ordinarily late in appearing at table and, as he took his seat, said with the air of one making a dramatic announcement, "Well, I'll begin cutting the rye in the morning!"

It was a warm morning and dry, ideal harvest weather, with a late-November bloom on it — just before the pallor of high summer — when everything you looked at seemed brighter than life and a size larger; and although work made you sweat quite freely you felt a bit larger than life yourself. The scythe-man, stripped to grey flannel and with a red kerchief around his neck to ward off sunburn, trimmed a few straggling stalks that had sprung on the headland, then swung into the crop, and soon the lane of shaved stubble was lengthening behind him, while the rye subsided in dark swaths above the shining arc of his blade.

The use of the scythe is an art and beautiful to see. It takes skill that has become part of nature to wield that python handle so that the blade neither stabs the earth with its point nor raises the dust with its heel, but shears close and even. The movements of the scythe-man's body are rhythmical like those of a ritual dance. His arms and shoulders swing wide above rigid hips, and the movements of his feet are timed to the sweep of the blade. In watching our scythe-man we forgot his stooped shoulders and stiff gait; youth and grace had returned to him. In the return swing his blade came clean from under the swath, leaving the windrows smooth for the binders who would come after him.

Twice in his first strip off the side of the crop Mr Sims turned to look back over his work in careful self-criticism; and when he had turned the corner of the field and was lost to us across the green from the chest down, he upended his scythe to whet it. His left forearm lay along the back of the blade to steady it. In his right hand the whetstone flashed back and forth as if it had a life of its own, and the blade sent a keen song into the morning air. After he had slipped the stone into the holder on the back of his belt he paused to mop his brow, and stared briefly over the crop. Perhaps the shades of old scythe-men had come to swing their blades with his; at any rate before he reversed the scythe he lifted his voice in a bar or two of his favourite lay.

Annie, Jessie, and I were the binders. We began when some of the rye had dried out a little. Mr Sims came back from the face of the crop and showed us how to take a handful from the swath, divide it, and by a dextrous twist of the hands knot the heads to make a band to bind a sheaf. After a few fumbles we caught the trick — to our immense satisfaction — and from then on we followed at a distance behind the scythe, gathering and binding the rye into sheaves and standing the sheaves by the head in stooks of half a dozen to cure ready for carting. It was warm work. The sun smarted on our bent backs. The stubble stabbed our hands and crackled under our feet. But it was good work, and we were careful to leave our stooks in rows as straight as could be desired.

Little by little as we followed the scythe around the field the green square in the centre grew less and less, until there came a time when we stood to raise a cheer as the last of it fell. Then Mr Sims joined us and we learnt to our surprise just how quickly sheaves could be made and stooks put together.

When the stooking was finished the field was a great pride to us all. It was let remain for a day or two until the hay was nicely dried; then we took the hood off the wagon, harnessed Billy, and drew in load after load of the sweet-smelling stuff until the twilit cavern of the store, between the stable and the wagon shelter, was crammed to the rafters — and the harvest was home.

The old road rewarded our hope of it, and we came to White's Turn-off just past where the bitumen road glides up out of the gullies to take over the running on top of the range. We turned onto the bush track. The tree-butts and saplings came close to the sides of the car, and we were near our journey's end.

I didn't expect — not after thirty-five years — to find the scene as I had left it. The selection was abandoned. I knew this much from a chance encounter a few weeks previously with a man who had known the Simses. Mr Sims had succeeded in making a living from the selection until, in his seventies, it had proved too much for his declining strength, and he and his wife had gone to live in the city. Here they remained until he died in his eighties, and she followed him within a few weeks. None of the sons had thought the place worth carrying on.

In returning for a day — a blessing on John — I was realizing a hope I had nurtured for many years and in far countries. Neither time nor distance had dulled the edge of happy recollection, nor robbed the old man of stature. In my thoughts he had come to stand for all humanity, holding to its dream while heart and nerve endure. I wanted to glimpse again the ground where he had fought the good fight — just as in telling this story I have sought with words to make him a memorial.

We reached our destination and alighted. As we passed through the broken gate I noticed that the area of the clearing had increased very little since I last saw it. The pasture paddocks had not materialized. The demands of the orchard as the trees grew in size — together, no doubt, with diminishing strength as the years passed — would explain this.

There was little to be seen; just a clearing in the bush with a thin coat of grass over the old plough-rumpled earth. Of the young apple-trees I remembered on the right there were remaining only a couple of hoary old stumps with broken and withered arms; and on the left just a green slope where the raspberries had been. Of the dividing fence only a couple of old grey posts were standing, and the grass now hid the cart-track.

The homestead buildings had vanished and the site looked strange, marked with a couple of tall blackwoods that I remembered only as seedlings fetched from the gully. There was a hard lump where the chimney had stood and a bare patch where the barn had been. That was all. The lips of the well had fallen in, like an old mouth turned to the sky.

We stood for a while, our minds busy with thoughts inevitable to such a place. I was wondering what the dark-haired lad in dungarees would have thought of the baldish man in city togs revisiting his morning scene, and what thoughts had been in the minds of the old man and his wife when it came time for them to retreat. The road to yesterday had brought us to the end of tomorrow — all tomorrows. It seemed odd that I hadn't counted on that.

It was a pleasant day, brightly sunny, blue-skied, and quiet. We could hear water trickling down the fern gully behind us, and there was a whiff of wild clematis in the air. A magpie was expressing its pleasure about something among the trees beyond the open grass, and we saw a fox trail his brush across the bottom corner of the clearing.

The fence around the clearing — once so trim and taut — was now in a state of collapse, rotten posts leaning awry, and wires missing or fallen slack. Saplings were thrusting up through the ruin, and a seedling shrub or two was growing on the grassland. Little by little the bush was reclaiming its own — though there would be an open green place in the wilderness for many a year.

On leaving the gate we encountered a couple of local bushmen; men at the turn of forty, they would have been toddlers when I was a lad; and from them I added a little to my knowledge of events since the days I recalled. Harry had fought right through the war from Gallipoli onwards. Jessie had afterwards gone with him wheat-farming in the Mallee, and there had married another veteran of the campaigns. Charlie and Annie were still in the district, along the new road, doing well in the red-soil potato-growing country, farther back in the hills. There was a grandson who was a young airman of some distinction. He had recently piloted across the Pacific the first of the new Constellation aircraft to reach this country from America. It was too late for visiting, but I made a note of addresses.

We went on then a few miles, and picnicked under the gums where King Parrot Creek comes singing from the high gorges over a bed of green and grey stones. After lunch we enjoyed climbing over the creek-bed boulders and mossy logs, spotting trout in the brown pools. We gathered an armful of bush foliage — harmony in low tones — and set out for the city again when the gullies were in shadow and the hill-tops golden. We travelled by the new road, gliding swiftly and smoothly around its sleek curves.

Rex
Ingamells

Slight Autobiography

When I was ten at Burra I would speak
with waterhen beside the reedy creek.
I was a Copper Miner after school,
taking it easy down there in the cool.

At lunch-time I would wander on the flat
beside the School, some notion in my hat
that Gordon's dying stockman went that way;
and there he goes for me until this day.

Down Murray reaches in a frail canoe —
though all the world should doubt me, this is true —
went Captain Sturt eleven years ago.
I tell you I was there and ought to know.

And any day in our King William Street,
if you would come with me, perhaps you'd meet
Deakin and Cook, just dropped along to see
if anyone has them in memory.

Lawson steps round a corner now and then,
flipping a wisp of rhyme from off his pen,
and that goes singing through my head as though
it holds a truth which everyone should know.

Garrakeen

Garrakeen, the parakeet, is slim and swift.
Like a spear of green and red he flashes through
the cumbered branches by the river-bank.
Watch him, brighter than the clouds, before the day is done;
watch him in the morning, when the gums are bathed with dew,
rivalling the spears of the sun.

When dawn flamed on the Murray I watched for Garrakeen . . .
Opaline purple and crimson was the river . . .
He came from the west with blood on his breast,
and the colours of the water were sluggish in sheen
compared with his fire in the air;

the voice of the water was shattered by one
shrill from the spear-bird hurrying there,
flying with the light of the east in his sight,
rivalling the spears of the sun.

The Tourist Dump

I found and lost Alcheringa;
I lost it by the bend;
I came too far, a chain too far,
to where it has an end.

On lofty bough and blackened stump
the kookaburras din —
but one is cock of the tourist dump
on a rusty kero tin.

Green and yellow reeds are here,
drinking the stream and sun;
overhead the parrots veer,
fifty that cry as one;
here, in the sleepy summer noon,
all frogs and crickets are —
but not till dimness of the moon
will be Alcheringa.

47

Marjorie
Barnard

The Persimmon-tree

I saw the spring come once — only once — and I won't forget it. I had been
ill all the winter and I was recovering. No more pain now, no more treatments
or visits to the doctor. The face that looked back at me from my old silver mirror
was the face of a woman who had escaped. I had only to build up my strength.
For that I wanted to be alone, an old and natural impulse. I had been out of
things for quite a long time and the effort of returning was still too great. My
mind was transparent and as tender as new skin. Everything that happened, even
the commonest things, seemed to be happening for the first time and had a
delicate hollow ring like music played in an empty auditorium.

I took a flat in a quiet, blind street, lined with English trees. It was one large
room, high ceilinged with pale walls, chaste as a cell in a honeycomb, and
furnished with the passionless, standardized grace of a fashionable interior dec-
orator. It had the afternoon sun, which I prefer because I like my mornings
shadowy and cool, the relaxed end of the night prolonged as far as possible.
When I arrived the trees were bare and still against the lilac dusk. There was
a block of flats opposite, discreet, well tended, with a wide entrance. At night
it lifted its oblongs of rose and golden light far up into the sky. One of its windows
was immediately opposite mine. I noticed that it was always shut against the air.
The street was wide, but because it was so quiet the window seemed near. I was
glad to see it always shut because I spent a good deal of time at my window and
it was the only one that might have overlooked me and flawed my privacy.

I liked the room from the first; it was a shell that fitted without touching me.
The afternoon sun threw the shadow of a tree on my light wall, and it was in
the shadow that I first noticed that the bare twigs were beginning to swell with
buds. A water-colour, pretty and innocuous, hung on that wall. One day I asked
the silent woman who serviced me to take it down. After that the shadow of the
tree had the wall to itself and I felt cleared and tranquil as if I had expelled the
last fragment of grit from my mind.

I grew familiar with all the people in the street; they came and went with a
surprising regularity and they all, somehow, seemed to be cut to a very correct

48

pattern. They were part of the *mise en scène*, hardly real at all, and I never felt the faintest desire to become acquainted with any of them. There was one woman I noticed, about my own age. She lived over the way. She had been beautiful, I thought, and was still handsome, with a fine tall figure. She always wore dark clothes, tailor made, and there was reserve in her every movement. Coming and going she was always alone, but you felt that that was by her own choice, that everything she did was by her own steady choice. She walked up the steps so firmly and vanished so resolutely into the discreet muteness of the building opposite, that I felt a faint, a very faint, envy of any one who appeared to have her life so perfectly under control.

There was a day much warmer than any we had had, a still, warm, milky day. I saw as soon as I got up that the window opposite was open a few inches. "Spring comes even to the careful heart," I thought. And the next morning not only was the window open but there was a row of persimmons set out carefully and precisely on the sill to ripen in the sun. Shaped like a young woman's breasts, their deep rich golden-orange colour seemed just the highlight that the morning's spring tranquillity needed. It was almost a shock to me to see them there. I remembered at home when I was a child there was a grove of persimmon-trees down one side of the house. In the autumn they had blazed deep red, taking your breath away. They cast a rosy light into rooms on that side of the house as if a fire were burning outside. Then the leaves fell and left the pointed dark gold fruit clinging to the bare branches. They never lost their strangeness — magical, Hesperidean trees. When I saw *The Fire Bird* danced my heart moved painfully because I remembered the persimmon-trees in the early morning against the dark windbreak of the loquats. Why did I always think of autumn in springtime?

Persimmons belong to autumn and this was spring. I went to the window to look again. Yes, they were there, they were real, I had not imagined them — autumn fruit warming to a ripe transparency in the spring sunshine. They must have come expensively packed in sawdust from California or have lain all winter in storage. Fruit out of season.

It was later in the day when the sun had left the sill that I saw the window opened and a hand come out to gather the persimmons. I saw a woman's figure against the curtains. She lived there. It was her window opposite mine.

Often now the window was open. That in itself was like the breaking of a bud. A bowl of thick cream pottery shaped like a boat appeared on the sill. It was planted, I think, with bulbs. She used to water it with one of those tiny, long-spouted, hand-painted cans that you use for refilling vases, and I saw her gingerly loosening the earth with a silver table fork. She did not look up or across the street. Not once.

Sometimes on my leisurely walks I passed her in the street. I knew her quite

well now, the texture of her skin, her hands, the set of her clothes, her movements — the way you know people when you are sure you will never be put to
the test of speaking to them. I could have found out her name quite easily. I had
only to walk into the vestibule of her block and read it in the list of tenants or
consult the visiting card on her door. I never did.

She was a lonely woman and so was I. That was a barrier not a link. Lonely
women have something to guard. I was not exactly lonely. I had stood my life
on a shelf, that was all. I could have had a dozen friends round me all day long.
But there was not a friend that I loved and trusted above all the others, no lover,
secret or declared. She had, I suppose, some nutrient hinterland on which she
drew.

The bulbs in her bowl were shooting, I could see the pale new-green spears
standing out of the dark loam. I wondered what they would be. I expected tulips,
I don't know why. Her window was open all day long now. Very fine thin
curtains hung in front of it and these were never parted; sometimes they moved,
but it was only in the breeze.

The trees in the street showed green now, thick with budded leaves. The
shadow pattern on my wall was intricate and rich, no longer an austere winter
pattern as it had been at first. Even the movement of the branches in the wind
seemed different. I used to lie looking at the shadow when I rested in the afternoon — I was always tired then, and so more permeable to impressions. I'd
think about the buds, how pale and tender they were but how implacable, the
way an unborn child is implacable. If man's world were in ashes the spring
would still come. I watched the moving pattern and my heart stirred with it in
frail, half-sweet melancholy.

One afternoon I looked out instead of in. It was growing late and the sun
would soon be gone, but it was warm. There was gold dust in the air, the
sunlight had thickened. The shadows of trees and buildings fell, as they sometimes do on a fortunate day, with dramatic grace. She was standing there just
behind the curtains in a long dark wrap, as if she had come from her bath and
was going to dress early for the evening. She stood so long and so still, staring
out — I thought at the budding trees — that tension began to accumulate in my
mind. My blood ticked like a clock. Very slowly she raised her arms and the
gown fell from her. She stood there naked, behind the veil of the curtains, the
scarcely distinguishable but unmistakable form of a woman whose face was in
shadow.

I turned away. The shadow of the burgeoning bough was on the white wall.
I thought my heart would break.

John
Manifold

The Tomb of Lt. John Learmonth, A.I.F.

"At the end on Crete he took to the hills, and said he'ld fight it out with
only a revolver. He was a great soldier." . . .
                                        —*One of his men in a letter.*

This is not sorrow, this is work: I build
A cairn of words over a silent man,
My friend John Learmonth whom the Germans killed.

There was no word of hero in his plan;
Verse should have been his love and peace his trade,
But history turned him to a partisan.

Far from the battle as his bones are laid
Crete will remember him. Remember well,
Mountains of Crete, the Second Field Brigade!

Say Crete, and there is little more to tell
Of muddle tall as treachery, despair
And black defeat resounding like a bell;

But bring the magnifying focus near
And in contempt of muddle and defeat
The old heroic virtues still appear.

Australian blood where hot and icy meet
(James Hogg and Lermontov were of his kin)
Lie still and fertilise the fields of Crete.

        *   *   *

Schoolboy, I watched his ballading begin:
Billy and bullocky and billabong,
Our properties of childhood, all were in.

51

I heard the air though not the undersong,
The fierceness and resolve; but all the same
They're the tradition, and tradition's strong.

Swagman and bushranger die hard, die game,
Die fighting, like that wild colonial boy —
Jack Dowling, says the ballad, was his name.

He also spun his pistol like a toy,
Turned to the hills like wolf or kangaroo,
And faced destruction with a bitter joy.

His freedom gave him nothing else to do
But set his back against his family tree
And fight the better for the fact he knew

He was as good as dead. Because the sea
Was closed and the air dark and the land lost,
"They'll never capture me alive," said he.

*   *   *

That's courage chemically pure, uncrossed
With sacrifice or duty or career,
Which counts and pays in ready coin the cost

Of holding course. Armies are not its sphere
Where all's contrived to achieve its counterfeit;
It swears with discipline, it's volunteer.

I could as hardly make a moral fit
Around it as around a lightning flash.
There is no moral, that's the point of it,

No moral. But I'm glad of this panache
That sparkles, as from flint, from us and steel,
True to no crown nor presidential sash

Nor flag nor fame. Let others mourn and feel
He died for nothing: nothings have their place.
While thus the kind and civilised conceal

This spring of unsuspected inward grace
And look on death as equals, I am filled
With queer affection for the human race.

The Bunyip and the Whistling Kettle

I knew a most superior camper
　　Whose methods were absurdly wrong;
He did not live on tea and damper
　　But took a little stove along.

And every place he came to settle
　　He spread with gadgets saving toil;
He even had a whistling kettle
　　To warn him it was on the boil.

Beneath the waratahs and wattles,
　　Boronia and coolibah,
He scattered paper, cans and bottles,
　　And parked his nasty little car.

He camped, this sacrilegious stranger
　　(The moon was at the full that week),
Once in a spot that teemed with danger
　　Beside a bunyip-haunted creek.

He spread his junk but did not plunder,
　　Hoping to stay the week-end long;
He watched the bloodshot sun go under
　　Across the silent billabong.

He ate canned food without demurring,
　　He put the kettle on for tea.
He did not see the water stirring
　　Far out beside a sunken tree.

Then, for the day had made him swelter
　　And night was hot and tense to spring,
He donned a bathing suit in shelter
　　And left the firelight's friendly ring.

He felt the water kiss and tingle.
　　He heard the silence — none too soon!
A ripple broke against the shingle,
　　And dark with blood it met the moon.

Abandoned in the hush, the kettle
　　Screamed as it guessed its master's plight,
And loud it screamed, the lifeless metal,
　　Far into the malicious night.

53

Stringybark Creek

Late one October afternoon
  When rain was in the sky,
A horseman shouting witless words
  Came belting madly by.

Straight for Benalla Town he rode
  And shouted as he came;
But no one recognised the horse
  Or knew the rider's name.

Silence came down behind his back;
  On countless cocky farms
The people watched the Wombat Hills
  Not moving eyes or arms.

None knew, and not for days we knew,
  That in the hour he passed
Lonigan died, and Kelly's hands
  Were dipped in blood at last.

And Kennedy was yet to die,
  And McIntyre in flight
Half-crazed upon a crazy horse
  Would scour the range all night.

But silence fell on all the farms
  As down the road they flew —
The horse that no one recognised,
  The man that no one knew.

Outer Suburbs

It seems you can't have gracious living and
Goannas. Shiny villas multiply
On what were quite attractive bits of land,
And we'll be getting sewerage by and by.

Down where Macpherson's smithy used to stand
They've built a supermarket on the sly.
"It's progress", says my neighbour; "Things expand."
But living creatures are in short supply.

We haven't had goannas in the yard
For six or seven years. They were the first
To leave, and then the frillies. That was hard.

The only newcomers are oversexed
Damned greedy sparrows, breeding fit to burst.
They drove the wrens away. It's our turn next.

The Map

Devil take our city-minded, imitative gran'dads who
Saddled us with Warwick, Ipswich, Bloomsbury (near Yalbaroo),
Surbiton on Belyando — names like these will never do!

Mount Mistake, The Risk, The Blunder, Wilson's Downfall make a change,
But the names I like are those that show a sense of somewhere strange —
One Tree Hill and Wild Horse Mountain, Razorback and Nightcap Range —

And at sundown, when the hills are monstrous and the bunyip stirs,
I am pretty sure the native names are what the land prefers:
Murderer's Flat was our invention, but Eurunderee was hers.

Jundah, Thunda, Nocatunga, Thargomindah, Gunnewin,
Tarrewinnabar, Canungra, Tabragalba, Coolwinpin,
Ulandilla by the Maranoa where the songs begin,

Binna Burra, Bindebango, Mullumbimby — these belong! —
Bunya, Quinalow, Nanango, Tallebudgera, Durong,
Xylophones among the timber,
      Bellbirds in the border mountains,
           Wallangarra, Woodenbong.

Bogong Jack and the Trooper

There's a story told about Bogong Jack
    And I'll not go bail it's true,
But I ran across it a few years back
    And I'm passing it on to you.

He wasn't in Kelly's class, of course,
    Nor a hero like brave Ben Hall,
But he couldn't stay off a beautiful horse,
    Branded or not; that's all.

This kept the traps in a state of strain
    From Omeo clear to Bright,
Till the squatters murmured they'ld not complain
    If Bogong were shot at sight.

A constable on his promotion once
    Attempted to do just that
When he sighted his man by the merest chance
    A mile above Clover Flat.

At the range, it was probably hopeless; still
    It made his intention clear.
So Bogong belted away up hill
    With the trap not far in rear.

He made for the Kiewa Fork like smoke
    Where the creeks ran high with the rains,
For he reckoned the trap was a willing bloke
    But his mount might show more brains.

Smash thro' the water went Bogong Jack
    And patted his mare's wet skin,
But the trooper's horse at the brink shied back
    And the trooper went right in.

Now you shouldn't go into those mountain creeks
    Unless you're a mountain trout,
For it may be a matter of days or weeks
    Before anyone hauls you out.

Well, the trooper wasn't. He simply clung
   To a rock with either hand,
And whenever the water bared his tongue
   He called upon Jack to "Stand!"

"Stand?" says Jack. "I'ld be grateful to,
   For it's been an exhausting game;
But it's hardly the thing for me to do
   When you can't do the same!

Are you going to be long in there? If so,
   I'll just have a bite and sup
From the saddlebag here. I should like to know
   How long you can keep it up."

The trap gave in. He'd begun to feel
   Like one of an angler's worms,
So he kicked the boot from each waterlogged heel
   And accepted Bogong's terms.

He let his belt and his pouches drift
   And settled himself to swim
On the blown-up waterbag — thoughtful gift —
   Which Bogong handed him.

Bogong rode for a mile or more
   On the bank as he drifted down,
Poling him carefully off from shore
   And seeing he didn't drown.

The trooper got home all right, it's said;
   But resigned from the Force next day;
And his boots are down on the Kiewa's bed,
   And there I suppose they'll stay.

This story may be a lot of tripe,
   But if that's so it's odd
That I once found a rowell of Government type
   In the craw of a Murray cod.

The Stranger

A stranger came into the district last week,
He wasn't a Balt and he wasn't a Greek.
We asked, was he Irish? He answered us, no;
He came from up North where the pineapples grow.

He answered so mannerly, quite at his ease,
Saying neither too much nor too little to please,
He was hardly a stranger by teatime, although
He came from up North where the pineapples grow.

We swapped the old stories of famine and flood
And the crook politicians that suck a man's blood;
We had reckoned they might have been local, but no!
It's the same in the North where the pineapples grow.

We tickled his fancy with peaches and cream,
We showed him Polled Angus as sleek as a dream;
He agreed they were ''mighty'', but still he must go —
He was needed up North where the pineapples grow.

The moral of this is too plain to be spoke:
The bloke on the land is a sensible bloke,
Be he brown as a berry, or black as a crow,
Or just from up North where the pineapples grow.

Gavin
Casey

Talking Ground

THE TROUBLE between Bill Lawton and Jim Sparrow was that the former knew the weakness of his mate. They had worked together for a year and been cobbers off the lease before Bill made the discovery that was to change the character of their relationship. But it had to come, and it came on the evening when the shift-boss took them from the face on the seven hundred level, and set them to work in the big stope at the twelve.

Bill knew the mine. He had worked in the stope before, and it was all the same to him. He led the way, because he knew every foot of the level and could make progress without peering ahead into the beam of his lamp. He voiced a warning of the locality of the chute as they left the plat, and when they were a quarter of a mile from the shaft, and the faint mutterings that had always distinguished the rickety old twelve hundred became audible, he thought nothing of it. He emerged from the tunnel into the great shadowy cavity, talking over his shoulder.

"It's a good level, Jim. There's plenty of air, and I like a place where there's plenty of air," he said, and then looked back. Jim was not there.

For a moment Bill was startled, but the sound of moving stones and a glow in the distance reassured him. Jim came out of the darkness, and stood his lamp on a rock behind him so that it shone on his back and his face was still in the gloom.

"What happened to you?" asked Bill. "You gave me a fright."

"Nothing," said his mate. "Just strange to the place."

Bill, who had moved off without waiting for an answer, was halted by something shaky in his tone. He swung his light so that the beam shone bright on Jim's face. Jim did not blink. His eyes remained wide and fixed, tense and alert as his white, drawn features.

"'Strewth!" said Bill. "You look like someone's ghost. What the hell's the matter?"

"Nothing," said Jim again. "She — she talks a lot down here, don't she?"

Bill's laugh of relief rumbled along the crevices and mingled with stifled, faraway grunts that indicate the minute movements of hundreds of tons of earth.

The chuckle cut its way into Jim's paralysed mind like an echo of the menace that he felt around him; but it could not have been suppressed. The man was frozen with fright, and Bill was amused. The very idea of a miner, one who had toiled in the depths for years, even noticing what he himself had long ago dismissed from his mind as the baffled bluff of ground held in check by its masters was funny. For the first time he had a warming, elating sensation of superiority over the mate who had never before shown a weakness, except of the kind that is admired among men.

"Snap out of it!" he said. "It's talked a lot for twenty years, and it'll talk a lot for another twenty. That's what it is — all talk, and the safest place on the Mile. You ought to know better, feller."

Jim knew it, but it was a flush of resentment that brought the colour back to his cheeks. He said nothing, but picked up his lamp, and soon they were making their insignificant contributions to the toil of the underground together.

But from out of the great black void of the stope the voice of the earth continued to protest. Whispers grew into muffled groans, and occasionally the hollow rattle of a little falling stone, diving down a rock wall, hitting the broken rock, and spinning and leaping to the bottom of a rill, made an exaggerated clatter in its higher key. Whenever this happened Jim's already taut muscles would stretch till they hurt, startled sweat would bead his forehead, and he would take a new grip of tattered nerves before he could go on.

But for Bill, Jim would have quit before the first week was out. He had walked off his last job — a good one, on profitable contract rates — before any one had discovered the reason. There, too, the ground had "talked", threatening and shifting about behind its deceptive face, day and night. It had creaked and groaned and grated above and around him, until it was no longer an interesting phenomenon, but a promise of doom. It had developed voices, suggestions of impending catastrophe that were almost articulate. The rock had pressed around him, stifling and startling, before he had decided not to go down into it again. He had got into a habit of staring, hypnotized, at a wall of solid stone until it first melted into vague, swirling, dark masses, and then leapt, toppling and tumbling, towards him. The seven hundred level, where the masses were quiet and still, and the only noises were those of humans and scurrying, friendly mice, had been heaven after that.

But now he was at the twelve, in the big stope that was always filled with vague hints of irresistible power, crushing weight and diabolical purpose, biding their time.

When Bill began to realize that his mate's inexplicable state was serious, he tried, with a clumsy good humour that was not free of patronage, to set his fears at rest. Standing with his heels dug into the rubble, he talked commonsense down to the pale face of a man whose mind had long since rejected logic as applied to his obsession.

"Crikey!" said Bill, in amiable, peaceful tones, unaware that all around him the earth was whispering promises to the devil. "It ain't the ground that talks all the time you've got to get the wind up about. When it starts all of a sudden, stand from under if you like; but this noise that goes on for years an' years don't mean a thing. She might come down, same as she might anywhere; but you ought to know there ain't any more chance of it just 'cause of all the silly row. Surely t' Gawd you've worked in a level where the ground's been gruntin' a bit before now."

Jim, a dozen feet below him, snarled. He had never admitted to Bill how he felt. He never would. He would wait for what was coming, and met his end when it did, just for the joy of seeing Bill Lawton go under first, with his grimace of animal astonishment on his ugly, unintelligent face.

"Damn you!" said Jim. "I know. I'm like you — I know everything — so you don't need to tell me. You don't need to tell me, do you hear? You're like the ground — you talk too much; but I don't give a damn for either of you."

After that they had little to say to each other, though Bill, who felt that he had a just grievance, aired it occasionally in ways that pricked and rankled. He took to watching his mate with the amused interest with which one might examine a freakish and eccentric insect.

"I've got an idea, Jim," he said one day. "Why let th' ground do all the talking? Answer it back a bit, lad. Tell it to go to hell a few times, an' they'll soon put you where it won't worry you any more."

"Listen to that one!" he would sing out when the fastness of the rock rumbled more heavily than usual. "It's giving you the raspberry now. If I was you, I'd shove a few plugs of fracteur into the cheeky cow."

Jim writhed, wavered at breaking point, and inwardly swore himself to what would be a joyous murder if he ever suspected that Bill had talked to any one else in that strain. But Bill never did that.

They were, of course, no longer friends off the mine. They kept as far away from each other as possible. And each eight-hour shift in the twelve hundred stope was an eternity of shameful misery for Jim. In the daylight, above ground, he knew it was ridiculous. In the mine he had no fear of a chattering rock-drill's hammering point striking an unexploded charge and splashing itself and the men around on the nearest wall. He had no fear of falls, or nervousness in the cage that dropped and leapt perilously in the narrow shaft. It was just the voices in the rocks, the secret evil conversations that went on in the bowels of the earth, that unnerved him. His face developed a permanent masklike stiffness of expression. He lost weight, and could not sleep for hating Bill Lawton.

Then one day when Jim, obviously a sick man, needed a lift on a job that was too heavy for him, Bill surprisingly made overtures towards friendship.

He was up on the rill, with his lamp illuminating the frowning rock behind and above him, and he sang out a little less confidently than usual.

"Wait a sec.," he called, "and I'll be down t' give you a hand." Then he straightened. "Crikey, Jim, we've been actin' like a couple o' nannies!"

Jim from the depths, looked up in silence.

"You're a bundle o' nerves," Bill continued; "and I know I've been kiddin' too hard. Git it straight, son. Forget the stupid noises for a week or two, an' we'll work a shift back to the seven hundred if I can manage it."

Just then the murmur of the uneasy earth became perceptibly louder, but Bill was too earnest in his persuasive arguments to notice it. Jim was listening more to the creaking of the rocks than to him, though he gazed as if fascinated at his mate. Away in some corner out of sight a staccato noise that was more like straining timber than grating stone joined the weird medley of sound; but Bill continued.

"It's a bit uncanny sometimes, I know," he said. "P'rhaps I been noticin' it more lately, with you all of a dither. A man wants a mate down these damn' holes that he can talk to, an' forget what lousy places they are. It's no use makin' 'em more unpleasant than they've got to be."

But Jim was not listening to his words at all now. The grunting of the mile-wide masses of stone was ringing in his ears like the sobbing breath of a giant struggling in bonds. A few tiny flakes dropped off behind Bill, and fell noiselessly into the rubble. Over his head a gigantic sharp-fanged lip of stone drooped slowly (like the lower jaw of a titanic, hungry beast) away from the main body. Jim's body seemed to slip away from him, and leave him standing, watching, without it. The tenseness was gone. He was not even afraid.

"If you'll call it quits ——" entreated Bill.

Then a scattered rain of small boulders was spewed from the crevice above his head. One of them caught him between the shoulders, and with surprising, elastic leaps and somersaults he came bouncing down the rill, with a little torrent of rubble in his wake. His lamp was out, but Jim's showed him, inert, at the bottom.

A few tons of rock peeled away, up above, with a rending noise, and settled with a sigh on the rubble. An ocean of dirt submerged the lower part of Bill, and pebbles pelting about his head brought him to consciousness. His face wore just that puzzled, uncomprehending expression Jim had often imagined upon it.

"Jim!" he called. "For God's sake ——"

But it was not that cry that affected Jim. A new river of dirt had started, near the top of the rill somewhere. The voice of the earth was angry, farther back, with the quaking upheaval that was upsetting it. The whispers had changed to a harsh challenge, and Jim snarled in reply, suddenly determined to beat the ground, to trick it of its prey. He leapt for his mate, and together they struggled against the mounting rubble.

It was only the loose stuff — the first light layer of the dirt that would soon be packed and hard beneath hundreds of tons of rock — that held Bill. He came out of it like a cork out of a bottle, and together they ran. Careless of fingers and faces in the fearful darkness, stumbling and scrambling forward with desperate energy, they made the level. And as they sped along it they heard the voice of the earth behind them change to a roar as the avalanche engulfed the big stope.

At the plat, under electric lights and in the comforting company of solicitous inquirers, the unruffled Bill tenderly examined bruises on his legs, and explained their narrow escape with a wealth of vivid detail. He made a hero out of Jim, though that worthy sprawled beside him, colourless and limp, and fit for nothing as yet.

And Jim, shivering and dumb with shock, longing for the surface and the sunlight, felt a glow of appreciation of his mate. A great chap — tough, straight and decent. As good a cobber as a man could wish for — a man upon whom one could rely. Such mates were scarce enough to be valuable. It would be a long while before he would find another. But seek another he would have to, for Bill would never, in any circumstances, understand how he felt about talking ground.

His only satisfaction was that now, at any rate, he would be able to get away from it, to walk off the lease for good, and still be able to enjoy a friendly drink and a yarn with Bill when they ran across each other on paydays.

When Jim was Different

THE HOUSE was not a bad one, in such a town of wood and iron and impermanent plasterboard, but it was pretty flimsy and drab. It was a copy of the brick and stucco shapes that adorn fashionable suburbs; but it was smaller, and the asbestos walls and iron roof showed it up as an imitation. There was a big yard around it, but no garden except a dying fig-tree and a square, plank-edged bed in which nothing at all grew.

Inside it was fairly comfortable, but there was generally red dust in odd corners. Mary had hated it when she first saw it, and she had never been able to become interested in it. On this Saturday afternoon there was a brisk wind sending ribbons of dust twirling along the street, and she had not worried to sweep up all day.

She went into the yard and chopped a few sticks of wood to start a fire for Jim's tea. The axe was heavy and blunt, its handle splintering near the head, and she hated the work, feeling that Jim should have done it. She hated even more the lack of privacy, the big yards and low fences which meant that any of the neighbours for three or four houses on each side could see her chopping wood. There was no privacy in the whole town, and everyone must know that Jim was going to pieces and how the pair of them were living. She whacked viciously at the wood, with her hair falling down over her eyes and sweat on her forehead. The woman next door came on to her back veranda, watched for a moment and then called out, "Don't do that, Mrs Peterson. I'll send Joey over to break up an armful for you."

Tears of shame and self-pity burned in Mary's eyes. She bent over the axe, afraid she would give herself away, but she had to say something. She started to gather up the pieces of wood.

"Don't worry," she called. "It's only a few sticks for kindling. I've finished now."

The woman came to the dividing fence and leaned on it ready to talk. She was comfortable and motherly, and for a moment Mary felt weak and tearful, ready again to break down and confide in someone. A corkscrew of sand, the beginning of a willy-willy, danced through the yard, tugging at her skirts as it went and making her drop the wood as she grabbed at the garment with both hands. She laughed foolishly.

"It's brutal weather," said the woman next door. "You'd think the wind'd make it a bit cooler."

"The wind only brings dust," said Mary. "I don't mind the heat so much — it's the dust."

"It's hard for a woman here," her neighbour said. "But you've got a better chance than a miner's wife. Your husband'll get a transfer one of these days, and you'll be sent somewhere nice and green, where there's no dust at all.''

"Oh, if only he would!" said Mary passionately. She remembered greenness so vividly that the tears almost started again. She remembered their garden at the coast, and the solid little house that had been her pride, and all the friends she had had, and how different Jim had been, too. It all hinged on him, she thought despairingly. If he'd be like he was then she'd put up with anything, even chopping the wood. But, of course, she'd never had to chop the wood then.

"It'll come," said the woman next door cheerfully. "Wait till you're my age, Mrs Peterson. The bad times in your life seem funny and interesting when they're over and done with."

But Mary didn't want to be the age of the woman next door, with most of her life over and done with. She wanted everything, and Jim in particular, to be as they'd been just a year ago. She went inside aching with the memory of the happiness she had had then, and lit the fire in the little wood stove.

For a while she was busy, getting the vegetables on and poking the fire into a good blaze, but all the time she thought about when Jim and everything were different. When the tea could look after itself she went through to the bedroom, and got out the snapshot album she'd kept ever since before she first met Jim.

She looked at pictures of herself taken when she had just left school, and, turning the leaves, at picnic pictures and yachting pictures and tennis pictures, most of them with both Jim and herself in them. It made her feel worse, but she couldn't stop. Why couldn't Jim always be as he had been then?

She should have got up and swept out the house, but she couldn't stop crying over the old pictures and feeling sorry for herself. Outside the wind increased, dust swallowed the town and the house and tongues of it licked in under the doors and spread on the linoleum, but Mary lay weak and tearful, thinking about the past when Jim had been different.

Down in the main street, where the pub and the bank were the only solid build-ings in the town, the dust was thick, too, but nobody noticed it much. The kerb was lined with cars of every kind, from the roughest sort of prospector's utility to the latest eight-cylinder sedan. Everyone was in from the district surrounding the little one-mine town, and someone had struck it rich, so celebration was in order. There were liquor and optimism and good-fellowship in plenty at the pub.

They were a democratic crowd around the bar, the local bank manager, and the boys who worked on the mine, and the manager of the State battery, and the storekeeper, and the newsagent, and the prospectors in for the week-end, all getting mixed up in indescribable but hilarious and friendly confusion. High hopes bubbled out of them as the beer soaked in, and they all had fortunes waiting around the corner, in claims or shares or holdings in syndicates. Their eyes gleamed as they spoke, and if the bank man had a moment of panic during a lull in the talk, hoping that the inspector was a long way away, that was no one's business but his. Everyone was in the running one way or another — even most of the toilers on the mine, who had good contracts in soft dirt.

Of course, there were only two prospectors in the mob who had really struck it, and had a signed option with a fat deposit as a basis for their optimism, but none of the others were more than the length of a pick-head away. They were on a leader that couldn't fail, and the lie of the land proved that, when they did strike it, it was going to be the lode that the Sunlight people lost in 1898. Or if it wasn't that — if their leader had fizzled out altogether and their store-bill had grown to frightening size — they were celebrating a move. And the move was worth celebrating too! They're cursing themselves for not having been out Yandarrie way months ago, and they tell the mob about the magnificent stuff they got there in '15 — only, of course, at that time Bordertown was shut up and dead, and there were no supplies and water, and a long, dry summer sent them in. It'll be different now with the Border thriving again, and they'll be back here just to buy for the boys in a few months, you can take their word!

"Hell!" someone says. "I worked the same dirt five years back. Tom was tellin' me he found one o' me old pegs, an' used it. The same damn' block, to a foot or two!"

"I'm pegged out right up against him," says someone else. "On the line o' reef, too. If they take up his option I'm a cert."

Among this crowd, Jim felt excitement and envy and a tremendous scorn for his safe job in the railways. It mightn't be as easy as it sounded, he thought, but it was having a lick at something. It made him restless, discontented with low pay and regular hours, doing small routine tasks. He wished he had the courage to break away, but he couldn't. He and Mary had never managed to save much, and she wouldn't stand for it anyway. Among the shouting, seething mob, he felt strange and out of it at first, but when he'd drunk enough and got talking he felt better. He hadn't done any of the things they were telling about, he'd only married young and worked hard in a lousy Government job, but he was just the lad that could have. It was hard to drag himself away. All the life and optimism of the town were here, anyway.

The mob grew noisier, and Jim grew happier, and after a while "Slogger" Priestly and a couple of his cobbers came over. Slogger was big and brown, with no coat, but an expensive silk shirt and well-cut slacks. He had two big trucks carting ore in from the Breakaway, and both of them were working two shifts. Slogger did twelve-hour stretches himself, but when he came in to have some fun he did it properly. He always had a thick bankroll, and Jim envied him his independence and his money. To-day he was complaining, but it didn't sound dinkum. He made it sound as if he was as pleased with himself as anyone very well could be.

"Jim here's the lucky one," he announced. "Proper meals an' a proper house, an' proper hours an' proper pay, an' a missus an' everything. Who wouldn't swap my humpy out at the Breakaway an' all my worries for that?"

Jim grinned half-heartedly, and felt more envious than ever. Slogger dragged a note out of his pocket, and thought to hell with the instalments on the trucks anyway; a man had to have some fun when he was working all day and all night to keep a lousy finance company going. The crowd was milling around, and drinking and singing and shouting, and Jim was pretty well under the weather, too. It was time he went off home, but there was another round on the counter, and he could see red dust cascading down the street outside. It was swirling on the floor and beginning to hang in the air in the pub, too, but it would be worse outside, and it was bright and comfortable in the bar.

It got dark and the dust kept blowing, making angry red rings around the street lights. Flappers and some of the lads of the village appeared on the pavements, parading up and down, waiting for the pictures to start. After a while the doors opened, and the gusty, dusty street emptied. A few of the cars backed out from the kerb and went charging through the flying sand, bound for distant leases, but the celebration at the pub continued, noisy and all mixed up and unsteady now. Tall talk about high hopes went the rounds. Jim decided that he might as well be hung for a sheep as a lamb and stayed where he was, pretty drunk, envying everyone else, and regretting the quiet years that lay behind him.

When he got home it was pretty late, and Mary wasn't there. There was a note to say that she had gone to the pictures, and the food she had cooked for tea lay cold on the dead fire. Jim didn't want to eat, but he felt aggrieved about it all the same. All the way up the road he'd been working out in a fuddled way how he was going to handle the row, and now there wasn't any row. There wasn't even Mary; only some cold, soggy potatoes and three greasy sausages.

The dust had drifted under the doors and lay in pools. The plates and knives and the bread and the butter-dish were powdered with red and the place looked as if it hadn't been lived in for a week. He lurched through to the bedroom and the counterpane was gritty, too, and hadn't been smoothed since Mary had lain on it that afternoon. The light jumped, as it always did, and it hurt Jim's eyes. Mary's album was lying on the bed, and he lay down with his clothes on and started to examine it.

He was pretty drunk and the figures in the snapshots danced under the dancing light, but he could spot himself and Mary, too, in the pictures. He jeered at himself in some sports outfit, and then his eyes focused properly on one of Mary. She'd been younger, sprucer, merrier when that was taken, he thought. Why didn't women stay the same? Thinking about the dust all over the house, and Mary away when he came home tired and a bit sick, he started to feel sorry for himself. Things were bad enough without her changing like she had. He thought of her now, lean and snappy and always complaining.

Outside, the dust-laden wind howled among the houses and the mine building, and a loose sheet of iron on the roof started to buck and flap. Turning the leaves of the album backwards, Jim grew more and more interested in Mary as she had been, before they were married, when he had first met her. Drink and misery welled up in him as he thought about it all, and he felt weak with grief and ready for tears. It was bad enough to live all the time knowing how he'd failed and envying everyone who was careless and free and full of high hopes, but he might have been able to put up with it if only Mary had been as he'd expected she would be, if only she hadn't changed!

Ian
Mudie

Street Vision

One night of mist the bush came back again
into the city street, I saw
glint of gum-sapling, rough trunk of blackwood
and the twist of mallee; there
the sheoak mourning for the dead, long dead,
red-gums that stood along the river,
shut out the neon lights and let the glare
of moon creep down the mist, and shine
to white the gums long gone.

That night of mist the bush came back again
into the city streets, I saw
a yacca pointing to the stars, near where
the great 'roo slept, undreaming of
the boomerang and spear; that night I heard
the mopoke call the hours where but
a dream before the clock-tower stood. — And then
the bush flowed back again; an English tree
drooped lifeless in the soggy square.

Galah

High in the wind, high against
clouds coloured as ash of vanished fires,
flies the galah.
Pink and grey, colours gilded by the last rays
of sun setting in unseen salt water,
beats slowly over.
His caged brothers, sensing him, shriek;
wings beat against the straight bars,
calling him.

Next year he will come again,
bringing a hundred others,
knowing it is time to return
to repossess the ancient
tribal grounds.

The Crab or the Tree

The crab or the tree
losing one limb
grows another.

The tiny lizard also
its severed tail
sprouts anew.

Can I be sure
my human mind
has the same power?

Losing faith and doubts
can I my doubts and faiths
ever renew?

As an experiment
let me lop off one finger
of thought.

You try it, too.

The Blue Crane

I am no poet of the fellowship of man,
I sing no universal brotherhood,
no oneness with all mankind
from furthest land to furthest land

— I sing only of the solitude,
the inner secret loneliness,
each one hugs happily unto his heart.

No graceful gregarious brolga I,
no flock-flying spadger, starling,
only a blue ungainly crane
stalking round muddy waterholes,
along the edges of tree-shadowed dams,
or fishing for thoughts
in swamps where none else seems to live,
only my ghost-like, tussock-crumpled reflection.

Alan
Marshall

Wild Red Horses

When the north wind moans thro' the blind creek courses
And revels with harsh hot sand,
I loose the horses, the wild red horses,
I loose the horses, the mad red horses,
And terror is on the land.

Marie Pitt, "Gallop of Fire"

A dark cloud of smoke mushroomed up from behind the crouching hills and rolled slowly towards the north. It marked the sky with a livid bruise charging the horizon with menace. It suggested sound, yet there was no sound; it proclaimed conflict, yet the violence of conflict was absent.

The air was still; the silence alert. A tense expectancy flowed from the trees and enveloped the small group of men working on the mountainside.

"We'd better get back to the mill, I think," said Blue. "Look at that smoke."

Leaves hung motionless on the slopes of Mt Campbell where the fallers were working. The summer sun had released the fragrance of fern and musk from the gullies. Young leaves were limp in the heat.

"Hey, Steve!" Blue called out to a man peeling the bark from a log some distance up the slope. "There's a big fire working up behind Barrets."

"How far behind Barrets?" Steve called back. From where he was working he could not see Splitters Ridge nor the dark cloud expanding behind its western end.

"About four miles. It's at the foot of Mt Gold."

"It won't do any harm out there," called Steve. "It'll creep back into the Crown Lands."

"What if a north wind comes up?"

"Right! I'll be down," called Steve.

A group of men standing near a tractor watched him making his way between the fallen trunks and the shattered limbs that littered the track above them. The tractor driver jumped down from his seat. His name was Paddy Dwyer and he lived with his wife and two children in one of the mill houses. Steve Johnson boarded with him.

"It's only a scrub fire, you know," he said to the men around him. "It'll burn itself out."

Steve joined the group. "It's a scrub fire now," he said, "but a north wind could whip it into a crown fire in a few minutes."

"I don't think there'll be any wind today," said Paddy, "but you never know. What do ya reckon?"

The men stood looking at the distant cloud slowly revolving and twisting, fashioning itself into blue-black domes and hollows that coiled slowly upwards.

"I don't like the look of it." Steve turned and looked down the mountain to where Tandaluk mill squatted in the valley. "Let's get back to the mill and see what's doing."

"You know, I don't think it's moving out into the Crown Lands," said Paddy. "It looks to me as if it's going to swing in behind Barrets. Do you know if any of the boys have come in from there?" He paused as he was about to climb onto the tractor and looked at Steve.

"I haven't seen any of them," said Steve. "Don't worry, they'll leave before it reaches them. They'll make for Tandaluk."

Paddy climbed onto the tractor seat. Its engine came to life under his hands and tossed its throaty roar across the mill valley. The treads tore at the bark-littered track then gripped as the tractor lurched forward. It heaved itself over the fallen trunks of tree fern and silver wattle, then reaching the track it moved down the hill, its upright exhaust coughing smoke. Behind it walked the fallers, carrying axes, wedges and cross-cut saws.

The fire was in no hurry. There was no wind to goad it to fury. It had been born of a lightning strike two days before and had crept unnoticed along a valley of tree fern and blackwood.

The ground was moist and there were times when its face contracted to a pointed tongue of flame creeping over dead leaves and through broken gum-tree branches that the sun had bleached. Dead wattles revived it when its strength waned and it flared into gusts of sparks and smoke and leaping flames for brief periods. The smoke of its burning drifted away in the still air.

On the morning of the third day it marched into an area where fallers from Barret's mill had left the earth like a battlefield. Tractors had pushed their way through tangled tree-heads and splintered trunks. The smashed bodies of silver wattle and dogwood were piled in chaotic heaps. From amid these lifeless heaps daggered trunks reared upwards, dry and brittle from the sun. The earth was soft with discarded bark. Yellow flowers of fireweed glowed beneath dead limbs and pale leaves. Where the giant mountain ash had fallen to the axe they had crashed through silver wattle and tree fern, crushing them into tortured heaps beneath their weight. Here the big trees had lain while awaiting the saw. Now they had gone and only the long curved beds where they had rested remained amid the litter.

The fire came to this area on a front of a hundred yards. It advanced across the littered earth with eager flares where the leaves were thick. Rivulets of flame merged and grew or subsided beneath rising smoke. When the exploring flames reached the heads of the fallen trees they suddenly grew in size and power. They leaped upwards amid the leaves, gasping a welcome to the main fire that surged forward and enveloped them.

The fire now had a voice. It roared as released gases sent flames like whips to lash the fallen timber. It grew with great speed. A wind now moved in to feed it, gusts of its own creating. Enormous clouds of smoke billowed upwards. Screams of flame pierced the smoke and then were engulfed. It extended its flanks. From a slow creeping fire it had become a scrub fire. It began to march through scrub at the feet of the mountain ash still untouched by the axe.

Tandaluk mill was built in a valley that lay between Splitters Ridge and the Wombat Ranges. It consisted of a mill, a number of men's huts, a boarding house and five houses occupied by the married men. All the buildings were constructed of undressed timber which had bleached to a pale grey over the years.

The huts were unlined. Shelves of undressed timber projected from the studs. Boxes acting as cupboards were nailed to the wall. Bunks were built along the sides with hessian bags strained between side pieces to make the beds upon which men slept.

The ground around the men's hut was strewn with chips. A grindstone stood near one door. Small benches built of new timber formed stands for chipped enamel washbasins. The benches were caked with dry soapflakes. Tree ferns standing at angles brushed the walls with green plumes. A few empty beer bottles covered with dust lay half buried in bark and shavings.

Below the huts Wattle Creek threaded the valley. It flowed along the foot of the Wombat Ranges until it passed out through a gap at the foot of Mt Nulla Nulla to the east. The track to Tandaluk, a bush township five miles away, followed the banks of the creek and afforded the only access road to the mill.

The screech of the twin saws greeted the fallers as they came down from Mt Campbell. They skirted the log yard where huge trunks, cut to a quarter of their length, lay on the skids before being rolled into the mill. Here the huge twin saws cut flitches from the logs. They fell away from the parent trunk and were slid back for further cutting. A huge steam engine drove the belts that flapped on pulley wheels above the benches.

The fallers stood for a moment looking at the men working. The mill was full of movement. Men stood at benches where circular saws screamed into planks a few inches from their hands. They staggered back from ripsaws carrying long beams which they stacked in heaps ready for carting to the timber yard. Men stood before docking saws severing the ends from measured planks. Men with cantle hooks levered huge trunks down skids then walked back for more. Sawdust floated through the mill and hung suspended in beams of sunshine.

Blue raised his voice to a yell so that he could be heard above the din.

"Knock off for a minute, will you! Take a look outside. There's a fire broken out behind Barrets. Where's McArthur?" McArthur was the owner of Tandaluk mill.

Levers were pulled. The circling belts slowed and stopped. Only the steam engine kept working, turning its mighty wheel to the slow hiss of steam.

"He's gone into Tandaluk. He said he was coming back this afternoon." The man on the docker, brushing sawdust from his arms, turned to answer Blue.

"Well, bugger him anyway," said Blue. "This is no time for working. Knock off and take a look outside."

The men left their benches. They followed Blue out into the open and looked at the distant smoke which was moving eastwards behind the northern range. Sometimes a convulsion in one of the billowing black clouds forced it into sudden expansion. The dark convolution of its crown rose upwards and burst. Through the rent shot a whirlwind of white smoke carrying with it a radiance from the fire below.

"Hell!" said the engine driver. "That's some scrub fire, I'm telling you. If we get a north wind we'll have a crown fire on our hands."

The sound of a car driven at speed made him turn his head. The car came into view from behind Mt Nulla Nulla and sped along the valley towards the mill.

"It's McArthur," said Steve. "He's woke up to this fire."

The car pulled up beside the mill and McArthur got out. He was a thick-set man with a round face and a red complexion. He had the confidence and manner that comes with money. He spoke rapidly, a habit of his, but now there was urgency in his voice.

"It's a scrub fire. There's no need to worry. The mill is safe. There's plenty of men at Tandaluk to check it. They've gone out to burn a break back to the main fire. They're doing that now. It won't come over this way but we'd better take precautions. Fill up all the barrels and drums you can get. Place them round the mill and round the back of the boarding house. Some of you come with me and we'll play some water over the timber stacks from the big tanks. Make sure the dugout's all right. Get wet blankets and hang them over the entrance. You all know what measures to take. Now get cracking."

"When do *we* make a dash for it?" asked one of the men. "That smoke looks crook to me."

"There's no danger," McArthur assured him. "It won't cross the break they're burning at Tandaluk. There's no wind. We'll take the women and children out after lunch just in case. We'll have the trucks back here to get you all out — that is if a north wind springs up. I want to see the mill safe first. We've got to douse those timber stacks with water. Come on.''

Blue and Steve did not go with the men following McArthur. They stood with Paddy who, with a sour expression, was watching them making for the stacks of timber.

"That's all right for him," he said. "What about my house?"

"I'll go over to the house now, Paddy," said Steve. "I'll give Mary a hand. Anyway I want to pick up some of my own things. What about you, Blue?"

"I was going to ask Paddy to come over to the boarding house with me. I want to get a pile of blankets and soak them. We could easily get caught getting out of here and if we do the blokes in the back of the truck will want something to cover themselves.''

"I'll give you a hand," said Paddy; then to Steve, "Put my gun out on the verandah, Steve. You'll find it on top of the wardrobe. Tell Mary I'm helping Blue at the boarding house. We're getting blankets.''

The proprietress of the boarding house was a stout, motherly woman who supplied the meals for mill workers boarding there. She was helped by her husband, a quiet man who walked with a limp, and two girls waited on the tables.

Paddy and Blue liked her. "Don't worry, Missus." Paddy spoke with his hand resting on her shoulder. "We'll look after you. Show us where we can get a pile of blankets, then you can go back to your cooking.''

She grinned at him. "Cooking's right. You take care you're not cooked yourself. You'll have to pull the blankets off the beds. Get them yourself; I'm busy.''

At midday, with a pile of blankets standing on the verandah, Paddy announced he was going home for lunch. Blue went back to his room where he began packing a suitcase.

A waitress came out onto the verandah carrying a small iron rod. She began striking a plough disc hanging on the wall. The sound carried across the mill and brought men hurrying to the boarding house. They sat on forms that stood along the sides of the two tables in the centre of the dining room.

"When are you and the girls getting out, Missus?" asked one of the mill hands.

"As soon as you lot finish your lunch. We're packing now. Mr McArthur is getting the two trucks to take us out. So hurry, will you?''

While the men were eating, the valley changed. The visitation of some pale spirit had softened its outline. The squat mill lay closer to the earth. The smoke from its stack no longer formed a contrast to the unrelated air but merged its pale outlines with a kindred presence. The pungent breath of burning eucalypts had crept in and filled the hollow between the mountains. There were no rolling movements of visible smoke. It came furtively. It brought with it a strange disquiet. It brought a fear smell — the smell of a bush fire. When the men emerged from their dinner they stood on the verandah in silence.

"Well, there it is," said Blue, "the breath of the bastard."

"I don't see what all the fuss is about," said a young man who was leaning against the wall. "It's only a scrub fire and besides there's no wind. Even if it does come this way we'll be able to stop it by burning a break."

"Let me tell you," said Blue, "the '26 fire started with a scrub fire. Once the wind comes up it'll whip that fire into a crown fire in two ups. You've never been through a crown fire yet, boy. Wait till you've experienced one. In the '26 fires I saw Cocky McKinney die in front of me in the sawdust and I couldn't do nothing because I myself was burning."

"I was at Warrens during that fire," said the engine driver, "and they only had two dugouts for thirty of us. Twenty of us came through but Old Joe, the yardman, lost his eyes for good."

"I've met him," said Blue.

"He loved the bush, Old Joe," reflected the engine driver.

"He was like Bill here, only he was old," said Blue.

"I saw him a month ago," said the engine driver, "and he says to me then, he says, 'The bush has no beauty for me now, Mac.' That's what he said."

"I've never seen a crown fire," said the young man.

"Those that see them hardly ever live to tell about them," said Blue.

"Show him your back," said the engine driver. "Let young Bill here have a look at it."

Blue pulled his flannel over his head and turned so that the group of men could see his scars. They stood in silence looking at them. As the dry skin on new paint slides and wrinkles at a thumb thrust, so had the skin on his back slipped over the weeping flesh when the fire had gone. Pale skin, glossy and bereft of pores, rose to soft ridges and wrinkles. Faint lines of tension converged on points of puckered flesh. Beneath this covering his muscles slipped and moved untouched.

"I felt my back drying out and wrinkling like a green gum leaf on coals," said Blue, "and not a flame touched me. The bloody air was burning."

"Christ!" said the young man. "I wouldn't like to go through that."

"If we get trapped here with a north wind we'll go through it all right," said Blue.

Paddy came back from his lunch followed by Steve. They were carrying blankets.

"We're going down to see if the dugout's all right, Blue."

"I'll come with you."

The dugout was a shelter erected down the hill just below the huts. An excavation had been made into the side of the hill and this had been roofed with logs. Over the logs soil had been thrown making a dome of earth now covered with grass. Earth had been piled in front of the dugout leaving an opening about three feet in height through which men could crawl and drop to the earth floor below the entrance. It was not an adequate dugout. McArthur had built it after complaints from the men about the mill's lack of bushfire shelters and though it could hold twelve men Blue claimed it was a smoke trap and that you would be lucky to get out of it alive.

Paddy dipped the blankets into buckets of water and Steve hung them in front of the dugout completely closing the entrance. He piled soil and rocks on the edge of the dugout to hold the blankets in place. They threw buckets of water over them leaving them saturated and dripping.

"We'll want a few blankets inside the dugout," said Steve. "Put three buckets of water inside while I go and get some more." When he came back they soaked them before throwing them inside.

Blue, who had been shovelling dirt onto the roof, came down and joined them. "Can you feel a breeze?" he asked. "I think that north wind's coming up. The smoke's thicker than it was. I'm going to find McArthur and see about getting the women out straight away."

"We'll burn if we stop here," said Steve. "Where is McArthur?"

They found him clearing grass around the mill. Men were raking it back from the walls and pitching it out into the open.

"We're going to take the women and kids out now," said Blue.

"Well . . . All right. If you want it that way." McArthur was in no hurry.

"And I mean now," said Blue angrily.

McArthur looked at him then rested his shovel against the wall. "Right. Get the two trucks and we'll load them up straight away. I think they've held the fire at Tandaluk but we'll take them out."

They gathered the women and children and helped them into the trucks. They threw in suitcases and blankets. Paddy had gone up to his house and brought down his gun. "Take this with you," he said to Mrs O'Connor who sat in the back of the truck trying to comfort her children.

She took it without comment. She understood Paddy.

Some of the women wanted to stay with their husbands.

"I won't go out without you, Bill."

"S'help me God, don't give me that now! I'm coming out, I tell you. Give me time."

"They'll all join you in Tandaluk," McArthur assured them. "As soon as we drop you at Tandaluk we'll come back and pick up the men. Will you drive the Bedford, Paddy?"

"No, I'll wait till you come back," said Paddy. "I want to close up my house and douse it with water. What about you, Steve?"

"I'll stop and help you," said Steve.

"Charlie Erikson will drive the other one," said Blue. He turned to Charlie. "Get back as soon as you can, Charlie. Don't waste any time. We'll be waiting."

The trucks moved down the track. The men watched them go then gathered in a group. They didn't say much. They were worried.

The wind was rising.

After sweeping behind Barret's mill the fire began to expand. A floating piece of burning bark landed on the dry grass near the mill wall as the fire swung back towards Tandaluk. The mill began to burn. The men who worked there had left it an hour previously. There was no one to fight the flames. The fire burnt unhindered until there was only a smoking ruin in the centre of a cleared patch.

The fire extended its face till it burnt on a three-mile front. It moved up valleys and over the steep spurs of ranges. It advanced with great vigour up mountainsides where the leaping flames could clutch the tea-tree and hopbush crouching on hillsides above them. It climbed the steep slopes through a tangle of scrub, leaving glowing skeletons to crumble to ash on the blackened earth.

Expanding gusts of air, seeking an outlet, rose through the treetops, expelling billows of dark smoke that rolled ahead of the flames like a mighty wave. Escaping flames feeding on gas writhed from the parent fire and laced the wave with red veins. They flickered a moment before being smothered in smoke.

The tall mountain ash stood knee deep in the flames of the burning under-growth. Their crowns shook violently as the heavy smoke gushed upwards. Flames reached for the high leaves then fell back thwarted. The combination of wind, temperature and humidity that would start a crown fire, a fire before which men were helpless, were not present on this Thursday morning. The fire raged on fed by erratic gusts and whirlwinds. It reached the crest of the range over-looking Tandaluk in the early afternoon where it first felt the breath of the north wind.

Ahead of the flames wild-life was fleeing. A flock of black cockatoos went over Tandaluk calling to each other as they passed. Wombats, scorched by flames and with smoke-blind eyes, came out of the hills and scurried across the track that stood between the fire and the bush township. A mob of kangaroos bounded down the mountainside, making for cleared land beyond the creek that skirted the cluster of houses. The dead limbs that lay half submerged in the running water formed a highway for insects seeking escape. They came crawling from the scrub and gathered in black masses on these limbs. They stood waving their antennae where water and limb met. They covered the half-submerged logs while the smoke thickened to a haze and the sky darkened.

The rising wind turned the fire. It bypassed Tandaluk and jumped the main road into messmate forest that lay between it and the mill. The fire fighters from Tandaluk were powerless to stop it. They fled, the sirens on their trucks screaming.

The wind rose, a burning north wind like the breath from a furnace. The smoking air smelt of eucalyptus gas. The fire burnt through the messmate forest with increasing fury. Little spiders of flame ran up the trunks of the messmate trees then went out with a puff. Some continued their scampering journey upwards until they reached the heads of the trees. The leaves took light. There was a dull roar and the crowns exploded into flame. The scrub fire leaped upwards and joined the flaming crowns. A vast sheet of flame shot hundreds of feet into the air. The flames in the treetops raced ahead of the main fire burning in the scrub below. Air currents generated by the heat developed into whirlwinds of flame that tore flaming branches from the trees and threw them high in the air. Saplings were hurled to the ground by the wind.

The fire marched like an army with banners flying. It roared its triumph while marching forward in a vicious, systematic advance. Before the blazing undergrowth went a mighty gust of expanded air which roared like a hundred trains going through tunnels. The fire in the treetops and the fire below marched almost together, the crown fire ahead of that in the undergrowth. From the treetops burning bark and leaves were swept upwards and away. These advance brigades started spot fires a mile ahead of the main blaze. The spot fires joined, releasing volatile gas from the burning eucalypts. The gas exploded with deafening booms when the main fire reached it. It threw its flames across valleys, starting fires on the opposite slopes. The very air burnt. Dead trees crashed in flames and were demolished. The terrific heat generated among the boles turned the foliage of the high trees from green to brown to flaming banners.

The wild red horses were galloping. They were heralded by a roar that came down upon the Tandaluk mill like the thunder of hooves.

Blue heard the roar. He dropped the pick with which he was diverting a water-race and ran towards the boarding house. He gathered some of the wet blankets stacked on the verandah and hurried to find Paddy and Steve. They came out of Paddy's house in a hurry and stood looking towards Splitters Ridge over which smoke was rolling. Paddy ran to the door of his house then dashed back to Steve. He kept looking from side to side like an animal seeking escape from a trap. Now that desperate decisions were called for he was incapable of making them.

Steve was calm. He took some of the blankets from Blue. "The creek or the dugout?" he asked quickly.

"There's too much scrub along the creek. You'll have a better chance in the dugout." Blue looked quickly at Paddy. "Do what Steve says, Paddy."

"I want to get my wallet. It has papers in it."

"Get it — and step on it."

Paddy dashed inside.

Russell Drysdale *Moody's Pub* 1941
Oil on wood panel 50.8 × 61.6 cm
National Gallery of Victoria

Roy de Maistre *Carol Singers* 1943
Oil on board 94 × 73.8 cm
Art Gallery of New South Wales

"I'll see he gets to the dugout," said Steve. "Where are you going?"

"To get the rest of the blankets at the boarding house. I'll be down later."

"Don't leave it too long."

Across the slope going down to the creek men were running. A man carrying a cage with a canary in it shouted at Blue as he passed. "Make for the creek. You'll smother in that dugout."

Heavy smoke rolled in over the mill and the houses, driven by the burning north wind. Men ran through a dense fog of smoke, nebulous figures that shouted and called.

"Over here, Jim."

"The creek's the best place."

The voices were full of urgency; some were full of fear.

Blue snatched the rest of the blankets from the verandah and made for the mill where some men were sheltering on the lee side. They were carrying possessions picked up as they fled.

"Leave your gear and run for it," he shouted. "Take these and cover your heads." He tossed them some blankets. "Make for the dugout. There'll be a blackout in a minute. Get moving."

"The smoke'll soon lift," said the young mill worker who had never been through a fire, "then we'll dash for the creek."

"Go now. Go now," screamed Blue above the noise.

They left at a run. One man remained.

"Oh God!" exclaimed Blue. He grabbed the man and shook him. The man's eyes were blank; comprehension had left him.

"The fire's down there." He spoke like a child who had lost its mother.

The blackout swooped over them as he spoke. It was light, then like the closing of an eye it was dark. It was a suffocating darkness, thick with an impenetrable smoke.

The man screamed and ran. Blue stood alone in the dark. He fell to the ground, wrapped in his blankets, gasping, with his face against the earth.

The roar of the fire beat down upon him like blows. There were explosions, whipcrack reports and the thud of stricken trees.

He concentrated on breathing while minutes passed. The darkness lifted. A radiant pink tinge suffused the earth.

Then came the flames.

When the blackout came Steve and Paddy were on their way to the dugout. They were running along the water course, an excavation no wider than a drain, along which water was trickling. It passed below the dugout on its way to the creek but in its passage it afforded some freedom from smoke.

The blackout had weight and substance. The impact of its coming flung both men to the ground in an effort to get air. The rolling darkness forced their mouths against the trickle of water where, just above the surface, was a layer of smokeless air they drew into their lungs. They breathed with great gasps.

Paddy lay without movement in the darkness. The blow that felled him had also paralysed him. He gasped the words, "Help me," in a remote voice then lay taut and still.

Steve raised his head from the earth. He shouted his confidence to Paddy. "It's all right. Hang on to me. We'll crawl there."

He began crawling, with his face close to the ground. Paddy followed, gripping his leg for guidance. He responded to every command from Steve. His reflexes were swift and immediate. Steve spelt survival.

They plunged and writhed through the dark, pausing after every forward drive to gulp the clean air from the earth.

Men had been hurling themselves into the dugout since the roar of the fire had first struck them and turned their fears into swift instinctive action. Those crouched inside were locked in their own thoughts. They wrapped wet towels around their heads against the smoke that entered every time the blankets covering the entrance were lifted.

A thick burst of smoke spilt into the dugout as a man jerked the blankets aside and jumped in carrying a dog. The dog was heavy and the man staggered as he landed on the earth floor.

"Shut that blasted door," someone shouted.

"I've got Bloody Old Dick!" exclaimed the man. He was known as Black Alec and was about fifty years of age. His once black hair was now grey and projected from his head like a clipped tussock. His stretched braces barely supported his trousers, which hung low from his hips. They concertinaed over his boots, the heels of which were worn away. He did odd jobs around the mill.

The dog, always referred to as Bloody Old Dick, belonged to the mill. His joints were stiff with age and he walked with difficulty. He was always to be found following Black Alec.

He lay on the dugout floor opening and closing his mouth and making strange gasping sounds. Black Alec knelt above him holding his head between his hands.

"Some water — quick," he shouted.

A man handed him a billy and he poured water down the dog's throat.

"The smoke's buggered him," a man said. "He's had it, poor bastard."

The dog quivered then lay still.

"Get up, Alec," said the man. "You're just about done yourself." He threw him a wet towel. "Cover your face."

Black Alec didn't get up. He sank closer to the ground, fighting for breath, his own survival now filling his mind.

The dugout was full of the sound of laboured breathing. Men stood with their faces pressed against the earth face that formed the dugout's rear wall. They were draped in blankets. They thrust their mouths against crevices in the wall. Smoke tears ran down their faces.

They all plunged to the floor when the blackout came. The darkness brought panic close to them. The engine driver, crouching on his hands and knees like a Moslem praying, kept repeating the Lord's Prayer. "Our father which art in heaven, hallowed be thy name . . ."

Some men swore savagely. Swearing at their helplessness, their frustration. Others were silent. Each man thought that safety lay where their mates had gone, not here where death by smothering seemed inevitable.

Steve and Paddy suddenly tumbled in leaving a wall of smoke behind them. No one greeted them. The men were too busy fighting for breath to speak. Paddy sat down with his back against the wall, his head between his knees. Steve threw a blanket over him then doused it with water.

Steve was still kneeling with his face against the wall when the darkness lifted and the world outside was tinged with a red glow. He straightened and raised a corner of the blanket while shielding his face with a towel against the heat that was preceding the flames. The smoke had cleared.

"Hell!" said one man looking over his shoulder. "It's like the sky's alight."

"A man's a bloody fool he never ran out of this," said another. "We had all this morning. Hell! there goes my winter supply of firewood."

"Take a look at your house, Paddy," said Steve. "Hurry up! Have a look."

"I can't, I can't," said Paddy still sitting against the wall. "You look, is she gone?"

Flames flapped like sheets from the wall of fire that marched into the clearing around the mill. As they leaped skywards above the buildings they brushed the walls of the houses with their fingers. The houses didn't burst into flame; they exploded. Sheets of galvanized iron were hurled fifty feet into the air. They whirled like propellers; they slid down slopes of burning air and sliced into the ground. Shattered beams were flung outwards. House after house went up, bursting like bombs before the flames swooped down and swallowed them.

The huge timber stacks were set ablaze as the fire swept over them. They burnt with a white hot glare throwing burning heat outwards like rays of the sun. The mill, ignited by the heat, did not burn section by section; it erupted into one huge rosette of flame tossing oil drums and oxygen cylinders high in the air. Battered and torn they rose slowly, turning over and over before plunging back into the inferno.

The howling face of the fire had only paused at the mill. Lifted by the north wind and fed by volatile gases it sped on, riding on air.

In the dugout Steve suddenly closed the opening in the blankets.

"Here it comes!" he yelled. He hurled a bucket of water over the entrance blankets and another over the crouching men, then dropped to the floor.

The thunder of the fire as it went over the dugout sent a convulsion of panic through those inside. There was a scream. Some rose to their feet, distraught.

"We're burning!" screamed old Alec. He jumped up and threw himself at the entrance, scrabbling at the blankets with his hands. Steve drove his fist into the old man's jaw. He fell and lay moaning.

As the roar increased men clasped their heads in pain. They writhed and clutched. They clenched their eyes. They tore at the earth like rabbits.

Then the face passed and all that could be heard was the crackle of burning ruins.

Blue gripped the earth. As the blackout fled before the onslaught of flames the smoke went with it. The mill and its buildings sprang from darkness and stood out in sharp detail, lit by a lurid glare. Blue leaped to his feet, wrapping the blankets around him like a shroud. He raced towards a low open tank that stood against the mill and flung the blankets into the water. He jerked them free almost in one movement and continued out into the open concealed within their folds.

He stood motionless in a bare space some distance from the mill. He stood like a grey stump while water dripped from him. He breathed through the saturated material, filtering the heat from the air, robbing it of flame.

A great roaring beat upon him. Detached banners of flame coiled around him then flicked away. They descended upon him from the flaming sky. They gulped and vanished. They swept in again tearing at him in a transitory frenzy then sped on with the fleeing eucalyptus gas.

The blanket steamed upon him.

When in a momentary lull the flames gathered over the mill and left the area in which he stood, he raced back to the tank, now being licked by fire, and flung the two outer blankets into the hot water. Then he bolted back to his stand, the saturated blankets heavy upon him.

Three times he made that trip; three times he faced the burning mill and returned.

When the fury of the fire had passed he still stood there, motionless, afraid of any movement that might bring back pain and dreadful knowledge. It seemed to him that with a return to life he would crumble to a pile of ashes.

It was here the men from the dugout found him. They had emerged from their smoke-filled shelter when the fire passed and stood for a moment looking at the devastation around them. Then they ran looking for their mates. They called men's names. They tore around in a panicky searching. It was Paddy who saw the still, blanket-clad man behind the mill.

"God! I hope it's Blue."

Steve reached him first. He lifted the blankets and held him in his arms. He was crying. "I thought you were dead," he said.

"Yes," said Blue in a remote voice. "Yes, I thought I was too."

He leant on Steve's shoulder, trembling a little. "The bloody heat . . ." He swayed on his feet.

Paddy held his other arm and they led him well out into the clearing where they sat him on a blackened bank. Behind him the ruins of the mill and the houses burnt quietly but now the thick smoke had gone and he could breathe in comfort.

"Sit here for a while," said Steve. "We have to look for the others. You'll be all right. Just sit here."

They left him and hurried to join the men. The men kept calling the names of their workmates. They shouted urgently.

"Are you there, Joe?"

"Give us a yell, Frank."

There were some answering shouts from the creek gully and in a moment a group of men came staggering up the bank and pushed their way through the burnt scrub and over the smoking ashes that an hour before had enclosed the creek in shade.

Some held their hands over their blackened and blistered faces. Some guided by mates were smoke-blind. From between clenched lids pain tears trickled down their cheeks. The clothes on all of them were sodden with water.

They stumbled into the open and for a moment the two groups faced each other. There was anguish on the faces of those who could see, anguish that changed to relief as they recognised mates.

They suddenly rushed towards each other. Arms gripped and held, cheeks were pressed against cheeks. They cried, unashamed. They greeted each other with words meant to comfort.

"Bill! Jesus! Oh, Bill!"

"You made it, Tiny. You made it, you old bastard."

"Don't worry over your eyes. They've got drops will cure you."

"I can still hear the roar of it in my ears."

"Where's Sammy?" asked one of the men, the man whom Blue had urged to run for the creek.

"I don't know," said Paddy. "He wasn't in the dugout."

"He's dead," said Steve. "I saw him. He must have panicked. He's lying up near the mill."

They were all silent.

"Any others?" asked the engine driver after a while.

"Young Peters and that bald bloke, the Swampie. They got caught on the sawdust heap." Steve had seen their blackened bodies lying there after he had left the dugout.

"God!" said the engine driver.

They all turned and began walking to where Blue was sitting. He had risen to meet them. He held himself together by an effort of will and clasped with both hands those hands held towards him. He held the smoke-blind men against him for a moment.

The sound of a truck jerked their heads around and they watched the rocking vehicle shoot out from behind Mt Nulla Nulla and make towards them.

"Charlie Erikson," said Blue. "I knew he'd make it."

Charlie was out of his scorched truck the moment he braked it to a stop. His face was blackened with charcoal. His eyes were bloodshot.

"I tink you all dead," he said and there was a quaver in his voice. He suddenly stopped and lowered his head.

"It's all right, Charlie," said Steve gently. "We've been waiting for you.

There's a lot here got to get to hospital. Their eyes are crook. Let's get them back as soon as we can.''

They were helping men into the truck when the cars began coming in from Tandaluk. They were driven by men who understood the shock experienced by those who survive a crown fire. They did not talk much. They acted. They loaded their cars with silent men and took them away.

Two policemen wrapped sheets around the charred bodies that were lying where they fell. They laid them beneath a tarpaulin at the back of a utility and followed the cars moving down Tandaluk Road.

Steve and Paddy tied a bandage around Blue's eyes then helped him into a car.

"We'll call and see you at the hospital, Blue,'' Paddy promised him.

After he had gone the two men stood looking at the pile of ashes and twisted iron that once was Paddy's home.

"We'll start clearing it up tomorrow,'' said Steve. "We'll build it closer to the creek next time.''

"Yes,'' said Paddy. "Mary would like it down there.''

A car driven by a Tandaluk youth pulled up beside them.

"Do you want a lift out?'' he asked. "You're the last.''

"We've been dwelling on you,'' said Paddy.

"Let us out at the pub,'' said Steve as they got in.

Singing to God

SHE WAS standing on a box in one of Sydney's side streets. A small group of people surrounded her, their upturned faces flushed from neon lights. It was a cold night and some wore shabby overcoats; but she had no overcoat, only a blue, woollen jumper above her grey, flannel frock.

She was a thin woman, with a smile that contained no mirth. Yet it wasn't an unpleasant smile. It gave one the impression of having been born of some astonishment experienced a long time ago; and the astonishment had never left her. Her eyes were wide open, a little distraught, as if she saw in the darkness beyond the group things that she did not understand.

I went over. I took out my notebook to record some impressions. I stood beside a man who glanced at the notebook in my hand. The self-satisfied thrust of his feet to the earth was in keeping with the smug expression.

"Are you a writer?" he asked.

"Yes," I replied.

"I thought so," he said and he turned to his companion. "I can always tell 'em," he told him.

"Besides Paul, who are the other ones, the mighty ones?" cried the woman from the box.

She waited for an answer. A fat man with puffed, unshaven cheeks who was standing directly before her in front of the group spat contemptuously. "Ah, keep quiet!" he said disgustedly.

"You are full of drink, brother," said the preacher.

The words galvanised the man into sudden action. He snatched off his hat and threw it to the ground.

"Who said that?" he cried, and staggered sideways as if an attack upon him was an imminent thing.

"Go ahead, lass," said a large woman, dismissing, on behalf of us all, this unimportant digression. "Yer'a great speaker. God bless ya."

This woman was very tall. She frequently turned and smiled benignantly on those behind her. Her powerful arms were folded across large breasts that lolled heavily upon her chest. Occasionally she nodded her head to selected ones as if confirming the arguments of the speaker.

"You see, dear people," the preacher continued, "if you accept God's word he writes your name down in the Lamb's book of God."

"Hell, he must have a lot of pencils!" said the drunk.

This flippant remark expanded the big woman's nostrils in the manner of a horse scenting battle.

"I'll hit him, s'elp me God I will," she informed us.

"Hey!" she addressed the man. "I'm big and powerful, you know. When I hit you'll stay hit. I'll slap you down, son. Shut up!"

This aggressive remark momentarily sobered the man, who exclaimed in astonishment, "Well, I'll go to buggery!" He gazed contemplatively at the ground, adjusting himself to this sudden revelation into woman's complexity. He fumbled for his pipe and, finding it, thrust it aggressively between his teeth.

"Smoking is a curse, brothers," cried the preacher, pointing at the man. "Smoking and drink. Ah, people!" she continued, clasping her hands in front of her. "You love your smoke better than you love God."

"Jesus would've smoked," announced the drunk in justification of the habit.

The preacher, stung by this sacrilege, drew herself indignantly erect.

"My God smoke — never," she cried.

"Good on ya, lass," cried the big woman.

"Didn't Jesus make wine come from the rock?" demanded the drunk.

"Do keep quiet, sir," pleaded the preacher.

"Shut up, you," growled the big woman making a threatening movement towards the man. She reached over and grabbed his tattered felt hat. She threw it to the ground where, a few minutes before, it had had the significance of a gauntlet.

Her action gave her the greatest satisfaction. She laughed in a manner that included, and made us, all a party to the deed. At the same time she subjected us to a leisured survey that forestalled criticism.

"You with the cigarette," cried the preacher pointing at me. "Where will you go when you die?"

I hastily removed the cigarette and wilted under the impact of many eyes.

"I will save you," she promised me at the top of her voice.

The drunk with great difficulty raised his leg and pointed the tattered boot towards the woman. "You old Jesus-chasers couldn't save the sole of me boot," he cried.

"Jesus will give you the crown of life," screamed the preacher exultantly.

A one-armed man, upon whose hollow cheeks the fluff and dirt of his last sleeping place still clung to the covering of stubble, pushed forward and called out wildly:

"For Christ's sake take my life and be done with it! What's the good of it to me."

"God said . . ." went on the preacher.

"He didn't say not to have a smoke," interrupted the drunk.

". . . That the rich with their silver and gold are going to burn," she shrieked.

"Listen to me," began the man with one arm.

"Go 'way will you," growled the big woman who moved towards him as she spoke. "You're only a lunatic."

The man raised his one arm defensively and backed into the crowd.

"God can make a man of you, sir," called the preacher as he turned away from her.

"Do ya reckon," he replied sarcastically over his shoulder.

A small woman, her face loosely wrapped in an excess of leathery skin, touched my arm and said, gently, "Give me half a cigarette."

I held a packet towards her. As she drew the white cigarette out she muttered fervently:

"I wish you luck. I'll ask the good old Saviour to give *you* a go. My old Saviour . . . I wish you luck. I'll pray for you."

She raised her eyes heavenwards and lowered them again. The one-armed man bumped her roughly as he forced his way through the group. She turned on him swiftly.

"I hope everything you do hurts you, s'elp me God I do," she said savagely.

"Why, it's only nineteen hundred years since he was here," shouted the drunk in answer to a declaration from the preacher.

"You know why he's not here," she answered triumphantly. "He's choosing a bride in his own image and the bride will be sealed."

This statement convulsed the drunk with mirth. He slapped his thigh and doubled up as if in pain. He staggered with laughter; then he suddenly straightened, feeling that the reason for his reaction was lost on those behind him. He faced them and, with one hand in the air, kept repeating:

"Didja hear that! Oh, my God, didja hear that!"

The woman on the box started to sway hypnotically. "Let your sins go. Let them go," she cried; then, with sudden power, she raised her voice to a scream, "We're all dying. Everyone here is dying."

This dire prophecy jerked the drunk from a temporary abstraction. He looked at the preacher with his mouth open; then he turned to me and said, fearfully, "There's *something*. There *must* be."

"Come to me all ye that labour," cried the preacher.

"By God I'm feelin' queer! I can see the light!" announced the drunk to those around him.

"Grace is the favourite of God."

The large woman who had moved so that she stood beside me bent to my ear and remarked:

"Grace Darling wrote a book, you know."

"Did she!" I answered.

"You are a writer, eh?"

"I do a little."

Her face assumed a conspiratorial expression. She opened a window in her eyes; then they narrowed and she whispered, "Like to come with me tonight?"

"No thank you," I said.

Her expression immediately changed, as if she had suddenly closed the window; and she exclaimed, with an air of dismissal, "Forget it."

"So you are a writer," she went on with a change of attitude. "So am I. Have you ever read 'Tess of the Storm Country'?"

"Yes."

"I wrote that."

"Very good, too," I said.

The preacher had finished her tirade and had left the soap box. She looked spent.

The big woman placed her arm around the preacher's drooping shoulders and said, "What us three ought to do is to worship God on our own — meet of a night, like, and do some worshipping where there ain't nobody drunk, or that."

She was interrupted by the drunk, who touched her shoulder and whispered, "Like a drink? I gotta bottle."

"Got any money?" asked the woman over her shoulder, her arm still clasping the preacher.

"I got a coupla bob."

"I'll be with you in a minute."

She again turned to us and continued, "Just the three of us, singing to God."

"Have you been saved?" the preacher asked me.

"Come on," demanded the drunk, becoming impatient.

"I think I have been," I said.

"I've got to go," said the big woman. She patted the preacher on the shoulder. "You did a good job, lass; God bless you."

She took the drunk's arm possessively and with confident steps piloted him away into the shadows of the little streets.

William
Hart-Smith

Columbus Goes West

Columbus looks towards the New World,
The sea is flat and nothing breaks the rim
of the world's disc;
He takes the sphere with him.

Day into night the same, the only change
The living variation at the core
Of this man's universe;
And silent on the silver ship he broods.

Red gouts of weed, and skimming fish, to crack
The stupefying emptiness of sea:
Night, and the unimpassioned gaze of stars . . .

And God be praised for the compass, oaths
Bawled in the fo'c'sle,
Broken heads, and wine,
Song and guitars,

The tramp of boots,
The wash and whip of brine.

The Ship's Cat

The cat comes ambling down the deck,
weaving a pattern of progression
round bollard-pin and stanchion, under shelves:
anything to guard her back from heaven.

She looks through slits, intelligence a claw
that hooks a golden curtain wide enough
to let inside a modicum of world:
bulwark is limit: all beyond is bluff.

Here is the ego all wrapped up in fur;
she does not mind if no one else responds
to her advances; takes her meat and sleep
and answers bounty with a rumbling purr.

She makes a show of loving when she's touched;
suffers a hand to tickle at her neck
or stroke her back, the parts she cannot reach.
Masts up her tail for this and rubs the deck,

extended upward into human legs.
Missing, the cook's boy finds her in his hammock,
ejects her, only to find a weight of fur
heaving on the ground-swell of his stomach.

No willing love, no faith, no pure affection,
returned for care, yet she's a benison
to man: she makes the most invidious
feel wondrous virtuous by comparison!

Mary
Durack

Red Jack

She rises clear to memory's eye
From mists of long ago,
Though we met but once, in '98 —
In the days of Cobb and Co.

'Twas driving into Hughenden
With mail and gold for load
That I saw Red Jack, the wanderer,
Come riding down the road.

Red Jack and Mephistopheles —
They knew them far and wide,
From Camooweal to Charters Towers,
The route they used to ride.

They knew them round the Selwyns where
The Leichhardt has its source,
Along the winding cattle ways —
A woman and a horse.

And strange the tales they told of them
Who ranged the dusty track:
The great black Mephistopheles
And the red-haired witch Red Jack.

She claimed no name but that, they said,
And owned no things but these:
Her saddle, swag and riding-kit
And Mephistopheles.

And often travellers such as I
Had seen, and thought it strange,
A woman working on the line
That crossed McKinlay Range.

Had seen her in the dreary wake
Of stock upon the plains,
Her brown hand quick upon the whip
And light upon the reins.

With milling cattle in the yard
Amid the dust-fouled air,
With rope and knife and branding iron —
A girl with glowing hair.

"Red Jack's as good as any man!"
The settlers used to own;
And some bold spirits sought her hand,
But Red Jack rode alone.

She rode alone, and wise men learned
To set her virtue high,
To weigh what skill she plied her whip
With the hardness of her eye.

I saw Red Jack in '98,
The first time and the last,
But her face, brown-gaunt, and her hair, red-bright,
Still haunt me from the past.

The coach drew in as she rode in sight;
We passed the time of day;
Then shuffled out the mail she sought
And watched her ride away.

And oh! her hair was living fire,
But her eyes were cold as stone:
Red Jack and Mephistopheles
Went all their ways alone.

W. Flexmore
Hudson

Mallee in October

When clear October suns unfold
mallee tips of red and gold,

children on their way to school
discover tadpoles in a pool,

iceplants sheathed in beaded glass,
spider orchids and shivery grass,

webs with globes of dew alight,
budgerigahs on their first flight,

tottery lambs and a stilty foal,
a papery slough that a snake shed whole,

and a bronzewing's nest of twigs so few
that both the sky and the eggs show through.

Nostalgia

I caught my tram and took my seat
in Swanston Street, in Swanston Street,
and I was then a water-hole
staring up at a sorrel foal
and two galahs, with wings full spread,
on a red-gum branch above his head.

At Prince's bridge, at Prince's Bridge,
I had become a quartzy ridge
watching the sheep on the plain below,
purple sheep in the afterglow,
and horses racing to drink at a trough
and frightening gusts of magpies off.

I barely noticed the windows glowed
as the sundown lit Commercial Road,
for I had turned to an eagle gliding
deep down gullies where hares were hiding;
and my shadow cast a quiet that stayed
a long while after my kill was made.

Before we had rattled through Prahran,
my starry night as a scree began,
with snow on my scarp, and falling rock,
the gully holding its breath for the shock,
while a rabbit gave a warning thump
and a wallaby peered from a wattle clump.

A frog dived, and the soak went plop!
at the Gardiner stop, at the Gardiner stop,
for I was a wind that swayed the reeds
and rolled the pods of the salt-bush seeds;
and so I reached my gate — too soon,
waving a she-oak across the moon.

John
Morrison

The Incense-burner

It was a one-way trip, and I paid off in London in the middle of winter with twenty pounds in cash, a wristwatch worth fifteen pounds, and a good kit of clothes, half on my back and half in a suitcase. And a fair bit of experience for my nineteen years.

I put up at somebody's "Temperance Hotel" near King's Cross Station because I was sick of the drunken orgies that had marked every port of call coming over from Australia, and was knocked up at eleven o'clock the first night by a housemaid innocently armed with dust-pan and empty bucket who asked me if there was anything I wanted. There wasn't. That also was something I'd got sick of on the way over.

At the end of a fortnight I had added something to my experience and was down to thirty shillings, a pawn-ticket in place of the watch, and the suitcase, still with contents. So I left the hotel, took a room in a seamen's lodging-house down near the East India Docks, and started to look for a ship home.

I wasn't long in finding out that I'd left my gallop a bit late. In 1929 a seaman looking for a ship out of London needed something better than thirty shillings and a brand-new discharge book. I had only one entry in my book, and Second Engineers and shipping officials weren't impressed. Thousands of good men were haunting the docks every day. Real seamen, with lifetimes of experience behind them, and rubbed old books to prove it. I came to the conclusion after a few days that my book was more of a handicap than a help. I'd had enough of London, and I wanted a ship bound for Australia and nowhere else. And my book made it all too clear. Second Engineers and Second Mates used to flick it open, drop the corners of their lips, and pass it back to me with a dry smile. I had it written all over me — Adelaide to London. They wanted men for a round voyage, not homesick Australians who would skin out at the first port touched.

I lasted two weeks; ten shillings a week for my room and ten shillings the fortnight for food. I did it by getting in sweet with a ship's cook, a Melbourne man, on one of the *Bay* ships laid up for repairs. I got breakfast out of the black pan every blessed day of the fortnight. Sometimes tea, too, until he told me not to make it too hot.

There were some good feeds, but not nearly enough, and it was all very irregular, and I was only nineteen, and as fit as they come, and walking up to fifteen miles every day, and I got hungrier and hungrier. There were days when I could have eaten my landlady. She was a skinny, sad-looking woman with bulging fish's eyes and a rat-trap mouth. I thought she was the toughest thing I'd ever met in my life. I was out all day every day, and on the rare occasions when I saw her she didn't seem to care whether she spoke to me or not. I used to turn in fairly early and lie reading, and until a late hour every night I could hear the thumping of a smoothing-iron in the kitchen at the far end of the passage. She was a widow; with only one other lodger, a pensioner, she had to support herself by taking in washing. It was a dark, silent, dismal hole of a place, smelling perpetually of wet clothes and yellow soap.

I saw the other lodger only once, an old man in a beard and long overcoat, vanishing into his room as I came in one night. I heard him often enough though. Too often. He had one of those deep, rumbling coughs that seem to come all the way up from the region of the stomach. He would go for minutes on end without stopping. He used to wake me up every night. Sometimes I thought he was going to suffocate.

His name was Burroughs — "old Burroughs" to Mrs Hall. I knew nothing about him — or about Mrs Hall either, if it came to it — until my last day in the house. I had sevenpence ha'penny left, and the rent of my room was due that night. It was a cold, raw day with skies you could reach up and touch, and a threat of snow. In the morning I did the usual round of the docks, missed out on a last feed on the *Bay* ship, and went back to Finch Street to tell Mrs Hall I was leaving. I'd had to recognize the fact that I was well and truly on the beach; that there was nothing for it now but the Salvation Army "Elevator", an institution about which I'd heard plenty in the past two weeks.

I was to learn that day that my landlady's forbidding manner was nothing more than a front deliberately built up over years of contact with tough London seamen. She had a heart of gold, but like a lot of good people had become afraid to let the world see it.

She talked to me at the kitchen door, and as I told her what I was going to do she stared past me down the length of the short passage with her grim little mouth tightly shut and an expression of sullen bitterness on her dour face. I felt I was telling her an old and familiar and hated story. She must have seen a lot of defeated men in her time. Behind her was a table piled with washing; two or three ramshackle chairs, a linoleum with great holes rubbed in it, and a stove with several old-fashioned irons standing at one side.

"It's a damned shame, that's what it is," she burst out with a vehemence that startled me. "Good, clean, respectable, young men walking the streets." She sniffed and tossed her head. For a moment I thought she was going to cry. Instead she asked me in for a cup of coffee. "I was just going to make one. It'll warm you up."

It was the worst coffee I'd ever tasted, half a teaspoonful of some cheap essence out of a bottle, mixed with boiling water. And a slice of bread to eat with it. Stale bread spread thinly with greasy margarine. But I was cold and hungry, and friendly words went with it. God help her! It was all the hospitality she could offer me. One glance around that wretched room convinced me that I had been living better than her.

I told her I didn't want to take any good clothes into the hostel with me, and asked could I leave my suitcase with her until my luck turned.

"You can leave anything you like. Only no responsibility, mind you." She went on to tell me that she never knew from one day to another who she was going to have under her roof, and in the middle of it there came a muffled sound of coughing from along the passage. She stopped to listen, holding her breath and pulling a face, as if she were actually experiencing some of the old man's distress. "I'm not saying anything about *him*. He's all right. I can go out and leave anything lying around. Poor old soul! There's many a time I give him a cup of coffee, and I'll swear to God it's the only thing that passes his lips from morn till night. Where he gets to when he goes out . . ."

"He's pretty old, isn't he, Mrs Hall?"

"Not that old. He was in the war. He's a sick man, that's what's wrong with him. One of these days I'll wake up and find I've got a corpse on my hands. You just ought to be here when he gets one of his foreign parcels."

"Foreign parcels?"

Mrs Hall finished her coffee, got up, and began sorting the things on the table. "Don't ask me where it comes from. He never tells me anything, and I never stick my nose into another body's business. But he's got somebody somewhere that hasn't forgotten him. Every few months he gets this parcel. Not much — a pair of underpants or socks, or a muffler — just bits of things. And a little bundle of dry leaves, herbs for his cough I suppose. My God, you just ought to smell them! He burns them in a bit of a tin pan he's got. They stink the house out. And there he sits and just sucks it in. It's beyond me how he can stand it. I've got to get out till he's finished."

Mrs Hall sniffed and blew, as if the smell of the herbs from the foreign parcel were in her nostrils even then. "He's been here twelve months, and if it wasn't for that I wouldn't care if he stopped for three years. He never bothers nobody, and he keeps his room like a new pin. I've never yet seen him with drink in, and that's a change from some of them I get here, you mark my words. I know *you're* not the drinking kind, otherwise I wouldn't have asked you in here."

Poor Mrs Hall!

She wished me good luck and promised to keep my suitcase in her own room until I came back for it.

Travelling light, I walked all the way to the Salvation Army headquarters in Middlesex Street, stated my case to a "soldier" just inside the door, and was sent over to an elderly grey-haired "officer" seated at a desk piled with papers. All this happened a long time ago, and many of the details are hazy, but I'm left with an impression of newness, of spacious floors, of pleasant faces, of friendly efficiency.

The officer asked me what it was I wanted them to do for me. I told him.

"I'm an Australian. I worked my way over as a ship's trimmer. I wanted to see London; you know how it is. Now I'm broke, and I'm looking for a passage back home. I've got to find somewhere to live while I look for a ship."

"Where have you been living?" Nothing inquisitorial about the question. He was taking quiet stock of me all the time. I had no reason to deceive him, but I felt it would be a waste of time anyway, that I was dealing with a man full of experience.

"In lodgings down in Custom House near the East India Docks. I've got to get out tonight, though; I haven't a shilling left."

"You didn't jump your ship, did you?"

Only a man who knew sailors would have asked me that. "No, I've got a clean book." My hand went to my pocket, but he stopped me with a gesture.

"It isn't necessary for me to pry into your affairs, my boy. You understand that if you go into the Elevator you won't have much time to look for a ship?"

"I know I'll have to work, but that's all right. I could get some time off now and then, couldn't I?"

"Yes, as long as you did your task. But that's the responsibility of the commandant down there." He reached out and picked a form off a little pile at his side. "I'll give you a note to take down. I can't promise he'll have room for you, but it's worth while trying. What's your name?"

"Thomas Blair."

"Do you know where Old Street is?"

They took me in, and for a little over three weeks I earned food and lodging by sorting waste string at the establishment known as the Elevator, down in Spitalfields.

It was the strangest three weeks I have ever experienced, and the most generally hopeless company of men I was ever mixed up with. There were about forty of us, of whom perhaps twenty were professional tramps wintering in. Of the others, fellows in circumstances more or less similar to my own, I got an impression that only a few were still trying to get their heads above water again. Conversation was not primarily around the prospect of finding employment, as

101

I expected it to be, but around the petty incidents of the day, that evening's bill of fare, a certain current murder trial, and every triviality of hostel administration they could think up. At the time I was thoroughly contemptuous of it all, but I understand better now. Those men had had a lot more of London than I had; I was still fresh to the struggle . . .

We worked nine hours a day; seven-thirty in the morning until five-thirty in the evening, with an hour off for dinner.

I was never able to find out why they called the place the Elevator, unless because it was intended as an elevator of fallen men. That's likely enough, but I'm not sure that it worked out in practice. I'm not questioning the good faith of the Salvation Army officers charged with its administration, but the prevailing atmosphere was far from elevating. On the first morning a short conversation with my immediate bench-mate served to reveal in a flash the spirit permeating the entire establishment.

"Been in before?" he asked me.

"No."

"Stopping long?"

"No longer than I can help."

"That might be longer than you think, chum. Y'ought to try and get on the staff. It's a sitter if they don't know you."

"What staff?"

"Here, and up at the hostel. Sweeping out, making beds, cooking and serving. They're all chaps that come in off the streets, like you. Not much money in it, but everything's turned on free. All you got to do is get saved."

"Saved?"

"Go out to the penitent form at one of the prayer meetings. Give your heart to Jesus . . ."

And that was it. It was a home for the destitute, largely run by some of the destitute. And if you weren't particularly anxious to move on, and were sufficiently unscrupulous, you could be one of the running brigade. And the way to muscle into the running brigade was simply to get "saved". I discovered that some of the old hands got saved every year as soon as the winter winds began to blow and the roads frosted up.

All the charge-hands at the Elevator were such brands clutched from the burning, and a more foxy-looking crowd I never set eyes on. They were on a sweet thing, and in their anxiety to stick to it they took good care that precious little of the spirit of Army benevolence got beyond the corner of the building where the commandant had his little office. Beggars-on-horseback, they ran the place with much of the efficiency, and even less of the humanity, of an ordinary factory.

The Elevator was simply a depot for the collecting and sorting and repacking of waste paper, rags and string. All day long motor-trucks, horse-drawn lorries and handcarts kept coming in heaped with salvage, which was unloaded and dragged to various parts of the great concrete floor for sorting out.

I was put onto the string-bench, and each morning was given a one-hundredweight bag of odds and ends of string which I had to disentangle and distribute into a row of boxes marked "cotton", "sisal" — I forget the other names.

That was my task for the day, the price I paid for three meals and a bed to sleep in at night. Anything I did over and above that was paid for, if I remember correctly, at the rate of half-a-crown a hundredweight. In the three weeks I was there I earned just enough cash to keep me in cigarettes, carefully rationed, and nothing more. And there was no getting out of it if you wanted those three feeds and the bed. I tried, on the very first day — seizing a moment when I thought nobody was looking, and ramming a double handful of unsorted string into the sisal box. But one of the foxes saw me from a distant part of the floor and made me drag it out again under the threat of instant expulsion.

We didn't live at the Elevator. An old shop next door had been converted into a dining-room, and every day at 12 o'clock we trooped in and received dinners served from hot-boxes brought down from some Army cookhouse. And at the end of the day's work each man was given three tickets on the hostel in Old Street a mile or so away, one for tea, one for bed, and one for breakfast next morning.

The Old Street hostel was one of the biggest in London, and was run on much the same lines, and in much the same spirit, as the Elevator. There was a washhouse with neither soap nor towels, dormitories — barrack-like but quite clean — and a spacious dining-room where the men could sit for the rest of the evening after eating. I understood that most of the food — "leftovers" of some kind or other — was donated or bought cheaply from hotels, cafes, shops and bakehouses. But it was priced so low that a man could usually eat plenty; it was dished up with every appearance of cleanliness, and I can't say I ever found it anything but appetizing. Meal tickets were valued at 1s 3d, and we could choose what we liked from the bill of fare stuck up at the end of the serving counter: slice of bread and margarine 1d, pot of tea or coffee 1d, soup 2d, roast beef or mutton 3d, stew 3d, kippers 1d each, vegetables 2d, apple tart 3d.

All a bit primitive, if you like, but I had a two weeks' hunger to work off, and they were the most enjoyable meals I ever had in my life. Food was, indeed, the only thing that made life at all worth living just then. I would open my eyes every morning thinking of breakfast, and when it was over I'd grit my teeth and stagger through the next four hours sustained only by thoughts of dinner. And when that was over there came thoughts of tea.

One red-letter day I cashed two tea tickets. My neighbour on the string-bench got on to something better for that evening, and gave me his. When I lined up at the counter the second time the fox in the white apron gave me a cold stare.

"What's this? I've served you once."

"Don't be funny," I replied. "How many tickets d'you think we get?"

Still staring, he became positive, threw the ticket into the tray, and turned to the next man in line, dismissing me with a curt: "Move on, chum, you've had it."

He should have known better, because there are two things for which a man is always prepared to fight, and food is one of them. I reached out and seized his wrist.

"Come up with it, Mister! I'm in the Elevator. I worked for that ticket —"

He shook himself free, but I must have looked as savage as I felt because he served me without further argument.

I was like that all the time, hostile on the whole infernal world and ready to take it out on anybody. Each week I got leave off for half a day and went the familiar round of the docks, but a ship seemed to be as far off as ever. I hated London as I'd never hated any place before, began to lose hope, and fell into a mood of gloomy self-pity that made me impatient and contemptuous of everybody around me. Those men didn't talk much about their private affairs, and with the egotism and intolerance of youth I assumed that none of their troubles was as great as mine. A man with youth and good health, and no responsibilities, should find any tussle an exhilarating adventure, but some of us don't realize that until youth is past. I used to try to cheer myself up by comparing my circumstances to those of old Burroughs coughing his life away down in the hovel in Finch Street, but that only made matters worse. Visions of the old man creeping along the dark passage, or crouched over his periodical burning of the herbs, positively frightened me. For he also had had a youth, and somewhere in the past there had been a beginning to the road that led to Finch Street, and that assuredly would go on from there nowhere but to the grave.

The hostel was full of them, shivering watery-eyed old men, who wandered the streets all day, and stumbled in at nightfall to stand for a long time studying the bill of fare with a few miserable coppers clutched in their stiff fingers. Nobody took any notice of them. No doubt they would have envied old Burroughs, for nobody ever sent *them* parcels with mufflers and "bits of things" in them. All the same, they moved me to horror and fear more than to pity, for were they not life-members of a fraternity of which I had become a novitiate?

And if during the day all my dreams were of food, then at night-time all my dreams were of home. The coughing of old Burroughs had nothing on the wheezings and mutterings of that refuge of lost men. Sleep came to me slowly, and was often broken, and in the wakeful moments I would lie with wide eyes and tight lips, deliberately torturing myself with nostalgic longings.

Some building close by had a clock that chimed the hours, and whenever I heard it I would think carefully and call up a scene in Australia that I knew was true and exact of that very moment.

At midnight I would say to myself: it's ten o'clock in the morning, and the hotels down Flinders Street are just opening and the wharfies coming away from the first pick-up are crossing from the Extension and dropping into the Hotham and the Clyde for a quick one before going home to lunch. And there's a white sky and a smell of dust, and trembling pavements which by noon will be hot enough to fry eggs on. And down at St Kilda beach lazy little waves are lapping in, and some of the Fortunate Ones are crossing the Promenade from the big apartment houses and spreading their towels on the sand for a brown-off. And even though it's a weekday, the Point Nepean Highway down the Peninsula is already lively with cars heading for the bush and more distant beaches. And there's a place down there in the heath country where my mates and I used to go rabbiting on Sunday afternoons. And the big loose-limbed manna-gum where we found the parrot's nest is still there, its thin foliage hard and sharp against the sky in that way that always reminded me of the figures on a Japanese willow-pattern plate. And somewhere on the scrubby slope that runs up to the road a wallaby sits with drooping paws and pricked ears. And the air is full of the scent of the paperbarks down in the swamp, and of the whistlings and twitterings of grey thrushes and honeyeaters and blue wrens. And every now and then, on the breathlike puff of a breeze that comes out of the north, there is another smell that I know well, and over in a saddle of the distant Dandenongs a column of smoke marks where the bushfire is burning . . .

For three weeks.

Then — suddenly, like most bad things — it was all over.

One morning at breakfast time I got talking with a stranger who turned out to be a sailor. And within a few minutes he knew what I was looking for.

"Why don't you give the *Tairoa* a go?" he asked me. "Ever done a trip as a steward?"

"No. What about the *Tairoa*?"

"She's leaving for Australia today, and they were signing on single-trippers yesterday. A lot of the New Zealand Company's packets do it. They go out stuffed with emigrants in the 'tween-decks. At the other end they dismantle the accommodation and fill up with cargo for home. They only want most of the stewards one way."

"How is it I've never heard about this? I've walked those docks —"

"Well, you wouldn't be looking for Chief Stewards with that book, would you? Anyway, the Shore Superintendent's the chap you want to see. He's got an office down at the East India somewhere. You'll have to look lively if you want to try the *Tairoa* — she's up for noon . . ."

She's up for noon — oh, the friendly, intimate jargon of the sea! There was a promise in the familiar phrase that raised my excitement to fever-heat. I never met that seaman again, but I'll love him till the day I die.

It took me two hours to find the Shore Superintendent, and less than five minutes to get the ship. He was a busy man all right. I was at his office by half-past eight, but they told me he had just left for a certain ship, and it was half-past ten before I caught up with him. I can't at this distance of time trace my wanderings in those two hours, but I must have visited at least six vessels at widely separated berths, always just a few minutes behind him. However, I was after something that drew me like the very Holy Grail, and I nailed him at last just as he was about to get into his car. I knew I was on the right track as soon as he stopped to listen to me.

"We don't want trimmers," he said after a glance at my book. "We want stewards."

"That's all right with me," I replied. "I want the passage. I'll sign as a steward. I've worked in hotels."

He passed the book back, taking me in from head to foot.

"Where's your gear?"

I could hardly speak for excitement. "Up in my room in Custom House —"

"You'd have to be aboard by twelve o'clock."

"I can do that. Where's she lying?"

He told me. "Give us your name." He pulled out a pocketbook. "Report to the Second Steward and give him this note."

She's up for noon . . .

Finch Street was two miles away, but I'll swear I made it in twenty minutes. There was plenty of time, but I had it in mind there was a suitcase to lug over the return trip, and I wasn't taking any chances. It was a cold foggy morning, but I was sweating from the long chase and the fever of success. And the grey buildings, and the shrouded figures that passed me on the pavement, were like things seen through the enchanted mists of fairyland. All the world had become beautiful, and I strode along puffed with triumph and springing on my toes with physical well-being. I told myself that youth and strength and pertinacity had to tell in the long run. You couldn't keep a good man down. Not when he had something big to struggle for. Those old men of the hostel had lacked the spur, inspiration, a vision . . .

No more Elevator. No doubt I wore a silly smile, because more than once I caught a curious glance directed at me as I hurried on. Perhaps my lips were moving too, because the magical phrase "she's up for noon" rang in my head until it took on the tune of a well-known military march. I could have danced to it, shouted it aloud.

She's up for noon . . .

I remember afterwards holding back to let an ambulance pass me as I was about to cross into Finch Street, but the fact that it was an ambulance didn't register at the time — only a car of some kind, and in a hurry.

But I did observe instantly the women out at their doors all along both sides, and the little knot of gossipers in front of my old lodgings.

I thought first of Mrs Hall, then of old Burroughs. But the humour of pitiless superiority was still on me, and I hardly quickened my pace. I'd come back for a suitcase, that was all, and in a few minutes these people . . .

They turned their heads and watched me as I came up. I saw Mrs Hall in the doorway, her popping eyes red with weeping.

"It's the old man, sailor. They've just took him off. The poor old soul."

Some of the arrogance and detachment left me. I wasn't interested in old Burroughs, but this woman had given me a cup of coffee and a few words of sympathy when I needed them most. The other women stood aside, and I moved into the passage, taking the landlady by her elbow and drawing her after me. Something tickled my nostrils, but all my attention was on something else.

"He's an old man, you know, Mrs Hall. What happened?"

"They think it's a stroke." She began to weep again, dabbing her nose with the lifted end of her tattered apron. "God help him! He tried to talk to me. He got one of them parcels this morning, them herbs. He's been sitting there — you got a ship, sailor?"

She could think of me too.

"Yes, I'm going aboard in an hour. Where've they taken him?"

But I didn't hear her reply.

Because that something which had been tickling my nostrils got right inside, and I lifted my head like a parched bullock scenting water, and stared along the passage, and sniffed, and licked my lips — and drew in a mighty inhalation that filled my lungs and sent me dizzy with the sickness that had been eating into me for five mortal weeks. I seized Mrs Hall with a violence that made her stare at me in sudden fright.

"Mrs Hall! — that smell — those herbs — where did they come from?"

As if I didn't know!

"Sailor —"

Burning gum-leaves! Oh, shades of the bush and smell of my home!

Pushing her from me, I was down the passage in two frenzied leaps and throwing open the door.

But nothing was left save the belongings of a lonely old man, a wisp of blue smoke rising from a tin set on an upturned box, and a digger's hat hanging on a nail driven into the mantelpiece.

Morning Glory

THE SHOT was fired about 4.30 in the morning. An hour before dawn, and a little more than an hour before the time set for the rising of the family. Poultry-farming involves early rising, but not necessarily 4.30. Everybody and everything was sleeping. Not a feather had shuffled in the long rows of white-painted pens perched terracelike on the hillside. Not a twitter had come from the starlings and sparrows crowding the cherry-plums and boobiallas behind the homestead.

For several seconds after the shot had broken the silence its echoes rumbled along the shallow valley and crackled back from the opposing slopes. Everybody was awakened, but they kept still for a moment, as people do at such a time, collecting their wits, separating dream from fact, waiting to see what would happen next. There were five of them: Arthur Brady and his wife Margaret, their thirteen-year-old son Lance, Grandfather Brady, and Hugh Griffiths, an itinerant labourer who had been doing some draining and was due to go on his way that day immediately after breakfast.

First reaction came from the Bradys' bedroom, the voice of Mrs Brady in an excited whisper:

"Arthur, did you hear that?"

"My oath I heard it!" There followed the sounds of a man hurriedly getting out of bed, and the click of a light-switch.

It had been a hot night, with all doors left wide open for free circulation of air, and the sudden flood of light in the bedroom dispelled the darkness all through the house.

Grandfather and Lance called out simultaneously from their separate rooms:

"That was a shot, Dad!"

"You awake, Arthur? Joe's had a go at something!"

Only on the back verandah, where the man Griffiths had a shakedown, was there still silence. The house filled with a buzz of voices and the soft swift sounds of people getting into clothes.

"Be careful now, Arthur! Don't go rushing out."

"Talk sense, woman! What d'you expect me to do . . . ?"

"We don't know what's happened . . ."

"Joe's got somebody, that's what's happened. He got something in his sights . . ."

"Can I come, Dad?"

"No, Lance, stop where you are."

"I'm up . . ."

"Stop inside, that's all I'm telling you."

Arthur Brady, a muscular little man in his early forties, came down the passage buckling a belt around a pair of trousers he had pulled on over his pyjamas. His lean brown face was grim and eager. Passing Grandfather's door he almost bumped into the old man, who was just coming out.

"I don't hear nothing else, Arthur."

"Neither do I. Perhaps he's killed the bastard."

Arthur hurried on, through the kitchen and out to the verandah, where he stood staring into the darkness, listening with cocked head and bated breath. But all he could hear was the low ceaseless rustling and clucking of a thousand frightened hens in the houses fifty yards away.

"You there, Joe?" he shouted.

A little way down the hillside a torch flashed and a strong voice came back: "Yes, come on down."

"Did you get him?"

"Come on down — quick!"

By now Mrs Brady, Grandfather and Lance were clustered behind Arthur at the top of the steps. They all started talking at once.

"Sounds like he got somebody, Arthur."

"D'you think he's killed him, Dad?"

"Lance, don't you say that like that!"

"But Mum . . ."

"You keep quiet . . ."

"I'll come down with you, Arthur . . ."

"You stop where you are, Dad. All of you stop here. I'll sing out if I want you."

Arthur Brady went off, running into the darkness. The others remained where they were, following his noisy progress down the garden path, out by the picket gate, across the open space to the fowlpens, and through the dry bracken ferns that clothed the hillside. Halfway down to the road the light of the torch remained on, moving about a little as if the man who held it were examining something. Voices drifted up to the house, but it was impossible to distinguish what the two men said as they came together.

"There's something doing down there, Madge," said Grandfather. "Better go in and put some clothes on."

"What d'you mean?"

He shrugged uneasily. "Oh, I dunno. There might be something to do . . ."

"Like what?"

"Joe's had a go at something, and he wouldn't sing out like that if it was a fox. We might have to get a doctor."

She didn't move immediately, just stood there staring in the direction of the torchlight, and frowning, as if the detailed implications of the shooting of a poultry thief were only slowly coming home to her.

"Will we have to get the police, Pop?" asked Lance, all boyish excitement.

"Course we will if Joe's hit somebody."

"I suppose I'd better put something on." Mrs Brady turned away, but in the entrance to the kitchen she stopped and looked back. "D'you think he could have killed him?" she asked in an awed voice.

"Kill him — no! Joe would hit him where he wanted to hit him. He had a flashlight rigged — go on in and get dressed. I'll stop here with Lance."

She went in, and for the first time Grandfather and Lance became aware of the hired man. He had a bag stretcher at the enclosed end of the verandah and had been sleeping without pyjamas. Even in the poor light that penetrated there they could see the white of his legs and short underpants as he put his feet to the floor and stood up.

There was no significance in the fact that he began to dress without speaking. In the two weeks that had passed since he came in off the road looking for work the family had become accustomed to his unobtrusive ways. He was a stoutish commonplace-looking man with an air of mild detached resignation that had baffled them from the first. Only Grandfather, however, really disliked him. He had remarked to Arthur that he always had a feeling that Griffiths was secretly laughing at them. Arthur was satisfied because he was a good worker; Mrs Brady because he was clean in his habits and kept to himself.

He came out now in trousers, singlet and heavy work-boots, and stood beside Grandfather. "That wasn't a gun, was it?" he asked.

"No, it was a rifle." Grandfather's reply came quite casually, but the instant it was made he turned sharply on Griffiths as if struck by a sudden suspicion of what lay behind the question.

Griffiths must have been aware of it, but he pretended not to notice.

It was quite warm, but a shiver passed over the old man and he noisily slapped his hands against his skinny stomach. "Go in and fetch me dressing-gown, will you?" he said to the boy. "It's hanging behind the door."

"Did he hit him, Pop?"

"We don't know nothing yet, Lance. We just got to wait till your Dad comes back."

Nothing passed between the two men while the boy was away. When he came back Grandfather, hugging himself in his dressing-gown, sat down on the top step. Griffiths stood over him, leaning against a post with one thumb hooked over his belt. Even the boy was aware of something in the air besides the actual shooting. His curious eyes moved from his grandfather to Griffiths and back again. He wanted to ask more questions, but the sullen expression on both faces kept him silent, and he went and rested his folded arms on the rail a few feet away.

All three of them watched the light down the hill. It remained fixed now, as if the torch had been laid on a ridge of earth or a stump. Now and then the little beam was broken as something passed through it. A murmur of voices came up almost continuously. It was very quiet, the deep hush that goes just before dawn.

In the fowlhouses the frightened birds had settled down again. The three people watched and waited and listened. When a dog rustled out from under the steps and reached up to sniff Grandfather's bare toes he pushed it away with the irritation of a man disturbed in anxious thought.

"Go and lie down, Bob. Go and lie down."

Suddenly the light of the torch went off and there came again the sound of a man tramping through dry ferns. The voices lifted for a moment, that of Arthur quite clearly:

"Don't you worry about it, Joe. You was there to do a job . . ."

All eyes were on him as he showed up on the garden path. He was breathing heavily, and would have climbed the steps without a word had not Grandfather, remaining seated, and moving only his knees out of the way, put out a hand to restrain him.

"What's the score, Arthur?"

"We got a dead 'un down the paddock, that's all."

"What!"

Grandfather stood up, but Arthur was already past, heading for the kitchen door. Mrs Brady, coming out at the same moment, frocked and combed, stopped on the threshold, fingers clapped to her lips.

"Arthur, did you say . . ."

"You heard me. I told you Joe wouldn't mess about if he got a go. Mind out of the way . . ."

He went in, and they heard the tinkle of the bell as he picked up the telephone at the far end of the passage. "Lil, give us D24 — quick! — yes, fair dinkum . . ."

At the back, Lance started to say something, but Grandfather hushed him down with an angry gesture.

Mrs Brady looked beseechingly at the two men. "Is that true? Joe's killed somebody?"

"Now don't you go getting upset over it, Madge . . ."

"He did — my God!" With hands pressed to the sides of her face she walked to the verandah rail and peered out at the scene of the shooting. There was a faint cool movement of air, carrying a smell of dusty herbage. In the east the sky was beginning to lighten. The first cock crowed. From somewhere close by there came the short, dry, tentative cackle of a kookaburra.

Griffiths was at the other side of the steps. He was standing very erect now, his hands gripping the rail, his head thrust forward, his brows knitted in an angry scowl. Grandfather watched him uneasily.

Arthur had finished his call to the police and got involved in conversation with the telephonist at the township. Every word came out clearly to the people on the verandah.

"I've seen too many dead 'uns not to know. What? — yes, of course she is

— I am myself — so's Joe. No, Lil, spare me days, you know Joe better than that! Listen — I got to go. They're all out here at the back . . .''

He hung up and came out again. Everybody turned to look at him but he addressed himself only to the boy.

"Get down to the bottom gate, Lance. Somebody's got to pull 'em up . . .''

"Who, Dad? The police?"

"You're always talking about D24 — hi, hold on!"

Lance was already on the steps. "Don't you go out on the road! You hear me? Just open the gate and stand on the side where they'll see you. Them blokes come like hell . . .''

Lance was gone. Arthur hitched up his trousers and tucked in his shirt. They were all watching him, but his eyes came to rest nowhere. His manner was ostentatiously defiant.

"This'll stop the bastards once and for all," he said. He began to roll a cigarette. Mrs Brady was studying his face, but Grandfather was watching his hands, which were shaking.

"Arthur, are you sure he's dead?" asked Mrs Brady.

"Wouldn't *you* know if you was looking at a corpse? Anyhow, Dr Noyes'll be here in a minute. Lil's calling him."

"Joe stopping down there?" This from Grandfather.

"One of us had to."

Silence fell, but it was the uneasy silence not of people who are content with their thoughts, but of people who are afraid of saying the wrong thing. Griffiths had moved away from the rail and was sitting on a box against the wall, filling his pipe. Dawn was breaking. The nearest trees were beginning to reveal themselves. A great chirping and rustling was going up from the cherry-plums and boobiallas. Wattle-birds called out in the garden.

Arthur began to pace back and forth across the creaking boards. Mrs Brady said something to him, but it was in such a low voice that he hardly heard her.

"What?"

"I said: what's he like?"

"What d'you mean? — what's he like . . .''

"Is he — young?"

"Young — no! Old enough to know what he was up to."

"Where did Joe — where did he hit him?"

"What does it matter where he hit him? Look, Madge, you'll get yourself and everybody else all stewed up." Arthur halted and faced her, emphasizing his words with short chopping gestures. "This has been coming for weeks, and you know it as well as I do. Joe . . .''

"But I never thought . . .''

"Neither did I. Nor Joe. Nor anybody else. It's still — oh damn!"

William Dobell *Billy Boy* 1943
Oil on cardboard on hardboard 70.2 × 53.4 cm
Australian War Memorial

Roland Wakelin *Black Mountain, Canberra* 1944
Oil on cardboard panel 59.5 × 68.5 cm
National Gallery of Victoria

Mrs Brady had covered her face with her hands. Arthur turned his back on her in exasperation, but Grandfather stepped in, and taking the distressed woman by the arm, gently urged her towards the kitchen door. "Go on in, Madge. This is man's work. It couldn't be helped. Nobody wanted to kill nobody, but it happened. Go on in. Go in and make us a cup of tea. Me and Arthur'll look after this."

She went in, but no sound of kettle or cups came out to the three men on the verandah.

None of them spoke for a minute or two while the glow of the lighted house began to weaken against the dawn. Then, suddenly, Arthur threw the butt of his cigarette to the boards and ground it with his heel.

"Why the hell do we have to have a scene like this over it! A bloke comes to steal my chooks. He knows I'm hostile on it and I'll do something about it. All right, he takes the odds and he gets shot. What do I do now — sit down and cry?"

"It's just that he got killed," said Grandfather gently.

"And whose bloody fault is that? Mine?"

"I'm not saying it was your fault."

"Joe's? We all put in and hired Joe . . ."

"No, I wouldn't say — don't let's argue about it, Arthur. It's bad enough."

"What d'you mean — bad enough. I say it's a good job that's been done. We set out to stop this thieving, and by jeez this'll stop it!"

"All right." Grandfather, not satisfied, but afraid to take the dispute any further, returned to his position at the rail. The sun had not yet risen, but there was enough light now to reveal the entire landscape: the small roughly tended garden, the dusty track leading past the gate and on towards outhouses and fowlpens, scattered wattles and stringybarks, and patches of brown ferns on a ground of yellow grass.

"Just whereabouts are they?" asked Grandfather after a discreet silence.

Arthur came and stood beside him, pointing. "See that clump of wattles in line with the corner-post?" he said sulkily.

"Yes."

"Over to the left — that gum forked at the butt, out on its own?"

"Yes."

"They're near there. Somewhere near that patch of ferns. It's a bit dark yet. You'll see Joe's head in a minute. He's sitting there . . ."

Grandfather nodded. "I heard you telling Lil he was running," he said cautiously. "That true?"

"Yes. Joe just let fly . . ."

"He hit him in the back?"

"Yes. There's a hole in him up towards the left shoulder."

"Bull's-eye. You know there'll be trouble over this, don't you?"

"Trouble. What kind of trouble?"

"The law says you can't kill a man for stealing a chook."

"The law says you can't steal a chook!"

Grandfather didn't answer that. He let a second or two pass. Then, with his eyes still fixed on the patch of ferns, he said sadly: "He might have needed it."

Arthur gave a scornful laugh. "By Christ, you're not too bad! How about me? Don't I need 'em? Who the hell am I raising chooks for? Any lousy bastard . . ."

"Sssh! You'll fetch Madge out." Grandfather, worried by Arthur's rising anger, held up his hands. "It's just the killing, Arthur. I got nothing against a charge of shot."

Unobserved by either of them, however, the woman had already appeared, standing in the entrance to the kitchen. She was looking not at them, but at the bowed head of Griffiths, as if she found his detachment puzzling and offensive.

Arthur thought of him at the same moment and turned to him for support. "What do you say, Griff? Don't you reckon that bloke got what he was looking for?"

Griffiths lifted his head, took his pipe from his mouth, and stared Arthur steadily in the eyes. "If a man's got property he's got to defend it," he said quietly.

"My bloody oath! And that's exactly how I see it."

Arthur, satisfied that his point had been made, resumed his restless pacing, but all Grandfather's attention remained fixed on the hired man. He began to breathe heavily, in the way of an old person caught up in a mounting excitement. His whole body shook, his head stuck forward like an angry parrot. He pointed an accusing finger. Mrs Brady called out to him from the doorway, but he didn't hear her.

"That bastard's laughing at you!" he shouted. Mrs Brady and Arthur moved towards him, but he evaded them, dodging sideways, his stooping body allowing the front folds of his dressing-gown to trail the floor. "What does it matter to him? He's got nothing. He never had nothing. He doesn't want nothing. He's just having a shot at you. He's one of them blokes that's crooked on the whole world." Arthur had reached him, hustling him back towards the rail. "That's all right, Arthur. You didn't see him. I did. He was smiling. That lousy sneering smile. I saw him . . ."

"What does it matter — break it up, Dad — I got trouble enough . . ."

Griffiths was on his feet, openly contemptuous. "Let him rave," he said curtly to Mrs Brady. "I've got my cheque. I'll eat on the road."

Arthur heard that. "What's up with you? I'm handling this. And you keep out of it, Madge . . ."

Snubbed on both sides, she stood there, silently watching Griffiths as he walked purposefully towards his bed. She saw him pull off the old grey blankets he had brought with him, spread them on the floor, and begin to throw onto them the few other odds and ends that comprised his worldly possessions: spare shirt and underclothing, a ragged jersey, a pair of worn canvas shoes, shaving gear.

Over at the rail the old man was almost weeping.

"I'm not crooked on you, Arthur. I'm not crooked on nobody. It's this killing, just the killing. I got no time for thieves, but nobody ought to get killed like that. They used to hang blokes once just for taking what didn't belong to them. What do we know about him? He's lying there — take your hands off me mouth! — I know what I'm talking about. I could have got killed myself more than once when you was kids. I never had nothing. I'm glad to see you getting on a bit. But I don't want to see you getting like the big 'eads — walking round what you got with a bloody gun. Your Mum . . ."

"Shut up, will you?"

Mrs Brady rushed over to them, pointing down at the road. "Arthur, look! Here's a car — the police . . ."

They stopped struggling. In the sudden silence that fell on the house there came only a clink of buckles as the hired man tightened his swag. All the lights were still on, but it was the new day that lit up the rich and peaceful earth and the grim immemorial burden of men.

Dog-box

I FIRST became aware of her just before the train pulled in.

Flinders Street Station in the peak-hour is a primitive place. You get pushed at from all sides, and if the pressure from one particular quarter is a bit more persistent than from anywhere else the odds are that you won't even notice it. That is, if you're a regular peak-hour traveller, have a long way to go, and are not as young as you used to be.

I was aware of this particular pressure, though. It turned out afterwards to be the edge of a wicker shopping basket, but it felt more like the lid of a garbage can. However, I held my ground and fought down a temptation to look around, because to have done so would have meant moving more than my head, thereby letting somebody else in.

The train came into sight running down from the yards, and a murmur of pleasant anticipation ran along the packed platform. Dog-box! We used to talk of the old dears with contempt, but have changed our attitude since the arrival of the Blue Hussies. It was like seeing the old brown teapot come to light.

It slowed to a stop. Those of us at the front pressed backwards as incoming passengers eased open the swinging doors. I was in a good position, but sensed immediate danger as I felt the lid of the garbage can slide round into my left side. I looked down, frowning, because for all the hurly-burly of the five-to-six rush, there is still a point beyond which most sufferers do not go.

She had Mum written all over her. I was close enough to get even the homely middle-aged smell of her; something of well-preserved clothes, wood-ashes, yellow soap, the stew-pot. Below a comfortable bosom she hugged her garbage can battering ram, a well-filled shopping basket topped with what looked like a folded woollen scarf. Two bright eyes flashed up at me out of a face full of character and rich experience.

"Sorry, mister!"

I gave her a smile, and a few more inches of precious ground, but I knew she wasn't a bit sorry. She was as good as past me, and already digging her basket into the backs of two other women who had moved in from the other side.

Nobody got hurt, but Mum was only fifth in. She was beaten by the two women, a big workman, and a little clerk type of fellow who must have been an old hand at the game, because he seemed to come from nowhere to take fourth place.

When I got in I found the two near window-seats occupied by the clerk and the workman. The three women were on the same side as the clerk, with Mum furthest from the window and apparently none too happy about it. In the fourth corner a tough-looking fellow wearing a black belted raincoat and a cloth cap sat watching us troop in with an expression of sleepy insolence on his unshaven face.

On his knees lay what was obviously a bottle wrapped up in brown paper. I sat down next to him before I realized that he was half drunk and that I hadn't noticed him before.

"Flinders Street," I said amiably. "This train's going back."

He turned on me a dull heavy-lidded stare. "Back where?" he asked with a strong Scottish accent.

"Lilydale."

"Lilydale." He gave that a moment's consideration. "An' supposin' tha's where I want tae go?"

"Sorry. I didn't see you get in."

"An' supposin' I didna get in?"

Now experience has taught me that the best way to deal with a quarrelsome drunk is to meet him halfway. So I said firmly: "That's what I was supposing."

"An' supposin' ye're richt?"

I shrugged my shoulders and looked away from him.

But to my relief he suddenly relaxed and clapped a heavy hand on my knee. "A'richt, Pop. I been sleepin'. A' the way there an' back. I wanted Nunawading. First thing I know I open ma eyes and there's the bluidy cricket ground flyin' past again, the wrong way."

"You're all right this time," I said. "I'm going to Croydon. I'll have an eye on you at Nunawading."

In the meantime the compartment had filled up, even with a few standing passengers. During my exchange with Scotty I'd been aware of Mum on the other side taking some interest in the proceedings. But not much. She was pre-occupied chiefly with the basket and with the two women on her left. The one in the window seat had lit a cigarette and seemed to want to keep to herself. The other, a stoutish matron in navy-blue overcoat and beret, and laden with parcels, was beaming at all of us, ready to take on anybody who'd give her a fair hearing. She had the air of a woman who has made some bargains and feels she has topped off a good day by getting herself a seat on a peak-hour train going home.

Mum looked as if she were still nursing a grievance over being beaten to a corner seat. Without moving her head she kept darting angry little sideways glances. Her leathery face was grim and anxious as she felt under the woollen scarf to see if everything was still there.

On Mum's right a pale youth in black trousers and pink windcheater had opened up a Superman comic. In the far corner the clerk was reading a paper-back. On my side there was Scotty, myself, two mates whose names I soon learned were Bill and Ian, and the workman, of whom all I could see were frayed trouser cuffs and a pair of big blucher boots. The standing passengers were reinforced at Richmond by a man who irritated Mum by flicking her face every now and then with the corner of a *Herald* hanging from a hand hooked on to the luggage-rack.

Bill and Ian were discussing an item in the news: Stanley Yankus, the American farmer who was migrating to Australia because he had been fined for growing too much wheat. Ian, sitting next to me, was doing all the listening, so that I picked up most of what Bill was saying.

"What good will it do him, anyhow? It'll be on here again any tick of the clock. I just heard the other night over the air that hundreds of acres of sugar-cane in Queensland ain't going to be cut this year. My old man told me the best job he ever had in his life was dumping butter during the Depression. He used to work all day carting butter down and tipping it into the Bay. Then go home at night to a feed of snags and fried bread. One of his mates got the sack because they found some butter in his bag . . ."

I began to get interested, but at that moment Scotty came to life again. No preliminaries. I thought he was sleeping until he whispered right into my ear:

"How about a whisky, Pop?" He tapped the brown paper parcel on his knees. "Nane o' your Australian tack. Real Scotch — White Horse. Have a nip."

I told him quite amiably that it wasn't my medicine. He frowned contemptuously.

"What do ye drink?"

"Beer."

"Supposin' I havna got beer?" He stared hard, as if I'd been demanding beer and what was I going to do about it now.

"That's my bad luck," I said.

"An' ye no want a whisky?"

"No, thank you."

On my left I caught Bill's voice: "I saw another case like Yankus only a few months ago. Only it was pigs. A bloke raising too many pigs . . ."

Ian must have moved, for the voice faded. And Scotty was still at me:

"Any objections tae me havin' a nip?"

"No," I replied, adding impatiently: "It's your whisky."

He knitted his brows, and for a moment I thought I'd gone too far too quickly. I tried to appear interested in Mum, but was acutely aware of him keeping me under observation while he decided what to do about me.

Mum had been captured by Mrs Blue Beret. The latter was obscured by one of the standing passengers and I couldn't make out what she was saying, but for the last few minutes her voice had provided a steady overtone to all the other noises in the compartment. Mum was only pretending to be listening. She kept turning her head and nodding sympathetically, but it was plain to me that her mind was never far from her basket. I began to wonder what was in it. She had it hugged close to her stomach, wrists braced against the arched handle, both hands turned inwards and spread out over the folded scarf as if ready to detect the slightest movement of something hidden beneath it.

Bill was flat out on the question of pigs. I'd stolen a peep at him and found him to be a man of middle age with a worried expression on the kind of face that goes with ulcers or a nagging wife.

"Blokes was getting paid for pigs they didn't raise. Now just you get on to it! Say you're a little bloke, just big enough to raise pigs up to the quota. All nicely organized, prices fixed and guaranteed. You get paid for, say, fifty pigs that stink and grunt and make pork. But I'm in it in a bigger way. I've got room for two hundred pigs. And I get paid for two hundred pigs. Only I get told to keep just a hundred and fifty — or else! So I declare a hundred and fifty pigs on the hoof and fifty on paper. And I get paid for them fifty paper pigs just like you get paid for your fifty pork pigs. And people everywhere screaming out for bacon. The game stinks!"

Ian murmured something which was inaudible to me, and nodded his head to agree that the game did indeed stink.

I waited, curious to see where Bill would go from there, but Scotty had returned to the attack on the other side. He must have been brooding, because he took up his grievance exactly where he had left off.

"What ye're tellin' me is: this is a free country, eh?"

I pretended not to grasp his meaning.

"If ye don't want tae drink whisky, ye don't have to. An' if I *do* want tae drink whisky — I drink whisky. That it?"

I smiled. "That's about it."

"It's as simple as tha', is it?"

"It was your idea!"

"I didna say it was my idea. I was suggestin' maybe it was your idea." He tapped the parcel again. "Supposin' a checker got in just as I cracked this bottle. Ye still say I can drink whisky if I want to?"

"That's a chance you'd have to take, my friend," I parried, still smiling.

"What ye mean is: this is a free country as long as I'm prepared tae take the odds. Is that it?"

I shrugged my shoulders, and once again he retired into his alcoholic whirligig. A moment later, under the pretence of identifying a station we were pulling into, I stole a glance at him. Chin resting on elbow, he was staring out through the window with an expression of sleepy triumph.

Mum also was watching stations. We were in Auburn, and she'd been checking off every stop as if on her way to an appointment of life or death. Conversation with the woman in blue had become clinical. I caught the sentence: "Anyhow, he gave me some tablets for him to take . . ." and guessed that the absent Mr Blue Beret was under discussion.

Mum was showing a little more interest, but still only between stations. Every time we stopped she leaned forward to peer out through the window, remaining like that until we were on the move again. She looked cold. She should have been wearing that scarf. It occurred to me that she had taken it off to protect something in the basket. A kitten? Chicken? Whatever it was she never for an instant removed her sheltering hands. Every now and then I saw the worn fingers spread out, feeling, probing. Next to her the pale youth had been through the comic and was fighting a losing battle with sleep. Mum had had to straighten him up several times with discreet little nudges. But I'm a leftwise subsider myself, and I knew that nothing she could do would make him collapse in the other direction. Motherly type as she was, I believe she'd have let him go to sleep on her shoulder if it hadn't been for the basket. I saw her shift it a little away from him and bring her right elbow forward as a barrier.

Bill was in the full tide of the subject of the paper pigs.

"Them pigs that nobody raises get paid for in real money. The blokes that whistles pigs up say you can't whistle money up — not for pigs, anyway. They say it's got to come from somewhere, and that somewhere always means you and me in the long run. Taxes. Say you're on the basic wage and you got a big family to feed. You'd give 'em all two cackles and a grunt for breakfast every morning if you could, wouldn't you?"

Ian must have agreed with that.

"But you can't, not on your pay. Eggs maybe, but not bacon as well. But, by jeez, you got to pay for bacon! Them paper pigs get paid for with Government dough. And that's you! Now just work it out. You pay taxes to pay blokes to raise paper pigs so that the bloke who raises pork pigs can get a price you can't afford! Now tell me the game doesn't stink."

Ian evidently was still not prepared to say that the game didn't stink, and a sulky silence fell on my left.

At Camberwell several passengers, including the woman in the corner seat, got off. Nobody got in. Mrs Blue Beret, in full voice on her husband's clinical history, seemed unaware that the corner seat had been vacated until Mum gave her an urgent push. Both of them moved along, and Mum settled herself one place nearer the window with obvious satisfaction. The pale youth lurched violently, collected himself with great embarrassment, apologized, and promptly moved in close to her again. I think he didn't like the look of the passenger who was ready to drop into the empty seat, and felt that if he was going to subside on to anybody it had still better be Mum.

In the commotion Scotty came to life again. I noticed his hand tighten convulsively on the bottle of whisky in the very moment that sleep left him. He shook his head, peered out for the name of the station, relaxed, and after a few seconds' contemplation to thoroughly digest the fact that I was still there, once again began where he had left off.

"So ye think it's a free country, do ye?"

"Look here, my friend," I began irritably. "I've done a hard day's work . . ."

"A'richt, a'richt, a'richt." I'd been prepared for a different reaction, and was rather disconcerted when he bent on me a dry smile. "Why don't ye go tae sleep then? Ye're sittin' there wi' your eyes wide open . . ."

"Any objections?"

"No, no objections. If a man wants tae sleep he's entitled tae sleep. If a man doesna want tae sleep . . ." he waved his hand in a way that made me want to hit him, "och weel, it's a free country!" And there he left me again, seething.

I decided to have a piece of him next time, whatever the cost.

Mrs Blue Beret was a foot or two further away from me now, but with the standing passengers gone I could hear more of what Mum had to put up with.

". . . little pink ones this time. And do you think I could get him to take them? Not on your life! He said they made everything he ate taste like burned cork. And the doctor had gone out of his way to tell me they didn't have no taste at all. It just goes to show what imagination can do for you."

Mum, carefully checking the train through Canterbury, nodded shrewdly.

"He was particularly crooked on them spoiling his tea. So he said, anyhow. He's always liked his cuppa. So d'you know what I did? I said to him: if you think they're not doing you any good then you'd better stop taking them. And I started putting them into his tea unbeknown to him! And now he's as happy as Larry. Says he hasn't felt better for years, and that them tablets must have been making him worse. Sometimes I could bust right out laughing at him. He looks at me across the table and winks and smacks his lips. 'By God, Sally,' he says, 'it's good to be able to enjoy a decent cup of tea again!' "

Mum chuckled, nodding vigorously, and, I thought, reminiscently. In other circumstances she might have told a good story back. At the moment she just didn't want to be involved in anything. There was that basket . . .

Bill was still getting a good hearing on pigs:

"The more you look at it the sillier it gets. If you ain't in the pig business you cop it three ways. You don't eat pork, even under the lap. You pay taxes to pay blokes not to raise pigs. And you pay more taxes to pay more blokes to see that the other blokes *don't* raise pork. Because it's like everything else, it's got to be administered. You got to have an office, clerks, paper for forms to fill in so that blokes can say exactly how many pigs they ain't raising. One time farmers just raised pigs, and there wasn't any office anywhere that had anything to do with pig-raising. They just took the little pigs to market. These paper pigs is different . . ."

We had come to a halt somewhere between Mont Albert and Box Hill, and

Mum was becoming increasingly worried. I believe she'd have given anything for Mrs Blue Beret's corner seat so that she could open the window and look out to see what was the cause of the hold-up. Mrs Blue Beret rambled on, regardless of the fact that Mum obviously wasn't listening. Mum looked thoroughly angry, as if nothing would suit her better just then than a chance to give the Victorian Railways Commissioners a piece of her mind. For the twentieth time I caught her withdrawing her hand from under the scarf, and had to fight down a temptation to lean over and ask her if it was still breathing. I wasn't sure how she'd take it.

More pigs . . .

"The trouble is, Ian, sooner or later the big blokes is going to take a wake-up to the lurk and go in for it in a big way. They'll monopolize it, get a corner in them paper pigs. They'll have 'em raising litters. They'll be claiming higher prices for 'em because of the rise in costs of all the tucker they don't give 'em to eat. They'll be going on overseas trips, tax-free, to study the latest developments in the paper pig-raising industry. They'll get their mates in Parliament to put a duty on imported pork so as to give the home-produced stuff a fair go — struth, we're at Box Hill! We made a quick run tonight . . ."

I felt a keen disappointment as the two friends reached for their bags on the luggage-rack. It would have been diverting to see how far Bill would have gone in his dissertation on the controls of private enterprise. I noticed that the moment they were out on the platform he started again.

Some other passengers got out also. More came in. Mostly teenage schoolboys.

Mum had just ridden out another lurch of the pale youth and informed him with a rather tight little smile: "You was nearly into me basket that time!" He was sitting stiffly now with a red face, trying desperately to find something in the comic that was worth rereading. Mrs Blue Beret announced that she was getting off at Blackburn, and with a new passenger standing against the door I saw Mum gather herself for the slide into the corner seat. With that in prospect she listened quite sympathetically to the final anecdote about Mr Blue Beret's stomach.

"He's supposed to eat brains, you know, but he says he's never sat down to the dirty things in his life and he ain't going to start now. So I give him fish-paste sandwiches in his lunch every other day. That's what he thinks, anyhow. If he's never tasted brains he can't be any the wiser. Sometimes he'll come in from work and say: 'By jeez, Sally, that was a nice bit of fish!' He thinks it's Japanese flat'ead paste . . ."

I'd have liked more on that, but just then the tenacious Scot came in again: "This free country business . . ."

"How about giving it a rest?"

"No offence, Pop. Ye're an Aussie, aren't ye?"

"Yes, I'm an Aussie."

"An' ye say it's a free country?"

"Yes, I do."

"You always cast your vote at election time?"

"You bet I do!"

"An' supposin' ye dinna like ony o' the candidates? You still cast your vote?"

"I can always vote for the one I dislike least."

The corners of his lips drooped. "Ye ca' tha' an argument? The real point o' the matter is: ye got tae vote, haven't ye?"

"Voting *is* compulsory, yes."

Again the pontifically waving hand. "Tha's jist ma point! A free country — an' compulsion wherever ye turn! In Scotland I never missed ma vote, simply because I was free tae please masel. Oot here the first thing they tell me is: Jock, ye got tae vote! That's enough for me. Ma hackles is up. If tha's wha' they ca' democracy they can keep it. I've never used ma vote since I set foot in Australia. I believe in real freedom."

And with that he retired, supremely confident of having finally flattened me, as indeed he had.

I was still reeling under the blow when we reached Blackburn and Mrs Blue Beret gathered up her parcels and got out. The man in the doorway stepped on to the platform to make way for her, so that Mum had no opposition in taking over the corner seat. I thought for a moment that she was going to open the window, but all she wanted was to make sure that it was in good working order. She just pushed it up a few inches, let it fall again, and immediately had another feel of the mystery under the scarf. If she hadn't looked so homely I'd have assumed then that she had some living thing she wanted to destroy, and was only waiting until the compartment was empty before pitching it out on to the line.

The schoolboys were involved in a lively discussion of TV. It might have been a golden opportunity for me to get an insight into juvenile perversion, but nothing now could divert me from Mum and her basket.

Except Scotty, who couldn't resist a final shot during the last lap to Nunawading. I knew for a good minute that he had turned his head and was watching me. I also knew, I don't know how, that he was smiling.

"Dinna let it worry ye, Pop."

"Do I look worried?"

"No, I'm no sayin' ye look worried. I'm referrin' tae oor wee dispute."

I said nothing, but was careful to keep a pleasant expression. In spite of everything he had succeeded in making me feel a bit of a nark. We slowed into Nunawading and he took a firm grip on his bottle of whisky and prepared to depart.

"No hurt feelings, Pop?"

"No hurt feelings, Mac. Good luck to you!" I was beginning to like him, but possibly only because he was going.

He lurched out, and, teetering alongside, gave me an ironic salute before banging the door.

"Never mind, Pop, there'll always be an England — as lang as there's a Scotland!"

On again, with Mum and I exchanging understanding smiles across the compartment. I believe she'd have said something but for the fact that, as I noticed with some excitement, she also was near the end of her journey. She was like a cat on hot bricks, measuring off the miles between Nunawading — Mitcham — Ringwood. She must have been feeling very cold. The pinched little neck, where that scarf should have been, was all gooseflesh. Every now and then a shiver passed over her. Her cheeks and the tip of her nose had turned blue. Her feet, which just reached the floor, kept up a ceaseless tapping. But in the keen eyes and on the thin lips there was a smile of joyous anticipation. Both hands vanished under the scarf as if to give added protection over the last mile or two. I must have looked vastly interested, because when she caught me watching her she gave me a you-mind-your-own-business kind of stare plain enough to be embarrassing.

Ringwood. No, she didn't get off. But for all practical purposes it *was* the end of her journey. Everything favoured her.

She must have known every stick and stone of that line, because, sitting with a firm grip on the catch, she shot the window up in the very instant that we hit the end of the platform. Out went her head and a frantically waving hand. A long line of waiting passengers rushed past, slowed down, stopped. Mum was hidden from sight as the door opened, but I heard her urgent piping voice:

"Hi, Bill!"

People were getting off, others crowding around to get in. I got a glimpse of a good-looking young station assistant, his startled face trying to see where the voice was coming from. He stepped forward and was blacked out at the other side of the doorway.

"Spare me days, Mum! Where've you been to?"

"In town. Here, cop this — it's a pie — it'll warm you up . . ."

"You beaut!"

"How's Elsie?"

"All right. How's Dad?"

"All right. How's Bubby?"

"Fit as a Mallee bull! Got another tooth . . ."

The changing passengers were clearing and I got a full-length view of him. He stood with one hand resting on the window ledge, carrying on the conversation while casting hurried glances right and left along the train. His other hand held a small brown paper bag with a grease stain on it.

As the last doors banged he stepped backwards, one arm uplifted. The guard's whistle blew. The train tooted. We jerked into a start.

Mum's head was still at the open window.

"Ta-ta, Bill — eat it while it's hot!"

I thought I'd never seen a sweeter sight than that little woman sitting there with a happy smile as she wrapped the woollen scarf around her frozen neck.

Dear old Mum! To hell with the railways! — eat it while it's hot.

Judith
Wright

Bora Ring

The song is gone; the dance
is secret with the dancers in the earth,
the ritual useless, and the tribal story
lost in an alien tale.

Only the grass stands up
to mark the dancing-ring; the apple-gums
posture and mime a past corroboree,
murmur a broken chant.

The hunter is gone: the spear
is splintered underground; the painted bodies
a dream the world breathed sleeping and forgot.
The nomad feet are still.

Only the rider's heart
halts at a sightless shadow, an unsaid word
that fastens in the blood the ancient curse,
the fear as old as Cain.

Bullocky

Beside his heavy-shouldered team,
thirsty with drought and chilled with rain,
he weathered all the striding years
till they ran widdershins in his brain:

Till the long solitary tracks
etched deeper with each lurching load
were populous before his eyes,
and fiends and angels used his road.

All the long straining journey grew
a mad apocalyptic dream,
and he old Moses, and the slaves
his suffering and stubborn team.

Then in his evening camp beneath
the half-light pillars of the trees
he filled the steepled cone of night
with shouted prayers and prophecies.

While past the campfire's crimson ring
the star-struck darkness cupped him round,
and centuries of cattlebells
rang with their sweet uneasy sound.

Grass is across the waggon-tracks,
and plough strikes bone beneath the grass,
and vineyards cover all the slopes
where the dead teams were used to pass.

O vine, grow close upon that bone
and hold it with your rooted hand.
The prophet Moses feeds the grape,
and fruitful is the Promised Land.

South of My Days

South of my days' circle, part of my blood's country,
rises that tableland, high delicate outline
of bony slopes wincing under the winter,
low trees blue-leaved and olive, outcropping granite —
clean, lean, hungry country. The creek's leaf-silenced,
willow-choked, the slope a tangle of medlar and crabapple
branching over and under, blotched with a green lichen;
and the old cottage lurches in for shelter.

O cold the black-frost night. The walls draw in to the warmth
and the old roof cracks its joints; the slung kettle
hisses a leak on the fire. Hardly to be believed that summer
will turn up again some day in a wave of rambler roses,
thrust its hot face in here to tell another yarn —
a story old Dan can spin into a blanket against the winter.
Seventy years of stories he clutches round his bones.
Seventy summers are hived in him like old honey.

Droving that year, Charleville to the Hunter,
nineteen-one it was, and the drought beginning;
sixty head left at the McIntyre, the mud round them
hardened like iron; and the yellow boy died
in the sulky ahead with the gear, but the horse went on,
stopped at the Sandy Camp and waited in the evening.
It was the flies we seen first, swarming like bees.
Came to the Hunter, three hundred head of a thousand —
cruel to keep them alive — and the river was dust.

Or mustering up in the Bogongs in the autumn
when the blizzards came early. Brought them down; we brought them
down, what aren't there yet. Or driving for Cobb's on the run
up from Tamworth — Thunderbolt at the top of Hungry Hill,
and I give him a wink. I wouldn't wait long, Fred,
not if I was you; the troopers are just behind,
coming for that job at the Hillgrove. He went like a luny,
him on his big black horse.

Oh, they slide and they vanish
as he shuffles the years like a pack of conjuror's cards.
True or not, it's all the same; and the frost on the roof
cracks like a whip, and the back-log breaks into ash.
Wake, old man. This is winter, and the yarns are over.
No one is listening.
     South of my days' circle
I know it dark against the stars, the high lean country
full of old stories that still go walking in my sleep.

Woman to Man

The eyeless labourer in the night,
the selfless, shapeless seed I hold,
builds for its resurrection day —
silent and swift and deep from sight
foresees the unimagined light.

This is no child with a child's face;
this has no name to name it by:
yet you and I have known it well.
This is our hunter and our chase,
the third who lay in our embrace.

This is the strength that your arm knows,
the arc of flesh that is my breast,
the precise crystals of our eyes.
This is the blood's wild tree that grows
the intricate and folded rose.

This is the maker and the made;
this is the question and reply;
the blind head butting at the dark,
the blaze of light along the blade.
Oh hold me, for I am afraid.

The Cycads

Their smooth dark flames flicker at time's own root.
Round them the rising forests of the years
alter the climates of forgotten earth
and silt with leaves the strata of first birth.

Only the antique cycads sullenly
keep the old bargain life has long since broken;
and, cursed by age, through each chill century
they watch the shrunken moon, but never die,

for time forgets the promise he once made,
and change forgets that they are left alone.
Among the complicated birds and flowers
they seem a generation carved in stone.

Leaning together, down those gulfs they stare
over whose darkness dance the brilliant birds
that cry in air one moment, and are gone;
and with their countless suns the years spin on.

Take their cold seed and set it in the mind,
and its slow root will lengthen deep and deep
till, following, you cling on the last ledge
over the unthinkable, unfathomed edge
beyond which man remembers only sleep.

Request to a Year

If the year is meditating a suitable gift,
I should like it to be the attitude
of my great-great-grandmother,
legendary devotee of the arts,

who, having had eight children
and little opportunity for painting pictures,
sat one day on a high rock
beside a river in Switzerland

and from a difficult distance viewed
her second son, balanced on a small ice-floe,
drift down the current towards a waterfall
that struck rock-bottom eighty feet below,

while her second daughter, impeded,
no doubt, by the petticoats of the day,
stretched out a last-hope alpenstock
(which luckily later caught him on his way).

Nothing, it was evident, could be done;
and with the artist's isolating eye
my great-great-grandmother hastily sketched the scene.
The sketch survives to prove the story by.

Year, if you have no Mother's day present planned;
reach back and bring me the firmness of her hand.

At Cooloola

The blue crane fishing in Cooloola's twilight
has fished there longer than our centuries.
He is the certain heir of lake and evening,
and he will wear their colour till he dies,

but I'm a stranger, come of a conquering people.
I cannot share his calm, who watch his lake,
being unloved by all my eyes delight in,
and made uneasy, for an old murder's sake.

Those dark-skinned people who once named Cooloola
knew that no land is lost or won by wars,
for earth is spirit: the invader's feet will tangle
in nets there and his blood be thinned by fears.

Riding at noon and ninety years ago,
my grandfather was beckoned by a ghost —
a black accoutred warrior armed for fighting,
who sank into bare plain, as now into time past.

White shores of sand, plumed reed and paperbark,
clear heavenly levels frequented by crane and swan —
I know that we are justified only by love,
but oppressed by arrogant guilt, have room for none.

And walking on clean sand among the prints
of bird and animal, I am challenged by a driftwood spear
thrust from the water; and, like my grandfather,
must quiet a heart accused by its own fear.

The Old Prison

The rows of cells are unroofed,
a flute for the wind's mouth,
who comes with a breath of ice
from the blue caves of the south.

O dark and fierce day:
the wind like an angry bee
hunts for the black honey
in the pits of the hollow sea.

Waves of shadow wash
the empty shell bone-bare,
and like a bone it sings
a bitter song of air.

Who built and laboured here?
The wind and the sea say
— Their cold nest is broken
and they are blown away.

They did not breed nor love.
Each in his cell alone
cried as the wind now cries
through this flute of stone.

Gum Trees Stripping

Say the need's born within the tree,
and waits a trigger set for light;
say sap is tidal like the sea,
and rises with the solstice-heat —
but wisdom shells the words away
to watch this fountain slowed in air
where sun joins earth — to watch the place
at which these silent rituals are.

Words are not meanings for a tree.
So it is truer not to say,
''These rags look like humility,
or this year's wreck of last year's love,
or wounds ripped by the summer's claw.''
If it is possible to be wise
here, wisdom lies outside the word
in the earlier answer of the eyes.

Wisdom can see the red, the rose,
the stained and sculptured curve of grey,
the charcoal scars of fire, and see
around that living tower of tree
the hermit tatters of old bark
split down and strip to end the season;
and can be quiet and not look
for reasons past the edge of reason.

Train Journey

Glassed with cold sleep and dazzled by the moon,
out of the confused hammering dark of the train
I looked and saw under the moon's cold sheet
your delicate dry breasts, country that built my heart;

and the small trees on their uncoloured slope
like poetry moved, articulate and sharp
and purposeful under the great dry flight of air,
under the crosswise currents of wind and star.

Clench down your strength, box-tree and ironbark.
Break with your violent root the virgin rock.
Draw from the flying dark its breath of dew
till the unliving come to life in you.

Be over the blind rock a skin of sense,
under the barren height a slender dance . . .

I woke and saw the dark small trees that burn
suddenly into flowers more lovely than the white moon.

Wonga Vine

Look down; be still.
The sunburst day's on fire,
O twilight bell,
flower of the wonga vine.

I gather you
out of his withering light.
Sleep there, red;
sleep there, yellow and white.

Move as the creek
moves to its hidden pool.
The sun has eyes of fire;
be my white waterfall.

Lie on my eyes like hands,
let no sun shine —
O twilight bell,
flower of the wonga vine.

Night Herons

It was after a day's rain:
the street facing the west
was lit with growing yellow;
the black road gleamed.

First one child looked and saw
and told another.
Face after face, the windows
flowered with eyes.

It was like a long fuse lighted,
the news travelling.
No one called out loudly;
everyone said "Hush."

The light deepened; the wet road
answered in daffodil colours,
and down its centre
walked the two tall herons.

Stranger than wild birds, even,
what happened on those faces:
suddenly believing in something,
they smiled and opened.

Children thought of fountains,
circuses, swans feeding:
women remembered words
spoken when they were young.

Everyone said "Hush;"
no one spoke loudly;
but suddenly the herons
rose and were gone. The light faded.

The Graves at Mill Point

Alf Watt is in his grave
These eighty years.
From his bones a bloodwood grows
With long leaves like tears.

His girl grew weary long ago;
She's long lost the pain
Of crying to the empty air
To hold her boy again.

When he died the town died.
Nothing's left now
But the wind in the bloodwoods:
"Where did they go?

In the rain beside the graves
I heard their tears say
— This is where the world ends;
The world ends today.

Six men, seven men
Lie in one furrow.
The peaty earth goes over them,
But cannot blind our sorrow —"

"Where have they gone to?
I can't hear or see.
Tell me of the world's end,
You heavy bloodwood tree."

"There's nothing but a butcher-bird
Singing on my wrist,
And the long wave that rides the lake
With rain upon its crest.

There's nothing but a wandering child
Who stoops to your stone;
But time has washed the words away,
So your story's done."

Six men, seven men
Are left beside the lake,
And over them the bloodwood tree
Flowers for their sake.

A Document

"Sign there." I signed, but still uneasily.
I sold the coachwood forest in my name.
Both had been given me; but all the same
remember that I signed uneasily.

Ceratopetalum, Scented Satinwood:
a tree attaining seventy feet in height.
Those pale-red calyces like sunset light
burned in my mind. A flesh-pink pliant wood

used in coachbuilding. Difficult of access
(those slopes were steep). But it was World War Two.
Their wood went into bomber-planes. They grew
hundreds of years to meet those hurried axes.

Under our socio-legal dispensation
both name and woodland had been given me.
I was much younger then than any tree
matured for timber. But to help the nation

I signed the document. The stand was pure
(eight hundred trees perhaps). Uneasily
(the bark smells sweetly when you wound the tree)
I set upon this land my signature.

The Forest

When first I knew this forest
its flowers were strange.
Their different forms and faces
changed with the season's change —

white violets smudged with purple,
the wild-ginger spray,
ground-orchids small and single
haunted my day;

the thick-fleshed Murray-lily,
flame-tree's bright blood,
and where the creek runs shallow,
the cunjevoi's green hood.

When first I knew this forest,
time was to spend,
and time's renewing harvest
could never reach an end.

Now that its vines and flowers
are named and known,
like long-fulfilled desires
those first strange joys are gone.

My search is further.
There's still to name and know
beyond the flowers I gather
that one that does not wither —
the truth from which they grow.

Counting in Sevens

Seven ones are seven.
I can't remember that year
or what presents I was given.

Seven twos are fourteen.
That year I found my mind,
swore not to be what I had been.

Seven threes are twenty-one.
I was sailing my own sea,
first in love, the knots undone.

Seven fours are twenty-eight;
three false starts had come and gone;
my true love came, and not too late.

Seven fives are thirty-five.
In her cot my daughter lay,
real, miraculous, alive.

Seven sixes are forty-two.
I packed her sandwiches for school,
I loved my love and time came true.

Seven sevens are forty-nine.
Fruit loaded down my apple-tree,
near fifty years of life were mine.

Seven eights are fifty-six.
My lips still cold from a last kiss,
my fire was ash and charcoal-sticks.

Seven nines are sixty-three, seven tens are seventy.
Who would that old woman be?
She will remember being me,
but what she is I cannot see.

Yet with every added seven,
some strange present I was given.

Brian James

(JOHN TIERNEY)

The Bunyip of Barney's Elbow

IF A TRAVELLER stood on the top of Tralgan Hill on, say, a clear day in autumn — good enough, as Sammy Bowen would put it, "to be killing the first pig for the winter" — a broad and a fair world would lie before him.

Asleep in the sunlight as it nestled beneath the high purple ranges, the town of Summerlea, its two spires looking as Mrs Thompson-Watts had said (in her role of "Melisande", poetess of the *Western Argus*), "like fingers pointing to a brighter world above". The long, wide, straight and dusty streets straggling and fading at last into lanes and paddocks and farms. The willows on the Cookabundy River already baring, and the tall Lombardy poplars touched with gold. On the flats, the brown patches of corn and the very last cocks of lucerne hay.

To the north the Grey Box, the land of ancient gold, too far just now to pick out more than the suggestions of farms and orchards and vineyards, but the Willow Ponds Creek, with its giant she-oaks plain to see.

Away to the south-east lies the Boolgi, the great spur from the Main Divide, and higher than it. To the east, stark, high and grim, the Cookabundy Ranges. To the west, the ridges tapering off in endless succession to Barney's Elbow and Sandy Ridges, and then going on for ever and ever.

A broad and a fair world.

Barney's Elbow, without more exact knowledge, would be suggestive of a man named Barney, with an unconquerable thirst, always giving exercise to his elbow. And that would be wrong. The Elbow was a sharp-angled turn like a bent elbow.

Barney himself had been an innocent, hard-toiling man, the first settler of Sandy Ridges, and the discoverer of the Elbow. At the foot of Barney's was Mick Cullen's Wild Cat Hotel. Originally this hostelry was named The Green Island.

The Green Island had no reference to any sort of island in the vicinity — really Barney's Creek was almost as lacking in water as in islands, so the name was probably due to the nostalgia of one Timothy Byrne, a villainous purveyor of poison in the golden days.

Timothy was eventually found hanging to the limb of a she-oak down by the creek, but whether he "done it hisself" or whether it was thoughtfully done for him was never properly discovered. But the fact that Timothy's ghost was frequently seen thereabouts for years after was strongly suggestive of what is popularly termed "foul play".

Mick Cullen was, strictly speaking, a newcomer, having run the Wild Cat only for the last twenty-five years or so. It would again be a mistake to think that this new name for the pub had anything to do with mining; Mick simply called it after his first wife. His first inspiration had been Spitfire — a good name, too, but connoting words rather than deeds. Wild Cat suggested both.

Mick was not one to talk overmuch of the past, but in the right time and mood he could be persuaded to expose for view a bony knob behind his right ear. His explanation went like a formula: "She done that. She did. Done it with a yammer. Just up with the yammer and cracks me there!" Mick would pat the bony excrescence tenderly.

Quite likely there were other marks of the "yammer" on Mick's skull, but they could easily remain hidden under a very thick growth of dirty-looking sandy hair. Mick never seemed to get it cut and it never seemed to grow any longer than the shaggy stage. His face was covered with a similar thicket of hair, of much the same colour. And out of it looked a pair of dull-green eyes. Mick wasn't really handsome.

"She must have been a terror, Mick."

Mick turned this over in his mind and puffed at a brier with a very broken rim.

"Yes, she was that. A regular wild cat, if you ask me." Then, in strict fairness, "But she had her points — only she was inclined to go too far."

Mick was reported as having told someone or other, at some time or other, that the first Mrs Cullen had, in a fit of rage, hit a Chinaman behind the ear with a hammer — and the Chinaman died a day or so after, very mysteriously, but it was all "hushed up" in some way or other. Also, it was that very same hammer that she used on Mick, and she always slept with that very same hammer under her pillow. *And* when she got pneumonia that winter, and the doctor said she was a "gonner", Mick's first thought was to bury the hammer with her. But before the end she looked so pitiable and small, and besides she forgave Mick everything, so that he didn't have the heart to bury the hammer with her after all. And then the hammer just disappeared, and Mick didn't know what ever became of it.

Mrs Mick, the second, was a widow when Mick married her — Mrs McCarthy that was. McCarthy had been a helpless little man with one eye, who seemed specially designed by Nature to die of pneumonia, which he did that very same winter, and was buried the very same day as the first Mrs Mick, and not twenty yards from her, and Father Moran merely moved from one grave to the other.

Such a series of coincidences was not to be taken lightly, and as a result Mick and Mrs McCarthy were married none so long after — and let people say what they like.

As a pub the Wild Cat was ordinary enough, shabby-looking, too, with its cracked and unpainted hardwood boards. There were six windows facing the road, and three doors and a long, narrow veranda. Mick attended the bar most times, but on occasion his two daughters assisted. Perhaps the cold, calculating eye might have noticed that Molly and Joan were useful as decoys.

The young men for miles round, when they had drinking silver, would ride to the Wild Cat and feast their eyes on Mick's girls. Shrewd and sophisticated were Mick's girls, and the hard of head summed up with great finality "You'd get no change there," or "They know how to look after themselves." Which was deemed a pity.

But, in all, the history of Barney's Elbow and of the Wild Cat was commonplace enough, apart from the exploits of Timothy Byrne and the first Mrs Mick; and so was the *ménage* of that pub if it came to that. And then it and the country round about leapt into fame — or notoriety.

One night in early winter a horse was heard descending The Elbow at a mad gallop. A runaway most evidently, and Mick went out into the starlight to see if he might recognize the horse.

He was surprised to find there was a rider on its back. The rider, with difficulty, turned off the road at the Wild Cat and with greater difficulty brought the horse to a trembling, lathering halt. The rider dismounted, and in a reflex sort of way patted the horse's neck.

"Gawd — it's you, Abe!"

"A whisky, Mick. Double-quick!"

Mick didn't move. His slow brain was dealing with visions of doctors, murders, snakes, premature births — any of the big, unexpected happenings.

Mrs Mick slithered out of the parlour. She was a shade faster in her mental workings than Mick.

"Come in, Abe, into the parlour fire. Mick will look after your horse."

Abe was wild-eyed, his hair was literally on end, and his thick lips were working in a curious manner. The indications were fear. And Mrs Mick felt frightened at the very appearance of him. With presence of mind she closed the parlour door. Then she took a candle into the bar and poured out a generous dose of whisky for Abe. It went down Abe's hairy throat in one gulp.

"Wh-what is it, Abe?"

Abe cocked his ear as though trying to hear something he didn't want to hear.

"Did you hear it?"

"What, Abe?"

"You didn't hear it?"

Mick had by now returned after putting Abe's horse into a ramshackle structure that bore the courtesy title of stable. "Did you hear anything, Mick? Abe's heard something."

Mick didn't think so, but after seeing Abe and his horse he was fully prepared to hear anything.

Abe was getting through his third glass, and Mick joined him in it — feeling that it was as well to be ready for the worst.

"Do you know that little apple-tree flat near the old selection of Morris's?"

Mick knew it well, of course — about three and a half miles back.

"Well, it was there!"

"What was? Good God, man, what was?"

"Look, Mick, old chap" — Abe was too scared to swear, which was a bad sign — "I don't know."

But Abe's horse was as full of terror as Abe was, so it *must* have been something.

"I was just coming down the hill — easy like — and across the little flat . . . You know the culvert over the creek, Mick?"

"Yes, Abe!" There was no use trying to hurry it out of Abe.

"It was there — Mick — as true as I am sitting here!"

Perhaps Abe had no desire to be dramatic about it, but Mick's hair was standing on end, too; that is, as far as Mick's tousled thatch could stand on end. Mrs Mick just stared at Abe.

"What was there, Abe?" Mick's voice was husky.

"The Noise. Mick, I never want to hear a noise like that again. I can't tell you what it was like — it came from under the culvert, and at the same time from up the creek and from the hill." Abe took a mouthful of whisky. "Gawd knows, Mick, what made that noise. But Something — it sounded like 'y-a-h—oo'."

"How often, Abe?"

"Just once. Christ, that was enough."

"Could it have been a bull?" Mick felt strongly within him that it wasn't a bull.

"A bull! A hundred bulls couldn't have made that much noise."

Mick's hair stood up a bit more as the thought of old Timothy's ghost came to him. But ghosts never made a noise like this. Then he thought of the Chinaman who had died of the hammer. But no, it could hardly be a ghost.

"When it came," continued Abe, "the mare stood and trembled — I thought she'd sag right down under me. And I was no better. And then she started off — she flew."

The girls came in. Abe went over the whole story again. The old pub was well and truly locked up that night, and the parlour lamp was kept burning. No one slept much — except Abe, and that was mainly whisky.

In the morning the hills looked innocent enough — dark-wooded ranges rising above Barney's Elbow, and in the nearer distances magpies warbling, kookaburras finishing off their morning's laugh, and a crow or two cawing as they flew towards the hills.

Innocent enough; and fears dissolve in sunlight. But out in those hills was a terrible Something. It was no dream — it was true. Abe's mare was found dead in the "stable".

Men called in at the Wild Cat and Abe took them out to look at her. It wasn't that they doubted that Abe had heard a noise, but they wouldn't credit it was terrible. Also, Abe was drunk and, in the retelling of his story, prone to exaggeration.

There was present a long slab of a fellow with pimples on his neck, shrewd in a mean sort of way. He was Jack Slade, and he worked on a station beyond Sandy Ridges.

"Look here, Abe," he said, throwing a wink to Molly. "Look here; you say that noise of yours came from under the culvert?"

"The main part of it did."

"But you said there was only one Noise."

A possible solution came to Abe. "The rest of it must have been hechos."

"What?"

"Hechos!"

Jack tipped another wink in sheer delight with "hechos".

But Abe stuck to the culvert as the chief source of the noise. And the upshot of it was that Abe should accompany Jack and several others going that way to Sandy Ridges. Abe was working on a chaff-cutting plant out there. Mick lent Abe a horse, and the party set out.

They came to the hill overlooking the creek and the apple-tree flat. It was a peaceful and beautiful spot, with a scattering of fine big apple-trees on the level flat below the culvert. The cattle usually feeding here and there among the trees were not to be seen, however. But the very appearance of the place stamped Abe as a liar, more so, perhaps, as Abe had a reputation for practical jokes and was always "up to his tricks".

They came to the culvert. "Now, Abe," said Jack, "we'll look underneath for tracks."

There was no water in the creek just there, only a fairly long stretch of nearly white sand. The only tracks in that sand were made by cattle passing up and down the creek under the fairly high culvert. Nothing else. Jack was delighted in his exasperating fashion. It is hard to say what Abe had expected to find, but the fact that there were no tracks of an untoward nature seemed to revive the worst of his terrors.

Margaret Preston *Drought — Mirage Country* 1946
Monotype on thin laid oriental paper 30.5 × 40.6 cm
Queensland Art Gallery

Arthur Boyd *The Mining Town* 1946–47
Oil, tempera on composition board 82.7 × 109.2 cm
Australian National Gallery

"Gawd!" he gasped. "Let's get away from the place!"

So Jack Slade spread the yarn of "Abe's Noise", and added all the necessary trimmings to make Abe look quite ridiculous. And Abe didn't even get wild about the banter, which was unlike Abe. No one else had heard the noise, so Abe was in a hopeless minority about it.

A fortnight later Jack Slade and his mate, Bob Felton, were riding into Barney's Elbow for a few drinks and the prospect of "doing a line with Mick's girls". They came to the culvert.

"Look out for Abe's Noise!" said Jack, laughing.

"Is this the place?"

"Too right."

It was a lovely night, with a frosty silver moon in the sky. They both laughed at Abe and clattered up the stony road beyond the culvert. At the top of the long ridge was a big patch of pine scrub — thin, tall trees, closely grown, a dark mass even in the moonlight. The road for some distance was like a cutting through this scrub. Jack and Bob had forgotten Abe and were indulging at the moment in certain shocking reminiscences. And then ——

Out of the scrub, from no defined point in it, came the "Noise" — a perfectly blood-curdling "Yah-oo-oo". Just one cry — long drawn out — and living in the ears for ever after. It was not the volume or pitch of the sound alone that froze the blood, but some indescribable quality of terror to it.

Jack and Bob were in an even worse state than Abe had been when they arrived at the Wild Cat. And for a long time, it seemed, they couldn't get in. This time Mick and his family had heard the cry and wouldn't open the doors.

There was no "doing a line with Mick's girls" that night. And though Jack and Bob didn't "belong" they were glad enough to join the family in the rosary — a whole long series of rosaries. It is doubtful if Mick had ever been so devout in his life.

Sydney papers got hold of the story, and treated it with entire disrespect in the main, though one afternoon journal took it seriously. One paper even had a cartoon depicting a hideous monster thrusting its head out of a whisky keg.

This was, of course, an explanation of the mystery; another explanation was that the whole thing was a hoax. And since Mick Cullen was undoubtedly selling more grog than ever, it was cunningly suggested that he "knows something about it — you bet he does", and Abe Newton "is in it, too".

However, a party of "sports" from Summerlea announced its intention of going out, well armed, to comb the hills round Barney's Elbow and shoot or capture the Yahoo. It had been heard, in all, a good dozen times now — always on clear, frosty nights, and of late in a tangle of scrubby gullies above the road over the ridge. Mick at once included the party in his prayers and set up supplications for its success. At the same time he thoughtfully got in huge extra quantities of whisky and beer.

Fairly early on a Saturday morning the party gathered at the Wild Cat. And they had, as mere afterthought, "a drink before we start". A few drinks in fact.

George Douglas, auctioneer and champion pigeon shot, was the leader and organizer. A shrewd, hard man was George, with great eyebrows of sandy bristles and a glib tongue. Some van-loads of hunters had come out from Summerlea with George. They were all heavily armed with a variety of weapons — mostly shotguns, though some had .32 Winchesters.

Of greater variety still were the hunters themselves. They ranged from Mr Simpson Butler, who was the Member, to old Pat Casey, who was nothing. Teddy Clarke and the other "sports" of the town were there, of course. So was Shoot, the undertaker. "We might need *him*, so we might," said Pat Casey. Also Peter Window, the blacksmith, and his rival, Sid Brown. There was quite a sprinkling of young fellows from the Grey Box and beyond — Doolans, Ryans, Rosens, Wenns, Notts, and so forth. Mostly they rode, if they had presentable horses. Everyone from Barney's Elbow and Sandy Ridges was there.

Simpson Butler was hardly a man of desperate action, but "it was decent of him to come along". He dressed for the part, too, looking something like a prosperous and retired bushranger. He was full of heartening cheerfulness and humour, and declared, "If we don't shoot It we'll legislate It out of existence."

Pat Casey came in an almost wholly ornamental capacity, and partly on account of an argument with Kelly, the publican. He was armed with a terrible-looking muzzle-loader, with the stock bound not over-neatly with wire. It was a great relief to everyone that Pat had no caps or powder for this ancient gun, though he had shot in great quantity, very aged shot, whitened and gummed with rust. Pat said he would be able to borrow powder and caps, surely. And if he couldn't it wouldn't matter, for the Yahoo was beyond "mortal encompassment", anyhow.

George Douglas got the crowd together at last, and divided it into two groups. The drivers, under Jack Slade, were to detour to the Sugarloaf, and then advance northward to the road, where George and his line would be waiting. Final instructions and warnings were given as to care in shooting, and the time of advance. Also hares, rabbits, wallabies, and kangaroos were to be ignored entirely.

Pat Casey and Mr Friar (of the *Western Argus*) were left at the Wild Cat with Mick, as a kind of home defence. Both of them by this time were fit for little else. Mr Friar, who was finding locomotion of any sort decidedly distressing, took up a position on a barrel in the bar, and later on a sofa in the parlour.

Jack Slade's party, in fine spirits, reached the Sugarloaf, but something of its courage vanished in the thick scrub. Often one could not see the next man, even at twenty yards or so, and there was a touchy tendency to fire at any movement or noise.

For, despite instructions, there was quite a deal of firing, with no result. An old wombat was most indignant at finding his peace disturbed and nearly skittled a driver in his haste to get to his burrow.

Now the waiting line of shooters opened fire — at hares and wallabies. The biggest thing that came through was a skinny old bull with an insane look in his eye. With two charges of shot in his hide, and possibly a Winchester bullet, he went down the slope at a speed that was hitherto thought quite impossible to bulls, sane or otherwise.

No one was shot in all this excitement, which could be ascribed only to the mercy of Providence, and not to human management. Courage flowed back as groups gathered. And disappointment mounted, too, that the Yahoo was not seen and dispatched. It was a kind of anticlimax after so much preparation and boasting; and a relief as well, a feeling that the best had been tried and a duty done, whatever the result.

The day was drawing into clear cold evening; the party moved down to the Wild Cat and Mick did a big trade. Mr Friar hardly took any part in the convivialities, except that of snoring on his parlour sofa. For one so frail and such a blending of the aesthetic and the tragic, Mr Friar's snoring was a thing to wonder at.

Pat Casey was fuddled in a logical sort of way. "You didn't see It at all, George?"

"No, we didn't."

"That's not to be wondered at."

"Why not, Pat?"

"It's not to be seen, and if It was to be seen you could do nothing."

"It wasn't in the bit of bush we drove."

Pat wagged his head solemnly.

A frosty moon floated in the sky. The night was growing late, and it was time to go. "Just one more, then, and that's the last."

Out of the frosty silence came the cry of the mysterious Yahoo, a cry that tingled to the very tips of the fingers, and was like nothing on earth.

"Christ!" And a glass shivered on the floor. Apart from that there was suspended animation, and the fixed look of men trying not to be afraid.

Outside there was wild commotion among the horses, and reefing and snorting and snapping of reins and halters, and a wild thud of galloping hoofs; while a few horses in Mick's stable screamed in terror. That panic of the horses made the fear of the men stark and absolute; and the Thing feared was nameless and undefined, a very personification of the most primitive fear itself.

Then Pat Casey blessed himself, saying loudly, "Holy Mary, preserve us — and I'll go to confession next Saturday — see if I don't."

All a matter of not so many seconds. George Douglas screwed himself together and with no conviction at all, "Now's-s-s our chance. It's just on t-t-top of the ridge!"

The sound had come from somewhere near the top of the ridge, somewhere in the area hunted that day. Just where was hard to say. Location was vague — the cry sounded very near and very far.

No one moved.

Through it all, snoring on the sofa, was the one man who could have immortalized that strange night at the Wild Cat. It was the very irony of things that Mr Friar, sceptic and genius, should be so oblivious. No one thought of trying to wake him. It would have been quite useless perhaps to make the attempt.

Outside were bright moon and pale stars, and world without end, and space without limit. A world of silence, and glistening leaves without number, and all the unnoticed sounds that are part of silence always. But no one looked out — not for a long time. Here were four walls, bright lamps, warm flesh, and breathing bodies; and brandy, whisky, and rum that could make a man cease to be himself, and as someone else face anything.

Mick's devotions interfered with his business capacity, such as it ever was, and his mortal terror increased his devotion. Even as he prayed he swallowed a fair deal of neat brandy which seemed to help him a deal. He passed round bottles instead of glasses. "Help yourself — we'll square up later — pray for us sinners now and at the hour . . ."

Pat Casey, exhausted, slumped in a corner with his head at a grotesque and impossible angle. Mrs Mick straightened his head and put it on a buggy cushion, and threw an overcoat over Pat. She hardly knew what she was doing, but in the tally of good deeds that will be remembered to her eternal credit.

The moon sank at last into the ridges, and out of the grey ghosts of trees came the harsh music of the kookaburras. There was the smell of morning in the air. Far and clear came the crowing of roosters. Nearer, the twitter of small birds. Night was over.

The high wooded ridges grew again into their wonted shapes, knowable, innocent and friendly. Men came out of the stale and rancid air of bar and parlour to sniff in life and freshness. They could face the things they could see. Pat Casey came out more tousled and dirty-looking than ever. He surveyed the big world and summed up things very comprehensively. "It's a bloody fine morning." Everyone took that as a healthy sign.

At long last, after almost insuperable difficulties about horses, most of the party got away. There was no concerted plan to comb the hills again — plenty of talk about it, however, and a vague understanding about "next time". Mr Friar stayed for the time being, alternating between snoring and muttering.

The ignominious failure of the Douglas expedition was a jest for ever after to those who had never heard the Yahoo's cry. Still, strangely enough, because of it, or in spite of it, the Yahoo was never heard again. It was gone, people just knew it was gone to join the Bunyip and other impossible terrors. What it really was was never discovered — beast, or bird, or devil.

Doolan's Devotions

MRS DOOLAN was out, and would be out till the morning at least. There was a new one expected over at Flanagan's — young Joe's place, of course, not old Dan's. Mr Doolan was, all things considered, glad. Not at the expected arrival, but that Mrs Doolan was out. She wasn't much company, that woman, nowadays, though she was good and pious; rather too much so; a trifle too much so. The two grandchildren were asleep in the spare room. They were Peter's boys. Their mother was dead, and Peter was in Tobruk or somewhere. Good kids, but of course the old woman spoiled them. Old women always do.

Doolan got more wood from the heap near the kitchen stove, and piled up the fire in the sitting-room. It was a cold night, even for June. At the same time, he brought out his private rum bottle from behind the wood and poured out a generous dose. It was a cunning plant, that woodheap, and cunningly constructed — the narrow space in the corner held the bottle quite cosily, and the old woman hadn't found it; not yet, shrewd and sharp of nose as she was. He kicked some of the new wood against the back log, and lolled back in the big chair. Well, you could afford an extra swig with the old woman away.

Doolan's conscience smote him or pricked him or stirred him, however. At least, whatever consciences do, it did. There was the Rosary to say, and the various trimmings thereon. Easy it would be to go to sleep and forget about it, or mumble it over and go to sleep in the first decade of it, or maybe the second, and trust to the good intentions being accepted. But would they? It was different in the old days when the children were all at home, and the chorus of young voices had sweet music in them. "H-o-l-y Mary, Mother of God . . ."

He went to the bedroom and groped in the semi-light for the beads. They hung on a nail near the holy-water font. Yes, there they were. But they felt different. He held them to the light that came in from the sitting-room, and confirmed the suspicion that they were not his at all. Eileen had taken his in her hurry to get over to Flanagan's. Hers were the black beads, and his were the blue. Blast the stupid woman! He was uncertain that Rosaries on other people's beads were much good. You should use your own. Eileen! That was a queer name for an old woman. Only young women should be called Eileen. Still, she was a young woman once. Hard to remember it now. Or to separate memory from imagination. Eileen! Gawd! She was fat and shapeless enough now — and most unnecessarily cranky.

Mr Doolan dipped his fingers in the font, and blessed himself very reverently. He went back to the sitting-room, still revolving in his mind the momentous question of the wrong beads. The rum bottle was on the sitting-room table — you could do that when Eileen was away. Eileen! Eileen!! He turned the name over a dozen times. Then he poured out another modest swig, and downed it with a feeling of glow, kicked the logs together again, and exasperated the back log with the poker till it leaped into tongues of flame. Eileen! Well, she hadn't always been like this. He looked at the rum bottle again, but instead of taking another nip went to see young Peter and Kevin. Good kids — pity the old woman spoiled them. Eileen! The name had never struck him like this before. What did she say to do with Kevin's throat? Rub it with? He *seemed* all right, so it couldn't matter much. Anyway, she always sprinkled them with holy water.

Mr Doolan went back to the bedroom and dipped all the fingers that would fit into the font, and hurried into the spare room, and went through the action of asperging. He wasn't too sure that any drops reached the boys, but the good intention was there. He was pretty certain, anyway, they got some of it.

He knelt on the mat before the fire, and propped himself in the big chair. He blessed himself, but the picture of Eileen recurred, and the humour of such a name attached to a fat, old, scolding woman. He chuckled and had to bless himself six times before the proper devotion was attained. But he got it, and was ready to commence. Then his eye caught the flickering light on the rum bottle, and as an act of decency he got up and put the bottle on the kitchen table. That meant blessing himself all over again. A difficult process, too, mixed as it was with the question of how far alcohol and sin were associated.

But at last again he was ready, and with brave concentration of devotion the beads trickled through his fingers. Smooth going, but it couldn't last. It couldn't. That Watson crossed in near the end of the second decade. Mean cow, Watson, and he'd tell him yet what he thought of him, see if he didn't. Make him squirm. Him and his lumpy red bullock! Methodists were like that. To hell with Watson, anyway; he'd spoiled the second decade. It might have to be said over again. Or should he say the lot from the beginning? It was a delicate point, but Mr Doolan decided that he'd just say over the bit that Watson ruined. Those Methodists had a deal to answer for. He droned on to himself, "H-o-l-y Mary —" Mary! Why the blue blazes should that Mary Sherry come to mind now? Mary Sherry! The Lord be praised that Eileen didn't know anything about *that*! Thirty-eight years ago, last March and April. There was a stimulating pungency about the memory of that girl. It was quite impossible to get away from the pleasure of the memory. "How many times?" said Father Moran. "A good many," he answered. Thank the Lord that Eileen didn't know! She'd be remembering it now. She *would*. Doolan groaned that the memory should come, and that there should be pleasure to it. But the second decade was gone again. Mary Sherry! Burned to death she was in that trapper's hut; and they not married at all. Just living in sin! A wicked lot were the Sherrys. And all those sins on her soul!

"Our Father —"

"Gink! I wanter gink." It was Kevin.

"Blast yer, don't yer know I'm at me prayers?" called Mr Doolan.

151

"Gink! I wanter gink." It was too insistent, so Mr Doolan got Kevin his drink, and pondered deeply what it was he was supposed to rub on the throat. Just like the old woman not to make things clear. But that Mary Sherry! He went to the kitchen, and took a gulp of rum straight out of the bottle. Peter shouldn't have enlisted like that — what had England ever done for Ireland? His old father used to say that in Tipperary. Mr Doolan blessed himself again, and decided that he would start all over again. It was better in the old days when the children were young. Then you were carried along, and were finished when you were finished.

He got through the first ten Hail Marys, and the Glory be to the Father . . . That horse that Hegarty sold him — a rankling raw deal that! A tenner for a straight-out jib! And Hegarty knew he jibbed. If he hadn't been able to sell him to those new people for thirteen quid, he'd have lost on the deal, for all that Hegarty cared. What a pious fraud Hegarty was!

Doolan started on the second decade, and wondered if the beads were any good, anyway. Might be as well to say them on the fingers.

"Hail Mary" . . . That Mary Sherry again! Wonder if she had time to repent — no priest or anything. The Sherrys were all . . .

The second decade started again. "Hail . . . I could have said to the stock inspector — a jumped-up flash fellow that! Next time he calls, I'll tell him . . ." The stock inspector ran parallel with the second decade, and it was debatable which got the more attention. Better let it go. It would *have* to be good enough.

The blaze died down, and the back log charred. Doolan got up and brought more wood from the kitchen, by-passing the bottle with a heroic effort. He blessed himself again, and decided to start on the third decade, and that he'd use the beads after all.

"Glory to . . ." That contract for the spuds was a crook deal. What a bloody government! Bloody! Right in the middle of his prayers. Oh, God and Father Moran! Bloody! Not that he meant anything really. But "bloody"! Miserable sinner indeed! This was really worse than Mary Sherry creeping in. After all, he'd done penance for her these thirty years ago. Ah well, nothing else for it, but back to the first decade again. Better in the old days when you could chorus through the Rosary with the children and be done with it. . . . Wonder if there is a hell, anyway. . . . Of course there must be. Hope Watson goes there; and that stock inspector . . . and all those who voted for the Country Party last election.

"Hallowed be Thy name . . ." The words went glibly forward, but mind and heart did not follow. Mr Doolan chuckled inwardly over a story. "Did you sleep with that red-headed woman, Barney?" "Divil a wink!" A good one that, and he'd be passing it on at the Contingent. It would bring a laugh, that would.

Then Mr Doolan groaned inwardly. A story like that creeping into his prayers! And he taking pleasure and not horror at it! Still — still — it was funny. God have mercy!

"Forgive us our trespasses as we . . ." Well, no one does *that*. Not even Father Moran and his brother-in-law. Hate each other like poison. (Doolan was not well acquainted with the theory of reservation.)

In a bedraggled way he struggled through the fourth decade, but he found the fifth much tangled in theology. If you didn't believe at all would there be a hell for you, and conversely if you thought all your sins were forgiven — and they weren't — what a horrible shock it would be! And how much worse off would you be if you didn't say any prayers at all — how would you get on? And if you managed to get a priest at the end would it be all right? And was it a sin not to love Eileen any more? And was it a sin ever to have loved her at all? And could he be forgiven about Mary Sherry, and Eileen not to know at all? And would she find out when they were up there?

The old head nodded and he slept for half an hour or so. He woke on the note, "Glory be . . ." He put the two bricks in front of the fire — just to be sure like. There were the "trimmings" yet — and that penance — a Litany of all things, and the print so small and his eyes so bad. He'd lie down a moment before he commenced.

The sun was shining and Peter and Kevin were making hell's delight when he woke. Joe Flanagan was standing at the back door with a big stupid grin on his face and saying it was a son — a boy, that is. It was like Joe, that sort of thing; or any Flanagan as far as that went. Still, it was Joe's first. And Eileen would be back after breakfast. Eileen! Well, she had her points after all.

Then he said, "Good luck, Joe, old man. I'm glad to hear it."

Joe and Sandy

THEY LIVED opposite us in a grassy and tree-lined street of Laidlaw. They were old identities — as the saying goes — but Laidlaw took little heed of them. They had never really stirred the still, stagnant surface of the pond that was Laidlaw, so why should it note them?

Joe's house was prettily hidden among orange- and lemon-trees and two poincianas. We could just see a part of the red roof and the clear top of the chimney. Every morning, as the sun blinked redly through the river mist, a long blue spiral of smoke rose from Joe's chimney. Joe believed in early rising, though there was really nothing for him to do — nothing that mattered much any more — but the habits of his ninety-eight waking years were made to last to the end.

The wife was always glad to see that thin breath of blue smoke: it meant that Joe was still alive. She said it was terrible to think of Joe all alone in the house, and that he might die in his sleep one night, and no one at all be by him. That was only sentiment, of course, for no one would surely deny Joe the boon of dying in his sleep. But the wife watched anxiously for the blue smoke that meant yet the grace of another day of loneliness to add to the countless tally of those ninety-eight years.

Sandy lived up the street a little. A mere youngster alongside Joe — only ninety-two he was. There was a time when those six years would have been an enormous disparity in age — if they had known each other then. Joe considered the difference still gave him a definite seniority, precedence, and richer experience, and that his superior age demanded a respect and deference that Sandy was often not willing to concede.

Sandy also lived alone, and his house, like Joe's, fronted the river. The Graham flowed broad and deep and slow before them always. It was an emblem of the resistless time that had swept away all the two old men's contemporaries and left them — two old river trees on a crumbling bank.

They had so much in common now — their loneliness and the generations long forgotten by everyone else. They should have been mates, by all comfortable reckoning, and, of course, they were not. And that was only natural. Still, they spent a portion of every day in each other's company, for there was a necessity that compelled it so. But these were not peaceful periods, and invariably they terminated in high dudgeon and a mutual retirement to lick the wounds engendered by the interview.

There were two visits a day. Sandy, as the younger, but by far the less active, would set out punctually at twenty past nine from his brick villa, and walk with upright dignity along the street to Joe's. His right hand grasped his polished black stick, and his left was free to manipulate his pipe when he wanted to spit. At Joe's paling gate he would halt and peer through the cracks. Joe let him do this for ten minutes before putting in an appearance. Then Joe would come down the back lawn with comparative sprightliness — and with *no* stick — carrying the *Laidlaw Times*.

Joe always did a bit of weeding in his garden to show that Sandy's visit didn't mean very much to him. Joe resented, too, having to bring the *Times* to Sandy, but he always brought it none the less. He reckoned Sandy was too mean to spend the twopence a day, while Sandy, on stout principle, declared he would never support a conservative rag like the *Times*. He just couldn't bring himself to do it. Then Sandy would fit steel rims on his nose — a real weakness that, for Joe never had to worry about spectacles — and read through the paper. He read the leading article first, and always condemned it. And there was an argument over that.

Then to the war news. He reviewed this in the light of what had happened in the American Civil War and the Franco-Prussian War. These two struggles were far more real to both of them than what was happening in Libya, Syria, or Russia. Joe and Sandy were in opposite camps in the matter of the Franco-Prussian War. There is no such thing as reconciliation of opposing points of view strongly held. And so Sandy would at last toss back the sheet with the worn formula, "You can keep your blasted paper!" Joe would tenderly straighten the crumpled pages and almost trot back along the garden path, and Sandy, with terrible dignity, would march back to his villa.

It seemed impossible after any one of these interviews that Joe and Sandy could ever come together again. But at five past four Sandy would set out and finally peer through the paling gate; and at a quarter past four Joe would amble down his back lawn. But Joe didn't hurry: he did a bit of weeding on the way among the vegetables. Then Joe would talk of horses, cows, bulls, pumpkins, maize, and all the things that were his life before he retired to town.

Sandy knew nothing and cared nothing about such things. He would talk of the things that meant so much before he very foolishly left Scotland. There was no sympathy of interest, and each departed with a strong impression of the other's intolerance and ignorance, and a strong resolve never to waste time again in such fruitless discussion. Sandy was more upright in dignity and dudgeon than ever as he marched off slowly to his home. He spat more vigorously and viciously, and between times clamped down hard on his pipe stem. If he hadn't had twine bound round the mouthpiece it was clear that he would have bitten the stem in two.

Joe watched Sandy's stately progress, leaning with one thin bony hand on the paling fence, and with a certain satisfaction, too, just as one might watch a retreating storm that had threatened dreadful things, but had done no great damage. Sometimes mutterings could be heard from the retiring storm, and then Joe would lean with both hands on the gate and chuckle, "*He* knows nothing about horses. And he doesn't like to be told he doesn't.''

One day Sandy fell off the bus — a nasty, shaking fall that marvellously left no broken bones. Joe happened to be on the bus, too, and saw it all. ''Wouldn't have happened,'' he said, ''if Sandy hadn't been so clumsy.'' Joe didn't believe in accidents — it was all a matter of cause and effect, he said. Anyway, there wasn't much to Sandy when all was said and done — bit of a weakling in spite of his size; couldn't walk without a stick; and blind as an owl, almost, without his spectacles.

They took Sandy to hospital. ''Pretty chicken-hearted he is. That's what *I* say!'' And Joe, by way of contrast, got out his scythe and swung youthfully into the paspalum. Undoubtedly Sandy had sunk very low in his estimation.

Sandy stayed in hospital. Evidently he was under the impression that he was badly hurt. He seemed to have deceived the hospital people about it, too. They insisted on keeping him there.

One morning Sandy died — as a crowning act of deceit, no doubt. Joe was really disgusted at the whole business, and found his worst suspicions amply justified. It was what he had always said about Sandy.

But next morning at half past nine Joe as usual ambled down his path with the *Laidlaw Times* under his arm. He did his bit of weeding on the way, and at last reached the gate. He seemed surprised to find no one there. And then he remembered. ''Yes, that Sandy *was* chicken-hearted!'' He looked up the street and down, leaned on the gate for a while, and then went back to the house. In the afternoon he was there again, and seemed to get the same surprise — and then he remembered once more. He consoled himself with, ''But what did *he* know about horses? Or Jerseys? *Or* pumpkins?''

Joe went through the routine every day. Then he would remember, and go off to the jobs that needed doing — a bit of woodcutting, scything, chipping, weeding, mowing, whatever it was. Even on a small place there were many things to be done, and you had to do them yourself if you wanted them done properly. Also, it saved money. Joe didn't like spending money. Not unnecessarily. It was good to save money. You never could tell.

The opinion hardened into conviction with Joe that Sandy hadn't been much of a fellow to know, and one was as well off without him really. He remembered, too, how mean Sandy had been. Never spend twopence on a paper, not he. Joe felt that he didn't like mean people. But he came down to that gate twice a day for all that. Sometimes he had a word with chance passers-by, but they always seemed to be in a hurry; but even that was better than nothing. It was good to have someone to talk to occasionally, even if they *would* leave before they had heard of the success of that Devon Bull he once bought.

The winter closed in dry and hard. Laidlaw had seen nothing like it since '02. Some of the old hands could remember that. Joe, of course, could go back to

'53 with much vividness, but he admitted there never had been such cold in Laidlaw before. His smoke banner in the keen, frosty air was bluer than ever. It always said, "Another day — at least." The wife watched for it fearfully.

One morning it didn't show. The wife knew, she said. And she was right; she and some neighbours went over, and they called the doctor in, though there was nothing a doctor could do now. There was a deal of commotion. Sons and daughters, old and stooped they were, came from down the river and up the river, and some middle-aged men and women who were grandchildren. Word went round that Joe had gone in his sleep. Children gathered round the fence to see all the unwonted excitement at Joe's place. Old blue and grey blankets were hung on the line to wave dejectedly and pathetically there. Then much smoke billowed from the chimney; cups rattled, and tea was handed round. Men mooned about under the orange-trees and talked in undertones. Neighbours said perfunctorily, "Poor old chap!" Heaven knows what they meant, for they had never known Joe and had never worried about him. The *Times* printed an account of his "career" in an issue that cost twopence — as all the other issues had done. Then they took Joe to the cemetery and buried him in the kindly earth, at about the same distance from Sandy as their homes had been apart on the banks of the Graham. Then the stooped old men and women who were the sons and daughters, and the middle-aged men and women who were the grand-children, went home, and wondered what the will would say — and felt that they were cheated in some way in being so old themselves.

Laidlaw promptly forgot Joe and Sandy, which was not charitable perhaps. But really it didn't matter so very much.

Bungally

TULLY SPOKE of the ragged space in the dense low scrub as "the clearin' ". He and the boys had taken the grubbing contract, five acres of it, at fourteen-ten an acre, with ten pounds added for the trees that had invaded one corner of the scrub. It wasn't a high price by any means, but times were hard, and a good man might make it pay. Hard work, too, for that low scrub was mostly bungally, a cruelly deceptive thing to the inexperienced. Among it was wild fuchsia in plenty, occasional iron-trees, and stubborn and stunted grass-trees, and many of the plants that are typical of coast scrub on the tops of sandstone ridges.

Tully had named the price. He was a good man, he said, and knew all about clearing. So he could afford to cut the margin fine. Besides, his boys, Henry and Dick, were out of work. It was really for their sake that he took the contract at all. Tully was like that — always doing things for his boys. They were good boys, he said — not just because they were his, of course — perhaps a bit raw to the game, but willing to learn. And he had the experience to teach them. In addition, he had the boss's nephew foisted upon him, a sort of condition to securing the contract. That meant sharing among four instead of three, but it would shorten the time. Anyway, it was generous to give the nephew a job. It was like Tully to be philanthropic.

They pitched camp on a rise off the clearing — a beautiful spot, as Tully remarked many times in the first day or two. Through breaks in the bloodwoods and stringybarks they caught sight here and there of the Blue Mountains, with an immensity of hazy space between, miles of wooded plain, a world in itself, and even more mysterious to the imagination than the mountains were. On clear mornings they could see the farms on Kurrajong and the very trees on Mount Wilson, and the Main Divide behind Jenolan would show in pale blue. On clear nights the whole plain would vanish and leave just the bright stars and the twinkling lights of the mountain towns. Yes, for two days Tully said it was beautiful. And then he appeared to forget all about it.

It took those two days for Tully to discover what a wretched job that bungally was. He said at starting that he would finish in a fortnight, but the little ragged space demanded a revised calculation. The scrub was malicious. The few insignificant boughs would come off almost at the touch, but beneath the surface were gnarled roots, hard as iron, and as thick as a man's thigh, branching into smaller roots as thick as a man's calf. They all burrowed into the subsoil, clinging desperately. Spud bar, mattock, and lever had to be applied endlessly to remove them.

It was outside Tully's experience altogether. He found himself somehow too old to compete with the new enemy. The scrub seemed to laugh at his efforts, jeer at the little hole in the brush that represented days of toiling and moiling.

It mocked him at every turn — he who had boasted of his prowess with big timber was to be baffled and beaten by underbrush!

Yes, Tully was beaten. But he told the boys that such scrub was only boys' work after all, and they might finish it now. He would go on to the big timber that had invaded the low scrub. That was a man's work — an experienced man.

So the boys had the bungally to themselves. They worked not the less harder than Tully did at the far end of the block. They were good boys. They ached and sweated and groaned and blistered; they slogged in early and late and drew what comfort they could from the doubtful blessings of profanity. But the days went by and grew longer and hotter and drier. The ground grew harder. And the bungally began to mock them, too. It told them that no band of novices would ever shift it.

The fortnight ended, and there was no very appreciable impression made on the scrub. It began to play tricks with their vision, and the part still to be cleared danced before them in a haze that blended with the haze of the plain. A kind of eternity with an endless and hopeless struggle in it.

They varied the work and tried softer-looking patches. But they only *looked* softer. They tried bigger levers; they burnt off the roots and rubbish to make the grubbed portions look more encouraging. It was hopeless. Then they spoke to Tully and begged him to throw it in. They'd never make tucker, they said, on the job. They'd starve on it. But Tully was afraid of the laws of contract.

Henry, the elder boy, was more enterprising. He broke out in boils, big painful boils. He grew quite affectionate towards his boils, particularly towards a livid specimen under his arm. It grew septic, and his heart rejoiced in the pain of it and the danger of it. It was better than bungally. Besides, his mother and the girls were at home alone. It wasn't right they should be alone, and they should know about that boil and have the chance of tending it. So Henry went home and stayed there, sending reports, from time to time, of new and more terrible boils.

Dick became a morose savage. The job was no longer work. All the zest a man may feel even in the hardest work had vanished. It was just gruelling exertion that called no longer for volition. He had been bred in the city, and the heart to learn bush work was dead within him. He dragged on, making the toil twice as hard as it should have been, and within him dully glowed a hatred of the nephew and the bungally, of the district, of his father, of the rough tools of trade, of the neighbours, and of all things that caught his conscious eye. He looked much the worse for wear, for the clothes he had brought were quite unsuited for the work. At first he stitched and mended the rents, and then he gave it up as useless. His only coat he left too near a clearing fire, and a big cinder fell on it. When he discovered the mishap there were only two sleeves and the collar left. Dick stamped out the smouldering rag, swore in a mechanical way, hung the tatters on a bush, and savagely attacked the next bungally. His only trousers were sketches of what those garments were originally intended to be. The mere wearing of them was concession to habit. Possibly it would have been far more honest, and no less decent, to have discarded them altogether. His face and arms were black with soot and smoke, caked with sweat and dirt; and as he hung pendulum-like from the end of a huge lever — which he never succeeded once in placing under the really vulnerable part of a root — he looked like a sadly overdone travesty of a half-civilized blackfellow.

Meantime, he prayed for boils, or incapacitating sickness, for Dick was too honest to malinger.

The nephew went at it more intelligently and with half of Dick's effort did twice as much effective work. The grubbing was hateful to him, too, but out of it he got at least a malicious satisfaction, for he had grown to hate the Tullys as fervently as they hated him. He had a secret and cynical delight in watching the job beat them, and in knowing that the boys must for ever lose faith in their father, and that he would live in their memories as a hopeless old liar. Stupid, petty hate perhaps, but common enough, too.

At the end of the third week the nephew broke out in boils. It must have been the food or the water. He was foolishly proud of his boils, particularly of a livid specimen that was far more dangerous looking than Henry's best and biggest. But he worked on as a silent reproach to the absent Henry, and to old Tully and Dick, who had no boils at all. He got satisfaction out of Dick's envying him his boils. Having demonstrated his fortitude in a most aggravating way, he secretly chewed cobbler's wax, and the boils vanished.

Then, from nowhere in particular, Davie appeared.

He said, "Good day!" and Tully said, "Good day!" Then he watched Tully spit on his hands and make a special effort on the trunk of a down white-gum with his axe.

"You're all wrong," said Davie.

"Eh?" said Tully.

"You know nothing about it," said Davie. "Show me the axe!"

There was such a breezy, half-rogue, half-honest, good-natured air about this gangling youth that Tully complied.

Davie took the axe, balanced it in his hands, and declared it was a very adjectively bad one. But still . . . And he started chopping the big log, holding the axe short, swinging effortlessly through small arcs and smothering grunts the while. But the big chips flew and the log parted. Tully knew the man was an artist.

Davie put through two more chops, levered the logs together for burning, and walked over to a big bloodwood. He circled it twice.

"I'll be over in the morning to start," he said. "That bloodwood will cost you

160

ten bob — follow the roots and all. You do the cutting up."

He left, and whistling very blithely moved over to the nephew and Dick. He stood watching them for a while, and then told them to stop and listen.

"I'm Davie," he said, "and you know nothing about your job. Not the first thing about it. You are nearly as bad as that old coot over there."

Filial pride was now dead in Dick. He didn't dispute the epithet.

"Give *me* that mattock!" And Dick complied.

"Watch!" Davie tore into the bungally at a killing pace, throwing out roots that appeared to leave the ground at his touch.

"That's the way to get out bungally. You chaps are mugs. You know nothing about it. I'll be over in the morning to start."

Off he went in long awkward strides that covered the ground amazingly, singing joyfully in a fine clear voice an utterly disgraceful song.

He was back next morning very early, bringing his worldly possessions in a bushel case and a sugar-bag. On top of the case sat Tim, a very slim tom-cat of no particular virtue.

Tully was in doubt about employing him, but Davie brushed doubt aside. "I'll start right now on the bloodwood. Ten bob and follow the roots. You cut up. The same goes for that white-gum."

Tully just nodded.

In less than five hours both trees were down. It was marvellous. Tully would have taken over a day with those trees. But a pound for two trees was a bit too much. Still, perhaps it was worth it for the moral effect. Even the trees had been mocking Tully of late.

Then Davie said that he would clear half an acre for nine quid.

"Nine quid!" Tully gasped.

"Shut up," said Davie, "or it will cost you a tenner."

Tully gazed through the straggling trees at the distant blue of the mountains. His mind seemed to be wrestling with the great problems of the dim future, and he gently sucked such portions of his moustache as drooped close enough to his mouth. Tully was really meditating upon the proposal.

"Well, now!" he said at last, "for myself I wouldn't hear of it. But for the sake of the boys —"

"Good-o!" said Davie. "We'll mark out the half-acre now."

Tully spent the rest of the day measuring out Davie's section, but its final location was really decided by Davie. At least, that it was not to include a very nasty-looking patch of gum suckers. Davie knew what was under gum suckers of that kind.

Davie's coming made a big difference, especially for the nephew. At least for him life became more bearable, and at night by the fire something like cheerfulness was restored.

Davie worked like a demon on his section — when he felt so inclined — and the patch he cleared made a brave show. But it was costing more than the original contract would pay. Tully brooded over that now and became more hopeless than ever.

The days grew hotter and drier, and the work went more slowly. Tully stepped-out again and again the cleared portions — it went in a face no longer — and calculated distances, areas and times. He would drop his hands to his sides as he figured out how much the job would return him. Then he would walk dejectedly to the camp to see how the mutton was boiling in the kerosene-tin. It was a bad sign. He would make a dozen trips to the fire to look at the mutton. It didn't help the clearing at all.

In the sixth week the boss came along, expecting the job to be finished, and to arrange for the ploughing. He was a queer mixture of simple faith and low cunning; sympathetic and trusting, and yet inclined to drive a hard bargain. He was disappointed at the muddle, and soon gathered how little Tully really knew about the job. He was genuinely sorry for the old fellow, but he did feel that he shouldn't lose through the foolish mistakes of others. However, it was impossible to let the job go on as it was. There was barely more than tucker in it — and the tucker was poor. Eternal boiled mutton, potatoes, bread, butter, and golden syrup.

He asked Tully to give a hand with straightening up the crooked edge of the clearing so that an acre or two at least could be ploughed. There were tons of shapeless knotted roots to burn. All set to gather these. Tons and tons of them, and every root represented drops of sweat and strain of muscle and fervent profanity. It was almost fascinating to gaze upon the huge heap of roots and calculate how much of each was represented by the pile. Then the white-hot flames consumed all in a general purification:

That done, the boss asked Tully about the floaters.

Tully just said, "Floaters!" and sucked at his moustache.

"Yes, floaters. All surface stone, you know. You can't plough properly with them lying about."

Tully said nothing, but his hands clutched at his thighs.

"It's in the contract," said the boss.

"I never did hear of it." Tully spoke like a martyr who wasn't too sure after all that he wanted to be a martyr.

"Well, it's in the contract, and the stone has to be shifted."

Tully's shoulders drooped till he looked ten years older. He just went off to the camp to look at the mutton. Then he went back to his trees. At dinner-time the boss reminded him of the stone.

"Oh, yes," said Tully, "the floaters. Yes, of course. Come on, Dick. We'll get those floaters off."

They dragged off some of the big flat stones with a bag and dumped them on the headland. There were not so many of them after all. But at last Tully threw down the bag. "That will be enough, Dick. That will be enough! We are being got at on all sides."

"Yes, father," said Dick. And Dick picked up his mattock and went back to the bungally. There seemed nothing in life to Dick now beyond bungally.

Some time later, Davie came to the boss and said, "Watch out for old Tully. He went mad just now and threw all his tools into a fire, and then waltzed in and kicked them out. Real cuckoo he is and talking to himself. Couldn't make out what he said, though."

It sounded like Davie's romancing.

Just then Tully appeared near a smouldering heap of roots. It had been a very big fire, and the ring of coal and ash covered a wide area. Tully walked to the edge of the ring, and then away to gather an armful of the small roots scattered round. He lifted these above his head and threw them savagely into the centre. Then he rushed into the hot coals and kicked the new fuel out. He danced around the fire and through it, and kicked charred skulls of bungally in, and then kicked them out again. At last he stopped and raised clenched fists to the heavens, and the floodgates of his wrath were broken. He cursed the bungally and the land it grew on and the sky above it. He cursed the boss and the damnable nephew. He cursed Davie. He cursed himself for taking the job, and Dick for helping him. He cursed Henry for getting boils. He cursed every soul that lived in such a district. He cursed the blacks who once owned the country — but, in fairness to them, he conceded that they were more decent than the "cows" who owned it now. Then he cursed the ancestors of all concerned.

It was a great performance, especially so as Tully had the reputation of being a religious man.

The boss was really scared. There was no telling what might happen next. But the matter had to be settled. So he went across as Tully was commencing to put a withering curse on the posterity of all who had conspired to push him into the job.

"Mr Tully," said the boss, "for God's sake calm down!"

Tully, strange to say, calmed down. There was not going to be murder after all. "Now, what is the trouble?"

There was plenty; and Tully said so. The contract, the bungally, the floaters, the price, the tucker. Everything. He was losing money, and the longer he stayed the more he would lose. And he'd never have taken the job only for the sake of the boys.

There was some argument on the points raised, but the upshot of it was an agreement to let Tully off the rest of the contract, and pay him *pro rata* for what he had done. Tully breathed like one who is reprieved on the scaffold. But he would have to ask the boys first, he said, just as a matter of form, though it was hardly necessary.

The tape was run over the cleared portions, and Tully was shocked to find that these amounted to two and a half acres. They measured them again to make sure. But the result was the same. Two and a half acres! And only just two and a half acres. An arrangement was come to about Davie's half-acre.

Tully and Dick gathered their belongings and prepared to depart. Luckily Dick possessed a long overcoat, or his journey to town would have presented new and interesting problems, although Dick himself was past caring about anything.

Two acres of bungally rustled crisply in the light evening breeze. There almost seemed to be an air of triumph about it as it watched Tully and Dick leaving for town.

Robert D.
FitzGerald

Edge

Knife's edge, moon's edge, water's edge,
graze the throat of the formed shape
that sense fills where shape vanishes:
air at the ground limit of steel,
the thin disc in the moon's curve,
land gliding out of no land.

The new image, the freed thought,
are carved from that inert bulk
where the known ends and the unknown
is cut down before it — at the mind's edge,
the knife-edge at the throat of darkness.

As Between Neighbours...

Be close in your corner; for the thing not said
is a wise thing, worthy the grey, wise head.
Surely the silent man saving every word
has right coin for living in his tight-held hoard.

The grave word spoken is soon proved wrong,
and the gay word's a feather that's afloat in a song;
and he who is hollow sees life as a jest,
and laughter is the sign of him; silence is best.

Chain your laughter, neighbour, put a lock on your tongue:
that the old should be merry is offensive to the young.
The young man has forgotten, though we remember, toys —
with the world in his pocket like a marble in a boy's.

Bog and Candle

I

At the end of life paralysis or those creeping teeth,
the crab at lung or liver or the rat in the brain,
and flesh become limp rag, and sense tap of a cane —
if you would pray, brother, pray for a clean death.

For when the work you chip from age-hard earth must pause,
faced with the dark, unfinished, where day gave love and jest,
day and that earth in you shall pit you to their test
of struggle in old bog against the tug of claws.

II

What need had such a one for light at the night's rim?
Yet in the air of evening till the medley of sound —
children and birds and traffic — settled in the profound
meditation of earth, it was the blind man's whim

to set at his wide window the warm gift of flame
and put a match to wick for sight not like his own —
for his blank eyes could pierce that darkness all have known,
the thought: "What use the light, or to play out the game?"

Yet could disperse also the fog of that queer code
which exalts pain as evidence of some aim or end
finer than strength it tortures, so sees pain as friend —
good in itself and guiding to great ultimate good.

Then he would touch the walls of the cold place where he sat
but know the world as wider, since here, beside his hand,
this flame could reach out, out, did touch but understand. . . .
Life in a man's body perhaps rayed out like that.

So it is body's business and its inborn doom
past will, past hope, past reason and all courage of heart,
still to resist among the roof-beams ripped apart
the putting-out of the candle in the blind man's room.

Macquarie Place

I will go out and hear the strain
of rat-bag orators at large.
There is a battery in my brain
which just that fever might re-charge.

The blends of curious craziness
which crank and anarchist extol
could fill with their electric stress
the run-down fury of my soul.

Whether some economic scheme
to conquer currencies, and spread
over the honeyed earth its dream,
moves them, that all men may be fed;

or whether warnings of the worst
in drink or diet or the boss,
or judgement coming with a burst;
they bring back vision gone as loss.

For nudist, atheist, or pest,
half genius and half distraught,
has in his frenzy of unrest
the drive of some determining thought.

God keep me sane until my last
of breath or knowing; but let faint
fervour still reach me from the vast
madness of prophet and of saint.

I could proclaim the world is flat
with reasonable skill and wit,
but need fanatic zest if that
I would persuade myself of it.

So I will cross Macquarie Place
and covet zeal as crude as loud
in lunch-hour lunatics who face
amused indifference of the crowd.

Quayside Meditation

This concrete city with glass, towering walls
grows newly up and does not share the years,
nearly two hundred now, which stone recalls

or harbour noise; and in this haunted time
I turn my back on it where in my ears
voices and ship-names from an older earth

echo out well beyond what I might claim
myself as yesterdays . . . though mine have known
(and longer gone than *Lawhill* from her berth,

that lone intruder upon steam and steel)
the masted ships (*Helen B. Stirling* one)
anchored in Birchgrove, five or six together.

For war brought back vessels of square-rigged sail;
but earlier still *Sobraon* off Cockatoo
tugged at fast moorings; and I see my father

point me out her rows of dummy ports
right to the waterline, which once would do
duty for cannon, make her seem, by bluff,

a bristling frigate. So in fabled parts,
the dangerous China seas, that skin-thin paint
had tricked Malayan pirates, scared them off.

And when you think of it this links my life
of not yet sixty years with what seems faint
in legendary lore and wholly lost,

namely the wooden ships of war. In brief
time is so shortened, since the day's brought near
of Nelson and Trafalgar and the rest,

that what's-to-come no longer looms a place
separate from all being but, joining here
the world we have walked thus far, is even our own.

Saying which, I can turn about and face
concrete and glass as things familiar — known
like brick, shell-mortar, and grey Hawkesbury stone.

169

Beginnings

Not to have known the hard-bitten,
tight-lipped Caesar
clamped down on savage Britain;
or, moving closer,
not to have watched Cook
drawing thin lines across
the last sea's uncut book
is my own certain loss;

as too is having come late,
the other side of the dark
from that bearded, sedate
Hargrave of Stanwell Park,
and so to have missed, some bright
morning, in the salty, stiff
north-easter, a crank with a kite —
steadied above the cliff.

Beginnings once known
are lost. Perpetual day,
wheeling, has grown
each year further away
from the original strength
of any action or mind
used, and at length
fallen behind.

One might give much
to bring to the hand
for sight and touch
cities under the sand
and to talk and trade
with the plain folk met
could we walk with the first who made
an alphabet.

But more than to look back
we choose this day's concern
with everything in the track,
and would give most to learn
outcomes of all we found
and what next builds to the stars.
I regret I shall not be around
to stand on Mars.

The Wind at Your Door

To Mary Gilmore

My ancestor was called on to go out —
a medical man, and one such must by law
wait in attendance on the pampered knout
and lend his countenance to what he saw,
lest the pet, patting with too bared a claw,
be judged a clumsy pussy. Bitter and hard,
see, as I see him, in that jailhouse yard.

Or see my thought of him: though time may keep
elsewhere tradition or a portrait still,
I would not feel under his cloak of sleep
if beard there or smooth chin, just to fulfil
some canon of precision. Good or ill
his blood's my own; and scratching in his grave
could find me more than I might wish to have.

Let him then be much of the middle style
of height and colouring; let his hair be dark
and his eyes green; and for that slit, the smile
that seemed inhuman, have it cruel and stark,
but grant it could be too the ironic mark
of all caught in the system — who the most,
the doctor or the flesh twined round that post?

There was a high wind blowing on that day;
for one who would not watch, but looked aside,
said that when twice he turned it blew his way
splashes of blood and strips of human hide
shaken out from the lashes that were plied
by one right-handed, one left-handed tough,
sweating at this paid task, and skilled enough.

That wind blows to your door down all these years.
Have you not known it when some breath you drew
tasted of blood? Your comfort is in arrears
of just thanks to a savagery tamed in you
only as subtler fears may serve in lieu
of thong and noose — old savagery which has built
your world and laws out of the lives it spilt.

For what was jailyard widens and takes in
my country. Fifty paces of stamped earth
stretch; and grey walls retreat and grow so thin
that towns show through and clearings — new raw birth
which burst from handcuffs — and free hands go forth
to win tomorrow's harvest from a vast
ploughland — the fifty paces of that past.

But see it through a window barred across,
from cells this side, facing the outer gate
which shuts on freedom, opens on its loss
in a flat wall. Look left now through the grate
at buildings like more walls, roofed with grey slate
or hollowed in the thickness of laid stone
each side the court where the crowd stands this noon.

One there with the officials, thick of build,
not stout, say burly (so this obstinate man
ghosts in the eyes) is he whom enemies killed
(as I was taught) because the monopolist clan
found him a grit in their smooth-turning plan,
too loyally active on behalf of Bligh.
So he got lost; and history passed him by.

But now he buttons his long coat against
the biting gusts, or as a gesture of mind,
habitual; as if to keep him fenced
from stabs of slander sticking him from behind,
sped by the schemers never far to find
in faction, where approval from one source
damns in another clubroom as of course.

This man had Hunter's confidence, King's praise;
and settlers on the starving Hawkesbury banks
recalled through twilight drifting across their days
the doctor's fee of little more than thanks
so often; and how sent by their squeezed ranks
he put their case in London. I find I lack
the hateful paint to daub him wholly black.

Perhaps my life replies to his too much
through veiling generations dropped between.
My weakness here, resentments there, may touch
old motives and explain them, till I lean
to the forgiveness I must hope may clean
my own shortcomings; since no man can live
in his own sight if it will not forgive.

Certainly I must own him whether or not
it be my will. I was made understand
this much when once, marking a freehold lot,
my papers suddenly told me it was land
granted to Martin Mason. I felt his hand
heavily on my shoulder, and knew what coil
binds life to life through bodies, and soul to soil.

There, over to one corner, a bony group
of prisoners waits; and each shall be in turn
tied by his own arms in a human loop
about the post, with his back bared to learn
the price of seeking freedom. So they earn
three hundred rippling stripes apiece, as set
by the law's mathematics against the debt.

These are the Irish batch of Castle Hill,
rebels and mutineers, my countrymen
twice over: first, because of those to till
my birthplace first, hack roads, raise roofs; and then
because their older land time and again
enrolls me through my forbears; and I claim
as origin that threshold whence we came.

One sufferer had my surname, and thereto
"Maurice", which added up to history once;
an ignorant dolt, no doubt, for all that crew
was tenantry. The breed of clod and dunce
makes patriots and true men: could I announce
that Maurice as my kin I say aloud
I'd take his irons as heraldry, and be proud.

Maurice is at the post. Its music lulls,
one hundred lashes done. If backbone shows
then play the tune on buttocks! But feel his pulse;
that's what a doctor's for; and if it goes
lamely, then dose it with these purging blows —
which have not made him moan; though, writhing there,
"Let my neck be," he says, "and flog me fair."

One hundred lashes more, then rest the flail.
What says the doctor now? "This dog won't yelp;
he'll tire you out before you'll see him fail;
here's strength to spare; go on!" Ay, pound to pulp;
yet when you've done he'll walk without your help,
and knock down guards who'd carry him being bid,
and sing no song of where the pikes are hid.

It would be well if I could find, removed
through generations back — who knows how far? —
more than a surname's thickness as a proved
bridge with that man's foundations. I need some star
of courage from his firmament, a bar
against surrenders: faith. All trials are less
than rain-blacked wind tells of that old distress.

Yet I can live with Mason. What is told
and what my heart knows of his heart, can sort
much truth from falsehood, much there that I hold
good clearly or good clouded by report;
and for things bad, ill grows where ills resort:
they were bad times. None know what in his place
they might have done. I've my own faults to face.

Society

Society, when I was young —
a word that bristled on my tongue —
meant fashion and milady's dress
and Women's Pages in the press
and girls who, prickly and polite,
would numb a fumbling lout with fright;
while *social* was a word (to give
society its adjective)
which went with brutes in modish clothes
with cultured manners that one loathes
if one is conscious of one's hands,
the way one speaks, the way one stands,
and hatches vengeful, inward plots
fit for the claws of sansculottes.

One knew that, sour residuum,
society had "dregs" and "scum"
whom *social workers* might retrieve —
an aim found stubborn to achieve
by church, police, or *socialist*.
But soon one learns how terms can twist
and definitions grow entwined
with bent assumptions of the mind;
and then *society* becomes
neither the mansion nor the slums
nor meeting-place of lad and lass,
but life's whole tangle and morass.

Therein — though I have neither graced
gay, brilliant company, nor faced
distresses, for mankind, and lent
to councils, unions, parliament,
the service of what gifts I had —
I yet, like most men, have been glad
to work and live and be exposed
to joys and ills that time disclosed,
and family matters, change and chance —
the tumbling dice of circumstance;
and since this churns me too within
the ferment of all human kin,
now, in these latter days, forgive,
Society, your fugitive.

Song in Autumn

Though we have put
white breath to its brief caper
in the early air,
and have known elsewhere
stiff fingers, frost underfoot,
sun thin as paper;

cold then was a lens
focussing sight, and showed that riggers' gear,
the spider's cables,
anchored between the immense
steel trusses of built grass. The hills were so near
you could pick up pebbles.

It is different at evening: damp rises
not crisp or definite like frost
but seeping into the blood and brain —
the end of enterprises.
And while, out of many things lost,
courage may remain,

this much is certain
from others' experience
and was indeed foretold:
noon's over; the days shorten.
Let there be no pretence;
none here likes the cold.

Sidney Nolan *Glenrowan* 1947
Enamel on composition board 90.4 × 121.2 cm
Australian National Gallery

Desiderius Orban *South Coast Timberland* 1948
Pastel on paper 50.2 × 65.1 cm
Art Gallery of New South Wales

Shared Ground

There have been days when some must thieve for food,
a family starving and nothing left to flog.
I rejoice to read of a pickpocket who made good
transported from poverty grimed with London fog,

and who, as trusty, dredged from our convict bog
promotion and the respect of a clean report
then later got into trouble over a dog
he seized for the pound; but won his case in court.

This, against all purse-privilege could distort
about the man's fair action, lets me discern
new citizenship and, tied with it in some sort,
justice in a new setting, awake to learn.

Time names the great whose achievements blaze, renowned.
I observe unknowns among them on shared ground.

Dal
Stivens

Warrigal

"YOU'LL HAVE to get rid of that dingo before long," my neighbour Swinburne said to me across the fence. "Why, he's an Asiatic wolf —"

"No one of any authority says that the dingo is an Asiatic wolf," I said. "The Curator of Mammals at the Australian Museum classifies the dingo as *Canis familiaris* variety *dingo* — that is, a variety of the common dog. Another eminent authority says it's most unlikely that the dingo is descended from the northern wolf —"

"I know a wolf when I see it," this classic pyknic said. "I don't care what some long-haired professors say. I was brought up in the bush."

As my wife Martha says, I can be insufferable at times — particularly when I'm provoked. I said: "So much for your fears of this animal attacking you — it's most unlikely as long as he continues to look on you as the *gamma* animal. Of course, you need to act like a *gamma* animal at all times."

I thought for a moment he was going to climb over the paling fence that divided our properties and throw a punch at me.

"You be careful who you call an animal!" he said. His big red face and neck were swelling like a frog's. It was pure Lorenz and Hediger I was throwing at him. This was during my animal behaviour period.

"I'm not calling you an animal," I said. "I'm just explaining how the dingo sees you. He sees me as the *alpha* animal — *alpha* is Greek for A. I'm the pack leader in his eyes. He sees my wife, Martha, as the *beta* animal. *Beta* is B and *gamma* is C. He probably see you and your wife and kids as *gamma* or *delta* animals. *Delta* is D. While you behave like *gamma* or *delta* animals, you'll be O.K. He'll defer to you."

He seemed a little assured — or confused, anyway.

"This *gamma* stuff," he began uncertainly. "You're sure of it, now?"

"I'll lend you a book," I said.

"All the same, he's got pretty powerful jaws," he said, pointing to Red, who was crouching at my feet, his eyes not leaving me. The jaws were, as he said, powerful, and the white shining canine teeth rather large. The head was a little too large, the prick ears a bit too thick at the roots for Red to be a really handsome dog, but there was a compact power in his strong tawny chest and limbs.

"No more than a German shepherd's," I said. There were two of them in Mansion Road — that wasn't the name but it will do.

"I suppose so," he said doubtfully.

"If I hadn't told you Red was a dingo you wouldn't be worrying," I said. "I could have told you Red was a mongrel."

"Are you trying to tell me I wouldn't know a dingo?" he started in belligerently.

Before I could answer, his own dog, a Dobermann Pinscher and a real North Shore status job, came out and began challenging Red. Both dogs raced up and down on their sides of the fence, the Pinscher growling and barking and Red just growling. (Dingoes don't bark in the wilds. When domesticated some learn to do so but Red hadn't.)

Red ran on his toes, his reddish-brown coat gleaming and white-tipped bushy tail waving erect. His gait was exciting to watch: it was smooth, effortless and one he could maintain for hours.

"This is what I mean," he said. "Your Asiatic wolf could savage my dog to death."

"Yours is making the most noise," I said. The Pinscher was as aggressive as his master.

"Noise isn't everything," he said. "Look at that wolf-like crouching."

"Innate behaviour," I said. "Dingoes have acquired that over thousands of years of attacking emus and kangaroos. They crouch to avoid the kicks."

"So your wolf is getting ready to attack, is he?"

"Not necessarily," I said. "No more than yours is. Of course, if one dog were to invade the other's territory, then there would be a fight. But they won't invade."

"Yours could jump the fence," he said. "I've seen him. He could kill my dog and clean up my fowls."

"Not into your place," I said. I was beginning to lose my temper. "He wouldn't. He knows it isn't his."

"So he's moral, is he?" he shouted. "This wild dog —"

"They're all moral although the term is anthropomorphic. Wild dogs or domestic dogs usually won't invade another's territory."

"So you say," he said. His face was purpling. "I warn you now yours had better not. If he does I'll shoot him. The law's on my side."

I was so angry I went inside and got a hammer. I started knocking palings out of the fence.

"Hey!" he shouted. "That's my fence. And I meant what I said about shooting that Asiatic mongrel."

"Pure-bred dingo," I grunted. I was out of condition and the nails were tough. "Our fence."

I got four palings out and, as I knew would happen, the dogs kept racing past the gap and ignoring the chance to enter and attack. I was dishing out pure Lorenz.

"It's just bluff," I said. "You can see it for yourself. They talk big. After they've said their bit, they'll knock off."

"Perhaps," he said, doubtfully.

"Call your dog out into the street," I said. "I'll call mine. They'll meet in the middle and sniff each other's anal quarters but they won't fight. There's nothing to fight about — none lays claim to the centre of the road. Of course, the footpath is different."

"I won't risk it," he said and he called the Pinscher and started off. "You may be right and your dingo ought to be at home in your garden."

It might have sounded conciliatory to you. But there was a crack in it. This was during my Australian native flora period. When I bought this block I had the house built well down the hillside and left all the trees and shrubs. I wanted a native bushland garden and I had left what the other people in Mansion Road called "that rubbish" in its near-natural state. I had planted some more natives — waratahs like great red Roman torches, delicately starred wax flowers and native roses, piquantly scented boronias, flannel flowers, and subtly curving spider flowers. This was in keeping with my newly acquired feeling for *furyu*, which is often used to describe things Japanese. It can be translated as "taste-ful", but the Japanese characters convey a fuller meaning of "flowing with the wind" — the acceptance of nature, of the material itself, and of the patterns it imposes. Transferring the concept to Australia, I was accepting nature and learn-ing to appreciate the muted beauty of Australian shrubs and flowers.

The neighbours didn't approve. They all had lots of lawns and terraces and beds of perennials and annuals. They'd chopped down most of the native trees and planted exotics. They thought my garden lowered the tone of the street. And they thought the same about our unobtrusive low-line house, blending with the slim eucalypts and the sandstone outcrops. They preferred double-fronted mod. bungs.

We'd have got on a lot better if we had lived in Mansion Street during my azalea and camellia period. At our last house Martha and I had gone in for landscaping — vistas, focus points, and the rest. And we'd used azaleas and camellias for much of the mass planting. I'd got myself wised up on azaleas, particularly, and I knew as much as most about Wilson's fifty Kurumes; I once engaged in some learned discussion in a specialist journal as to whether or not some experts were correct in thinking 'Pink Pearl' (*Azuma kagami*) was, indeed, the progenitor of all the pink-flowered forms.

That was some time ago, and although I still like azaleas, the love affair was then over. Not everyone appreciates Australian natives. We went away for a week once and when we came back someone had dumped two tons of rubbish into our place. We had no fence at the street level and someone had thought it was a virgin block. The house is well down the slope and hard to see from the street. Of course, he should have noticed the rather heavy concentration of native flora. He had tipped the rusting tins, galvanized iron, mattresses, and so on, onto a stand of native roses, too.

We didn't really fit into Mansion Road for a number of reasons. First, there was my profession as a journalist and writer. And moreover, Martha and I were in our Chagall period; our earlier Rembrandt love affair might have been accepted.

And there was the car business. They all had one or two cars but we didn't see the need when there was a good taxi and hire car service. When they finally got the idea that we could afford a car but wouldn't have one, it struck them as un-Australian or something.

The dingo business was merely another straw, though Swinburne seemed to be trying to push it a bit further.

"Why get yourself angry?" Martha reproached me when I went inside.

"A conformist ass!" I said.

"You can't educate him," she said.

"I know," I said. "I was having a bit of fun."

"Whatever you call it, we'll probably have to get rid of Red," she said.

"Where?" I said.

That was the question. I wasn't giving him to the Zoo, as some in Mansion Road had hinted I should. Dingoes are far-ranging, lively, intelligent creatures and it would be cruelty to confine him. And I couldn't release him in the bush now that he was a year old and had had no training in hunting for himself. Normally, he would have acquired this from his mother, but I'd got Red as a pup. A zoologist friend had brought him to Sydney and then found his wife wouldn't let him keep a dingo.

I didn't see Swinburne again until the next week-end. He called me over the fence.

"What you say about that dingo might be true at present but he'll revert to type," he said. "The hunting instinct is too strong. It will be someone's chicken run eventually even if it's not mine."

"He hasn't been taught to hunt fowls — or anything else," I said. "So why should he? He's well fed."

"Primitive instincts are strong," said Swinburne.

"We don't know what his primeval instincts are," I said.

"He's a wild dog."

I said, insufferably: "Professor Konrad Lorenz, who is one of the world's greatest authorities on dogs, says that the dingo is a descendant of a domesticated dog brought here by the Aborigines. He points out that a pure-blooded dingo often has white stockings or stars and nearly always a white tip to its tail. He adds that these points are quite irregularly distributed. This, as everyone knows, is a feature never seen in wild animals but it occurs frequently in all domestic animals."

"Has this foreign professor ever seen a dingo in the wilds?" he asked.

I couldn't see what his question had to do with the paraphrase I had given him, but I told him that while Lorenz had not been to Australia as far as I knew, he had bred and studied dingoes.

He changed the subject abruptly.

"You seem to know all about animals and birds," he said. "Perhaps you have a cure for a crowing rooster? Mine is upsetting some of the neighbours by crowing during the night. He answers other roosters across the valley." (There were farms there.) "In a street like Mansion Road, you have to fit in."

He was getting at me but I ignored it.

"I think so," I said.

"I'd like to hear it," he said, too sweetly.

"You have to get on with people, as you say," I said, also too sweetly. "But roosters can be stopped from crowing in a very simple fashion. A rooster, as you know, has to stretch its neck to crow. I'd suggest tacking a piece of hessian over the perch, a couple of inches above his head. When he goes to stretch his neck, he'll bump the hessian and won't be able to crow."

He took it in after a few questions and said he'd try it. It took him and his fifteen-year-old son most of the afternoon. I must say they were thorough. It took them ten minutes to catch that White Leghorn and then they held him with his feet on the ground and measured the distance to a couple of inches over his head. They measured the hessian meticulously and then they had a conference during which they kept looking towards me. I was sowing some flannel flower seeds. I'd gone to the near-by bushland reserve several times to observe the soil and aspect of flannel flowers so that I could plant the seeds in the right place in my garden.

Swinburne came over to the fence finally. "I'm sorry to trouble you," he said. This was a change. "But there are several perches in the hen house."

"The top one," I said. "He's the *alpha* animal."

They fixed it there and Swinburne asked me to come and have a beer at his place. But he hadn't changed his mind much about the dingo because he and his wife started telling me about the merits of budgerigars as pets.

"Now, budgerigars make marvellous pets," he said. "Our Joey is a wonderful talker."

The bird, a male pied blue, was perched on his hand, and while Mrs Swinburne smiled dotingly, it displayed and then, with wings down-dragging, it tried to copulate with Swinburne's big red hand.

"Isn't he quaint?" asked Mrs Swinburne. "He does that by the hour."

Poor bloody bird, I thought.

"No wonder," I said aloud.

"What do you mean?"

"Nothing," I said. "I mean it's wonderful."

"And they tell me budgerigars don't talk in the wilds," said Mrs Swinburne.

"No," I said. "Only when they're caged." I refrained from saying anything about mimicry being due to starved sexuality, to banked-up energy.

I couldn't see Mansion Road letting up on Red — Swinburne was just the official spokesman as it were, one of the *alpha* members in the street, the managing director of a shoe factory. I knew the others were saying the same things among themselves.

They said them to me a few nights later. Mrs Fitter called. If Swinburne was an *alpha* male, she was *the alpha* female. Her father had been a drapery knight and had built the big house in which the Fitters lived with a feature window and two cars.

"I've come on behalf of the mothers of Mansion Road," she started in. She was a large dark woman with a hint of a moustache. "They're very frightened that ravening wild dingo will attack their children. They have to pass it on their way to school and it crouches in the gutter."

She was laying it on. Most of the children were driven to school.

"It won't attack them," I said. "He lies in the gutter because that's his territorial boundary. Like ourselves animals are land owners."

"And what's more he barks at them," she said, going too far.

"Dingoes don't bark," I said, gently, but I was getting angry. Martha was making signs.

"And at cars, too," she said. "I had to swerve to miss him. And he slavers at the lips."

"He has well-developed salivary glands," I said. "I assure you he won't attack anyone, but in any case the solution is simple. Your Schnauzer owns your footpath, Mrs Fitter — or thinks he does. I respect his property right and don't walk on his footpath and we get on very well."

It wasn't tactful but I didn't want to be.

After Mrs Fitter had left, Martha said, "Red has been going out after cars the last couple of days."

"But not barking?" I asked.

"No," she said.

Three nights later a young policeman called. Mrs Fitter had complained that

Red had killed one of her fowls.

"Did she see him?" I asked.

"No, but she is convinced it could only have been the dingo," he said.

"Well, constable, you know the legal position as well as I do," I said. I didn't like it but I had to tack a bit. "Every dog is allowed one bite — but not two. I don't admit that Red did kill the fowl. It could have been any one of the dogs in the street. And, further, Red is not necessarily a dingo. He could be a mongrel. I don't know his parentage. He was found in the outback by a friend and brought to Sydney."

He went away but was back the next night.

"Mrs Fitter says that you have admitted that the animal is a dingo," he said.

"I admit nothing," I said, tacking again. "I have called the dog a dingo without any accurate knowledge and purely out of a spirit of fantasy. I wanted to indulge in a little fancy. It has been fun to think of Red as a dingo."

He was a bit shaken and I went on, "I'm no expert on dingoes, nor is anyone else in this street. Have you ever seen a pure-bred dingo?"

"I think so — at the Zoo —" he said, uncertainly.

"Exactly," I said. "And how do you know it was a pure one and even if it was, would you be able to point to any dog with certainty and say that is a dingo or that another was a Dobermann Pinscher —"

"A Dobermann what, sir?"

"Mr Swinburne's dog is a Dobermann Pinscher. Mrs Fitter, on the other hand, has a Schnauzer. Of course, the two have points in common, according to the experts. I am told that a Manchester Terrier is even closer in appearance to a Dobermann Pinscher and that only the well informed can pick one from the other. Now when you come to mongrels, the question of identification is much more complicated —"

There was a bit more of it. He fled in some confusion and Martha and I rolled around the floor, helpless with laughter, and went to bed earlier. But it was getting serious. If I didn't cure Red of going out on the road, Mrs Fitter, or someone else, wasn't going to swerve next time.

What I did was undiluted Lorenz.

If you want to stop a dog chasing cars you have to fire a small stone at him from behind from a catapult when he is in the middle of chasing. When you do it this way the dog is taken by surprise. He doesn't see you do it and it seems to him like the hand of God. That is anthropomorphic, but you know what I'm getting at; it's a memorable experience for the dog and usually cures him completely.

I stayed home the next day. It took me an hour to make a catapult that worked properly and I had to practise for twenty minutes. Then I was ready. I cured Red that morning with two hits, which were, I hope, not too painful. The gutter and the street were abandoned by him. Encouraged, I decided to cure him of establishing himself on the footpath. I achieved that, too.

I knew it only won a respite for the dingo. I had to return him to the wilds. The alternatives of giving him to the Zoo, or having him put away, I'd already rejected. Swinburne came home early that day.

"I see you're still insisting on keeping that Asiatic wolf," he said.

"*Canis familiaris* variety *dingo*," I corrected. "But you're wrong about keeping him. I'm returning him to the wilds."

"But they're sheep killers."

"Not where there are no sheep."

"There are sheep everywhere," he said stubbornly.

"Australia's a big place," I said. "There ought to be a place somewhere where he can live his own life. But he'll have to be taught to hunt before I can release him."

"You mean on wild animals?"

"What else?" I said.

"You'll soon have the fauna protection people after you," he said.

"Rabbits aren't protected," I said.

"They're vermin — and so are dingoes!" he said.

They didn't give me time to put my plan into operation. I had thought it just possible that they might give Red a bait. But I couldn't believe they hated him so much. Besides it's an offence to lay baits and they were most law-abiding in Mansion Road. They didn't poison Red. What happened was that Red went wandering off one day through the bushland reserve and a poultry farmer on the other side of the valley shot the dingo, as he was legally entitled to do.

"Sorry to hear about that dog of yours," said Swinburne later.

"But why should he go off?" I asked.

"I know a bit about dingoes," he said and his eyes were gleaming. "Most likely he followed a bitch on heat. It's a question of studying animal behaviour."

I knew then that he'd done it with a farmer in on the job. They were legal in Mansion Road. But I wouldn't be able to prove anything.

"It's better to keep budgerigars as pets," I said, blazing inside. "You keep them sex-starved and they'll try to mate with your hand." Only I used a blunter word. "It's all nice and jolly and they'll talk, too."

I was sorry afterwards for losing my temper. Swinburne wrung the budgerigar's neck the next time it displayed on his wife's hand.

We sold out soon afterwards. I was coming to the end of my Australian native flora period, anyway.

W. E. "Bill"
Harney

West of Alice

We are travelling west of Alice Springs, and Sam is at the wheel;
Riding the diesel-grader I am watching its blade of steel
Roll back the dark-red sandy loam or grind the limestones grey,
And the wheels whirl in a red-dust swirl along the new highway.

We pass where Sturt-peas clothe the earth with a scarlet sweep of flowers,
And burst through green acacia-trees that send down golden showers;
The parakeelia's purple blooms are crushed in the dry, red sand
When the bright blade sweeps as the grader creeps over the stern, strange land.

The mulga, mallee, desert-oaks fall prostrate as we pass,
The lizards, pigeons, porcupines crouch low in stone and grass;
We brush the spinifex aside; tear down the bush-rat's shade,
And the desert mole in its sandhill hole digs faster from our blade.

The honey-ants are rooted out to roll upon the sand,
But ever the ramping, stamping fiend goes roaring through the land;
The tyres grind and the steel blade cuts the pads where camels trod
And claws at the ground of a stony mound where tribesmen praised their God.

We cross the desert rivers, formed when the world was new,
And churn to dust the fossil-bones of the giant kangaroo;
I wave to naked native kids upon Erldunda's plain,
And we fill our tank where the black men drank from rock-holes filled by rain.

We camp in Kulgera's weathered hills, scarred core of an ancient range,
Where the camp-fire flame throws out its light on a scene that is ever strange
As a dingo wails by the painted wall of a sacred cave near by
And the stars shine bright as we lie at night beneath a frosty sky.

We rise as mulga-parakeets go whirling through the dawn,
We see old star-man Manbuk rise from depths of midnight drawn;
We hear the grader's engine roar with Sam behind the wheel,
And I sing my song as we plunge along to the chatter of wheel and steel.

Roland
Robinson

Waratah

Fierce and holy flower
burning, in the drenched
depths of blue-grey bush,
solitary, unquenched.

Sprung from Eden earth
named with sacred name,
from stiff serrated leaves
rises the chaliced flame

Misted mauve-grey light
brightens, glistens, fades
through the crowding depths
of fronds and spears and blades.

Silence, save the one
thrush's piercing call,
save, from fern-hung heights,
hush of the waterfall.

Holy, holy flower,
through centuries, again
sprung from the mould to burn,
burn in the bush and rain.

Ma-poor-am

Related by Fred Biggs, Ngeamba tribe

Go out and camp somewhere. You're lying down.
A wind comes, and you hear this "Ma-poor-am."
"What's that?" you say. Why, that's a Ma-poor-am.
You go and find that tree rubbing itself.
It makes all sorts of noises in the wind.
It might be like a sheep, or like a cat,
or like a baby crying, or someone calling,
a sort of whistling-calling when the wind
comes and swings and rubs two boughs like that.

A Wirreengun, a clever-feller, sings
that tree. He hums a song, a Ma-poor-am:
a song to bring things out, or close things up,
a song to bring a girl, a woman from the tree.
She's got long hair, it falls right down her back.
He's got her for himself. He'll keep her now.

One evening it was sort of rainy-dark.
They built a mia-mia, stripping bark.
You've been out in the bush sometime and seen
them old dry pines with loose bark coming off.
You get a lot of bark from them dry pines,
before they rot and go too far, you know.
The woman from the tree, she pulled that bark.
It tore off, up and up the tree. It pulled
her up into the tree, up, up into the sky.
Well, she was gone. That was the end of it.
No more that Wirreengun could call her back.

"Ma-poor-am. Ma-poor-am." "What's that?" you say.
Why, that's two tree-boughs rubbing in the wind.

Altjeringa

Nude, smooth, and giant-huge,
the torsos of the gums
hold up the vast dark cave
as the great moon comes.

Shock-headed black-boy stands,
with rigid, thrusting spear,
defiant and grotesque
against that glistening sphere.

In clenched, contorted birth
black banksias agonise;
out of the ferns and earth,
half-formed, beast-boulders rise;

because The Bush goes back,
back to a time unknown:
chaos that had not word,
nor image carved on stone.

Bees

Related by Percy Mumbulla, Wallaga Lake tribe

From the holler trees in their native home
them old fellers cut the honey-comb.
On honey an' little white grubs they fed,
'cause them young bees was blackfellers' bread.
That's why they was so mighty an' strong
in their native home at Currarong.
An' them old fellers' drink was honey-bul,
honey an' water, a coolamon full.
Naked through the bush they went,
an' never knew what sickness meant.
Them little dark bees would do you no harm,
they'd crawl all over your honey-smeared arm.
But them Eyetalian bees, they'd bung
your eyes right up. When we was young
we used to rob their honey-trees.
Savage! They'd fetch your blood. Them bees
would zing an' zoom an' chase a feller
from Bomaderry to Bodalla.
Well, old uncle Minah, old Billy Bulloo,
Jacky Mumbulla, King Merriman too,
them fierce old fellers, they're all gone now.
An' the wild honey's still in the gum-tree bough.

Elizabeth
Riddell

Carnival in the Park

Two thicknesses of dark trees and air
And then the flowering fair
With its bright blooms of light
Its trunks of wire and its mane-tossing horses
Galloping the summer pastures of the night.

The birds to make the music are shut in boxes
Silver paper falls in a silly stream,
The gold is gilt, the promises tissue paper
But in the soil sleeps the persistent grass
And when the trumpets and the showmen pass
It will thrust back to light.

Meanwhile the wooden hooves of the carnival horses
Gallop the summer pastures of the night.

Suburban Song

Now all the dogs with folded paws
Stare at the lowering sky.
This is the hour when women hear
Their lives go ticking by.

The baker's horse with rattling hooves
Upon the windy hill
Mocks the thunder in the heart
Of women sitting still.

The poppies in the garden turn
Their faces to the sand
And tears upon the sewing fall
And on the stranger's hand.

Flap flap the washing flies
To meet the starting hail.
Close the door on love and hang
The key upon the nail.

James
Devaney

The Willows

Dawn, and the stars yet there,
Like revellers overstayed,
And I watch the shadowy twilight
Vaguely the dark invade;
I see slowly emerging
The river willow-lined,
And a strange winter daybreak
Looms the hill behind.

The kingfisher head-heavy
His first patrol has tried
Along the falling willows
That love the river-side.
You poets city-weary,
I'll tell you a lovely thing:
Shadows of trees on water
At the day's first wakening.

The misty breath of morning
Like a cool hand on the brow,
And skies begin to opal,
And day is here now.
Poets, I know a poem
That never shall be old:
Willows along a water,
And their green hair going gold.

Nan
McDonald

Wet Summer: Botanic Gardens

Under the low dark sky and the sodden leaves
Poor Summer bared her shoulder with coy grace,
Her marble flesh streaked with mortality,
Her sheaf of wheat lay mildewed on her arm,
Her eyes stared vacant from her tear-stained face
On paths empty at noon, on glooms beneath
Great fig-trees, where the drop of rotting fruit
Broke the warm, damp hush, on unbelievable green
Of wet grass still unfaded by the sun
In this strange season. Once we laughed to see
That foolish white thing named for the brazen queen
Whose sword we knew, the fierce and splendid one.

But tonight, alone with the steady sound of rain,
I do not smile, seeing her image there
On the haunted edge of sleep — the blackening marble,
The blind and weeping eyes, the ruined grain —
Seeing this season of the world's despair.

David
Martin

Bush Christmas

Stuffed with pudding to his gizzard
Uncle James lets out a snore,
Auntie Flo sprawls like a lizard
On the back verandah floor.

Grandpa Aub sits with a flagon
On the woodheap 'neath the gums,
And he thinks he's seen a dragon
Where the pigs are munching plums.

Cousin Val and Cousin Harry,
Cousin May and Cousin Fred,
Play the goat with Dulce and Larry
By the creek below the shed.

In the scrub the cows are drowsing,
Dogs are dreaming in the shade.
Fat and white, the mare is browsing,
Cropping softly, blade by blade.

It is hot. Mosquitoes whirring.
Uncle Jamie rubs his knee:
"Flo," he whispers, "are you stirring?
It's near time to get the tea."

The Other Map

When the native names are mentioned
With a throb in the old throat,
Seems to me it's time for striking
A more realistic note.
Gerringong is nice for rhyming,
Illalangi, Burradoo:
Having killed the rightful owner
Must you pinch his handle too?

All around the outer suburbs
Murdered tribes still act the host,
Werrigulla, Niavanda —
Septic sewers and a ghost.
Corryong and Birambiral,
Koorali and Dandaloo:
Does it matter none can tell me,
Which is which and who is who?

Up the street stands Mia-Mia,
Looking down on Warrawee.
Murambeen is round the corner . . .
God preserve the bourgeoisie!
Millimgimbi is my neighbour —
Might as well be Kangaroo.
Wannawong is up for auction:
Takes all sorts to make a zoo.

From the monstrous hills at sunset,
When the lonely bunyip stirs,
And the lamps are lit at Braebrook,
Hiawatha and The Firs,
Comes a whisper to Yarringa,
Terrigal and Coomaloo:
"Thanks for nothing. Men aren't judged by
What they say but what they do."

A Supplication in the Bush

The travelling parson took his seat.
The free selector and his wife
Drove off the flies, took fork and knife,
And silently cut up their meat.

The parson, looking at his plate,
A flickering smile athwart his face,
Asked if they ever said a Grace
Before they settled down and ate?

The bushman stroked his beard. "It's true,
We don't go much on prayer, though
If you would like to pray, you know
We should be very pleased, so do."

The parson smiled again. "I may.
But God would like it better still
If your own son, your eldest, Bill,
A benediction cared to say."

The old man nodded to his lad,
Who awkwardly got up and stood
Still like a figure carved in wood.

"For this here food we thank you, Dad.
You raised the cow, you built the pen,
You killed the calf and dressed the veal.
And Mum, we thank you for this meal
You cooked for us today. Amen."

A Girl Rode into Goulburn

A girl rode into Goulburn,
Her hair was like the sun,
The bell-bird chimed her singing,
The magpie mimed her fun.
What made her sick of singing
Before the tale was spun?

A girl went up the country,
Her hair as raven's breast,
In Bool Bool's snow-cool waters
Her song has found its rest.
The bush larks that are singing
Under Monaro's sun
Must keep her laughter ringing
As long as ten creeks run.

Kenneth
Mackenzie

My Friend...

My friend who lives with men
has fled to flowers and birds
to satisfy his restless questing pen
and slake its thirst for words.

I who live with trees
and birds and beasts and flowers
can safely turn to men without unease
to test my pencil's powers.

And of the two of us
I feel the more secure.
Man's life is drawing downwards to a close
but all else will endure.

Drought

I drink to the bitterness of drought,
the drying pool, the dying tree,
the barren flower that cannot fruit,
the sun's embracing anarchy.

Skeleton cattle stand like stone
in a stone landscape, where the shade
is whittled to a blackened bone
etching the fallow and the road.

Poor helpless life! The anarchist
has laid his hand upon my heart;
and yet beneath the gripping fist
the soil, the land cannot be hurt.

All that dies will be renewed.
The leaf will spring as green as god.
The draught that bitter drought has brewed
will sweeten suddenly to good,

and I shall laugh and I shall sing
and bend my back above the soil
in praise of that new burgeoning,
quenched and made fair again by toil.

Geoffrey
Dutton

The Island Day

No day ever began like this.
The sun our love, the sea our kiss,
The shells of night upon the beach
Are mysteries within our reach.
A blue wren on a broken tree,
Brighter than this clear sky could be,
Sings that silence must be broken,
That we must keep this day as token
Of all the days since we were lovers.

This island that our love discovers,
Blessed by sun and windless air,
Shall for one perfect day we share
Be lapped by seas of happiness,
Guarded by sands of idleness.
The hungry ocean shall be fed,
The gales, like us, lie soft in bed.
Fan-shells and cowries on the sand
Shall wait below your gentle hand,
The bottlebrush in flower shall burn
On every tree when you return.

If I were time's geographer
This island day I would confer
On you, and your gift would be mine.
Why can we not make one day fine?
Oh, we have no control at all
Of things that we find magical.
The morning's calm is blown by noon,
Clouds wrap the sun, the bird-song soon
Grates to the cruelty of the crow,
The flowers are stripped till the twigs show,
And the sea throws high upon the sand
Drops salt as tears that flow on land.

Winter Sunlight

To sleep like a cat in the sun
And leave my work undone
Curve like a duck on its nest
And let my brain have rest.

It is the gulf of doing
Parts us from being.

John
Thompson

Married Quarrel

Regard those luckier lives
That skid or plod upon surfaces, embrace
Fictions or nullities, are hardly aware
Of how the deep sweet root of joy goes rotten
Under the false fact or the act without
Philosophy — light lives that never allow
The moths of misunderstanding and estrangement,
The moths of hate and fear (born of the mind
Within the mind, the shadow within the shadow),
To clog their sense with anguish.

Me you have dimmed and hollowed and diminished.
Me you have shown the meaning of old age,
The greyness of defeat, and the once-too-often
Plunging from peak to pit. Now there is nothing
Of good favour or savour; mists that are grained
Like harbour water with the fat moon's rays
Hold no enchantment; breezes bring no message;
The huge and singing dawn is mean and dumb.
Yet, though I pray ''O let this grief dissolve
In some sublimer grief, or burn me dry
With idiot sunshine till I keep no sap
To feed the branch of sorrow, wash me with music,
Or with toil crush me'' — still in my bitter heart
My balm is this: You suffer too, thank God.

Now with our terrible words,
With silences tenfold more terrible,
With many words and with denial of words,
We each lay waste the other. Our wily hatred
Presses and hits and cuts at every nerve
Which love would always with a delicate knowledge
Please and assuage. That knowledge, grown malignant,
Rips at our inmost frailties. We have no screen
Against these private evils, precise hurts,
Most intimate betrayals, and no disguise
Nor means of refuge. We are still at one,
A double self-tormentor twined and twinned
In the one system, grafted each to each.

Ronald
McCuaig

The Steam Tram

FROM *SCENES FROM CHILDHOOD*

If a dream can start the steam tram where the beggar used to whine
At the corner near the hoardings about "P.C. Fortynine",
Spitting steam around its pistons, blowing smoke out of its stack,
As the fares blow smoke and spit from the compartment at the back,

I'll take the turn from Hunter Street through Wickham dredged from silt,
And Hamilton and Islington, and Tighe's Hill, shanty-built,
Where, round the bend a little way along the Maitland Road,
The grocery, the butchery, and the old sweet-shop stood.

It's a short walk from the tram-car, left verily in the lurch,
Up past the kindergarten, the tennis-court and church,
And against the farther hillside, with the river flats beyond,
I'll find a wooden cottage in its hard-worked bit of ground:

A lawn of which my father said it never seemed to stop;
It was time to start the bottom when he'd mown it to the top;
And a pepper-tree full of beetles, and a little silky dog
And, on a fence of sweet-peas, an emerald-green frog.

There'll be butterflies and chrysanthemums, and snowdrops near the hedge,
And petals of a huge white rose flaked on the grass's edge,
And violets in shadow, and sunflowers to burn:
My flowers make the single season that is gone beyond return.

Then it's only up a flight of steps, and knocking on the door:
Will the ghosts be disconcerted? Will my welcome still be sure?
They are so much dust and ashes; they can well survive the shock:
What have I to be afraid of? Go up, you fool, and knock.

Au Tombeau de Mon Père

FROM SCENES FROM CHILDHOOD

I went on Friday afternoons
Among the knives and forks and spoons
Where mounted grindstones flanked the floor
To my father's office door.

So serious a man was he,
The Buyer for the Cutlery. . . .
I found him sketching lamps from stock
In his big stock-records book,

And when he turned the page to me:
"Not bad for an old codger, eh?"
I though this frivolous in him,
Preferring what he said to them:

They wanted reparations paid
In German gold and not in trade,
But he rebuked such attitudes:
"You'll have to take it out in goods."

And what they did in time was just,
He said, what he had said they must:
If Time had any end in sight
It was, to prove my father right.

The evening came, and changed him coats,
Produced a rag and rubbed his boots,
And then a mirror and a brush
And smoothed his beard and his moustache;

A sign for blinds outside to fall
On shelves and showcases, and all
Their hammers, chisels, planes and spades,
And pocket-knives with seven blades.

Then, in the lift, the patted back:
"He's growing like you, Mr Mac!"
(The hearty voices thus implied
A reason for our mutual pride.)

And so the front-door roundabout
Gathered us in and swept us out
To sausage, tea in separate pots,
And jellies crowned with creamy clots.

And once he took me on to a
Recital, to hear Seidel play,
And Hutchens spanked the piano-bass,
Never looking where it was.

When I got home I practised this,
But somehow always seemed to miss,
And my cigar-box violin,
After Seidel's, sounded thin.

And once he took me to a bill
Of sporadic vaudeville.
A man and woman held the stage;
She sneered in simulated rage,

And when he made a shrewd reply
He'd lift his oval shirt-front high
And slap his bare and hairy chest
To celebrate his raucous jest.

Then, as the shout of joy ensued,
Uniting mime and multitude,
And mine rang out an octave higher,
A boy-soprano's in that choir,

My father's smile was half unease,
Half pleasure in his power to please:
"Try not to laugh so loudly, Ron;
Those women think you're catching on."

But far more often it was to
The School of Arts we used to go;
Up the dusty stairway's gloom,
Through the musty reading-room

And out to a veranda-seat
Overlooking Hunter Street.
There in the dark my father sat,
Pipe in mouth, to meditate.

A cake-shop glowed across the way
With a rainbow-cake display;
I never saw its keeper there,
And never saw a customer,

And yet there was activity
High in the south-western sky:
A bottle flashing on a sign
Advertising someone's wine.

So, as my father thought and thought
(Considering lines of saws he'd bought,
Or, silence both his church and club,
Feeling close to Nature's hub,

Or maybe merely practising
Never saying anything,
Since he could go, when deeply stirred,
Months, at home, without a word,

Or pondering the indignity
Of having to put up with me),
I contemplated, half awake,
The flashing wine, the glowing cake:

The wine that no one can decant,
And the cake we didn't want:
As Mr Blake's Redeemer said,
"This the wine, and this the bread."

Eve
Langley

Australia

The brown round of the continent tonight
Rises up, shoulder on shoulder, searching for the sun;
And all the white French rains that once took flight
Into the earth, rise slowly, one by one,
Remembering Villon who left a rag on every tree.
Perhaps he walked Australia long ago,
Mourning for all those women white and sad as snow.
Verlaine perhaps enchanted by our seas
Cried in his lyric voice that purple hours
Lay waxen-mitred in our purple flowers . . .
The wildflowers of Australia; a thin brown
Veil of lost Autumn is somehow caught around
Their stalks unspeaking, as though Springtime at the core
Was a small child lost in the bush for ever more.

Judah
Waten

Neighbours

OUR NEXT-DOOR neighbours arrived in the morning. It was still cold, for the sun had not yet risen over the roofs.

The street re-echoed with the stamping of horses' hooves and the voices of neighbours who had just come out from breakfast. Our street was a narrow, cobbled one — a cul-de-sac of nondescript houses with tiny verandas and wooden fences right on the footpath.

The new-comers' wagon was piled higgledy-piggledy with stretchers, chairs, wooden boxes, pots and pans. There were ten in the family.

The older ones helped their father to carry the furniture into the house while their mother saw to the younger ones. She ushered them to the veranda and fed them with biscuits and apples.

We children clustered round the wagon, getting under the feet of the workers and gingerly patting the stamping, steaming horses. We chattered and laughed and furtively peered into the dark, musty recesses of the open door of the empty house. It was like all the others in the street and had a low, slanting, galvanized-iron roof, a rusty, crooked chimney, and blistered, brown wooden walls.

As the commotion grew one of the boys who had been helping his father abruptly left his work. With his hands on his hips, he said challengingly to the boys around, "I'll race you to end of the street."

We stared at him with curious eyes. He was about eleven years of age and came somewhere in the middle of the family. His straight black hair and his narrow slits of eyes immediately earned him the name of "Chinaman". He was short and slender, but he gazed at us as boldly as a lion. Like his brothers and sisters he was poorly dressed in some blue, cheap stuff and his sandshoes were grimy and threadbare.

"Tell us your name and we'll race you," said Joseph, eyeing the new-comer with a sceptical look. Joseph was the tallest and strongest boy in our group and our acknowledged leader.

"Benny Smutkevitch," came the instant reply.

We lined up in the middle of the road, completely absorbed in our new interest. Forgotten were the horses, the wagon, and Benny's family. And the adults standing behind the fences and in the street scarcely gave us a glance, so accustomed were they to our noisy play.

Benny made us look very foolish. He shot off the mark and flew to the end of the street, leaving the rest of us behind running clumsily like broken-winded old horses.

"Give in?" he said cheekily, fixing a triumphant gaze on us.

"No, I won't give in," said Joseph, still panting from his strenuous efforts to catch Benny.

"You won't?" said Benny. "Well, I'll race you back hopping."

"Hoppo bumpo first," said Joseph with a sly look. Confident of his strength, he was anxious to beat Benny in a bumping contest on one leg.

"Make a ring," shouted several voices.

Benny and Joseph hopped towards each other with a business-like air. Arms folded, each endeavoured to bump the other to the ground. Excitedly we closed in on the combatants. Despite our dwindling confidence in Joseph we shouted words of encouragement to him. He looked much the stronger of the two.

Benny hopped with an incredibly long step like a kangaroo and all Joseph's efforts to reach him were in vain. He soon tired of missing Benny and he stopped in the centre of the ring, biting his lips with vexation.

One boy shouted to him, "Don't rush! Take your time."

"Your legs are made of wood and your bottom is too large," another voice said in disgust.

Joseph turned to his detractor with a threatening air and in that moment he was bumped off his feet by Benny, who came at him with great speed.

"Foul!" shouted several boys.

Our leader sprawled on the cobbled ground. We made one more attempt to best Benny before admitting his superiority. The same boys who had shouted, "Foul!" now cried, "All together, at him!"

The howl of voices brought Benny's elder brothers to the scene. They stood on the edge of the compressed ring, frowning bad-temperedly. But Benny was in no need of their assistance, for he was scattering us to the ground like a chaff-cutter. With deadly purpose he had increased his tempo, and shouting insults he leapt first at one and then at another.

At the height of the mêlée a little girl more curious than the others strayed into the moving, swaying ring. She was promptly knocked over and lay on the ground whimpering and sobbing. Her mother, who had been watching us from a distance, came running distractedly towards us.

"Stop this hooliganism!" Mrs Katz shrieked. "You young hooligans! You will bring eternal shame on your parents!" she went on as she stooped to help her daughter to her feet. She cast angry looks at us, staring fixedly at one and then another as if attempting to discover who had knocked her daughter over.

Her shrill agitated voice brought the encounter to an end; only Benny was still dancing round, his black, glossy hair tossed over his forehead, his fists clenched in readiness.

"Who did it?" she inquired of her daughter loudly. We shuffled backwards, trying to efface ourselves. None of us was eager to brave Mrs Katz.

She was a short, big-bosomed woman with a fat and rosy face. Her life seemed to consist of keeping an eternal eye on her only child. She had already quarrelled with all the other women in the street over the misdemeanours of their boys and girls and she was for ever upbraiding us.

"It was him," the little girl tearfully pointed to Benny.

Mrs Katz turned angrily to face Benny.

"Look," she said in her shrill voice, indicating with her hand a bruise on the girl's leg and dust marks on her white dress. "Look what you have done to her."

I sighed with relief, and so did the other boys, that Benny was blamed and not us. Benny reluctantly moved towards the wagon, pushed forward by Mrs Katz.

Her shouts had meanwhile drawn the attention of some of the other women who began to call their children inside. As if to pour salt into his wound, Joseph's mother cried to him, "Come inside at once!"

Thoroughly shamefaced, his eyes averted from us, our former leader ran quickly at his mother's call. Cruel voices shouted after him, "Sissy! Cry-baby!"

From then on we deserted Joseph and our new allegiance was to Benny. We watched him admiringly from afar. His short, lithe body stood beside his father at the back of the wagon in front of the low wooden house. He seemed full of a reckless vitality.

"You should control your boy," Mrs Katz waved an aggressive finger. "He's not a boy, he's a wild animal. That's what he is, a wild animal," she stammered on a grating top note into Mr Smutkevitch's face.

His short-sighted, red-rimmed grey eyes darted round piercingly from Mrs Katz and her daughter to Benny.

Mr Smutkevitch was a middle-sized, thick-set man with red hair. His huge red beard covered all his face except the eyes and nose, and it was stained with black snuff marks round his hairy nostrils. There was only a tight slit to mark his mouth.

He swayed impatiently on his slightly bowed legs as Mrs Katz continued her recital. All the time his face was swelling with anger like a turkey-cock. At last he raised a gnarled, freckled hand.

"Enough," he said gruffly.

Without making another sound he suddenly turned to Benny and struck him quickly and dexterously once, twice, on both cheeks. Then, casting an unfriendly glance at Mrs Katz, he climbed back on the wagon, beckoned to his two elder sons, and began handing down pieces of furniture. Not a word did he speak.

All this happened so quickly that Mrs Katz remained standing open-mouthed, her brows knitted in perplexity. This was not what she had expected and it seemed to me that she was assailed by a sudden pity for Benny.

"Mr Smutkevitch," she began, looking up at the unresponsive face. "Mr Smutkevitch —" and then she stopped and cleared her throat.

Meantime, Benny's mother, who had witnessed the scene from the veranda, shuffled with a sideways gait into the street and looked round at the strange faces. With motherly concern she made for Benny. She whispered to him as she stroked his head.

Mrs Smutkevitch was like her boy; the same long slits of black eyes, thick spreading line of brows and olive skin. Her smoothly combed, gleaming black hair, gathered in a heavy knot at the back, showed her anxious, unhappy face.

"What have you got against my child?" she asked, suddenly turning to Mrs Katz. "Why did you have to interfere with the children?" she went on in a flat, whimpering voice.

"Don't get upset," said Mrs Katz. "Let's talk it over reasonably."

"Grown-ups should keep out of children's affairs. You interfered cruelly," Mrs Smutkevitch said, looking down at the ground.

"Please listen to me for a moment," Mrs Katz began. But Mrs Smutkevitch interrupted her, not permitting her to finish a sentence.

Then Mr Smutkevitch, standing on the tailboard of the wagon and without glancing at the two women, shouted as if into the air, "Stop that old wives' quarrel!"

His gruff, impatient voice resounded down the street. There was silence. Fixing his short-sighted stare on his wife, he shouted again, "Take the boy inside! I don't want to hear another word."

The new family was on the lips of everybody in the street. My mother thought very badly of Mr Smutkevitch. The way he had spoken to his wife was insufferable! Why, he had shouted at her like a sergeant-major! Others said they could see that Benny was no precious toy. They would have to watch him with cats' eyes.

We boys, however, regarded Benny as our new leader and hero. Each of us separately sought his special favour. We gave him marbles, picture-books, penny dreadfuls, Buffalo Bills, cigarette-cards, pocket-knives, and other odds and ends. He quickly understood that we were like putty in his hands and preferred none of us as his best friend. So he soon acquired a prodigious fortune out of our generosity, though his father never gave him any pocket-money and never bought him presents. But Benny soon tired of these petty dealings. He was full of plans for adventures in which we figured as his followers.

Thus began a new chapter in our lives.

Unbeknown to our parents we sneaked away from the street one summer day. My mother had always forbidden me to go beyond the street, but what could I do when Benny asked me to go with him and the others in a jaunt to the river that flowed through the city? His confident face, his narrow slits of mocking eyes, and his careless hands on hips shamed me into violating Mother's orders.

Another time Benny took us to a circus and we stood outside the tent and listened to the bandsmen in blue and gold uniforms play "Pack up Your Troubles" and "It's a Long Way to Tipperary". We caught a glimpse of the elephants and the monkeys, and Benny, who had read tales of hunters and explorers, airily told us that one day he would leave for a place far away to hunt animals as remarkable as the bunyip. We believed him and marvelled at his nonchalant courage.

Then another time, not far from our street we met a group of boys playing in a vacant paddock. Benny sat down on the uncut grass and we slavishly followed suit. Insolently he began to jeer and laugh at the playing boys. They stopped their game and stared at us. Then they cried, "Ikey Mo!" and wagged their outstretched palms under their chins. Before we could rise to our feet they began to throw clods of earth and stones at us. Benny was ready for them. Using a kerosene tin as a shield he shied empty jam tins at our enemies. He was playing at war but his army was badly trained and quite unused to such earnest encounters. We turned tail and ran and our backs bore the marks of our defeat.

Our secret life was not known to our parents, but on this occasion the tell-tale marks of dust and grime on my clothes had given me away. My disreputable appearance loomed tragically in Mother's eyes and she spoke scathingly of this new land where children defied their parents and roamed the streets like wild dogs.

But my mother, like the other women in the street, found excuses for her own child. It was all Benny's doing. Benny was to blame for everything. And so the women began to think that perhaps they should approach Mr Smutkevitch and appeal to him to restrain his son for the good of the street. Although Mr Smutkevitch rarely spoke to anyone and his gruff, frightening manner had not been forgotten, the women began to think better of him, and even Mother said that perhaps he was deserving of some sympathy on account of his wayward and vagrant son.

Two women were deputed to talk to Mr Smutkevitch and they waited for him at the gate of his house. As soon as the wagon approached Mr Smutkevitch pulled tightly on the reins, stood up in the driver's seat, and shouted above the heads of the women to his little girls playing on the veranda, "Tell your mother to have my tea on the table! I'm in a hurry."

Without turning his eyes in the direction of the women or bidding them a good

215

day, he jumped off the wagon with sure-footed agility and ran into the house. The two women shuffled their feet and coughed and said nothing. They became ashamed of their previous good words about Mr Smutkevitch and hurried back to their homes, loudly cursing the family that had brought such unpleasantness to the street. Too proud to discuss things with women, they said, "A plague on him and that boy of his! Like father, like son!"

We were forbidden to play with Benny or to call at his home. I ignored Mother's orders and one morning just before breakfast I peered through the kitchen door of the Smutkevitch house. I hoped to see Benny and to arrange to walk to school with him.

I was met by the sight of father and sons, their hats on their heads, standing facing the eastern wall of the room, reciting morning prayers. Mr Smutkevitch and the two older boys wore phylacteries and read from their prayer books, but Benny and the younger ones were not yet old enough to wear the tiny sacred leather cases containing the holy parchment. They mumbled the words, their eyes moving idly towards the door.

Mr Smutkevitch's phylacteries were carefully adjusted to his head and arm and the thong was neatly tied on the arm, palm, and finger. He prayed slowly, enunciating each holy word in a rapture of loving tenderness. His stern face was wrinkled by a secretive smile, something between him and God.

But the phylacteries seemed a burden on the two older boys. They continually fingered the leather-covered cases and gabbled the prayers with sullen expressions on their faces. With sleepy eyes they shot malevolent glances at Benny, and I guessed they were filled with envy of him, who would soon run freely into the street while they would have to go to their daily work, the elder to help his father on the bottle-cart, the other to a tailor's shop.

As soon as the prayers were over Mr Smutkevitch lovingly bound up his phylacteries and replaced them in their embroidered velvet bag. His face again became angry and stern and I sidled out into the yard.

Suddenly Mr Smutkevitch's voice filled the small kitchen and I listened intently.

"You heretic!" I heard him shout at Benny. "Your father's ways don't suit you? Ah? You think your ways are better? If I ever catch you staying away from the scripture lessons I will break every bone in your body!"

Then Mrs Smutkevitch's flat, pleading voice floated out to me.

"I will see he goes to his lessons. Benny will be a good boy, won't you, Benny? You will do what your father tells you?"

But the next sabbath Benny sidled out of the synagogue under the very nose of his father. I saw Mr Smutkevitch's face darken and his body swayed more vigorously as if seeking solace in his prayers. Without taking his eyes from the prayer book in front of him, he laid one hand gently on his eldest son's arm to deter him from following Benny into the street. It was as if he had decided that for the moment it was better to let one carry the sins of the family.

We knew that Benny had hurried out to meet his new friend, Martin Gallagher, and his departure threw us into a state of agitated curiosity so that we were deaf to the ardent praying round us. A bolder one amongst us stole towards the door. Then we all rose from our pews and guiltily tiptoed right out of the darkened, murmuring synagogue into the sunlit street outside.

On the next corner Martin and Benny were whispering together in some strange gibberish. They had manufactured their own language, and we offered them new marbles and tops to disclose the secrets of the fascinating code to us, but without any success. They regarded themselves as something apart from us.

Martin and Benny were a strange contrast; Martin was as fair as Benny was dark and he was at least a head taller. He was dressed in a thin, butcher-blue suit and he was barefooted. His great boast was that he could walk on broken glass without cutting his feet. They were leathery and always caked with brown dust. Martin came from a mysterious world. His father was at the war and he never mentioned his mother or sisters or brothers, if indeed he had any.

"Coming with us?" Martin said with a mischievous wink at Benny. They looked at each other knowingly.

We were flattered by the invitation, for Martin as a rule never spoke to us without screwing up his face and jabbering in his own mysterious language.

"Cross your hearts," he commanded us.

And we had to swear not to tell our parents.

I crossed my heart fearfully, with one reluctant finger, feeling all the world like a traitor and an apostate and imagining that the beadle was standing on the steps of the synagogue and watching my heretical motions.

Martin and Benny led us through streets and lanes to a park crowded with men and women. They were standing round a man in a brown cloth cap who spoke from a pulpit-like wooden platform in the shade of an elm-tree. His face red with exertion, he said in a loud voice that the war was for the master class. His words roused shouts of disapproval and there was a movement of people towards the speaker. The excitement infected every one of us and our hesitation and fears left us.

Following Martin and Benny we wove through the crowd, stepping on feet and being jostled and pushed in the back. As we came closer to the platform the speaker's words resounded in our ears. He was denouncing the conscription of men for the army, and this was something that had begun to stir our street.

Angry voices again rose from the crowd and several men in uniform pushed their way towards the platform. Other men formed a ring round the speaker and blows were struck as the soldiers tried to push the platform over.

Suddenly a woman screamed. The wooden platform lay on the ground and the crowd behind merged with the milling soldiers and men gathered round the hapless speaker. A squad of policemen appeared from nowhere and mingled with the crowd. Wildly excited, we boys ran to the outskirts of the moving, swaying mass of people and shouted words that had no meaning.

Very soon the police drew their batons and the dull, empty thud of wood on flesh resounded sickeningly. We stopped in our wild caperings and gazed open-mouthed.

Barely able to restrain a sob of fear when a policeman with baton in hand brushed past me, I fled from the park. Some of my companions soon caught up with me. We glanced back for a moment and behind the trees at the end of the park rose the tall buildings of the city. We could hear the sharp clatter of the cable trams and we walked on in bleak silence, towards our homes. Neither Martin nor Benny was with us.

The news of our behaviour in the synagogue reached home before we did. Mr Applebaum, the beadle, had shuffled along from house to house apologetically blowing his nose as he complained of us. And Mrs Katz stood in front of the gate of her home and shook her head at us as we hurried past and shouted, "You young scoundrels! You will drive your mothers to their graves!"

Mother was not at all surprised at Mr Applebaum's information. She had a premonition, she said, that her son would become like Martin if we stayed in this country. In a few years' time Benny and her own son would be strangers to their parents.

Father made light of the whole affair and tried to placate Mother.

"Don't take it so much to heart," he said. "There are many attractions outside a synagogue for a boy of his age. Why, even I ran away myself when I was a boy."

And then he plunged into a story of his childhood, boastfully relating how he had tormented his old Rabbi in his town in Russia. I laughed more than was necessary and he suddenly broke off his story and fixed me with an angry glare. My laugh had unexpectedly offended him and he went pale in the face.

"I'll give you something you'll never forget if you cause your mother any more anguish," he said. "Now, pick up your Hebrew book and go into your room and don't let me hear a whisper out of you. Now go." His voice brooked no contradiction. You can't rely on Father, I thought, as I hurried out of the room.

I was not the only boy who was punished. Others suffered more severely, and Benny was thrashed by his father and then locked up in the shed with the horses and bottles.

Mr Smutkevitch was still in a savage temper at Mr Frumkin's bottle-yard the following Friday. He was arguing heatedly with Mr Frumkin as we drove into the yard.

It was just past noon. The sky overhead was blue and bright and there was a pleasant late spring heat in the air. There were many men in the big yard and they were moving about with great determination. They carried sacks into open sheds and stacked bottles into crates.

Suddenly they looked up from their work and turned towards the two quarrelling men. Father jumped off the cart, leaving me holding the reins, and moved with the others over to Mr Smutkevitch and Mr Frumkin.

Mr Frumkin had grown stouter. He still wore the same dust-covered trousers but the top buttons were undone and his open waistcoat was held together by a massive gold chain. From under his new black borsalino hat he squinted sideways at Mr Smutkevitch, who was angrily demanding a better price for a neat stack of glossy new chaff-bags lying at his feet.

"I won't give you that price," said Mr Frumkin, jingling a pocket full of coins with his thick, sausage-like fingers.

"How am I to feed my family?" asked Mr Smutkevitch with a momentary expression of despair on his red-bearded face. "I work like a horse but I'm not fed like one," he added bitterly.

He spoke so feelingly that Mr Frumkin smiled secretly to himself as though pleased and flattered that the unbending and taciturn Mr Smutkevitch was thus forced to appeal to him.

"Well, I'll lend you some money," said Mr Frumkin expansively. "I won't see you starve."

Mr Smutkevitch's short, stout neck went red with anger and for a moment I was afraid he would have a fit. Clenching his fists, the muscles of his cheeks quivering, he spoke with great difficulty as if suppressing a torrent of frightful words.

"You grind us into the earth and then you offer to buy us a coffin."

"Are you doing me a favour by turning my offer down?" Mr Frumkin turned to the others with a humorous gesture of the hands. "If you are so independent," he continued slowly, "you can work the whole of Friday and even Saturday. I keep my yard open for those who are not Rabbis."

"How dare you talk to me like that, you apostate!" Mr Smutkevitch cried to Mr Frumkin in a hoarse, panting voice. "You wicked apostate!"

With quick, impulsive movements Mr Smutkevitch tossed the bags on his wagon and as he placed one foot on the step he glanced back at Mr Frumkin. Turning his head from side to side he made as if to spit on the ground and then, swinging the reins over his horses' heads, he drove out of the yard.

I saw Mr Smutkevitch again near the door of the synagogue on the sabbath. I was surprised to see him outside, for the service was not yet finished. He was talking to Mr Applebaum. The beadle had one leg inside the synagogue and one outside and he was chewing at his nails, as was his habit, and looking at the ground. Mr Applebaum was tall and lean and he had a pale, melancholy face. He now seemed more melancholy than ever.

With an impatient shrug of his shoulders Mr Smutkevitch abruptly turned his back on the beadle and advanced towards me.

"Have you seen my Ben?" He stared at me with a mournful, vexed expression in his short-sighted, red-rimmed eyes.

I made no reply, merely shaking my head nervously.

"I will find him," he said, scowling at me.

Instead of going on into the synagogue I followed Mr Smutkevitch. He stopped a passing boy, who was carrying in his hand a velvet bag containing a prayer book and shawl, and appeared to be making inquiries.

I knew where Benny was to be found. He had gone to a church hall in the street behind the synagogue. There was to be a fair in the afternoon and Martin had asked us all to go with him and watch the preparations.

Even now, when I was resolved to warn Benny that his father was looking for him, I hesitated to go near a church. It was a warm, windy December morning and a fine grit assailed my face and hands as I walked with a heavy heart towards the hall. Pieces of paper flew past me. Behind me the swiftly-moving white clouds seemed peppered with a grey dust.

I stopped outside the wooden hall. Benny and Martin and several other boys were standing in the doorway. From within came the sound of merry voices and the noise of feet sliding on the polished floor.

I looked up at the plain wooden cross above the door. My heart fluttered with terror as I sidled closer to Benny. I whispered to him about his father and pleaded with him to hasten away with me. Although I knew that stalls and lucky-dip bins were being placed in position for the afternoon fair, I was terrified of looking inside. I trembled at the thought of standing under the cross on the sabbath.

Benny seemed no more comfortable than I was, but he was unable to make up his mind to leave. In the meantime the other boys had walked into the hall, leaving him and me standing at the door.

Minutes seemed to pass. I stared at the street and in the distance I could already see Mr Smutkevitch walking towards us. He peered intently. Then he caught sight of Benny. Their eyes met and Mr Smutkevitch stopped at a distance, but neither spoke.

At that moment Martin and several other boys came out of the hall, excitedly calling to us, "Come in."

They stopped and their gaze followed ours.

Mr Smutkevitch beckoned Benny with one broad, heavy finger. Suddenly Martin and his friends began to mimic Mr Smutkevitch with their fingers. They shouted at him in their strange gibberish. He looked bewildered and grinned foolishly, his red beard parting for a moment.

Out of the corner of my eye I saw Benny wince. He tried to efface himself behind the backs of the boys. His eyes darted nervously to and fro in their narrow slits. His face quivered and beads of sweat came out on his forehead.

The boys quickly tired of their mimicry and ran shouting back into the hall, leaving Benny and me to face Mr Smutkevitch.

There was a stubborn, angry look on Mr Smutkevitch's face as he cast a last glance at us. He turned away slowly, his shoulders momentarily hunched as if he had suddenly become an old man.

As his broad back and bowed legs became smaller in the distance Benny ran into the street as if to follow his father. Then he stopped. There was a look of anxiety in his dark, nimble eyes and we did not speak to one another as we walked on, but neither of us knew that there could be no reconciliation with the ways of our fathers.

A. D.
Hope

Australia

A nation of trees, drab green and desolate grey
In the field uniform of modern wars,
Darkens her hills, those endless, outstretched paws
Of Sphinx demolished or stone lion worn away.

They call her a young country, but they lie:
She is the last of lands, the emptiest,
A woman beyond her change of life, a breast
Still tender but within the womb is dry;

Without songs, architecture, history:
The emotions and superstitions of younger lands.
Her rivers of water drown among inland sands,
The river of her immense stupidity

Floods her monotonous tribes from Cairns to Perth.
In them at last the ultimate men arrive
Whose boast is not ''we live'' but ''we survive'',
A type who will inhabit the dying earth.

And her five cities, like five teeming sores,
Each drains her, a vast parasite robber-state
Where second-hand Europeans pullulate
Timidly on the edge of alien shores.

Yet there are some like me turn gladly home
From the lush jungle of modern thought, to find
The Arabian desert of the human mind,
Hoping, if still from the deserts the prophets come,

Such savage and scarlet as no green hills dare
Springs in that waste, some spirit which escapes
The learned doubt, the chatter of cultured apes
Which is called civilization over there.

The Brides

Down the assembly line they roll and pass
Complete at last, a miracle of design;
Their chromium fenders, the unbreakable glass,
The fashionable curve, the air-flow line.

Grease to the elbows Mum and Dad enthuse,
Pocket their spanners and survey the bride;
Murmur: "A sweet job! All she needs is juice!
Built for a life-time — sleek as a fish. Inside

"He will find every comfort: the full set
Of gadgets; knobs that answer to the touch
For light or music; a place for his cigarette;
Room for his knees; a honey of a clutch."

Now slowly through the show-room's flattering glare
See her wheeled in to love, console, obey,
Shining and silent! Parson with a prayer
Blesses the number-plate, she rolls away

To write her numerals in his book of life;
And now, at last, stands on the open road,
Triumphant, perfect, every inch a wife,
While the corks pop, the flash-light bulbs explode.

Her heavenly bowser-boy assumes his seat;
She prints the soft dust with her brand-new treads,
Swings towards the future, purring with a sweet
Concatenation of the poppet heads.

Beyond Khancoban

Beyond Khancoban the road winds into hills
That lead to the High Monaro of my birth.
I emerge from a pass to a vast blue valley which fills
My mind with those august presences of earth,

Austere in their stillness, great mountains that watch and abide,
Where trees stand tier above tier in the tranquil air,
Crown that great theatre, pack it from side to side,
Feasted with music of which I am not aware.

A sky full of light pours down its viewless rain
On a landscape lost in its thoughts, as I in mine.
Places and names that echo and remain,
Khancoban, Kosciusko, Tom Groggin, Jindabyne,

Signal my way as I drive through the afternoon,
A silent pilgrim fulfilling an ancient vow.
The road winds, rises and veers like a difficult tune
Known always, but mastered for the first time now;

For the heart of this utter solitude has been tapped;
As I move on, the brooding landscape comes alive.
Now I catch the music that holds this audience rapt:
I am turning its world into music as I drive.

The car winding on becomes a centre of this
Perpetual wheeling of trees in their solemn dance,
Just as earth seems at night to spin the galaxies,
All illusory motion to our illusory stance,

Yet not a total illusion when all is said:
Though it does not happen out there, but in the mind,
The music itself is real; we are not misled,
But have glimpsed a mysterious function of mankind.

We have sampled a fragment of that mystery
By which the inanimate wakes to life and thought
And the universe shakes itself free from entropy
In whose dull net all frames of matter seem caught.

In our minds is it able to enter the dance;
Moved by our music things learn themselves and rejoice.
I would count it worth while to spend life for this single glance,
To have made them conscious in me, to have lent them my voice.

Now the blue-gums crowd in close to a tunnel of shade;
The car labours up to the pass. I think of the spot
To which I return, from which long ago I was made,
Cooma, and wonder whether it made me or not.

Man is made by all that has made the history of man,
But here the Monaro claims me; I recognise
Beyond Khancoban the place where a mind began
Able to offer itself to the galaxies.

Patch and Mend

Patch and mend, patch and mend;
Borrow and scrape or lavish and spend
As much good fortune as God may send:
Naught shall avail you;
All things shall fail you;
Nothing shall profit you in the end.

Meditation on a Bone

*A piece of bone, found at Trondhjem in 1901, with the following runic inscription
(about A.D. 1050) cut on it:*
I loved her as a maiden; I will not trouble Erlend's detestable wife; better
she should be a widow.

Words scored upon a bone,
Scratched in despair or rage —
Nine hundred years have gone;
Now, in another age,
They burn with passion on
A scholar's tranquil page.

The scholar takes his pen
And turns the bone about,
And writes those words again.
Once more they seethe and shout,
And through a human brain
Undying hate rings out.

"I loved her when a maid;
I loathe and love the wife
That warms another's bed:
Let him beware his life!"
The scholar's hand is stayed;
His pen becomes a knife

To grave in living bone
The fierce archaic cry.
He sits and reads his own
Dull sum of misery.
A thousand years have flown
Before that ink is dry.

And, in a foreign tongue,
A man, who is not he,
Reads and his heart is wrung
This ancient grief to see,
And thinks: When I am dung,
What bone shall speak for me?

The Walker

Who walks round my house all night?
None but lanky Tom.
　　　　　An Old Children's Game

Who walks round my house all night,
Stepping sad and slow,
Ghost or woman, child or sprite?
None that I do know.

Who is she that haunts the dark
When the moon is down,
Street or garden, pale or park,
Through the sleeping town?

When the frost falls thick and chill
And the stars slide by,
In my bed I hear it still,
Hear her walk and sigh.

Sultry midnights when I wake
In the clutch of fear,
Though my bones with fever shake,
Nothing do I hear;

Nothing, nothing can I spy
Through the darkened pane;
Yet, when on my bed I lie,
Come those steps again;

Comes the sound of mortal grief
And the tread of woe —
Is it woman, spirit, thief,
Pacing to and fro?

"Lover, keep your careless bed,
Turn you to the wall.
Not the living, not the dead
Answers here your call;

"But a witness from the void,
Banned with drug and knife,
Whom your coward heart destroyed
In the gates of life."

227

Agony Column

Sir George and Lady Cepheus of Upper Slaughter
Desire to announce to family and friends
That the death has been arranged of their only daughter
Andromeda, aged twenty — Sir George intends

To avoid undesirable pomp and ostentation:
A simple ceremony, a quiet funeral feast
And the usual speeches; a train will leave the station
For the Virgin's Rock at four. No flowers by request!

Owing to the informal nature of the occasion
Guests are requested to wear ordinary dress.
It is hoped that, in view of Sir George's official station
The event will be treated discreetly by the press.

In accord with religious custom and public duty,
The populace is expected to maintain order and quiet;
But, because of her daughter's quite exceptional beauty
And numerous suitors, to discourage scandal or riot,

Lady Cepheus wishes it to be distinctly stated
That any attempt at rescue has been banned;
Offenders will be summarily emasculated;
Heroes are warned: the police have the matter in hand.

As the victim is to be chained wearing only her skin,
The volunteer armorers will be blinded at once.
On the following morning her lovers and next-of-kin
May assist in gathering any remaining bones.

Ode on the Death of Pius the Twelfth

To every season its proper act of joy,
To every age its natural mode of grace,
Each vision its hour, each talent we employ
    Its destined time and place.

I was at Amherst when this great pope died;
The northern year was wearing towards the cold;
The ancient trees were in their autumn pride
    Of russet, flame and gold.

Amherst in Massachusetts in the Fall:
I ranged the college campus to admire
Maple and beech, poplar and ash in all
    Their panoply of fire.

Something that since a child I longed to see,
This miracle of the other hemisphere:
Whole forests in their annual ecstasy
    Waked by the dying year.

Not budding Spring, not Summer's green parade
Clothed in such glory these resplendent trees;
The lilies of the field were not arrayed
    In riches such as these.

Nature evolves their colours as a call,
A lure which serves to fertilize the seed;
How strange then that the splendour of the Fall
    Should serve no natural need

And, having no end in nature, yet can yield
Such exquisite natural pleasure to the eye!
Who could have guessed in summer's green concealed
    The leaf's resolve to die?

Yet from the first spring shoots through all the year,
Masked in the chlorophyll's intenser green,
The feast of crimson was already there,
    These yellows blazed unseen.

Now in the bright October sun the clear
Translucent colours trembled overhead
And as I walked, a voice I chanced to hear
    Announced: The Pope is dead!

A human voice, yet there the place became
Bethel: each bough with pentecost was crowned;
The great trunks rapt in unconsuming flame
    Stood as on holy ground.

I thought of this old man whose life was past,
Who in himself and his great office stood
Against the secular tempest as a vast
    Oak spans the underwood;

Who in the age of Armageddon found
A voice that caused all men to hear it plain,
The blood of Abel crying from the ground
    To stay the hand of Cain;

Who found from that great task small time to spare:
— For him and for mankind the hour was late —
So much to snatch, to save, so much to bear
    That Mary's part must wait,

Until in his last years the change began:
A strange illumination of the heart,
Voices and visions such as mark the man
    Chosen and set apart.

His death, they said, was slow, grotesque and hard,
Yet in that gross decay, until the end
Untroubled in his joy, he saw the Word
    Made spirit and ascend.

Those glorious woods and that triumphant death
Prompted me there to join their mysteries:
This Brother Albert, this great oak of faith,
    Those fire-enchanted trees.

Seven years have passed, and still, at times, I ask
Whether in man, as in those plants, may be
A splendour, which his human virtues mask,
    Not given to us to see?

If to some lives at least there comes a stage
When, all the active man now left behind,
They enter on the treasure of old age,
    This autumn of the mind.

Then, while the heart stands still, beyond desire
The dying animal knows a strange serene:
Emerging in its ecstasy of fire
    The burning soul is seen.

Who sees it? Since old age appears to men
Senility, decrepitude, disease,
What Spirit walks among us, past our ken,
    As we among these trees,

Whose unknown nature, blessed with keener sense
Catches its breath in wonder at the sight
And feels its being flood with that immense
    Epiphany of light?

A Windy Afternoon

Two beards laughing
Slashed by teeth;
Four legs walking
Underneath;
A great gale blowing;
Trees awhirl;
Skirts fly, showing
Essential girl;

Leaves and laughter
And legs hurl past
And I stride faster
Against the blast.
Where am I going?
What shall I care,
Buoyed by the blowing,
Living air?

Moschus Moschiferus

A Song for St Cecilia's Day

In the high jungle where Assam meets Tibet
The small Kastura, most archaic of deer,
Were driven in herds to cram the hunters' net
And slaughtered for the musk-pods which they bear;

But in those thickets of rhododendron and birch
The tiny creatures now grow hard to find.
Fewer and fewer survive each year. The search
Employs new means, more exquisite and refined:

The hunters now set out by two or three;
Each carries a bow and one a slender flute.
Deep in the forest the archers choose a tree
And climb; the piper squats against the root.

And there they wait until all trace of man
And rumour of his passage dies away.
They melt into the leaves and, while they scan
The glade below, their comrade starts to play.

Through those vast listening woods a tremulous skein
Of melody wavers, delicate and shrill:
Now dancing and now pensive, now a rain
Of pure, bright drops of sound and now the still,

Sad wailing of lament; from tune to tune
It winds and modulates without a pause;
The hunters hold their breath; the trance of noon
Grows tense; with its full power the music draws

A shadow from a juniper's darker shade;
Bright-eyed, with quivering muzzle and pricked ear,
The little musk-deer slips into the glade
Led by an ecstasy that conquers fear.

A wild enchantment lures him, step by step,
Into its net of crystalline sound, until
The leaves stir overhead, the bowstrings snap
And poisoned shafts bite sharp into the kill.

Then, as the victim shudders, leaps and falls,
The music soars to a delicious peak,
And on and on its silvery piping calls
Fresh spoil for the rewards the hunters seek.

But when the woods are emptied and the dusk
Draws in, the men climb down and count their prey,
Cut out the little glands that hold the musk
And leave the carcasses to rot away.

A hundred thousand or so are killed each year;
Cause and effect are very simply linked:
Rich scents demand the musk, and so the deer,
Its source, must soon, they say, become extinct.

Divine Cecilia, there is no more to say!
Of all who praised the power of music, few
Knew of these things. In honour of your day
Accept this song I too have made for you.

Spätlese

A late picking — the old man sips his wine
And eyes his vineyard flourishing row on row.
Ripe clusters, hanging heavy on the vine,
    Catch the sun's afterglow.

He thinks: next vintage will not be too bad.
The *spätlese* at last, as I recall,
Has caught the grace I aimed at as a lad;
    Yet ripeness is not all.

Young men still seek perfection of the type;
A grace that lies beyond, one learns in time.
The improbable ferment of the overripe
    May touch on the sublime.

Old men should be adventurous. On the whole
I think that's what old age is really for:
Tolstoy at Astapovo finds his soul;
    Ulysses hefts his oar.

The Lamp

FROM SIX SONGS FOR CHLOË

Night and the sea; the firelight glowing;
We sit in silence by the hearth;
I musing, you beside me sewing,
We glean the long day's aftermath.

After the romping surf, the laughter,
The salt and sun, the roaring beach,
These flames glancing on wall and rafter
Are tongues of pentecostal speech.

And while their whispers come and go, I
Turn to watch you in your grace,
My gallant, radiant, reckless Chloë,
Who love and lead me such a chase,

To find it vanished, that incessant
Fulfilment of the urgent Now:
For here, absolved from past and present,
There broods a girl I do not know.

The clear, the gay, the brilliant nature
Matching your body's pride, gives place
To a soft, wavering change of feature:
This grave, remote and troubled face;

A face all women have in common
When, lost within themselves, alone,
They hear the demiourgos summon
And draw their ocean like the moon.

The moon is up; the beaches glisten,
The land grows faceless as the sea;
And you withdraw and, while you listen,
Put on your anonymity.

I hear my pulses, as they travel,
Drop one by one to the abyss;
I feel the skein of life unravel
And ask in dread: who then is this?

Who is this shade that sits beside me
And on what errand has she come:
To drive me on the dark, or guide me,
To tempt, or bring my spirit home?

Or is she lost herself, uncertain
And helpless on that timeless track?
Whichever way, I draw the curtain
And light the lamp that brings us back.

"With Thee Conversing..."

Talking with you each day would seem
To pass unnoticed into night,
And, borne on that enchanted stream,
Time but its pulse of dark and light;

And even busied or apart,
I feel the current's restless sweep:
A conversation fills the heart,
Or voices answer in my sleep.

Nor does it move by words alone:
Beneath our smiles, our talk, beneath
All words, a colloquy goes on
Which runs as strong and still as death.

Where did it rise, that mighty flow
On which, chance travellers, we embark?
What cordilleras feed with snow
Its cataracts raging through the dark,

I cannot guess, nor yet foresee
What hour the flood, as we descend,
Will turn and sweep us to the sea
In which all rivers have their end.

Talking with you, I cease to care
Where the springs rise and where they flow;
The goal of all my search is here
And here my everlasting Now.

Hay Fever

Time, with his scythe honed fine,
Takes a pace forward, swings from the hips; the flesh
Crumples and falls in wind-rows curving away.
Waiting my turn as he swings — (Not yet, not mine!)
I recall the sound of the scythe on an earlier day:
Late spring in my boyhood; learning to mow with the men;
Eight of us mowing together in echelon line,
Out of the lucerne patch and into the hay,
And I at the end on the left because I was fresh,
Because I was new to the game and young at the skill —
As though I were Time himself, I remember it still.

The mild Tasmanian summer; the men are here
To mow for my minister father and make his hay.
They have brought a scythe for me. I hold it with pride.
The lucerne is up to my knee, the grass to my waist.
I set the blade into the grass as they taught me the way;
The still dewy stalks nod, tremble and tilt aside,
Cornflowers, lucerne and poppies, sugar-grass, summer-grass, laced
With red-stemmed dock; I feel the thin steel crunch
Through hollow-stalk milk thistle, self-sown oats and rye;
I snag on a fat-hen clump; chick-weed falls in a bunch,
But sorrel scatters; dandelion casts up a golden eye,
To a smell of cows chewing their cuds, the sweet hay-breath:
The boy with the scythe never thinks it the smell of death.

The boy with the scythe takes a stride forward, swings
From the hips, keeping place and pace, keeping time
By the sound of the scythes, by the swish and ripple, the sigh
Of the dying grass like an animal breathing, a rhyme
Falling pat on the ear that matches the steel as it sings
True through the tottering stems. Sweat runs into my eye.
How long to a break? How long can I hold out yet?
I nerve my arms to go on; I am running with, flooding with, sweat.

How long ago was it? — Why, the scythe is as obsolete now
As arrows and bow. I have lived from one age to another;
And I have made hay while I could and the sun still shone.
Time drives a harvester now: he does not depend on the weather.
Well, I have rolled in his hay, in my day, and now it is gone;
But I still have a barn stacked high with that good dry mow,
Shrivelled and fragrant stems, the grass and the flowers together
And a thistle or two in the pile for the prick of remorse.
It is good for a man when he comes to the end of his course
In the barn of his brain to be able to romp like a boy in the heap . . .
To lie still in well-cured hay . . . to drift into sleep.

Country Places

Hell, Hay and Booligal!
Banjo Paterson

I glean them from signposts in these country places,
Weird names, some beautiful, more that make me laugh.
Driving to fat-lamb sales or to picnic races,
I pass their worshippers of the golden calf
And, in the dust of their Cadillacs, a latter-day Habbakuk
Rises in me to preach comic sermons of doom,
Crying: "Woe unto Tocumwal, Teddywaddy, Tooleybuc!"
And: "Wicked Wallumburrawang, your hour has come!"

But when the Four Horsemen ride their final muster
And my sinful country sinks in the fiery rain
One name shall survive the doom and the disaster
That fell on the foolish cities of the plain.
Like the three holy children or the salamander
One place shall sing and flourish in the fire:
It is Sweet Water Creek at Mullengandra
And there at the Last Day I shall retire.

When Numbugga shrieks to Burrumbuttock:
"The curse of Sodom comes upon us all!"
When Tumbarumba calls for spade and mattock
And they bury Hell and Hay in Booligal;
When the wrath of God is loosed upon Gilgandra
And Gulargambone burns red against the west,
To Sweet Water Creek at Mullengandra
I shall rise and flee away and be at rest.

When from Goonoo Goonoo, Underbool and Grong Grong
And Suggan Buggan there goes up the cry,
From Tittybong, Drik Drik and Drung Drung,
"Help, Lord, help us, or we die!"
I shall lie beside a willow-cool meander, or
Cut myself a fly-whisk in the shade
And from Sweet Water Creek at Mullengandra
Fill my cup and whet my whistle unafraid.

When Boinka lies in ruins (more's the pity!),
And a heavenly trump proclaims the End of Grace,
With: "Wombat is fallen, is fallen, that great city!"
Adding: "Bunyip is in little better case;"
When from Puckapunyal and from Yackandandah
The cry goes up: "How long, O Lord, how long?"
I shall hear the she-oaks sough at Mullengandra
And the Sweet Waters ripple into song:

Oh, there's little to be hoped for Grabben Gullen
And Tumbulgum shrinks and shudders at its fate;
Folks at Wantabadgery and Cullen Bullen
Have Buckley's chance of reaching Heaven's gate;
It's all up with Cootamundra and Kiandra
And at Collarenebri they know they're through;
But at Sweet Water Creek at Mullengandra
You may pitch your camp and sleep the whole night through.

God shall punish Cargellico, Come-by-Chance, Chinkapook;
They shall dance no more at Merrijig nor drink at Gentleman's Halt;
The sin of Moombooldool He shall in no wise overlook;
Wee Jasper and Little Jilliby, He shall not condone their fault;
But though I preach down Nap Nap and annihilate Narrandera,
One place shall yet be saved, this I declare:
Sweet Water Creek at Mullengandra
For its name and for my sake the Lord shall spare.

Coda

Alas! my beautiful, my prosperous, my careless country,
She destroys herself: the Lord will come too late!
They have cut down even their only tree at One Tree;
Dust has choked Honey Bugle and drifts over Creeper Gate;
The fires we lit ourselves on Mt Boothegandra
Have made more ruin than Heaven's consuming flame;
Even Sweet Water Creek at Mullengandra,
If I went there now, would it live up to its name?

The Death of the Bird

For every bird there is this last migration:
Once more the cooling year kindles her heart;
With a warm passage to the summer station
Love pricks the course in lights across the chart.

Year after year a speck on the map, divided
By a whole hemisphere, summons her to come;
Season after season, sure and safely guided,
Going away she is also coming home.

And being home, memory becomes a passion
With which she feeds her brood and straws her nest,
Aware of ghosts that haunt the heart's possession
And exiled love mourning within the breast.

The sands are green with a mirage of valleys;
The palm-tree casts a shadow not its own;
Down the long architrave of temple or palace
Blows a cool air from moorland scarps of stone.

And day by day the whisper of love grows stronger;
That delicate voice, more urgent with despair,
Custom and fear constraining her no longer,
Drives her at last on the waste leagues of air.

A vanishing speck in those inane dominions,
Single and frail, uncertain of her place,
Alone in the bright host of her companions,
Lost in the blue unfriendliness of space,

She feels it close now, the appointed season:
The invisible thread is broken as she flies;
Suddenly, without warning, without reason,
The guiding spark of instinct winks and dies.

Try as she will, the trackless world delivers
No way, the wilderness of light no sign,
The immense and complex map of hills and rivers
Mocks her small wisdom with its vast design.

And darkness rises from the eastern valleys,
And the winds buffet her with their hungry breath,
And the great earth, with neither grief nor malice,
Receives the tiny burden of her death.

The Return of Persephone

Gliding through the still air, he made no sound;
Wing-shod and deft, dropped almost at her feet,
And searched the ghostly regiments and found
The living eyes, the tremor of breath, the beat
Of blood in all that bodiless underground.

She left her majesty; she loosed the zone
Of darkness and put by the rod of dread.
Standing, she turned her back upon the throne
Where, well she knew, the Ruler of the Dead,
Lord of her body and being, sat like stone;

Stared with his ravenous eyes to see her shake
The midnight drifting from her loosened hair,
The girl once more in all her actions wake,
The blush of colour in her cheeks appear
Lost with her flowers that day beside the lake.

The summer flowers scattering, the shout,
The black manes plunging down to the black pit —
Memory or dream? She stood awhile in doubt,
Then touched the Traveller God's brown arm and met
His cool, bright glance and heard his words ring out:

"Queen of the Dead and Mistress of the Year!"
— His voice was the ripe ripple of the corn;
The touch of dew, the rush of morning air —
"Remember now the world where you were born;
The month of your return at last is here."

And still she did not speak, but turned again
Looking for answer, for anger, for command:
The eyes of Dis were shut upon their pain;
Calm as his marble brow, the marble hand
Slept on his knee. Insuperable disdain

Foreknowing all bounds of passion, of power, of art,
Mastered but could not mask his deep despair.
Even as she turned with Hermes to depart,
Looking her last on her grim ravisher
For the first time she loved him from her heart.

Hills

Says Tumble-down-Dick to Pretty Sally:
"Why are you so very far away?
Were we divided by just one valley
We could roll together and we could play."

Says Pretty Sally to Tumble-down-Dick:
"That is just the trouble with being a hill:
Though lying nearer might do the trick
The valley would fall between us still;

"And if, by the force of hugging and heaving,
We should make the bed of that valley our own,
We could get no good of this longing and grieving
For each of us harbours a heart of stone."

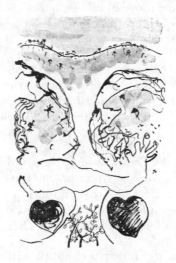

The Waters

We sit in the deepening twilight in my room,
Talking of this and that as we always do,
Events of the day, things we remember, news from home:
And then, as always, the unforeseen breaks through.

My heart, at some chance remark, stilled with surprise,
Brings things together and finds their meaning plain,
Towards which I have groped for years; some vast surmise
Takes shape and life from you. Now it happens again.

You say: I see you always, a wide, calm lake,
Shining, serene, biding some ultimate call;
But underneath, though the surface does not break,
Things surge in the depths which are not calm at all.

And I: But you are a river, questing bound
On its timeless errand; I see you range and veer
Round mountains or, when you must, run underground,
Crying at every turn: Not yet! Not here, nor here!

A quicksilver torrent, deep and swift in the gorges
Of Custom; threading its prairies, secret and alone,
With the liquid strength of urgent floods, whose urges
Sweep away cities and tunnel through sentinel stone.

Yes, I wait in my stillness; you vary your restless course;
But both must reject what other waters crave:
The assurance of ends that match their means, the resource
Of those whose answers settle for what they have.

All round us they call to us, dam and canal and pond:
Life is here and now, the given, the useful task.
Crazy Waters! What *is* there to wait for beyond?
What answers are there to questions one does not ask?

What can we say to them; how can they understand?
They have never heard of that universal sea
Which swallows whole continents, yet rebuilds their land;
Whose summons is our blood; whose service keeps us free.

So we sit in silence; our darkening room is haunted
By the voice of those ageless waters sweeping by.
I think of the earth's great rivers whose names enchanted
My boyhood, its vast lakes naked to the sky.

Water to water, smiling, we turn to each other,
The quest, the questions we live by hover between
And the wells of "non-existence", that most are content to smother,
Break through to the surface and make our wilderness green.

Those springs are the answer to all who tease and task us;
The prophet's response to the leper's angry appeal:
"True, Abana and Pharpar, rivers of Damascus,
Are sweeter than Jordan; but can they save and heal?"

Winterreise

The mountains are covered with snow;
Birds crouch deep in the nest;
O where shall my true love go?
Where shall the delicate breast
Be warm in its world of woe?

My house is empty and bare;
Ash lies cold on the hearth.
She walks in the icy air,
Falls on the stony path
And calls in her last despair:

Come to me, warm me, save!
There is not much time: Come soon!
The world is an open grave
And under the riding moon
Your arms are all I have.

But where shall I find her? Where,
As I grope through these winter storms,
Is the house, the hearth, the stair
Where I held my love in my arms
And slept in the folds of her hair?

Aubade

She will not come now,
Turn and sleep again;
Hear the winds blow
Listen to the rain.

Lying here awake
You already knew.
Day begins to break,
What is left to do?

No step on the stone,
No hand at the door;
You must sleep alone
Now and evermore.

E. O.
Schlunke

The Enthusiastic Prisoner

HENRY HOLDEN decided to get an Italian prisoner-of-war after he had seen several at work on Esmond's farm. Esmond was building a shed, and it was beautiful to see how they rushed to carry anything he picked up, and how they seemed to take it for granted that they were there to do all the heavy work while the boss gave the orders.

When the captain in charge of the P.O.W.C.C. had a preliminary look over Henry's place he tactlessly asked him if he were an invalid; he saw so few signs of work being done and so many of neglect. He wasn't at all keen on letting Henry have a P.O.W.; he didn't think he was the type to handle them successfully, but, on the other hand, he was eager to get his "hundred".

When the P.O.W. arrived Henry was decidedly disappointed with him at first sight.

He did not look obliging and polite; he didn't even look like an Italian. He had a tremendous amount of fuzzy brown hair, his eyebrows were so large and dense they nearly surrounded his eyes, and thick hair grew all round his neck and jutted out of his ears. His small bright eyes glinted sharply from among all the hair, not at all like the large, soft and servile eyes of the Italians at Esmond's.

In fact, he reminded Henry of a big brown bear, with his air of having great physical strength and tremendous determination. When the military truck drove away Henry had an uncomfortable feeling of having let himself in for something.

He directed Pietro to his room and, while he was settling in, tried hurriedly to work out a plan of what to do with him. There was, of course, plenty of work to be done, but it wasn't easy to start a man who didn't understand English, or know Australian farms. In a few minutes Pietro appeared.

"Worrk," he said, briefly and determinedly.

Henry abandoned his half-formed plan to let Pietro have the first half-day off. He thought of a number of jobs, only to realize that he didn't have the necessary materials. In desperation he decided to repair a fence. He pointed to the fence and to some tools and tried to explain to Pietro.

"Unnerstan', *reparare*," said Pietro.

He picked up a shovel and pick, and started hunting for a "*leva*". Henry soon realized that he meant a crowbar, but he couldn't remember where his was. Pietro looked at him in astonished reproval. When they started off, Pietro carrying all the heavy tools while Henry carried the wire-strainer, Henry felt better, though he was sure Esmond's men would have offered to carry the wire-strainer, too.

They did little good with the fence, though Pietro was obviously eager to work. It really needed a lot of new posts and wires and Henry had neither. They tightened what wires were there and braced and stayed some of the key posts in a makeshift manner. Pietro liked the wire-strainer. Apparently he had never seen one before, and was greatly intrigued with the way it worked.

"Very ni', very ni'," he said.

But when they were going home for dinner he glanced disapprovingly at the propped-up posts. "No good, no good."

After dinner, Henry usually had a nap that lasted well into the afternoon if the day happened to be warm, but Pietro apparently didn't know about dinner hours. He waited outside the door for a while then knocked and said, quite politely but very firmly, "Worrk."

Henry went out, and remembered the woodheap. It cheered him immensely. He had recently brought in a load and it would take Pietro several days to chop it up. It would be a great standby. Pietro could work there all the afternoon.

He lay down while Pietro chopped with great vigour, but he could not sleep or even relax properly because of his problem. His wife and family, too, kept asking him questions; they were rather awed by Pietro.

He heard the rumble of the wheelbarrow on the veranda several times and sounds of cut wood being tipped out. Then Pietro knocked on the door. He pointed to the great pile of wood and said, "*Sufficiente.*"

"No, not sufficient," said Henry. "Chop more."

Pietro looked at him with a blank expression.

"No unnerstan'," he said, and before Henry could work out another way of expressing himself, he inquired, "*Sufficiente* one day? Two day? T'ree day?"

"T'ree day," Henry admitted reluctantly.

Pietro smiled broadly and looked surprisingly pleasant as he did so. "Plenty sufficient," he said, closing the argument.

Henry went and got his hat. He could hear the wind banging a loose sheet of iron on the roof of the machinery shed. They would begin by nailing it down. But when they climbed the roof Pietro discovered that half the sheets were loose. Henry gave him the nails and directed him to nail down the flapping sheet. But Pietro was hunting round for causes. He discovered that the rafters were rotting and demonstrated it by giving one a hard hit with the hammer. It split from end to end and a couple of sheets immediately blew off the roof.

They spent the afternoon cutting trees in the scrub and trimming them for rafters, though nothing had been farther from Henry's intention and inclination. He cut down a few little trees while Pietro cut a lot of big ones. Pietro always took the heavier end when they loaded the rails, but even so Henry became exhausted. Round about four o'clock he decided to go home.

"Sufficient," he said.

Pietro consulted a diagram he had made.

"No sufficient," he said. "*Ancora* four."

They went on working.

At tea that night Pietro met all the family. There were a flapper daughter, three younger boys, and a baby. He was particularly interested in the baby.

He made some queer foreign noises at it, and to everyone's surprise it showed unmistakable signs of affection for him. He asked Mrs Holden if it were breast-fed, and when she told him, in some confusion, that it was not, he wanted to know why. Then he gave her detailed and intimate directions, mainly by signs, about how to ensure an abundant flow for the next baby. The flapper daughter half smothered a lot of embarrassed giggles, and the boys nearly "busted" trying not to laugh. Henry felt that he should reprimand Pietro for his indelicacy, but didn't know how he could make him understand.

The next day Henry felt stiff and sore. He decided to relax, but Pietro kept calling him onto the roof, sometimes for advice, but mostly to help him in fitting rafters which were too big to be "*possibile solo*".

They finished re-roofing the shed by the week-end. Pietro wanted to know if they would cut some fence-posts next week to repair the fences. Henry thought of how he would suffer if he had to work on the other end of a cross-cut saw with a tireless bear like Pietro. "No," he said, "some other work."

But he didn't like the way Pietro looked at him, so he decided to hide the cross-cut saw.

On Sunday Esmond's Italians came to visit Pietro, and told him all about what was going on at their place. On Monday morning Pietro wanted to know why Henry was not preparing his soil for his crops like Mr Esmond. Henry looked a bit guilty, then tried to explain that he used different methods from Esmond. Pietro was not satisfied.

"Mr Esmond good *resultati*? No good *resultati*?"

Henry had to admit that Esmond's results were good. He also had to confess that his results were often bad.

"*Provare* similar Mr Esmond," Pietro suggested enthusiastically. "*Possibile* very good oat, very good weet."

"Tractor broken," said Henry. He was always overwhelmed by a feeling of hopeless apathy in the autumn, and he couldn't face the strain of all the preparations necessary for his worn-out plant.

"Me look?" asked Pietro, and was off before Henry could say anything.

Pietro had a thorough look over the tractor and scarifier. He made a list of all the new parts needed, which he laboriously translated into English with the help of his little dictionary. He explained that he was not a mechanic, but he had had a lot of experience with military vehicles.

He suggested that Henry go to town and buy the necessary parts, and Henry went, glad to escape from the responsibility of Pietro for an afternoon. While Henry was away Pietro "polished" the toolshed and the farmyard.

When Henry came home, rather late in the evening and somewhat the worse for wine, he thought he had come to the wrong farm until Pietro emerged and carried his parcels for him. He was in an exalted mood and gave Pietro an orange for his services. But Pietro spoiled the effect by telling him several things he had forgotten to bring.

At the table that night Pietro objected to Mrs Holden giving the baby honey to stop it crying.

"No good 'oni, no good," he said.

She continued to exercise the lawful rights of a mother. Suddenly the baby vomited. Pietro made an angry noise, jumped up, and put the honey-pot away in the cupboard.

"No good, no good," he said so emphatically that she was startled and impressed.

Henry found that he couldn't tell Pietro much about overhauling farm machines. He stood by to explain where tools, parts, and materials were kept, but frequently found it easier to fetch them than to explain; sometimes when Pietro was held up he became so impatient that Henry found himself running just like one of Esmond's Italians, until he remembered his dignity as a *padrone*.

They had an auspicious rain when everything was ready, and Henry's land was never worked into better condition.

The tractor ran very well. Pietro assumed a jealous control of it, and appeared to be perfectly happy on it no matter how long he worked. The arrangement suited Henry excellently.

He felt free for the first time since his prisoner arrived. He had plenty of time to turn over all the vague plans forming in his head.

When Pietro finished working the land he suggested again that they cut some fence-posts. But Henry was ready with his own plan. Pietro was to paint the house. Pietro agreed heartily; the house certainly needed painting. They went to have a good look at it. Not only had the paint peeled off, but much of the plaster was cracked and loose.

"No good paint," said Pietro. "*Prima* plaster."

The thought of all the work and expense involved in plastering horrified Henry.

He said, authoritatively, "Paint sufficient", and took a trowel and demonstrated how the rough plaster could be smoothed off.

He handed the trowel to Pietro, who made what appeared to be a similar movement. But the result was vastly different, at least a wheelbarrow-load of plaster fell off the wall.

"Plenty similar," Pietro said, and knocked off another square yard. Henry gave in.

Henry was kept very busy mixing and carrying plaster to Pietro. It had to be mixed in small lots and applied immediately, Pietro said, otherwise it would fall off just like the previous plaster.

When this job was finished Henry brought out the paint. Pietro was very interested in the "*colore*". When he discovered that it was to be a drab, uniform stone-colour all his eagerness vanished.

"No good, no good," he said. "Similar mud."

He wouldn't take the brush when Henry offered it to him.

"Brush no good," he said. "*Troppo* old."

Henry tried the brush and had to admit it was worn out. He decided to go to town and buy a new one. Pietro wanted to go, too, to have his hair cut. Henry left him at the Control Centre and went to do his shopping.

When he walked into the general store where he did most of his business he had an uneasy feeling that he was being followed. He turned and saw Pietro carrying the two big cans of stone-coloured paint. He had that brown-bear look about him which Henry hadn't liked the first time he saw him.

The manager of the hardware store came up to them. He saw by the expression in Henry's eye that he wasn't sure of himself, so he turned to Pietro, who appeared to know exactly what he wanted. Pietro held up the tins.

"*Colore* no good," he said.

The manager remembered having advised Henry against a uniform drab colour, and immediately set out to help Pietro. He quite ignored Henry's somewhat indistinct, "No, it's all right. I'll keep it."

He showed Pietro a colour-card, from which he selected a very light cream, bright blue, and a black.

"One big creama, one little blue, one little, little *nero*," he said.

The manager was, as he would have said, intrigued. He tried to discover what design Pietro had in mind, and Pietro demonstrated as best he could, attracting a lot of attention from other shoppers, who began to gather round.

Henry became most uncomfortable. "I won't have it at any price," he protested. "Everyone who goes past will die laughing."

"Ah, garn!" said a big voice from the back. "Let him have a go. It couldn't look any worse than it's looked for the last twenty years."

Then a couple of ladies joined in.

"How interesting!" said one. "The Italians are so artistic, aren't they?"

The other one said, "I remember seeing the adorable Italian cottages painted just like that. You must let us come and see it, Mr Holden." She happened to be the wife of Henry's long-suffering mortgagee, and her word carried some weight with him. Quite a number of others voiced favourable opinions before Henry and Pietro carried out the cream, blue and black paint.

Pietro took endless pains over the painting, and all the time he was at it Henry felt resentful, despite the fact that many people came and admired it. He comforted himself by compiling a long list of heavy jobs Pietro would have to do when he was finished. He had the interpreter prepare a translation and when at length the house was finished he gave Pietro a week's programme, consisting mainly of firewood-carting and post-hole digging.

But that day it rained, a splendid soaking rain, and during the night it cleared.

Henry was awakened early in the morning by the roar of the tractor starting. He was puzzled and rather annoyed; Pietro was up to something. Then he realized that Pietro had made the all-important decision of the year, to start sowing the wheat.

Henry thought, with some indignation, of the programme he had given Pietro, but he also realized that it was much more important to have the wheat sown while the soil was moist. He lay thinking for a long time of ways in which he could reassert himself, and all the time he heard the noises of Pietro's preparations. He stayed there because he always hated the worry of working out the proportions of wheat and fertilizer and adjusting the machines accordingly, and all the other important details necessary for a successful sowing season.

When at last he went out Pietro hurried up to him, his face aglow with enthusiasm.

"Oh, rain very nice!" he said. "*Possibile* very good weet this year, similar Mr Esmond."

He pointed to the tractor hitched to the sowing combine and the farm cart loaded with supplies of seed, fertilizer, and tractor fuel.

"After brekfus I take tractor and weet machine. You bring *carro. Allora* we commence before Giuseppe and Leonardo on farm Mr Esmond."

"Yes, Pietro," said Henry.

The Man Who Liked Music

ALEX DENHOLM was a pleasant enough man who could have been popular with his neighbours if it had not been for his queer streak. Alex had no sense of proportion. Until the neighbours got to know him they would hurry across to his farm to help him fix his tractor or his combine, only to find that there was nothing wrong with them; Alex had actually stopped work in the middle of the wheat-sowing season to go inside to listen to the Music Lover's Hour on the radio. And he would come out with his red hair standing up from the way he rumpled it in his excitement, his reddish-brown eyes glowing like fire, and his face, which was rugged and ruddy, shining in an absurdly delighted and boyish manner, to tell them he had just heard the Vienna Philharmonic Orchestra playing Mozart's E Flat Symphony.

Opinion about Alex's wife was divided. Some said she was a heroine for putting up with him; others that she was a fool for not leaving him.

The neighbours were very amused when they heard that Alex was getting an Italian prisoner-of-war to work for him.

"That'll be two of a kind," said some.

"Don't be too hard on the Ities," said the others.

The Control Centre men were a bit apologetic about the Italian they brought to Denholm's place. He was a small, obsequious fellow, who looked exactly like a waiter in a second-rate Italian restaurant.

"I don't think he knows anything about farm work," said the sergeant-major, "but you'll have no trouble keeping him in order."

All the C.C. staff chuckled at this and Mario looked at them nervously, with his big soft brown eyes sliding from one to the other. Alex gave his prisoner a cheerful smile, as if he were sure he would discover some good in him. It did not take him very long. The very first night when he took him in to tea and they were both feeling awkward and embarrassed because they could understand only a few words of each other's language, Alex switched on his radio to his usual programme of classical music. An orchestra was playing selections from Italian operas. Mario looked and listened with intense interest.

"Rossini," he said.

"Rossini good," said Alex.

"Good! Good!" said Mario enthusiastically, and they smiled delightedly at each other. The orchestra played the first three notes of the next air and Alex shouted, "Mascagni!"

Mario looked at him admiringly. "Mascagni good!" he said.

They went on "Verdi good", "Leoncavallo good", "Bellini good".

After that Mario could do no wrong. Alex taught him to milk the cows and do the odd jobs about the place. For a prisoner-of-war Mario had a very happy existence. He liked milking the cows, and gave them new Italian names — the names of girls he had loved in Bari. The beautiful friendly red one with fat round hips he called after Domenica, his latest and best love, even though she had not written to him for three years. He always sang while he milked, and while he milked Domenica it was always "*Che gelida manina*" from *La Bohème*. He sang it very feelingly and very sadly, just like the ill-fated lover in the opera, and Alex wasted a great deal of time listening outside the cowshed. Mario was really good. Alex boasted about it to everybody he met. He had a sister who was a music teacher in the near-by provincial city of Waghurst. He lost no time in telling her about his sensational discovery, and bringing her out to hear him.

Theresa Denholm was a Dip.Mus., an S.T.S., and an A.T.M. She was also a master of the art of attracting large numbers of pupils and keeping them paying tuition fees long after they should have realized that they had neither the physical nor the intellectual gifts required in an interpreter of music. She was a bright, attractive, and lively young woman, though not so young that she wasn't somewhat troubled by the problem of keeping her hips and bust within the limits of elegance. On the way to Denholm's place she listened with every appearance of rapt attention, though with the inner boredom of the professional musician, to Alex's praise of his Italian singer.

But when she saw Mario come in to sit at the "low" end of the old twelve-foot family table, looking so foreign and exotic, and really rather fetching with his big eloquent eyes and sensitive face, she was greatly interested.

"Is that the man who sings so well?" she said, letting her big and somewhat babyish blue eyes roll admiringly at him.

Mario had been a prisoner and had lived a harshly masculine life for four years, and here was a *bella donna* with curves like the most alluring Italian girl *and* blonde hair. Mario could not take his eyes off her, and though he was only a poor, wretched prisoner-of-war Theresa blossomed under his admiration. She was gay and bubbled with laughter; she joked with Alex; she teased his wife; she caressed and played with the children. Mario couldn't swallow a single mouthful.

Ina, the girl carrying plates in and out, full of resentful bewilderment because Mrs Denholm had impressed on her most emphatically not to play up to the Italian because it was a condition of his parole that he was to have no contact whatever with women, pointed meaningly at his plate each time she passed him. But Mario heeded her not at all, though usually his glances followed her hungrily enough.

When Mrs Denholm rose from the table it was the signal, among other things, for the Italian to retire to his hut. But tonight Theresa stopped him with an entreating cry. She wanted to have Mario in the lounge-room so that she could hear him sing at the piano. Mrs Denholm objected. The prisoners should be kept in their places, she said, and she told them the nasty things the neighbours were saying about Alex for being too friendly with a P.W. There were some brisk exchanges between Mrs Denholm and Theresa, Mario not understanding a word, but looking on with an expression of embarrassed self-pity. Theresa finally won through sheer egotistic inconsideration.

But Mario appeared very reluctant to go into the lounge. He eyed the carpet as if he dared not step on it; he would not take a chair but remained standing, tense and nervous.

"No *possibile* me siddown," he said, "me *prigioniero*."

Theresa gave him a melting smile, and a roll of the eyes that made him momentarily sag at the knees. She went to the piano and played softly and sentimentally. She began to sing, flashing glances at Mario until she saw that he was so full of music that his throat muscles had relaxed. She invited him to sing, tactfully helping him along when he had difficulty with the rather elaborate piano accompaniment. Theresa certainly knew the job of music-teaching. She soon had him going with great enthusiasm, leading him into exaggerated expressions of passion and sorrow until the tears ran down his cheeks. She stopped abruptly.

"Very good," she said, giving him an up-and-down look as if it were decidedly incredible.

But Mario shook his head with a sort of pessimistic modesty. "Me no good. Plenty *prigionieri* sing similar me." Then he caught the look in Mrs Denholm's eye, and hastily departed with many "Scusami's", taking long steps to avoid treading too much on the carpet. Alex turned triumphantly to his sister.

"Isn't he as good as I said? Did you notice his marvellous *forte*?"

"It's the best natural singing voice I've ever heard," said Theresa enthusiastically. "Do you know what I've been thinking? I'll have to have him in my pupils' concert."

Mrs Denholm said with deceitful sympathy, "It's a pity you can't, but he's under strict military discipline. Otherwise it wouldn't really matter that he isn't a pupil of yours, would it?"

Theresa gave her sister-in-law a blank unreceptive look.

"I must have him," she said. "That man Foll has a fine young tenor. His voice is so good that even Foll's ridiculous old Marcesa methods can't ruin it. His opera singing is supposed to be particularly good, but Mario would make him look silly."

Alex's eyes began to shine. "Wouldn't he make them sit up? A beautiful, fresh young voice like that."

Mrs Denholm said, "For goodness sake Alex, don't let Theresa make a fool of you again."

Alex tried to remember what she was referring to, but soon gave it up as unimportant.

"He really *must* be heard, he's so good," he said.

Theresa turned her eyes up in her thoughtful pose.

"Isn't that Captain Adkins in charge of the prisoners?" she asked, then she broke into contented smiles. "I know him. He's an awfully nice man."

Captain Adkins was an amiable gentleman who ran the Waghurst P.W. Control Centre as if it were a welfare centre for Italian immigrants. The large room where the staff worked was always cluttered with prisoners whose employers had brought them into town for a hair-cut, to see the doctor, or just for an afternoon off. They always made a great deal of noise, seizing each other by the hands, exclaiming like long-lost brothers and even embracing and kissing each other. Theresa soon became quite well known at the Centre. She cultivated Captain Adkins, learnt the names of all the sergeants, corporals and other ranks, and dropped *buon' giorno's* to the prisoners, who soon got the notion that she was the *prima donna* at the local opera house. When she felt that she had established so much goodwill in Captain Adkins's heart that he could deny her nothing, she asked him if Mario could sing at her pupils' concert. The Captain looked somewhat taken aback.

"Now," he said, looking at the ceiling, "if it were just a private entertainment of invited guests, held at your brother's place, at which the prisoner would make a brief appearance dressed in his maroon uniform, and all the guests were informed beforehand of his position and had no objections, then it would be quite all right."

Despite her carefully cultivated woman-of-the-world control, and her rather lavish make-up, some disappointment was discernible in Theresa's face. Her pupils' concerts were always held in one of the biggest halls in the city, the public was bidden to attend by cunningly and rather deceitfully worded advertisements, and a charge was made for admission. She smiled very warmly on Captain Adkins and put a hand on his sleeve in an innocently beseeching manner.

"So many people want to come to my concerts ——" she began.

But the captain held up a warning hand.

"Those are the regulations," he said, and then he smiled, "but then, I don't know any more about your concert than you choose to tell me."

Theresa nearly blushed as she realized how close she had gone to being guilelessly confidential. She rose and said, "I'm having a little cocktail party at my studio tomorrow afternoon, I do hope you can come."

On her way out she didn't remember as many of the sergeants' names as usual. She was too preoccupied in thinking of ways and means. The advertisement, for instance, might be worded as an invitation — and a charge could still be made to defray expenses. She went and bought the most expensive tie in the town, and sent it to her brother, omitting to remove the price tag. She had an idea she would need a lot of co-operation from him.

The story went the rounds of the musical circles in Waghurst that a mysterious Greek tenor was going to sing at Theresa Denholm's concert. It transpired that he was a famous partisan patriot deep in the confidence of the Allied War Council. Every blossoming young soprano was dying to meet him, but the Nazis still maintained a fabulous price on his head, and all his comings and goings were made in the utmost secrecy.

On the night of the concert Alex smuggled Mario into the hall dressed in a suit of his own clothes, with a very bright blue shirt and crimson tie to give him a bit of dash and to make him look less like an Italian waiter. He faced the audience rather nervously, but he sang very well, with Theresa at the piano giving him great moral support. The audience loved him; they thought his modesty becoming in a foreigner of his reputation. Captain Adkins was there and seemed to enjoy his performance as much as anyone. The crowd clapped for an encore, but Theresa was pushing him out of the back door, where Alex seized him and rushed him away, the well-disciplined prisoner carrying out the orders of his *padrone* without question. Only when they were safely at home did a glimmer of pride light Mario's eyes.

"Me sing good?" he asked.

Mr Foll, the eminent music-teacher, went about with one of his handsome iron-grey eyebrows sardonically elevated, telling people there was something phoney about the whole business, that the story of the tenor's romantic origin was only a poor publicity stunt, and that any Mediterranean would have a much more convincing Italian enunciation. He personally recognized the voice as belonging to a yodelling milkman employed by a dairy-farmer just outside the town. It was a freakish, unnatural voice, and nobody would be fooled by it for long.

But the *Waghurst Daily Diverter* said, "Here is the voice which Waghurst can match with pride against the cream of Sydney and Melbourne at our forthcoming eisteddfod."

Queues of new pupils blocked the way to Theresa's studio door, where she received them with a most winning and gracious condescension. Next week-end she was at Alex's place again, still seething with excited triumph.

"Now I'll just have to enter him in the eisteddfod! I could win one of the major sections with him, against all comers. Then I'd be able to double my fees."

Mrs Denholm said darkly, "That would be very nice for you, but do you know what we've found out? The penalty for supplying a prisoner-of-war with a suit of civilian clothes is five to ten years jail."

"There isn't much risk," Theresa said brightly.

"What about Mr Foll and all the other jealous music teachers? They'll be nosing round," said Mrs Denholm.

But Alex sat with a bemused smile on his face.

"I believe Mario could win the operatic aria," he said, as if everything else were unimportant.

Theresa said with brisk, easy confidence, "I'll go and have a confidential talk to Captain Adkins. He'll fix everything for me."

She started training Mario immediately. Mrs Denholm interrupted rather frequently to send Mario to do some job, and stayed to criticize.

"Is it necessary," she asked, "to hold his hands and tell him how good he is all the time?"

"That's building up his confidence," said Theresa professionally. "Voice without personality will get him nowhere in an eisteddfod. He's got to learn to put it over. I have to make a study of his psychology, and find out how to put a bit of backbone into him."

Back in Waghurst Theresa took the first opportunity to call at the P.W.C.C. As soon as she entered she was aware of a difference in the atmosphere. There was no noise except the sounds of men at work. There were no surplus personnel in either khaki or maroon loitering about. The few N.C.Os were so busy at their desks that they barely had time to glance up at her. She felt quite relieved when a prisoner-of-war came in, bowing with extravagant politeness and smiling at her in the friendliest manner. She was greeting him warmly when she suddenly saw his face go blank and pale. She turned round in surprise to see a huge man towering over her with the pips of a captain on his massive shoulders. A pair of cold, opaque, hardened blue eyes were fastened mercilessly on the cringing prisoner. He said in a well-controlled, but definitely menacing voice, "Take that fellow out of here."

Two sergeants and a corporal sprang from their seats and advanced so swiftly and threateningly on the Italian that he fled like a rabbit to the cells at the back of the Centre, hitherto used for storing blankets. After he had heard the clang of the door Captain Pillory turned his eyes on Theresa. She searched his face for something that might suggest a line of approach. It was the face of one in authority — one who knew what he knew, and knew it so well that it was futile to tell him anything else. He said to her with all the arrogant assurance of a man securely entrenched in a man's world, and bolstered by an infallible set of man-made rules, "Now, madam, just what is your business in here?"

Theresa looked round at all her friends at the desks, but none of them offered to introduce her. She looked back at Captain Pillory and knew that it was neither the time nor the place to make an impression on him.

"Oh, I must have made a mistake," she said with an airy smile, "I wanted the place next door.''

The next Thursday was ''canteena'' day at Denholm's place. Captain Adkins had always left the tours of inspection and supply to his staff, but Captain Pillory came personally to see that his new order was established. Mario's smile of welcome dribbled off his face when he saw the new ''uffishaal''. Pillory reproved him sharply for the way he was dressed, for not polishing his boots, for the way he kept his room. Captain Pillory scorned to make use of the interpreter. Experience had taught him that if he glared hard enough, shouted loudly enough, and towered high enough, the b——s understood him very well. Mario certainly understood that he was very unpopular with Captain Pillory; he stood at a rather lopsided attention, his face pale yellow with fright, trying hard to be correct and respectful. The N.C.Os treated him severely, too. They handed out only half the usual tobacco ration without making any explanation. They refused to issue new clothing unless the old were worn to disgraceful shreds, and they didn't allow Mario more than five minutes of his favourite futile sport of trying to get into a pair of boots two sizes too small for him.

When they had finished Pillory had Mario paraded before him again. He said to Alex, sternly, ''How has he been behaving?''

''Splendidly,'' said Alex. Pillory looked quite disappointed.

''Isn't this the fellow who sings?'' he asked, with something very like a sneer. Alex's face lit up.

''Oh, marvellously!'' he said, with his usual enthusiasm. ''A true lyric tenor with only a little development required in the upper register to make him one of the great *bel canto* singers of our day.''

Pillory looked hard at Alex, as if he were having some trouble in militarily classifying him.

''Is that so?'' he said, feeling his way, but letting his face relax a bit so that his staff could think he was pulling Alex's leg.

''Yes,'' said Alex, ''it is. His voice has something of Gigli's quality, with Schipa's lightness of inflection.''

The captain cleared his throat and set out to do some intelligence work.

''Tell me, who are these fellows, Gigli and Schipa? Sounds to me as if they're just a couple of dagos.''

Alex's ruddy face flamed with indignation. ''Gigli and Schipa are the greatest operatic tenors in the world. Thousands of people flock to hear them whenever and wherever they sing.'' He ran his eye over the captain's various insignia of rank with a none too respectful glance, and burst out again. ''Why, Gigli would be paid as much for a tour of a few weeks as ten generals would get in a year.''

Captain Pillory maintained his undaunted and unimpressed expression, but he repeated, ''As much as ten generals'', as if that had got through the responsive core of his being. An incredulous and vastly curious look crept slowly over his face.

"But surely this —" he glanced towards Mario as if he couldn't think of the word to describe him — "this Italian isn't good enough to get among the money like that."

"Would you like to hear him," Alex said eagerly, "and compare his voice with gramophone records of the world's best tenors?"

But Pillory was not going to be led in beyond his depth. He glanced at his watch, and said, "Not today, thanks, we haven't time."

One glance round and the N.C.Os sprang onto the truck. They roared away to terrify some more prisoners.

When Theresa came out next week-end Alex had a copy of the eisteddfod agenda, and was shouting with excitement.

"Look here," he said, "the very thing for Mario, 'Selection from Italian Opera in Costume'. He can sing some of Canio's part from *Pagliacci*. No one would know who or what he is in a clown's make-up."

Theresa gave him a shrewdly calculating look to make sure he was determined, then said, "Oh, you wonderful man, to think of that, and to be willing to take such a risk for me!"

"There's no need to worry," Alex said. "That new captain might be strict, but he's not very bright. Would you believe it, he'd never heard of Gigli or Schipa! I've got it all worked out. Mario can wear his red uniform and pull the clown's overall over the top of it. That will give us a chance to talk our way out if Pillory does stumble on us. See? No civilian clothes, no disguise that would help him escape, and wearing his red uniform."

Mrs Denholm, who had come in with her face full of suspicion of Alex's excited talk, said ominously, "Did you hear about the man who took his prisoner into a hotel for a drink? The mob threw both of them out and Captain Pillory sent the prisoner back to the camp for punishment."

Theresa looked at her with a dead, bored expression, then rushed out and called Mario to come and have a practice. He was just about to go and milk the cows, but he dropped the buckets and came. Alex went out and picked up the buckets.

A week before the eisteddfod Theresa invited Alex and Mrs Denholm to give Mario an "audience test". She asked them particularly to notice his growing confidence. It was apparent as soon as they entered the lounge. Mario was relaxing comfortably in an armchair, but he sprang out of it quickly enough when Mrs Denholm gave him one of her looks.

Theresa stood Mario where he could watch her while he sang. They noticed his eyes turning to her continually, and the way he responded to her every look and gesture. He sang extremely well. Alex complimented both Theresa and Mario profusely.

But Mrs Denholm said, "He'll be all right, provided you can keep him hypnotized until after the eisteddfod's over."

When Mario had gone Theresa confided, "He's not going to fail, because I've taught him to be more afraid of letting me down than he can possibly be of the audience or adjudicators."

Mario went about the farm with an earnest expression, practising conscientiously at all hours of the day and night. While he milked the cows, instead of his old light-hearted singing, he ran through his scales and arpeggios or roared dramatically his *"Ridi pagliaccio"*. Even the cows seemed to know there was something portentous about it all, and gave (on the average) a pint less of milk per day per cow. Alex took elaborate precautions against Mario getting too hot or too cold, and running the risk of a chill. His wife went about wearing an expression of apprehensive resignation.

There was tremendous public interest in the Waghurst eisteddfod that year. Mario was greatly impressed with the throngs of people about the town hall.

"Me similar Caruso," he said, thinking they had all come to hear him.

They kept him discreetly in a closed car until it was nearly time for him to sing, then they brought him into the wings "to get the feel of the theatre". At the back of the stage there was a concourse of people in every degree of excitement. Young girls nearly palsied with fright, proudly holding sheets of music in their hands to show they were competitors, but getting sudden pitiful expressions on their faces as if they would have sold their souls to be back at home washing the dishes; teachers hovering; neurotic women combining the solicitous protectiveness and fierce aggressiveness of mothering hens; temperamental men teachers, and young men performers affecting calm self-possession but forgetting themselves to fall into fits of passionate nail-biting.

Most of them forgot their troubles to stare at Theresa Denholm's Greek tenor, who could easily have been a Dutchman or a Negro under the heavy clown's make-up that Theresa had plastered on him for safety. Mr Foll came drifting to Theresa's side, despite her uninviting look, and, glancing at Mario's costume said loudly enough for him to hear, "Singing *'Vesti la giubba'* I see. Unfortunate, that. Another man sang it a while ago. A strange thing happened. The note the accompanist gave him was half a tone flat. The poor fellow sang flat all the way through."

Theresa thanked Mr Foll and smiled more warmly than he expected, because she was thinking how ineffective his nerve war was on uncomprehending Mario. She encouraged him to retire and mind his own business.

The mysterious Greek tenor got a great reception. It seemed as if most of the audience really had come to hear him. And they were not disappointed. Theresa and Alex hugged each other in the wings as he went on from one thrilling phrase to the next. Even before the adjudicator announced his decision, everybody recognized it as a great triumph for him and for Theresa Denholm. Captain Pillory was there, to everyone's surprise, looking as if he were determined to get this singing business by the throat.

He was still thinking about it when he next visited Denholm's place. He didn't have much time to spare, but he insisted on Mario singing for him, unaccompanied and in the open air, while the N.C.Os were getting the issue forms ready for him to sign.

He listened with a very judicial expression, but soon stopped Mario with a curt gesture.

"Quite a voice," he said commendingly, "but nothing like that Greek tenor at the eisteddfod. That was the man who has the chance of getting among the big money."

For once Alex let an obviously wrong opinion about music go unchallenged. He did not encourage the captain to speak any more about the matter, being quite relieved to see him departing. But the interpreter, a mild, soft-spoken, dark little man, who had been ignored by the captain ever since he came, paused by Alex's side for a brief moment, and murmured to him, "You've got away with it twice, but for goodness' sake don't try it again, because I'll have to do my duty and report you."

First Flight

The Manager,
Air Outback Ltd,
Bourke, N.S.W.

Dear Sir,

I hereby apply for a transfer to another district, as it is not in the interests of the firm for me to remain here, since an unfortunate misunderstanding has arisen, following the death of a client of ours, the late Mr Alan Wilcox. At the outset I wish to assure you most emphatically that no offence was intended, and that any that may have been taken was due to a complete misinterpretation of my actions. However, I shall describe the incident and leave it to you to judge.

As a matter of fact, I wasn't really going to Wilcox's place that trip, but the doctor asked me to drop in with some sulpha tablets for him, as he wasn't well, which I did as I was going past his place to Marracumba. Having completed the business at Marracumba (you may remember the five hundred fat Hereford steers I got there at a very satisfactory price) and having no urgent appointment, I decided to drop in at Wilcox's on the way back to see how he was getting on. I had always thought a lot of the old chap, and I think he liked me. He loved to hear about what they were doing on all the other stations I visited, and he took a great interest in flying, too. Every time I dropped in at his place he'd say to me, "My boy, some day you must take me up and let me see what it feels like to go through all those loops and turns you always do."

I always meant to, too, but every time I arrived there was the usual rush to get his stock mustered and inspected; then, likely as not, urgent telephone or pedal-radio calls from this or that station wanting me to call, so that I could never work it in.

Well, I arrived at Boronoro and did my usual stunts over the homestead to let him know it was me. But when I put the plane down and got out they told me he was dead. I tell you, I felt very bad about it.

The relations were arriving in cars from all over the back country — the Wilcox family occupy a terrific lot of land over the west. And then, while the men were still talking about funeral arrangements and arguing about the details in the stiff-necked Wilcox way, down came the rain in bucketfuls.

I had to stay there for the night and listen to all the women moaning about how they were going to get him to the cemetery. And how were they going to have a decent funeral with all the creeks up and the roads impassable? And the men weren't much better, though they pretended that *they* could manage everything very well, if only the women wouldn't fuss.

Well, it rained all night, and though it was clear in the morning, Boronoro homestead looked like Noah's Ark with water all round it. All the morning there was a string of men queuing up at the telephone, trying to persuade the under-taker to bring out the hearse. Each of them swore that he could get through, though I noticed that none of them was game to try to take *him* in in a car (there were about a hundred and twenty miles to go and three or four sizeable creeks). But the undertaker wasn't going to risk his new Cadillac, and I didn't blame him, it being so low-slung and heavy.

Well, in the end I had to come to their rescue. I told them that since they were so sure they could get through to town, they should go. I would wait until the afternoon to give them time to arrive (and to let the water dry away a bit so I could get the plane up) and I'd bring the old man in myself. There was an all-in debate about that. Some of the women even seemed to think I was insulting the family. But in the end they agreed that it was the only thing to do.

So they all went sloshing off through the mud while I went to see if I could pick out a strip of higher ground to get a run. I found a place that would do; then I went inside and the cook gave me a Number One dinner.

A couple of station-hands had been detailed to give me a hand with the old man. He'd been left in his pyjamas and dressing-gown, so we carried him out like that. We had some trouble getting him to sit in the cockpit properly, but we managed and got the straps fastened round him.

But he looked wrong, sitting there in his check dressing-gown and his bald head sticking out. So I got them to put a tough, windproof gaberdine overcoat on him (because it gets damn cold up aloft, even in this weather), and we put a thick cap on his head and tied it under his chin.

Conditions for the take-off were still very bad; I had to put all I knew into it; I didn't want to have a crack-up with that cargo, especially after what the women had said. Then, when we were up, and going along beautifully above all the mud and water, like a bird, I took a look round to see how he was taking it. He was sitting there in his sturdy, calm old way, with his head tilted a little over one side as if he was having a last look at Boronoro Downs, and liking the look of it very well, with all that rain on it and plenty of autumn feed assured. I tell you, it gave me quite a turn to see him looking so alive and interested in everything, I didn't look back for quite a while, but the next time I did he was looking over the other side, and looking so intently that I had to look, too. We were right over Tenterby, and I remembered straight away that his old crony Evans lived there. We had our last look at Frank Evans's place.

I don't suppose you will understand how I felt, because you've never flown over the lonely Western Plains with only a dead man for a passenger, and him acting as if he was alive all the time. But it got me that way that, if he happened to be looking the wrong way when we passed a homestead he knew, I'd yell out to him and point it out. And sure enough, he'd turn that way and give me a little nod with his head, as if to thank me. Of course, when I come to think of it now in cold blood, I realize that the plane must have rocked a bit; I might even have banked her to make him lean over the other side, but I wasn't aware of it at the time.

Then, quite suddenly, we were over the town, and I remembered that I'd never have another chance of giving him that spot of aerobatics he'd always wanted. So I gave the old bus the gun, and put her into a loop; I rolled off the top, coming down slowly over the 'drome. Each time we turned over I could see the relations' cars drawn up, waiting, and the hearse; and all the people getting out of the cars, looking up at us. I zoomed up again, did a long barrel-roll that was as good as anything I've ever seen an instructor do, came down in a couple of tight turns that were really tight, and put her onto the 'drome in a beautiful three-point landing.

Believe me, sir, I came down to earth in more senses than one. I'd got myself all stirred up about giving the old chap his last request; doing the very best that was in me for a man I had liked and respected. But those relations! They took a very different view of it.

Now, sir, I trust that you will not take an unsympathetic view of this incident. I am still eager to serve the firm in my present capacity, but I think you will agree that this locality is no longer the most favourable for my operations. I have heard that you are opening up a branch in the Northern Territory. If that position has not yet been filled, I most respectfully suggest that it is the ideal place for me.

Yours faithfully,

J. S. Bunkle.

The Garden of Dreams

For two hundred miles of travelling, always westerly, always into more sparsely settled and arid country — through the familiar box- and pine-trees of the wheat-farming lands, into the vast grazing land of the grey-green, drooping wilga-trees and ephemeral western grasses — we had been thinking with pleasurable anticipation of the big riverside town ahead of us. For the last twenty miles the road had approached and retreated from the river, giving us glimpses of the immense serpent of green formed by the rows of river-gums, dense along both banks; there were patches of private irrigation, small areas of bright green sorghum, or ambitious projects, almost as far as the eye could see over the flat plains, which must have cost tens of thousands of pounds to establish and had produced a paradisaical richness of growth that seemed incredible and miraculous in that kind of country. It made the river appear to be an exciting and almost magical thing; and the town, which I had never seen before, would be worthy of the river, I felt sure.

"We shall be entertained royally in this place," my friend Robert Stevens said to me. "A man called Sampson has been writing to me off and on for years, urging me to come and visit Nangotta." Then he went on to give me quite a biography of the man. Stevens is a member of parliament, and talking about everything comes easily to him.

"Sampson is one of those born with a silver spoon in his mouth. Son of a big grazier; sent to a Great Public School and Sydney University, though I imagine that what he chiefly learnt there was the first steps in becoming a man of the world: a big place of his own as soon as he reached his majority, and a beautiful woman for his wife. He gets around a great deal; he is well known in Sydney and Melbourne, as well as all over the country."

"He certainly seems to have been lucky," I said, recalling the stories of hardship and struggle we had been listening to in the last few days.

"Well, not entirely. His wife's people are family friends of mine, close enough to get me involved in her affairs. I was shocked recently to have a letter from her saying that she thought she would have to leave him. But, as I said before, he's going to see that we have a wonderful time in this town."

That sounded promising to me. We couldn't exactly say that we'd had wonderful times in the towns we'd been calling at in the past few days. Towns in the marginal farming areas; towns planned optimistically in the boom days after the first world war, when it was thought that all that was needed to turn the dry areas into prosperous wheat-farms were railway lines and closer settlement, but which had never revived after the setback received in the depression of the nineteen-thirties. Towns where there was no electricity, and no water-supply except the minimum quantity of rainwater that each householder collected off his galvanized-iron roof; hence there were no gardens and no lawns, and a parched, dried-out, and dusty aspect wherever one looked. Places in which it was the oddest sight to see how the first keen businessmen had made their choice of corner sites to build their shops, garages, or hotels in the new and coming towns, and now, thirty years later, still to see no buildings between the original ones. Unless you could visualize the surveyor's pegs and the markings of the proposed streets, you might think that the citizens hated each other so much that they couldn't endure to be near each other. Sometimes this seemed to be actually the case; someone would be waiting for us, hot with his all-consuming grievance against another inhabitant, usually one vested in a little authority in the comically far-flung, skeletal, footpathless village.

My friend's secretary had sent telegrams ahead of us, saying: "Mr Stevens will be at —— on Tuesday afternoon", or whatever the anticipated time might be; and it was always a matter of interest to discover what response the telegram had evoked. His tour was both official and informal; a forestalling of the possible complaint, "He never comes to visit *our* town." Always we were entertained in the public bar of a hotel — *the* hotel, in the smaller places — normally a tolerable enough way of being entertained, but when it started at ten in the morning at Aramah, and ended at ten at night in Zandibingal, the beer was as hard to get down as if it were dishwater, while whisky or gin merely had a scarifying effect on the stomach, without the slightest exhilaration accompanying it.

The character of the towns, and of our receptions, seemed to depend to quite a degree on the size of the population, which we always calculated by the number of hotels. In one-hotel towns our coming was an important event. Here the chairman of the local branch of our political organization would be on the look-out, with his telegram in his pocket, to tell us how many hours he had been waiting. He was usually an aggressive type of farmer who ran all the public bodies (and the smallest towns seemed to have as many as the largest) — the Parents' and Citizens', the Show society, the recreation ground, the public hall and the cemetery trusts; sometimes even a progress association in towns which seemed to have made no progress in thirty years.

The first concern of the local man would usually be some vital and secretive matter: some shortcoming he'd discovered in the local postmaster, or some check he'd received from a government department in connection with his public responsibilities, which it would give him enormous satisfaction to circumvent by making use of the powerful intervention of the local Federal member. All these requests, no matter how fantastically puerile some of them might be, Stevens recorded in a little brown notebook, to take up conscientiously with the proper authority in due time.

Then the local gentleman, having set the world to rights, would rush around the village and collect everyone who was at a loose end at the moment. A mixed lot, composed of the indolent aged and the idle youth, a few impatient farmers waiting for broken parts of their tractors to be repaired at the garage; always an entirely masculine audience, unless there happened to be a barmaid at that hotel, who would watch the goings-on with a blandly indifferent curiosity.

There was some reward for Stevens in the awe and respect with which he was treated in these places; ejaculations of amazement followed his pronouncements, and the most obliging laughter greeted every sally. It was relatively easy to get away from a one-hotel town. The audience was likely to start breaking up fairly soon; terrifically important things had to be done in those little unheard-of villages, which the presence of even their parliamentary member must not be allowed to delay. It ended with Stevens thanking the chairman cordially for what he had done.

"You know," he'd say to me after we'd got going again, "I've got to admire a man like that; doing all that onerous voluntary work in a little, thankless place, which very few men would think was worth their while."

Two-hotel towns were likely to pay us less public attention, but the people we met generally had a little more sophistication. There was the same deplorable lack of water, though usually a local electricity-supply, generated by an enterprising garage-owner with a big diesel engine. The gaps between the houses were filled in a little more, they had pavements of a kind in certain sections, and they invariably had a big Greek or Italian café, gleaming with lacquer, chromium, and glass, reminding one of Russell Drysdale's paintings, such as "Joe's Garden of Dreams", picturing the owner and his shop set against a background of hot, dry, treeless plains.

In these cafés my parliamentary friend was always immediately recognized and made much of by the proprietors. At first I put it down to a surprising political awareness on the part of the Greeks or Italians, but Stevens told me that it was due to the fact that these people were always applying to him to get them landing permits for relatives whom they wanted to bring out to Australia. In two-hotel towns the party officials did not wait expectantly for our arrival. They were likely to be storekeepers or bank officers, busy at their jobs, but willing to neglect their duties while they took us to the better of the hotels, where an audience of a kind accumulated gradually, with the usual requests to be written down in Stevens's little notebook. It took us a bit longer to get away.

"I have to be grateful for what is done for me there," Stevens always said. "It's a grim and tedious job keeping an organization like ours going between elections."

But now at our beautiful river town, where the inhabitants splashed and sprayed the abundant water extravagantly on parks and gardens as if impelled to create a verdant oasis that would compensate for the millions of arid acres surrounding them, we had the promise of the man Sampson that our reception would be worthy of a parliamentary representative and his friend.

Naturally, we couldn't expect to be welcomed immediately on arrival, as in the small towns where nothing could happen without everyone knowing about it; so, since we'd had no lunch and it was already three o'clock in the afternoon, we went to one of the characteristic chromium, glass, and lacquer cafés. This was owned by an elderly Italian who, as I might have expected, was one of Stevens's far-flung acquaintances. He had a lined and ravaged face that was not without a certain dignity, and an air of immense and perpetual seriousness. He was proud of having fresh fish on the menu for us, something rare and inviting so far inland — perch and yellow-belly, taken that morning from the river which flowed close past the back of his shop. He invited us to have a look at his river view while our meal was being prepared.

There at the back of the café, we discovered, he had tried to recreate a little of old Italy with a fountain, fishponds full of little golden fishes, garden seats and flower-beds, even some broken columns made of cement, though all on so small and economical a scale that beside the broad river and the endless plains that stretched beyond, it rather failed in its effect. Yet we gave him credit for it, and commended him. Undoubtedly it was his Garden of Dreams, and represented the investment of a considerable sum of money from which there would be no hope of a return — always a matter of serious concern to an Italian café-proprietor.

The fish was really good, done with loving care, tender and palatable, though having the slightly flat flavour of inland river fish. Our host watched over us solicitously, or stood silently and unmoving behind his counter (it being the quiet time of the afternoon for cafés), with his sad and ravaged face composed, while he watched his young assistants bustling about the shop, tidying and cleaning in the tireless, efficient way of Italians.

"That man has quite a story," Stevens said to me. "He came out here about thirty years ago with nothing, and worked prodigiously hard for many years, until he was able to buy this café. Then he arranged, in the way that the Italians do, for a girl to be sent out for a wife. She was a lovely young woman and the marriage turned out to be remarkably successful, as these arranged marriages among Greeks and Italians so frequently do (don't ask me why). They were idyllically happy, had three beautiful children, but then a terrible thing happened. She was taking the children on a visit to some café people in a neighbouring town, in a car they'd recently bought, and, through some mishap or lack of experience, she stalled it on a level-crossing, right in front of an oncoming train. They were all killed."

I looked at the man's face and could see the story written there.

"Some people have the most dreadful misfortune," was all I could think of to say.

"Oh, that's not all," said Stevens. "For years he seemed to suffer appallingly. He kept the café going in an automatic and half-heedless manner, mainly because of the excellent assistance he got from these two young fellows; then finally he got the idea that he hadn't much longer to live, and that he ought to do something about the pretty good inheritance there would be for someone when he died. He started writing letters to Italy, and at last it was decided that his youngest sister, with her husband and family of five, were to come to Australia at his expense. That would mean a big outlay for him, but it was the only way, because his sister's family was extremely poor. This was the stage at which I became involved in his affairs. They had trouble about getting landing permits, and I was asked to look into the matter.

"The confidential department explanation I got was that the husband's state of health was the obstacle; he was a bad case of T.B. That started another spate of correspondence with the relatives. At first they denied that there was anything wrong with the husband's health; they said he'd never had a day off work in his life, which might have been quite true too. But presently the tone changed; the man was desperately ill, and the wife and children destitute. By this time Pelagio had come to feel responsible for the family, and so a lot of money which had been set aside for the fares went to maintain them.

"After a cruelly long period of suffering, the husband died. That seemed to be the chance to get the family out, but there were more delays; the sister was terrified of bringing out the children on her own, and our medical authorities were apparently cautious about giving a clean bill of health for the family without a precautionary interval. All this, let me tell you, took years to happen. Now, at last, everything is cleared up, and the family is on the way over."

At this point Pelagio, who had been watching us at intervals, and who was, I had no doubt, well aware in the supersensitive Latin way, that he was being talked about, took some letters off a shelf, and after sorting through them came over to our table in a hesitating manner with some photographs in his hand.

"Excuse me," he said, in his sad, old, guttural voice, "this is my sister with her children. Quite big children they is now." They looked very much like the photos one sees in newspapers or on the newsreels, of Italian peasants dressed in drab clothing, with round, dark faces and big, apprehensive eyes. It brought home to one with a shock just what pangs the decision to emigrate must have cost them; and just how forlorn and fearful they would feel when they arrived in this country.

"Yes, nice big children," Stevens agreed. Then he added with a great amount of circumspect kindness in his manner, "They must be about the same age as yours would have been."

Pelagio gave a great, heartfelt sigh. "Oh, yes," he said, without apparently taking the point that they would be a recompense for him, "soon they will be here, and at last the end of the great expense."

"It will be wonderful for you," said Stevens, who was never willing to see anything but the best in people, "to see your sister again."

"Yes, yes," Pelagio agreed, without cheering up to any great degree, "but she knows no word of English to work in the shop."

"The children will learn quickly enough, and they'll soon be able to help you."

"Yes, yes," Pelagio said, still a little doubtfully. Then he went back to the counter to serve a customer with cigarettes.

"These Italians," I said, "have a very keen appreciation of the value of money. He's worried that he won't get enough back in assistance, to justify the expense the family has been to him."

"You do him an injustice," Stevens rebuked me. "He has the profoundest affection for that family; but he's so sure he's going to die soon that he's worried about the prospects of getting them familiar with running the business before they're left without him."

"Your sentiments do you great credit, Rob," I said.

Just then a man came swinging into the café who looked as if he owned all the town and the surrounding country within a fifty-mile radius — one of those substantial grazier types, short, solid and robust of physique, somewhat ruddy in the face, dressed a bit carelessly in the very best kind of sports-coat and slacks, the characteristic wide-brimmed, flat-crowned felt hat, a silk shirt, and a woollen tie to show his faithfulness to the interests of his industry.

"Hey, Pelagio," he called out, regardless of the fact that the proprietor was serving a customer, "have you seen any distinguished visitors in the town? I'm expecting a Very Important Person."

"Oh yes, Mr Sampson, he is here." He made a delighted gesture towards our table. "There he is — Mr Stevens."

The man came charging across, scattering the afternoon-tea people who were beginning to fill the place.

"Rob, old boy, I'm delighted to see you here. Sorry I didn't find you in time to take you to lunch, but I've been shockingly busy."

He sat down as if he was suddenly exhausted, pulling off his hat as he did so. Close up he looked both younger and more dissipated, and not so impressive as when he'd appeared at the door. He had obviously been drinking. He greeted me with polite cordiality, but he had an air of being on his guard in the presence of a stranger; a little uneasy that he wouldn't make just quite as good an impact as he would like to. Pelagio came fussing over to him.

"Mr Sampson, you like some nice fresh fish, too? Perch or yellow-belly? You ask these gentlemen; very nice."

"No thank, Pelagio, this is one of my fast days."

Pelagio looked at him, greatly concerned. "To eat, a very good idea."

Sampson turned to us. "Good old Pelagio; great friend of mine; always trying to mother me." He waved him away and turned to us urgently. "Say, if you're finished here, what about coming where we can be comfortable and have a good talk?" He led the way briskly to the nearest hotel.

"I didn't think," Stevens said, looking a bit surprised, "that you'd patronize *this* place; I remember it as rather seedy and run-down."

"As a matter of fact," Sampson said, continuing with his headlong stride, "it still is seedy and run-down. But it's near, and that's something." He gave us a speculative grin. "In fact, it's a hell of a lot." He grabbed a shirt-sleeved cigarette-sucking individual by the arm and said "Scotch" with the same kind of fervour and reverence that you see in the whisky advertisements in the expensive American magazines. He led the way to what was obviously a hastily improvised beer garden, done out after ten o'clock closing had been introduced. It had a floor of rough, unevenly worn bricks, and garden furniture of hard wooden slats. Knowing country hotels, I immediately realized from the steady through-traffic in both directions that it had previously been, and still actually was, the passage from the public bar to the lavatory, now covered with a bleak galvanized-iron roof, and sprinkled with potted palms.

"We're coming on," I said. "It's the first time we haven't been entertained in the public bar."

"The only civilized way to drink," Sampson said, dropping into one of the hard seats with a resounding clatter. But he soon bounded out again to hurry the drinks.

"That man," Stevens said, "has a beautiful, charming, and cultured wife, three delightful children, and a magnificent home, but he seems to prefer to spend his time in places like this."

Soon Sampson was back with an enormous tray full of drinks, and an assorted company of gentlemen at his heels. They looked much more sophisticated than the men we'd been meeting in the smaller towns, and I soon discovered them to be stock-and-station agents, owners of considerable businesses, professional men, and landowners of substance. Some of them knew Stevens, and all the rest of them were soon calling him by his first name. The majority of them looked the definitely hard-drinking type. They surrounded us and submerged us in a dense, high-pressure area of volatile fumes and cigarette smoke, while beating upon our ears with a battery of high-spirited conversation. Here there was no awed waiting upon the oracle. Stevens was allowed to speak, if he was quick enough to seize the opportunity, and out of some concern for him the subject of politics cropped up now and then, but most of the time it seemed to me that everyone was talking at once, and anyone who lacked a listener immediately bustled away to the service hatch to order another tray of drinks, thrusting it upon us with a fervid cordiality that could not be denied.

The only admittedly legitimate way of getting a little temporary relief from the flood was to join in the ever-increasing procession that went through the beer garden to the lavatory. However, that respite could be only brief, partly because the place was so nauseating, but mainly because one of the party would soon turn up, take one by the arm urgently and say, "Come on, we'd better hurry back, or we'll be missing a round." Then the chairs and the tables and the suffering drinkers hurrying out, swirled and eddied around us, and the uneven floor harassed our feet, till it seemed to be something achieved to be safely seated again.

I shouted to make myself heard above the noise, "Rob, we'd better get out and see more of the townspeople before the shops close!"

But Sampson overheard and cut in. "Don't worry," he said, his speech now slower and more deliberate, "you'll see everybody without moving. I've had the word passed around, 'Rob Stevens is at the Royal'. If you go away now, you'll be missing people who want to see you."

Then he looked at his watch and with difficulty focused attention. "Four o'clock, by hell! I had a terrifically important appointment with my solicitor at three twenty, to fix something up for my wife. Got to hurry like damnation. Now, don't move from here. I'll be back quite soon to look after you some more."

He charged off, leaning forward in his eagerness, with a bemused look on his face, getting into traffic difficulties when he had to dodge around people, and as he was going through the door. But that didn't lessen the pressure on us. New people, just as Sampson had promised, kept turning up, each eager to buy a drink for his parliamentary representative, and each obliging him, by the inviolable law of the liquor trade, to return the compliment; each, of course, included the entire party that waxed and waned about us, and started another cycle that had to be worked to its conclusion.

"Have to go now, Rob," I said, "or we'll miss dinner at our hotel."

But then two men came in with outstretched hands, and as soon as they had been accommodated there were others. Even on his several walks out to the back, Stevens would be tagged by men seizing the chance for an urgent request to get them out of their troubles with the taxation department, and these men, on returning, expressed their gratitude by speeding up the tempo of the rounds. It seemed that the town was too large and Stevens's fame too great for the party ever to come to an end naturally. An hour went by, with no notice taken of the compulsory six-thirty break, while the liquor-logged participants leaned blurrily upon the whisky-spattered table, or lurched out over the beer-soaked floor.

"Your ulcer, Rob," I said, becoming inventive as a last resort. "If you don't get some bland food wrapped round it you'll be a cot-case tomorrow."

That made an impact on the dazed wits about us. "Ulcer!" they said, perturbed.

"Yes, I've got to look after him."

"My word, yes. We'll never get another member like him."

Stevens rose — gratefully, I'm sure — and we hurried out before someone else could come in and start the cycle off again.

On the way out through the public bar we were surprised to find Sampson, deeply immersed in another party.

"Did you fix your business with your solicitor?" I chipped him.

He looked at me as if he could vaguely remember seeing me somewhere before; then recognition came slowly. He put out a hand as he laboured for words. "Matter of fact, I telephoned him when I found I'd missed my appointment. Made another appointment for five fifteen."

"You'll have to hurry, then," Stevens admonished him. "It's after seven now."

Sampson looked at Stevens as if he had difficulty in identifying him, too, then laboriously at his watch.

"Ah, damnation! Have to phone him again." He started off, but at the door his host's responsibilities overtook him.

"Where are you going now? I'm going to take you to dinner at the best hotel. Don't forget that."

We reminded him of the time, and that there was nothing for it but Pelagio's.

"Meet me there. Meet me there in ten or fifteen minutes. Remember, it's on me." We saw him walking down the street quite jauntily, though when people nodded to him he seemed to have difficulty in recalling who they were.

Pelagio welcomed us. He overlooked our sodden condition, and urged hot soup, coffee, and other restoratives upon us. "Mr Sampson," he said anxiously, "he not with you?"

"He's gone to his solicitor's," I said, not meaning to give him away, "has to sign an important document."

But Pelagio was quick to reach his conclusion. "Oh, poor Mr Sampson. Too much whisky, too many times. And he with the beautiful wife and the beautiful children. Why in the name of God should he drink so much?"

"Oh, he's a nice fellow," Rob said to redeem my slip.

"Oh, yes, yes, he is a very nice man. He is my friend for a long time. Always speaks to me and makes me laugh."

This gave me a new light on both of them. I hadn't thought it possible for anyone to make Pelagio laugh. We ate our food and drank our coffee, feeling distinctly better; taking our time and, for my part, at least, hoping that we'd seen the last of our eager host Sampson. But just as we were about to leave and get some rest at our hotel, he arrived.

"I must apologize. Terribly sorry. Couldn't get on to my solicitor anywhere. Rang all the places I could think of, then I started a round of the pubs to see if he was in any of them."

It wasn't really necessary for him to tell us the latter part. Sampson was now very close to the state when he could no longer be respected. When he lurched, Pelagio held him up by the arm and looked most distressed.

"You sit down here, Mr Sampson, eat some nice hot soup, drink some strong coffee. I get you some quick."

"No, no, Pelagio. I'm all right. I'm not hungry today. Besides, I've got social obligations. I've promised a lot of fellows to take Mr Stevens round to the club, so they can buy him a drink or two."

Pelagio did not presume to say anything, but he looked at us as if he had a vast amount of compassion for people whose social eminence obliged them to consume great quantities of liquor. He made a covert sign to one of his assistants, and presently took a cup of coffee from his hands. He offered this to Sampson.

"Very hot, very sweet," he said, as if this had occurred a considerable number of times before.

Sampson took him by the arm and shook it. "I'm drunk, am I?" he demanded.

"Oh, no, no!"

Sampson's face broke into a slow smile, the stiffened facial muscles of the alcoholic responding tardily to the impulses from his muddled brain. "You're a good friend of mine, Pelagio," he said. "I'll drink your coffee, even if it kills me."

"Coffee will never kill you." It was the nearest Pelagio went to a reproach. He watched Sampson drinking the coffee, with a touching look of sympathy on his face. Sampson put down his cup. He looked at us, and it took him so long to formulate his thoughts that for a while I wondered whether he was going to say anything or not.

"Pelagio is getting his sister and her five children out from Italy. That will be a great thing for him, won't it?"

We agreed. Then suddenly we were all alarmed. A dreadful greeny-yellow colour had suffused Sampson's face; perspiration stood out in drops on his forehead. He rose giddily to his feet. Immediately Pelagio had him by the arm and supported him out the back door. Stevens looked very upset. "There's no hope for a man like that," he said regretfully. "He has to go on being a dreadful worry to his wife and an increasing embarrassment to his children until he dies."

Presently Sampson returned, trying to look as if there was nothing wrong with him. "Now to the club," he said, with a courageous attempt at jauntiness.

"Look here," said Stevens, "let's drop the club. We need some rest. We've had a hard day, and I have phone-calls to make and letters to write."

Sampson was perturbed. "A promise is a promise. A lot of fine fellows are expecting me to bring you around. If I don't bring you, I'll have to spend the rest of the night explaining and apologizing and consoling them with drinks."

We got up to go. There was nothing else to be done.

At the club we met some of the people who had been entertaining us in the afternoon, and a lot more like them. For a while Stevens contrived to maintain a lively political discussion, with the attention off the drinking, but it soon turned into the usual cyclic bout, and the man most responsible for speeding up the intake was, of all people, Sampson.

When the club at last closed down, I thought we had reached the end of our orgy, but Sampson had other ideas. He had got an invitation to a friend's place, a doctor who apparently rated highly in the social life of the town. It was round eleven, and Stevens and I were full of misgivings that the invitation had really been for a more suitable hour. But Sampson was adamant and in such a state of mind that he would have been deeply offended and most difficult if we had refused to go with him. The hosts had obviously given us up, after expending any pleasurable anticipations they might have had while they waited; now they were deadly weary.

We spent an embarrassing hour there; it was much worse than in the hotel or the club, because in a bar-room crowd at least there is a sort of individual indistinguishability, but in the tired doctor's house whatever anyone did stood out in bold relief. We flogged along a dreary, inanimate conversation; we tried to cover up poor Sampson's deplorable condition; we made many resolute efforts to move him, but did not succeed until there was not a drop of liquor left in the house.

The only thing to do with him, we decided, was to take him to our hotel and see if we could find a place for him to sleep — a not very hopeful prospect, with all the staff undoubtedly in bed. But he was determined to drive his twenty miles home.

"Get a drink of coffee from Pelagio, and I'll be right."

Pelagio's was closed, but he opened the door after a lot of knocking, and quite uncomplainingly made coffee for all of us. And that wasn't all he was prepared to do. He got into the car with Sampson to see him safely out of the town, through the difficult creek-crossing where the bridge was unsafe, and onto his long, straight road home. We made a rather half-hearted offer to drive out with them and bring Pelagio back, but Sampson was quite outraged at the suggestion; he was our host, and it would be unpardonable of him to cause us any inconvenience.

We went to bed thankfully, and slept as well as the conflict between our drugged brains and our outraged stomachs would allow us. We were late for breakfast in the morning, and the injured waitresses declined to talk to us, though we suspected, from the excited way they were going on among each other, that something extraordinary had happened.

"We'll go and say good-bye to Pelagio before we leave."

But at the café the young assistants told us, with dramatic voices and anguished faces, that Pelagio was dead. Sampson too. The car had been wrecked at the damaged bridge, and both men had been killed instantly.

We went back to the hotel and had a drink of our own volition.

"Well, that's that," Stevens said. "One could have expected it for Sampson. But Pelagio — that was a real tragedy." He got out his little brown notebook. "We'll have to send wreaths to both the funerals, and a condolatory letter to Sampson's widow." Then he looked at me with troubled eyes. "But what am I going to do about that poor unfortunate sister of Pelagio's? Arriving in Sydney next week, and not one person in the whole wide continent that she knows?"

We left our drinks unfinished, finding them unbearably distasteful.

Then he said, "Come on, my boy; off to the next town. See what's waiting for us there."

Douglas
Stewart

Nodding Greenhood

The slim green stem, the head
Bent in its green reverie;
So like the first discovery
Of what the hands could make
Or spirit dream out of rock
In the deep gully's shade . . .

All that has come to pass
Where gum-trees tower in millions
Lies in the globe of silence
The little wild orchids hold,
Lifting each hollow hood
Nine in a row from the moss.

Terra Australis

1

Captain Quiros and Mr William Lane,
Sailing some highway shunned by trading traffic
Where in the world's skull like a moonlit brain
Flashing and crinkling rolls the vast Pacific,

Approached each other zigzag, in confusion,
Lane from the west, the Spaniard from the east,
Their flickering canvas breaking the horizon
That shuts the dead off in a wall of mist.

"Three hundred years since I set out from Lima
And off Espiritu Santo lay down and wept
Because no faith in men, no truth in islands
And still unfound the shining continent slept;

"And swore upon the Cross to come again
Though fever, thirst and mutiny stalked the seas
And poison spiders spun their webs in Spain,
And did return, and sailed three centuries,

"Staring to see the golden headlands wade
And saw no sun, no land, but this wide circle
Where moonlight clots the waves with coils of weed
And hangs like silver moss on sail and tackle,

"Until I thought to trudge till time was done
With all except my purpose run to waste;
And now upon this ocean of the moon,
A shape, a shade, a ship, and from the west!"

2

"What ship?" "The *Royal Tar!*" "And whither bent?"
"I seek the new Australia." "I, too, stranger;
Terra Australis, the great continent
That I have sought three centuries and longer;

"And westward still it lies, God knows how far,
Like a great golden cloud, unknown, untouched,
Where men shall walk at last like spirits of fire
No more by oppression chained, by sin besmirched."

"Westward there lies a desert where the crow
Feeds upon poor men's hearts and picks their eyes;
Eastward we flee from all that wrath and woe
And Paraguay shall yet be Paradise."

"Eastward," said Quiros, as *San Pedro* rolled,
High-pooped and round in the belly like a barrel,
"Men tear each other's entrails out for gold;
And even here I find that men will quarrel."

"If you are Captain Quiros you are dead."
"The report has reached me; so is William Lane."
The dark ships rocked together in the weed
And Quiros stroked the beard upon his chin:

"We two have run this ocean through a sieve
And though our death is scarce to be believed
Seagulls and flying-fish were all it gave
And it may be we both have been deceived."

3

"Alas, alas, I do remember now;
In Paradise I built a house of mud
And there were fools who could not milk a cow
And idle men who would not though they could.

"There were two hundred brothers sailed this ocean
To build a New Australia in the east
And trifles of money caused the first commotion
And one small cask of liquor caused the last.

"Some had strange insects bite them, some had lust,
For wifeless men will turn to native women,
Yet who could think a world would fall in dust
And old age dream of smoke and blood and cannon

"Because three men got drunk?" "With Indian blood
And Spanish hate that jungle reeked to Heaven;
And yet I too came once, or thought I did,
To Terra Australis, my dear western haven,

"And broke my gallows up in scorn of violence,
Gave land and honours, each man had his wish,
Flew saints upon the rigging, played the clarions:
Yet many there were poisoned by a fish

"And more by doubt; and so deserted Torres
And sailed, my seamen's prisoner, back to Spain."
There was a certain likeness in the stories
And Captain Quiros stared at William Lane.

4

Then "Hoist the mainsail!" both the voyagers cried,
Recoiling each from each as from the devil;
"How do we know that we are truly dead
Or that the tales we tell may not be fable?

"Surely I only dreamed that one small bottle
Could blow up New Australia like a bomb?
A mutinous pilot I forbore to throttle
From Terra Australis send me demented home?

"The devil throws me up this Captain Quiros,
This William Lane, a phantom not yet born,
This Captain Quiros dead three hundred years,
To tempt me to disaster for his scorn —

"As if a blast of bony breath could wither
The trees and fountains shining in my mind,
Some traveller's tale, puffed out in moonlit weather,
Divert me from the land that I must find!

"Somewhere on earth that land of love and faith
In Labour's hands — the Virgin's — must exist,
And cannot lie behind, for there is death,
So where but in the west — but in the east?"

At that the sea of light began to dance
And plunged in sparkling brine each giddy brain;
The wind from Heaven blew both ways at once
And west went Captain Quiros, east went Lane.

Mosquito Orchid

Such infinitesimal things,
Mosquito orchids flying
Low where the grass-tree parts
And winter's sun lies dying
In a flash of green and bronze
On the dead beetle's wings
Among the broken stones.

Such infinitesimal things
And yet so many, so many,
Little green leaves like hearts,
Bright wings and red antennae
All swarming into the cold,
It seems the whole hillside stings
And glints from the grey leaf-mould.

The Snow-gum

It is the snow-gum silently,
In noon's blue and the silvery
Flowering of light on snow,
Performing its slow miracle
Where upon drift and icicle
Perfect lies its shadow.

Leaf upon leaf's fidelity,
The creamy trunk's solidity,
The full-grown curve of the crown,
It is the tree's perfection
Now shown in clear reflection
Like flakes of soft grey stone.

Out of the granite's eternity,
Out of the winters' long enmity,
Something is done on the snow;
And the silver light like ecstasy
Flows where the green tree perfectly
Curves to its perfect shadow.

from *The Birdsville Track*

1 THE FIERCE COUNTRY

Three hundred miles to Birdsville from Marree
Man makes his mark across a fierce country
That has no flower but the whitening bone and skull
Of long-dead cattle, no word but "I will kill".

Here the world ends in a shield of purple stone
Naked in its long war against the sun;
The white stones flash, the red stones leap with fire:
It wants no interlopers to come here.

Whatever it is that speaks through softer earth
Still tries to stammer indeed its broken phrases;
Between some crack in the stone mosaic brings forth
Yellow and white like suns the papery daisies;

The cassia drinks the sky in its gold cup,
Straggling on sandhills the dwarf wild-hops lift up
Their tufts of crimson flame; and the first hot wind
Blows out the suns and smothers the flames in sand.

And man too like the earth in the good season
When the Diamantina floods the whole horizon
And the cattle grow fat on wildflowers says his proud word:
Gathers the stones and builds four-square and hard:

Where the mirage still watches with glittering eyes
The ruins of his homestead crumble on the iron rise.
Dust on the waterless plains blows over his track,
The sun glares down on the stones and the stones glare back.

2 MARREE

Oh the corrugated-iron town
In the corrugated-iron air
Where the shimmering heat-waves glare
To the red-hot iron plain
And the steel mirage beyond:

The blackfellow's squalid shanty
Of rags and bags and tins,
The bright-red dresses of the gins
Flowering in that hot country
Like lilies in the dust's soft pond:

The camels' bones and the bullocks',
The fierce red acre of death
Where the Afghan groans beneath
His monstrous concrete blankets
That peel in the heat like rind:

Where life if it hopes to breathe
Must crawl in the shade of a stone
Like snake and scorpion:
All tastes like dust in the mouth,
All strikes like iron in the mind.

10 THE HUMORISTS

The red cow died and the Hereford bull,
Two figures more to cancel:
Dan Corcoran took a bullock's skull
And wrote on it with a pencil:
"Here I lie on the Birdsville Track
Driven to death by Scotty Mac."
Scotty Mac laughed fit to kill,
Saw it six months later;
Took another and tried his skill:
"Here I lie like an old tin can
Kicked down the Track by droving Dan" —
Thus drover joked with drover.
Whether the bullocks laughed as well
Nobody knows or cares;
But what they wrote on a bullock's skull
A bullock could write on theirs.

11 Ruins

Two golden butterflies mating over the ruins
Of the iron house that is nowhere's dark dead centre
Stark on the rise in the huge hot circle of the plains
All doors and windows gaping for the wind to enter —
Lord, Lord they think that nowhere is all the world
And, so they can dance their golden dance of love,
One hot blue day in the desert more than enough.

And in that same dark house when her husband perished
The woman, they say, lived on so long alone
With what she could think and the household things she cherished,
Staring at that vast island of purple stone
Without one break until the mirage unfurled
Its ocean of steel, it tore a great gap in her mind
Harsh as the loose sheet of iron that bangs in the wind.

13 Place Names

Ethadinna, Mira Mitta,
Mulka, Mungerannie —
Dark shadows blown
With the dust away,
Far from our day
Far out of time,
Fill the land with water.
Where the blue sky flames
On the bare red stone,
Dulkaninna, Koperamanna,
Ooroowilanie, Kilalpaninna —
Only the names
In the land remain
Like a dark well
Like the chime of a bell.

19   Night Camp

Sleep, traveller, under the thorn on the stones.
Somewhere on earth a man must lie down in trust
And though behind you, cold as it breathes on your hand,
Thudding like surf through the desert, foaming with dust,
Rushes the wind that moves the hills of sand,
What need of more than a bush to turn the gale?
Sleep, all's well.
Look where the dusty blossoms shake on the thorn
Over your head, like motes in a shaft of the moon
Climbing and falling, fluttering their wings now come
Tiny white moths that call this desert home.

25   The Branding Fire

The dust, the smoke and the yellow fire on
The red plain heating the branding-iron,
As though the sun's long white-hot blast
Had struck the stones to flame at last.
And where the stockmen bronze and hard
Roll their smokes in the high stockyard
And watch that wild young bull break loose
Defiant from the calves and cows,
And bellowing with rage and pain
Run mad across the vast hot plain
With tail out stiff and tossing horns,
Kicking the stones up when he turns
To meet the blackboy cantering after,
Like smouldering coals I hear their laughter;
Like man's own will I see that fire,
Who stamps the stones with his desire,
Who herds his beasts and burns his brand
Like red-hot iron on this red land.

The Silkworms

All their lives in a box! What generations,
What centuries of masters, not meaning to be cruel
But needing their labour, taught these creatures such patience
That now though sunlight strikes on the eye's dark jewel
Or moonlight breathes on the wing they do not stir
But like the ghosts of moths crouch silent there.

Look it's a child's toy! There is no lid even,
They can climb, they can fly, and the whole world's their tree;
But hush, they say in themselves, we are in prison.
There is no word to tell them that they are free,
And they are not; ancestral voices bind them
In dream too deep for wind or word to find them.

Even in the young, each like a little dragon
Ramping and green upon his mulberry leaf,
So full of life, it seems, the voice has spoken:
They hide where there is food, where they are safe,
And the voice whispers, "Spin the cocoon,
Sleep, sleep, you shall be wrapped in me soon."

Now is their hour, when they wake from that long swoon;
Their pale curved wings are marked in a pattern of leaves,
Shadowy for trees, white for the dance of the moon;
And when on summer nights the buddleia gives
Its nectar like lilac wine for insects mating
They drink its fragrance and shiver, impatient with waiting,

They stir, they think they will go. Then they remember
It was forbidden, forbidden, ever to go out;
The Hands are on guard outside like claps of thunder,
The ancestral voice says Don't, and they do not.
Still the night calls them to unimaginable bliss
But there is terror around them, the vast, the abyss,

And here is the tribe that they know, in their known place,
They are gentle and kind together, they are safe for ever,
And all shall be answered at last when they embrace.
White moth moves closer to moth, lover to lover.
There is that pang of joy on the edge of dying —
Their soft wings whirr, they dream that they are flying.

The Blacktracker's Story

FROM *FISHER'S GHOST*

There is a thing that I have found
In the creek of Fisher's ghost
Would make a white man blench with fear
And a black man run, almost.

It is a creek like other creeks
(Fisher's ghost is lonely)
That sleeps on sandy beds for weeks
Or stumbles where it's stony.

Through paddocks brown, through crops of corn
(Oh where is Fisher now?)
I followed it and thought it knew
A thing no creek should know.

I saw the little clear brown pool
(Oh where is Fisher buried?)
Where water-beetles chase the sun
And dragonflies are married.

I saw the floating water-spinners
(What's that beneath the rocks?)
Whose shadows lie on the sand below
Like footfalls of a fox.

I saw the mudhole in the bank
(It seemed a thing to fear)
And there the yabbie crawled to drink
With claws out like a spear.

The moon was on the standing corn
(Fisher's ghost is lonely)
And every pool and easy turn
The creek was white and moony.

I took a sheaf I stripped the leaf
(Dead man's fat floats up)
And skimmed that cold white water there
And drank it like a cup.

Lord come and wash you, little creek,
From mountain to the coast,
For I have tasted murder there
In the creek of Fisher's ghost.

B Flat

Sing softly, Muse, the Reverend Henry White
Who floats through time as lightly as a feather
Yet left one solitary gleam of light
Because he was the Selborne naturalist's brother

And told him once how on warm summer eves
When moonlight filled all Fyfield to the brim
And yearning owls were hooting to their loves
On church and barn and oak-tree's leafy limb

He took a common half-a-crown pitch-pipe
Such as the masters used for harpsichords
And through the village trod with silent step
Measuring the notes of those melodious birds

And found that each one sang, or rather hooted,
Precisely in the measure of B flat.
And that is all that history has noted;
We know no more of Henry White than that.

So, softly, Muse, in harmony and conformity
Pipe up for him and all such gentle souls
Thus in the world's enormousness, enormity,
So interested in music and in owls;

For though we cannot claim his crumb of knowledge
Was worth much more than virtually nil
Nor hail him for vast enterprise or courage,
Yet in my mind I see him walking still

With eager ear beneath his clerical hat
Through Fyfield village sleeping dark and blind,
Oh surely as he piped his soft B flat
The most harmless, the most innocent of mankind.

Arthur Stace

That shy mysterious poet Arthur Stace
Whose work was just one single mighty word
Walked in the utmost depths of time and space
And there his word was spoken and he heard.
Eternity, Eternity, it banged him like a bell
Dulcet from heaven sounding, sombre from hell.

Sometimes it twinkled to him in the sand
As though God winked at him, and then he smiled
And scooped it up to sift it through his hand;
Sometimes it roared upon him vast and wild
When the green seas rolled heaving from the Gap;
Appalled he stood, to think a man might leap

And swim those waves, and could if he had strength,
Could count the sand, if he had time enough,
And yet the sea was not one inch in length
Against those endless miles his thought slid off,
And though you counted the sand-grains ten times over
You'd not begun Eternity's awful number.

One two three four, sometimes he counted all day,
Five six seven eight, and on far into the night
By tens, by thousands, hoping to reach half way,
And still before his eyes like swans in flight
Though he got up to billions and to trillions
The numbers streamed away into the silence.

O it was in the sky that had no end
Where fiery worlds hung glittering in the void;
He thought of Heaven where man had his big friend
And that was safe he knew and that was good,
But at the back of heaven he felt, he feared,
The hellish dark ran on, the wild eyes glared.

And it was here in Monday, Tuesday, Friday,
In yesterday, tomorrow, morrow, morrow,
In Caesar's day, thought Arthur Stace, and my day;
It moved in him, it struck him deep with sorrow
That men should live in time with all its vanity
Or think they did, and yet were in Eternity.

For it was like a dark wind in their hair,
It burnt their eyes, it roared in their dull ears,
It flowed between their fingers with the air.
How could they be obsessed with worldly cares,
How could they sin, how waste one precious minute
When every step they took plunged deeper in it?

This must be told, he knew. But how to do it?
He was a quiet man and he was shy
And had no gift to speak, but like a poet
Must write the word that reached him from on high.
Eternity he'd heard great preachers shout
And shook to hear, but say it he could not.

No, it must come like moonlight or like frost
Silent at night like mushrooms quietly growing
To wake the wicked and redeem the lost;
Like a white feather in the dawn wind blowing,
Perfect and white, like copperplate in chalk;
And that was when Arthur Stace began to walk.

All night he walked and most nights of the week,
Treading with silent steps the silent town
Where none but drunks and whores were still awake,
His great word burning where he wrote it down;
Eternity he wrote, clear pure and pale
And underlined it with the y's long tail.

No night-bird saw him for he was an angel
Or almost that, upon his holy mission;
Unseen he passed the copper with his cudgel,
Unseen he climbed the steps at Town Hall station,
Invisible, like ectoplasm, he swam
Where shops were empty and where lights were dim.

Sometimes when midnight chimed in Martin Place
Behind the arches of the G.P.O.
A shadow moved, but was it Arthur Stace?
Some flickering thing perhaps crept soft and low
On the dark pavement by the Opera House
But was it hands that moved there or a mouse?

No one could say, one only knew for certain
That here, that there, in unexpected places
Somewhere that night the great word had been written
And Arthur Stace once more had left his traces
And bright and spry now like a leprechaun
Was stepping home to Pyrmont in the dawn.

Eternity, it fades like morning dew,
Like morning dew and he is lost in it;
Yet one can say, as one can say of few,
It was the greatest of all words he wrote
And if it hardly changed this wicked city
God rest his soul, his copperplate was pretty.

Cave Painting

Look there are dark hands in the black rock,
Man's hands, woman's hands, child's hands hiding in a cave,
Shadows of hands, but with such a living look
They seem to waver and beckon, they seem to move
In a language of gesture startling and piercing as speech.
Up from the green water here we clambered
Say the hands and the bodies of the hands, to hold and to touch,
And here we camped, and here we shall be remembered.

And they are so close and yet so far and wild
They seem to breathe and speak for all humanity
Who made their camp so, man and woman and child,
And flowed with the green river down to infinity;
And beautifully and terribly they wave
In the black rock, like hands alive in a grave.

For Kenneth Slessor

Hang it all, Slessor, as Pound once said to Browning,
Why have you sailed so untimely out on the water
To vanish up in a cloud or down by drowning
Whichever it was? You should have died hereafter.

For though you've left your verse to make amends
And so it does, as much as verse can do,
You were a man who liked to meet his friends
And here we are but where in the world are you?

Still at the top of your stairs I see you stand
Bowing a little in your courtly manner,
Smiling and gracious, shining and pink and rotund,
Bidding us into the privilege of your dinner.

And in your dining room that you've made noble
With walls of books that climb up shelf by shelf
From floor to ceiling, there's your dark wood table
Gleaming with silver you've laid out yourself,

For men must eat their beef in decent splendour
Wherever their wives and mistresses have flown
And since those bright mad girls had all gone under
The ocean somewhere, superbly you cooked your own.

I think of how we sat there light and lucky
While the soft candlelight flowed round the room
And heard you talk of Pepys and William Hickey,
Tennyson's verse and drunken pranks of Lamb;

Or venturing forth, where oystery rocks were waiting
At Bobbin Head and you were Captain Slessor,
Staunch on your launch I see you navigating
Like Captain Dobbin, your great predecessor,

And can't believe you've sunk; yet sunk you have,
Or flown or gone, and so with due apology
I raise my voice in necessary grief
And trespass in your private field of elegy.

And yet the day you died when I went walking
— Where else to go? — restless to Circular Quay
There had come in a tide so huge and sparkling
It filled all Sydney with the open sea,

And while it flowed from Manly to Balmain
With seagulls white on it, the great blue tide,
And washed the harbour sparkling clean again
As though no man had ever drowned or died,

I thought how with your spacious hospitality
In its high tide you'd made all life a feast;
And how your verse in its rich lustrous quality
Flowed round us still though you were far and lost,

And suddenly knew it still was good that morning,
Whatever else might happen in the world,
To see that noble tide now full and turning;
And in my grief I was half reconciled.

Well, round and ripe and rich with years you went
As if you rode that great tide out to sea
And we salute you even as we lament
And drink your health wherever you may be.

Peter
Cowan

The Island

THE SQUARE of lawn before the house, and the small rose-bed, were neat and clean, but as he looked at them he thought that the roses needed pruning.

He said, "But there is no reason now for us to go on like this."

"You want me to divorce you," she said. "I'm not going to."

"We can do it decently. A separation. I'll go away."

"You want to go away. I'm not quite sure where you want to go, but I know you have something planned."

"I never denied it," he said. "I just want us to be divorced — decently and without a lot of trouble. Surely we don't have to pretend, at our age. We're nothing to one another now. Why not be reasonable about it?"

"You may say that." Her voice was controlled, but as if she were determined he would not provoke her. Her plump cheeks were flushed. "Why should I be humiliated in front of my friends — give up this place after all these years —"

"I've explained that you can have the house."

"And the children — why should they be humiliated?"

"They are independent now. And they've known how things are for long enough. Which could be why they don't live at home."

"I'm not going to do it."

"It's a mean enough pride," he said, "that would rather we dragged on not even hating each other any longer, just so that people won't talk."

"I don't see why I should put up with their gossip. I'm not going to."

"I see," he said.

"Besides," she looked at him with a mockery that irritated him almost with the strength of forgotten feeling, "besides, I think you will get over this."

"I see. And come back to heel."

"If you put it like that. I didn't."

"But we will go on?"

"We can.."

"You mean until we're too old to care. So that no one will gossip. So that your pride won't be hurt."

293

"I don't see why you should want to humiliate me in front of people I've known all my life."

He wondered if all they had achieved in their years together were to be seen in this expensively furnished but stiff room that looked out upon the square of lawn, the rose garden, and the suburban street.

"I don't," he said. "I don't want to humiliate you at all. This could be a decent separation."

"No. I've told you."

"People will talk," he said, and he thought how he hated the way she did her hair, with its fair, set waves, its stiffness. "They will talk if I get out of here and live in a flat."

"If you do they will think you are mad," she said. "If you do it. I don't think you will."

"You're very sure."

"After all, you've said things like this before."

"Yes," he said. "I suppose I have."

The wide window of the flat looked out across the city buildings, the view blocked to the north by the rise of other walls, but open southwards to the river bank and a small curve of dark water. In the short time he had been in the flat he had often found himself standing at the window, simply looking out across the buildings and the river, and it had seemed at first that the smooth square of lawn and the diamond-shaped rose garden of his suburban home might have risen like some image on a cinema screen to become imposed upon and, growing, to obliterate the view that held the rise of the hills and the buildings on the river bank.

He turned from the window to answer the telephone, realizing as he spoke that he had acted without thought, and was helpless before his wife's voice.

"David." She was patient, it was rather as though she spoke to their children when they were young. "The Harveys are coming to dinner tonight. It would be a pity if you missed them."

"Not really," he said.

"They will want to see you."

"You mean they will expect to see me."

"And why shouldn't they?"

"Look," he said, "can't we drop this charade? I'm not mad, and I'm not sulking. I've not run off in a fit of temper. I'm just not coming back."

"Very well," she said. "I'll explain that you can't be in tonight."

He put the receiver down, and only a sense of tiredness held him from anger. And the stirring of humour. For it was funny. She could defeat him. If he could not act in some decisive way, and quickly, she might well defeat him, conventionality, habit, reassert themselves, and the pair of them remain in the strange bondage of distaste and denial until it no longer mattered.

"No," he said. He stood looking down upon the buildings and the cars that passed endlessly on the curve of road by the river. "However it is to be done. Whoever gets hurt. It cannot be that."

He went downstairs and took his car from the garage. He drove out along one of the main suburban streets, avoiding particular destination, finding in the easy manipulation of the car and the sense of movement a satisfaction that the unresolved fragments of his own problem denied him.

Near an intersection where he stopped for the traffic lights, he saw on the opposite corner the parking lot of a hotel, and when the lights changed he drove across into the parking area. There were chairs and tables along the wide veranda of the hotel, and on the grass among the gardens. He bought a drink and sat at one of the tables on the lawn, for a time watching the others about him drinking and talking.

By a small side entrance he had noticed a girl alone at one of the tables. Her faint air of impatience, the fact that she once or twice looked at her watch, attracted his attention among those others who seemed happy in the endless afternoon, and he thought perhaps her friend had made a too prolonged trip to the bar. But there had been no one with her, and it seemed more likely that whoever she was expecting had not arrived. He began idly to speculate how long she would remain alone, who would make the obvious approach. Yet there was something about her that perhaps discouraged the opportunist. That she was not attractive would in this place have been irrelevant; her features were irregular, her nose rather sharp, her brows were darkened heavily as if she felt they achieved some balance to her face; her hair might have been tinted, or, being originally a dark brown, she had lightened it. He thought ironically that if she could have made up her mind about it, her hair might have been attractive; she wore it longer than the prevailing style. These things he realized might have been disregarded by those who wandered among the tables, would at least have been unlikely to deter them; but there was about her an air of self-sufficiency, almost of hardness, now intensified perhaps because she found herself alone and was annoyed. She did not look about, her glance seemed restricted to the small table top and the single glass upon it.

He got up slowly and went to the bar. Carrying his drink, he walked in a different direction back through the tables towards the side entrance. As he stood by the table she looked up, aware suddenly he intended to sit there, and he wondered briefly what she felt at this intrusion of some middle-aged stranger.

"Do you mind if I sit here?" he asked.

She looked pointedly about at the other tables that might have held vacancies. "Oh no."

"Thank you."

"Actually I'm expecting someone. A girl-friend."

"I'll leave if she comes."

He talked idly, touching only on those things which lay about them awaiting the obvious comment, so that she might feel only that he, like herself, filled in some small space of time. She answered him with an indifference he felt to be real enough, and which he began to be afraid might prevent the plan that he had abruptly, as he watched her at the table when he had first arrived, felt to be so simple. It was simple, he knew, so much so that it frightened him, for it seemed impossible.

She allowed him to buy her a drink. Finally she said, "I think I'll have to go. My friend is not coming now."

He then knew his idea of a gradual approach must fail. She would go, and he was quite certain he would never bring himself to the attempt again with someone else.

"Could I drive you home? I've got the car over there in the parking lot."

"It's all right, thanks," she said. "I can catch the bus outside. I've not far to go."

"I'm going, anyway, myself." He had risen with her, and she stood close to him, looking at the small handbag she held.

"It's quite all right." There was the beginning of impatience in her tone.

He said, "I've rather a shocking proposal I want to make to you. If you'd let me drive you home I'll explain on the way. Then if you don't agree, I'll simply drive off and — that will be that."

"Well!" she said. She looked at him directly, as if he were telling some joke the point of which must come soon.

"It's quite straightforward," he said. "Couldn't I just explain to you — it's really not improper."

"Only shocking."

He laughed. "I'm afraid it might be."

"If it's what I think," she said, "at least I've never known anyone use your way of trying it."

"I imagine it's not at all what you think. Will you risk finding out?"

"You've got me curious enough. Can't you give me some sort of an idea?"

"Not like this. It's rather awkward standing here." He smiled. "People will think we're arguing."

"It's a one-sided argument. I can't win. Oh, all right."

She walked with him to the parking area, and he opened the door of the car for her. As he got in she said, "This is quite a car."

"I like cars," he said. "They've been my extravagance. That, and deep-sea fishing."

"Is that all you fish for?"

"All right," he said. "I'll explain." On the road outside, as they waited for the lights, he said, "My name is David Taylor. I have a small business in town. Importing. I do fairly well. At present I have a chance to go into partnership with a friend in Sydney. We'd probably put a man in here, and I'd go over to Sydney. To live there."

She said, looking at the dash of the car as if the instruments might have held her attention rather than his words, "I see. So far."

"That part is simple. Now, the rest is not. I'm married. I don't want to take my wife to Sydney. Late as it may be, this is to be a new start, you see."

"No. Does she know you feel like this?"

"Oh yes. Only I haven't told her about the partnership. Or Sydney. Or she'd simply come with me. I — this is the part I don't suppose I can make clear — we just haven't got one thing left for one another. We fight — we just seem to bring out the worst in one another now. And it's so senseless — we'd both be much better people alone. Does that make sense?"

"I think so. Yes. Yes, it does. And if you just went away — she'd follow?"

"Yes. She won't agree to a decent divorce. It might damage her hopeless suburban pride. And perhaps — I don't know — perhaps she knows she can make me suffer. Fair enough. I've caused her enough of that, I suppose. But I don't know why we should go on with it."

"I don't think I would want to have anything to do with it," she said.

"But listen — oh, I don't even know your name — let me tell you what I've thought. It's all I can think of. I've got to do something. You're young, you haven't seen the last bit of your time running out and felt that you had to watch it go. Then nothing."

"How do you know what I've felt?" she said.

"Listen — this is what I want to ask you. I want someone who will go to places with me — be seen with me — so that people will talk and it will get back to my wife. It will be quite harmless. I can only give you my word, but it's just to make it look . . ."

"I know what you mean. You turn just at the shop, ahead. To the left."

"All right. I wouldn't expect it to be done for nothing. I'd be glad to pay a couple of hundred pounds."

"You should be able to buy someone for that."

"I didn't mean it that way. The money is the least of it. It's just that if I could find someone to help me . . ."

"It's a funny thing to want help in. Why me?"

"I don't know. I thought — you were alone — I had to approach someone . . ."

"And I looked as if I hadn't got anything to lose by a thing like that."

"I'm sorry," he said, "if it seemed like that. And I suppose it did. No — I just didn't think about it at all, I'm afraid. I was desperate and something just seemed to click. Haven't you ever done something on the moment like that?''

"Oh yes."

"Anyway, I'll never have the nerve to do it again. I'm sorry."

"It's this place," she said. "Here. The two-storey place."

He stopped before an old house that had perhaps once been set in wide grounds that now held modern buildings, itself already in disrepair, as if an anachronism.

"I'll keep my bargain," he said, "and leave you here. Thanks for being so patient."

She made no movement. She looked at the road ahead, a few cars parked along the kerbs. She said, "What would my family think?"

"What would they think? Oh. Yes. I didn't reckon on that, either. Sorry."

She laughed suddenly, looking up at him, and he realized it was the first time she had laughed since he had seen her earlier that afternoon at the table alone.

"I live by myself," she said. "There's only my father, anyhow. And he's in the country. I never see him."

"Do you think," he said, "we could go to a film tonight? Or a show some-where?"

"As part of your plan?"

"Not as part of the plan. The plan does not operate unless you agree. But it would — well — round off a strange day."

"It would, I suppose. All right."

"I'll call for you."

He closed the door and for a moment watched her walk up the path to the outmoded porch of the old house. She did not look back.

The house was different in the darkness, as he drew the car to the pavement, after the cinema. Its disrepair was less evident, and its symmetry, its original design, less circumscribed by the buildings on either side of it.

He said, "The old place looks altered — quite attractive."

"It's nothing inside," she said. "But it's not expensive."

She looked at it without interest. She seemed not aware of his own gaze. He thought her hair, touching the wide collar of her light-coloured coat, attractive; it was loose and soft, brushed simply, its lack of artifice strangely different from the way her face was made up. Her brows were darkened strongly, her eyes heavily accented, the eye shadow grotesque. The rest of her face seemed colour-less; it might have been the light that sccmcd now to make it mask-like, without animation.

"Well?" she said abruptly.

His surprise was evident, and she said with a kind of impatience, "Will I do?"

"Will you do for what, Janet?"

"For what you had in mind."

"I haven't said any more about that. If that's what you mean."

"I don't mean anything else."

"I said I'd leave it if you didn't agree."

She did not answer and he said, "You haven't had second thoughts about it?"

"Do you still want to do it?"

"Yes. I realize it's a one-sided arrangement. That I've everything to gain."

"Oh," she said, "I'd be taken out. And I'd have the money."

He said, "Janet — I didn't mean . . ."

"I'll try," she said. "If I'm no good you'll have to find someone else."

She opened the car door and stepped out.

"Thanks for tonight."

He leant awkwardly towards the open door. He was afraid she would be gone before he could speak. "How will I . . ."

"I'll be here. Good night."

In the flat, when he had changed, he turned out the light in the main room and pulled a chair to the window that looked down upon the lights of the buildings. The step he had taken no longer seemed so preposterous or so difficult. He reflected in an amused relief that the afternoon might have offered some extremely embarrassing moments if the girl had refused or become angry. But her attitude of seeming indifference made their contact easier. And the evening had not made any clearer what she felt, if in fact she had any real feeling about it at all. She might have had a kind of contempt, perhaps. He could stand that. There would be others to share it later. It would not matter. Those who knew him would reckon it his own business. Others could judge and condemn. He would no longer be there. The girl would have her money. He wondered idly what she would do with it.

In the streets below the traffic had thinned, the buildings darkening. He yawned and got up from the chair. His hand reached for the cord to pull the blind across the wide expanse of glass.

The hall of the two-storey building was poorly lit, a single globe giving a light that was lost before it reached the corners of the dark skirting-boards. On one wall near the door was a print of the city, very early, the few houses small among the scrub, and along the banks of the wide stretch of river there were trees down to the beds of rushes at the edge of the water. Looking at it, he did not hear her come into the hall, or see her stand for a moment beneath the light as though she had expected him to turn from the print upon the wall.

When he realized she was behind him he said, "This could be quite rare — probably valuable."

"I don't doubt," she said.

"The light's so wretched — I'd like to see it in daylight."

"It's not much easier to see in here at any time."

He laughed. "Well, if you say so. Ready?"

"Is that hard to see, too?"

"Eh?"

"Nothing. Come on."

As they drove he said, "I think this thing of ours is working."

"Well," she said, "I'd begun to wonder."

"My wife has stopped phoning me. There was a certain amount of unpleasantness. But, now, I've quite obviously been dropped."

"That's what you wanted, wasn't it?"

"Of course it's what I wanted," he said, momentarily irritated. "And there could be another thing — I've noticed a rather obvious character outside the flat, in a car."

She looked at him quickly. "You mean . . ."

"Perhaps I'm being watched," he said with exaggerated emphasis. He laughed. "I'd rather expected a polite note from a solicitor, but perhaps this is a preliminary."

The hotel had made a feature of its dining-room, and its floor shows and entertainers, so that it was currently fashionable. At their table the girl said, "I've never been here. It's quite a place."

He had found that her terms of approval often did not go beyond the phrase; not, he suspected, because her vocabulary was necessarily limited, but because in some way she seemed niggardly of words, using them with a kind of contempt, almost, he felt at times, afraid they betrayed her and she would reject them.

He said, "I bring clients here occasionally. One of the benefits of a business."

She said, "It's given you most things, hasn't it?"

He looked at her quickly. "My business?"

"Yes."

He laughed. "I won't rise to that one. Let's just say, some things."

He had become used to her silences, often enough he was glad of them; and as he looked at her across the table he realized he had also, after their first meeting, taken little notice of her appearance, as if to that, too, he had become accustomed. He was aware that his disregard was probably because he did not particularly like her features, the way she made herself up, which seemed to enhance the kind of hardness, at times almost sullenness, he had first noticed in her and which she seemed unconcerned to disguise. But now he was forced to a recognition that in the deep-blue evening dress she had an attractiveness he had not expected. It was the first time they had worn formal dress. He had hardened himself to the flamboyance of some of her clothes, but this was different. It was quite plain to him that others about them would have disregarded those facets of her appearance he did not much approve for the beauty of her arms and shoulders, her fine skin, clear yet with its own colour, her body which the gown more discreetly than usual but quite firmly suggested. And he thought that he would have been less than human if he had not risen to her appearance, to the regard of others which flattered him in a way he knew he had done nothing to deserve: a complex of feeling in which they might approve her as his mistress, covet her themselves, and disapprove his conduct. He felt a sudden elation at the whole misconception, and at the fact that he was at least here with her.

He began to laugh quietly, and she asked, "Is it a good joke?"

"Yes," he said. "Very."

"Tell me."

"You're too young. Look, could we dance? Now?"

"Why not?"

She danced, he found at once, far better than he did, and he realized suddenly how little he knew of her. But they seemed caught in some exhilaration he would willingly give himself to, and through the evening his restraint became lost; acquaintances spoke to them, they exchanged drinks and jokes, and if occasionally he thought there might have been irony in the glances of some of those he had for so long known in another role, it was not unfriendly, the tentative gestures passed to acceptance, and a gaiety included them all. When the evening ended and they went outside among people finding their cars, slamming doors, calling jests and farewells, he felt surprise that it had all passed so quickly, as if it were something he had not planned.

He stopped the car outside his flat. She said, "Well, we had quite a time."

"Yes. Should we have a small drink?"

"What about — your man?"

"If he's not in bed by this time, we might give him some encouragement."

"Is that what we're going to do?"

"A small drink, was all I said. And we leave the car here in the street. With the parking lights on. It's very respectable."

She laughed suddenly. "Of course."

They climbed the stairs and on the small landing he opened the door and turned on the light. She looked about the room.

"This is nice."

"Yes," he said. "I've become quite attached to it."

While he made their drinks she walked across to the window. She stood looking down at the lights of the traffic and the buildings, the long glow of colour upon the dark water. As he came in she said, "It's lovely."

She took the drink. She said slowly, "And you're going to leave it."

"I have to. A lease on one of these flats is not easy to come by."

"You're going away, anyhow. Perhaps you'll get another in Sydney."

"I hope so. If I'm lucky."

"Where we went tonight — did you go there because — of someone specially who would see us?"

"In a way. It should bring things to a head, I think."

For a time they looked at the night beyond the window, and the lights that made variations upon it, and when she put the glass down she shook her head slightly as he moved his hand towards it.

"No, thanks. I'd better go now. If your man has earned his keep."

He drove slowly through the streets that still held traffic, until in the side-streets the houses were in darkness. He walked with her along the few steps of path to the curiously jutting porch of the old house, and she pushed the door that seemed never to latch.

As she stood in the doorway he said, "I think I went there tonight to show you off."

She smiled quickly. "You didn't. But it's nice of you."

"It was as if I knew you better than our bargain. I'm sorry. It would have been wrong."

"Not really. No. Anyhow — thanks."

The door moved slowly as if it erased some pattern of the dimly lit hall. He walked down to the car. The door handle was cold; he thought there was already a fine moisture of condensation from the night air upon the metal.

The phone seemed to ring for a long time unanswered in the old lodging-house, and he wondered if for once there was no one to answer it. The success of a call always depended on someone's generosity, the odds were always too great against getting the right person at once. When a voice answered and he made his request there was a brief pause, then a disappointed agreement to find the girl.

Her own voice came quickly, as if she might have been coming to the phone herself, and he said, "Could I call for you in about half an hour? And go somewhere? Perhaps a run in the car?"

"All right," she said. "I'll be ready."

"I feel restless — like just going somewhere . . ."

"Yes."

"In half an hour."

"Yes."

As he put the receiver down he thought she might have been someone in his office, obeying requests that were instructions, showing no curiosity or feeling, and he was faintly nettled. He poured himself a drink and sat near the window.

He was aware that the radio was euphemistically presenting the news, and he got up to turn it off.

She carried a coat, and wore a light short-sleeved dress that he thought he had not seen before. As he started the car he said, "You've had dinner?"

"Oh yes."

"Shall we just drive? Go out of town somewhere?"

"All right."

Her acquiescence irritated him. He knew his feeling to be illogical. He concentrated on driving, the car going away fast through the gears down the suburban street, and they skirted the city, going over the causeway at the eastern end, the traffic beginning to thin as they followed the main road.

After a time he asked, "Where will we go?"

"Anywhere," she said. "Just driving is good."

The suburbs seemed to have passed suddenly and they were on a dark straight road, the lights of the houses set some distance back in the darkness. He worked the car up without fuss and he saw she watched the rev counter.

"That thing doesn't make sense," she said.

He laughed. "It does, of a sort."

"How fast are we going?"

"About seventy-five."

"Is that as fast as it will go?"

"No. But I'm not a speed man, really. Particularly at night. I've never explored its top speed properly."

"You'll take it with you, I suppose?"

"Take it — oh yes. I don't see myself buying another. And I'm fond of this one."

They began to climb into the hills, the car easy on the grades and turns. She sat back, relaxed, her eyes on the cone of light ahead. At the top of the climb they came into a small town, and he pulled in to the kerb outside a café.

He said, "Let's have some coffee."

He opened the door, taking her arm as she straightened from the low car. For a moment as she steadied herself her weight was against him, and her arm was cold under his hand.

"You're not cold?"

She looked up at him, and smiled, shaking her head. "No." He wished she would not use eye shadow, that her brows were not so emphasized. As if she had read his censure she looked quickly away, her features without expression. He let his hand drop from her arm and they crossed the pavement.

The café held only one other couple. They took a table against the garishly decorated wall, near the front where the light reached out across the pavement and towards the vehicles along the kerb. The proprietor, neatly and rather flashily dressed, served them.

"They have good coffee," she said.

"Yes. I felt like a drive somewhere."

"It's wonderful, just to get away like that."

He said, "I've a thing to discuss with you."

She moved her spoon as though she traced a pattern in the dark liquid.

"I thought you did."

"Oh."

"Why? Was it to be a surprise?"

"No. No."

"We didn't come up here just for the pleasure of my company. Was it your man?"

"No. Not actually."

She sipped the hot coffee.

"Then I don't know," she said.

"It's a bit difficult . . ." He felt that she mocked him, waiting to see him formulate the words she would not help him with.

"Our plan is going very well," he said.

She nodded. "I'm glad."

"If — you see, what I thought we should do . . ."

"Save it till we're going back," she said. "If you like."

He grinned. "Thanks. We might as well. Do you think they'd give us more coffee?"

"Not for me. But you have some. It's quiet here, isn't it?"

"The hills. Yes."

As they returned, the road beyond the car seemed to fall to the darkness of the valleys, and away to the west there were the lights of the city and the long ribbon of suburbs that reached towards the hills. He drove slowly and she looked out at the lights that patterned the blackness below them.

"It would be quite something to live up here. To see this at night."

"Too far out from town," he said.

He watched the steep curve, the white posts lifting along the beam of the headlights.

"You want me to go away somewhere with you."

He looked at her quickly, but she was still watching the dark plain below them. He said, "I'm sorry. You see, I thought if we went to some place — a hotel . . ."

"Yes."

"Then in the eyes of the law the thing is done."

"When do you want to do this?"

"I thought — the week-end after this coming one . . ."

"It's for you to say."

"You — don't mind?"

"I agreed in the first place. I won't go back on it."

"I'm sorry — I don't want you to be unhappy about it. There's a place down the coast a bit . . ."

"I agreed," she repeated, this time with something of impatience. The road dropped steeply and there were trees about the sides. They could no longer see the lights of the coastal plain, and then the road itself was straight and level. He began to accelerate the car.

The beach below the raised promenade was dark, broken from the sea only by the thin whiteness of small irregular waves.

"It's very still," he said. "The tide is well out."

"Yes. It's more like the river." From behind them the reflections of lights stretched briefly across the darkness. "That was a wonderful dinner we had."

He laughed with her. "The drive down must have given us an appetite."

"It was good, though. And the drive."

She had paused, standing near the edge of the promenade, her foot resting on the wooden beam.

"Is it to places like this you go fishing?"

"I've fished out from here. I like to get fairly well outside."

The swift shaft of light from the lighthouse on the island swung at the land and was gone. She did not move, she might have forgotten him, and he waited. After a time he stepped towards her, touching her arm, and as she made no movement, he turned her towards him, her arm firm beneath his hand. She looked up at him, the whiteness of her face mask-like, as he had seen it before, so that it told him nothing.

He asked gently, "No second thoughts?"

She shook her head. "No."

"You're — unhappy."

"Oh no. No. I was happy."

"Janet — if this bothers you — if you're worried . . ."

"No. You wouldn't understand. You don't need to worry about me." She smiled. She stood quite still, close to him, and he realized he still held her, and she let him turn her so that they began to walk close together along the broken surface of the promenade.

The hotel room was small, bare; sufficient, he thought, for those who came in summer for the fishing, and to swim. Or those whose purpose was what his own must seem to be. He smiled wryly, and she said, seeing him before the mirror, "You have private jokes, don't you?"

"Sorry," he said. "It's a kind of habit, I suppose."

"You'd forgotten me."

"No." He looked at her and began to laugh. "Indeed no."

She laughed with him, sitting upon the bed, her light robe about her, her feet tucked under her.

"It's silly, isn't it?"

"Very silly," he said. "How did we get like this?"

"You made a shocking proposal."

"I did, too."

"And I accepted it."

"Then there's not much to choose between us."

"Not really."

He saw that the sullenness she had always held like reserve before her, her refusal even to admit words as if somehow she feared them, was gone, and that she was attractive. Her face was now lightly made up, almost as though only her lips held slight emphasis; and then he knew himself as a middle-aged man whose business it was to divorce his wife. But she said quickly, "Don't — you don't have to be like that . . ."

"Like that?"

"You'd gone back to how it's always been — as if I wasn't human. For a minute you looked at me as if I was . . ."

"You are real," he said. "However it was before. But that was not the way I had meant to think of it."

"Why?"

"No."

"I can look after myself."

"Perhaps," he said, "I've realized that."

"Then just while we're here you can think of me as someone."

"That's not really as difficult as you make it sound, either."

She laughed quickly. "After all, I suppose we do know one another a bit by now."

In the morning the boats along the waterfront rode light and buoyant out by the dark line of the deepening water, the early sun upon them. In the distance the outline of the island was dark against the sky, the ridges of the sand dunes beginning to lighten above the hollows that lay in shadow. The boards of the jetty rang beneath their shoes as they walked, and she asked, "Why can't we go out there?"

"To the island?"

"Yes. It's not very far."

"A few miles. Too far to swim."

"I didn't think of trying that. We could hire a boat."

"We could," he said. "Are you serious?"

"I'd love to go. And you could fish."

"Except I've no gear. There's a man down past the hotel who hires boats. If he's got a reasonable inboard we'll go."

"I'll get something for us to eat," she said. "And I can change while you're seeing him."

He had the boat in at the jetty, and had been looking over the engine by the time she returned. He saw her walking quickly along the jetty. She had changed to shorts and a blouse, a light scarf about her hair, and was carrying a small bag and a heavy sweater, which she tossed to him. His own preparations had consisted of removing his shoes and rolling his trousers up to the knees. He said, "You came prepared."

"Why not?" She laughed. "I don't do this every week-end." He steadied the boat as she stepped down. "I saw your man back there. But let's not think of him any more today."

"I don't think we'll have to again," he said.

The boat curved away from the jetty across the deep channel where the rays of the sun slanted into the greenish, opaque water like shafts they might have touched with their fingers from the boat. After a time the water shallowed and without wind was still, so that they could look down and see the weed and the clear pools, the sand faintly yellowed. She sat looking into the water as the boat went steadily but without haste. As they neared the island the long banks of weed became isolated, and there were reefs that lay as brown stains on the surface. He slowed the engine, beginning to cruise along the edge of the shallows.

"Anywhere in particular, captain?"

"Just around there," she said, pointing, "where those rocks are, looks a good place."

He worked in slowly, where a high limestone headland eroded by the waves enclosed a small beach, and he took the launch in past the broken reef. In a clear patch he let it drift towards the beach from the anchor, and she stepped into water about her thighs, grimacing at the cold. They placed their few things on the coarse white sand at the edge of the thick fringe of rushes. Behind the beach the low scrub covered the steep rise, in patches forming heavy thickets.

"Let's walk round the rocks." She laughed, looking at him. "And you can dry out."

"Yes," he said. "I didn't come prepared like you. I won't mind drying."

The limestone was sharp to their feet, and they walked carefully, round the base of the headland and along the broken beach.

He said, "If it starts to blow it could be rough going back."

"I wouldn't care. I've always liked boats. I used to go out with my father when I was a kid. We lived near the beach, and he was out fishing every week-end. He used to take me."

"And now he lives in the country."

"Yes. It's strange, I suppose. I never see him now. Perhaps he misses the sea. He went into the country when mother died. It was a better job, but she would never have gone to a strange place."

"Can I ask you something?"

"Of course."

"This — what I've asked you to do — hasn't interfered with your own private affairs?"

"I suppose I wouldn't have done it," she said, "if it had." The water in the shallow pools along the edge of the sand splashed beneath their feet and he saw the clear drops of it held upon the smoothness of her legs. "When I told you that time that I was waiting for a girl-friend, I was waiting for someone I'd finished with." She laughed. "That sounds silly, but he used to go there, and I suppose I hoped I'd see him. It had been no good for either of us. But — well, I was lonely, I suppose. I just went there. I'm glad now he didn't come."

"Then perhaps all this has fitted somehow," he said slowly.

She looked up at him quickly. "Yes."

Near a high eroded rock platform they turned back, along the smooth sand where the tide was ebbing. Their foot-marks showed plain before them, and she tried to walk in those her own feet had made earlier, laughing as they were lost where a small wave had washed up onto the sloping beach.

On the small beach shut in by the limestone headland she prepared the food she had brought, and he lay upon the sand, watching her. She had taken the scarf from her hair, and he remembered what he had thought of her hair when he had first seen her. It was now without the tinting he had disliked, a deep brown, not striking perhaps as once she must have tried to make it appear, but he liked the way she wore it, loose, touching her shoulders. A rarity, he felt, in the days of jagged hair-cuts, or upswept beehive-like effects. His old age showing, he supposed wryly. And he wondered how old this girl before him might be. Not as old, perhaps, as he had first thought. Sullenness, a deliberate hardness, had seemed to give her age. Now he was not sure.

"You've never liked the way I look," she said. "Have you?"

For a moment he could find no reply.

"I was thinking," he said, "how much I like your hair."

"Never mind. Look, here's our lunch."

When they had eaten they lay in the sun, the thick white sweater she had brought spread beneath their heads, and they let the sense of sleep come on them from the heat. They could hear the gulls on the beach, as they drove one another from food, and he thought of the high cliffs and the waves that washed at them, the long sloping rise of the island that cut across the sky, the dull-coloured scrub that spread down at the grass and reeds and the white beach. It moved in the sun, lazily, beneath his half-open lids, like the turning sky.

He woke slowly, raising himself on his elbow. Where she had been lying the sand was compacted to the shape of her body, smooth, the edges broken where her hand had dragged across. He was suddenly afraid.

The launch had swung out from the beach, its bow pointed at him, the rope clear of the water. He called, hearing his own voice self-consciously.

"Janet . . ."

He began to walk quickly along the beach. Against his will he called again, as if he might momentarily have missed her along some street. Then he heard her laugh.

In the pool that deepened towards the line of the reefs he saw her head and the whiteness of her body distorted beneath the water.

"You'd better go away," she said, "while I come out. It was so hot I couldn't resist it."

"You might have woken me."

"I thought you'd never wake. I was going to be dry and respectable long before."

"You're not having it to yourself," he said.

They swam out near the reef where the water darkened above the weed. He paddled easily, his head just below the surface, trying to see the weed that waved slightly in some current he could not detect, the thick strands blurring strangely, unreal to his eyes, and then he felt her hands suddenly on his shoulders and she pushed him down. He let himself sink, and she went down with him. He caught her arms, their bodies were against one another, weightless, their motion magnified beyond their own volition. Their faces were close together, grotesque, her hair drifting strangely before his eyes, and abruptly he felt her lips upon his own, and then the opaque water cleared about them as they broke the surface. She shook her hair back from her face, laughing, and they swam slowly along the edge of the reef, the brown weed upon the rock just clear of the water, washing slowly in the turning tide.

The high limestone headland dulled in the pattern of shadow upon the thin layers of rock and the hollows driven by the wind. Along the sand-bar that was rippled with the small growing waves the gulls and terns stood quietly. The rushes made a sharp line of shade along the sand. She sat looking down at the sharp dry sand and he leant towards her, touching his lips to her arm, her skin warm and with the faint bitterness of salt.

"We'll have to go soon," he said slowly.

"When you called me," she said, "when you woke — what did you think?"

"I don't know," he said. "You were not there — I didn't know . . ." Suddenly she began to laugh.

He asked, "What's so funny?"

"Oh — it's just — just that your man should have been over here. Not at the hotel."

"You're an immoral woman," he said. "But it is funny. Yes. When you put it like that. But I thought we weren't going to think of him."

"I just couldn't help it. It's a pleasant last thought of him anyway. I'd come to hate him. But I don't care now. Because he wasn't here."

She picked up her small bag and the white sweater, and he waded out to bring in the launch. The boat moved from the shelter of the small bay, so that soon they could feel the wind. The swell was rising behind them, lifting the boat easily in a patient rhythm. Behind them the outline of the island grew slowly, elongating, until the length of it stretched dark against the sky, the shadows reaching down the slopes and over the scrub-filled hollows.

As he came back from the door of the flat the phone was ringing and for a moment he thought not to answer it.

"I got your note," she said.

"I wanted to let you know I was leaving — to thank you."

"I suppose you've been busy?"

"I have been. Most of it is straightened out now."

"Could I — see you?"

"Yes," he said. "Yes — shall I call for you?"

"I'm in town. I could come up."

"All right. I'll expect you."

He walked across to the window. The flat seemed bare, with so many of his own things packed. He looked out at the buildings, and beyond them the small crescent of the river was faintly ridged by the wind. He thought of the afternoon he had stood like this, and then driven haphazardly through the suburban streets. For the formalities that were left now, he need not stay. His wife had, in some phone calls and a long letter, turned a savage bitterness upon him, and then it had all seemed to fade. An admission that their real hurt had all died long ago. He would have had it so. He looked idly across the water to the hard sharp line of the hills with the late afternoon shadows beginning to move across them, and her knock upon the door startled him. He got up quickly.

For a moment she looked at him. She said, "You look as if you didn't recognize me."

He stood aside to let her enter the room. It was as if he saw her as he had on that first afternoon at the hotel. Her face was made up heavily, unnecessarily, achieving some deliberate over-emphasis, whose purpose was not obvious, there was the hardness, the sullenness, about her mouth that had perhaps first enabled him to speak to her.

He said, "The place looks a bit like a morgue. Most of my stuff is packed.

Sit down, I'll get you a drink.''

As he handed her the glass he said, "It's been a bit hectic lately. Getting the partnership in order. Quite a bit of business to do at both ends. I flew over to Sydney for a few days.''

"Yes," she said. "I got your message that you had to go suddenly.''

"It was a rush trip. I — couldn't meet you . . .''

"I understood.''

"I've been so infernally busy . . .''

"I understood.''

"I — got my boat away finally. I could have bought another for what it cost me.''

"Why didn't you?''

"I don't know. Perhaps I'm getting too old to part with things.''

She looked away, her glance taking in the bare room. "You've not much left now.''

"I've only to get myself off.''

"Your car?''

"I was going to drive it to Kalgoorlie and put it on the train for Pirie. But — I don't know — it seemed too far on my own.''

"And you had no passenger.''

"No. So it goes crated.''

"That should be everything.''

"Yes." He leant forward suddenly. "Thanks, Janet, for all this.''

"Think nothing of it. You paid me.''

He said slowly, "All right. But it wasn't quite like that.''

She swung her leg, crossed over one knee, restlessly, her shoe seeming to slip upon her heel as if she would free her foot of the plain brown leather, and abruptly he was reminded of her beauty when they had swum in the still water by the reef and they had walked out onto the beach, their bodies wet, touching, to lie upon the warm sand. And he looked at her as she sat near him in the flat from which almost all personality had been removed, seeing her faint air of aggression, like defiance, the counterpart to her over-made-up features.

"Janet — what will you do?''

"Do? Oh, go for a trip, I suppose, with the money.''

She put the glass down. Her fingers twisted about the gold-coloured clasp of her small brown handbag.

"Did you have anywhere special in mind?''

"No." She stood up. "I haven't really thought.''

As if from some strange distance, from which he could not recall them, he heard his own words: "Look — I'll be at this address — if your trip should take you over in that direction — you never know . . .''

311

He thought she would deny the suggestion, then she took the card he had written upon.

At the door she said, "Don't come down. I know my way."

He walked along the passage with her, and they went down the stairs. On the pavement she turned.

He said, "Then don't forget your trip."

"No. And if it doesn't take me over there . . ." She smiled at him quickly. "You did so want to be free. Be happy, David."

Incongruously, he thought it was the first time she had called him by his name. She had begun to walk down the pavement. He moved uncertainly, lifting his hand as if he might have beckoned to her. Then he heard the sudden high-pitched shout of an evening newsboy swooping a bicycle at the pavement, and he shifted back as the roll of papers was flung past him to skid along the entrance hall of the flats.

Mary
Finnin

Of Bacchus, in the Marsh

Gently time spins,
And humming, sings
Of the lost stories,
The mind-emptied things;

Bald Hill is mute on Coomaidai,
But the grey-box dream of days
When curlews drowned the frog bells
Along the waterways,

When Lairederk and Werribee
Had meetings on Main Street,
Before men crippled them with weirs
And locked their wandering feet.

Men overlanded from the south,
Men overlanded from the east,
Mountains no more were barriers —
But hills of home for man and beast.

And when Black Thursday broke in fire,
Darkened cloud-acres of the sky,
The road dust spelt the runic wrath
Of maddened horsemen flying by;

And racing them through Melton Plains
A wall of flame lit Beremboke,
Men fought it on the pasture flats
While Parwan farms went up in smoke.

From Buninyong, from Forest Creek,
The gilded diggers passed, and sang;
From Travellers' Rest to Stamford Bridge
Their clinking quart-pots rang.

One crossed Deep Creek on a knife-blade plank
While the troopers lurked at the ford below,
When Moonlight robbed the Egerton Bank —
Seventy years ago.

And lost is Finnin's lucerne flat
Where the grave kestrels hover,
And faint the track round Stumpey Hill
That wind and rain discover.

Like drums that beat for passing shades,
I hear bronzewings on Lairederk,
The dingoes bay round Rockbank stones,
And Peter Lalor speak in Bourke.

Here, where a soldier squatted,
In country grand and harsh,
They gave the place his happy name
Of Bacchus, in the Marsh.

Rain in Glenrowan

An Irish rain is creeping round,
Seeking a Kelly ghost;
Up screes it moves, and searches still
Behind each granite crest.

A mist dissolves the crags
As paper wraps up stone;
(But to paper comes the knife
As winds bleach the bone).

As the dead believe in life,
Believe in the Warby Hills;
Lost in the rain, they'll come again,
When the sun rain's shadow kills!

The shorn sheep huddle in the fine,
The folding rain, and cry:
Since Kellys went, both Ned and Dan,
The crows as often fly;

And shearing is a surer way
Of getting gold today,
Than robbing banks, and shooting folk
In the old Glenrowan way.

A Farmer's Dirge

The doctor and the parson,
The lawyer and the clerk,
They clamber on my bare, broad back
And hinder there till dark;
And hinder there till dark, me boys,
And I am growing grey
And getting groggy in the legs,
And *still* there's bills to pay!

Great rains are riding the Divide;
But will they come in time
To green the flats, fill bullock hide,
And bring the lambs in prime?
And bring the lambs in prime, me boys,
And bring me a release
From those dunning lawyers' letters
Re the fence round Murphy's Piece?

A drought will come, as sure as eggs
Grow stale when waiting long
For clerks to pass them fit by Regs
Of Boards that make a song —
Of Boards that make a song, me boys,
About googs' tint and weight,
While chooks are croupy, neck and crop,
'N the season's running late.

With measles all the kids are down,
The missus in a tear —
The quack he can't run out from town —
Bad roads, and petrol's dear —
Bad roads, 'n petrol's dear, me boys;
But we bring the cream cans in;
The tractor runs the kids to school,
And fills the silo bin!

The parson sobers Sunday's air
With hymns, and ancient Word;
I snooze and fidget in me chair,
'N dream that crow's a bird;
'N dream that crow's a bird, me boys,
And not the devil's wonder
Gathering by the dozen
When parson ploughs me under.

Vincent
Buckley

Day with its Dry Persistence

In day with its dry persistence
In night warm with the first star
Down the midnight-passages
Or in the small corners of silence
Or at the bedside hot with death
A restlessness that clings and will not
Be rubbed off on paper.

Yet there are some tempos that prefer me,
Some twigs that burst with shaking
Blossom and dew, some lights that are constant,
Some movements of the earth that bring me
In constant pilgrimage to Genesis,
To the bright shapes and the true names,

Oh my Lord.

Market Day

Market, or pitched battle, or Galway Hunt?
The dunged boots and sweaty heads
Following where the money leads;
Their women craning a goose's neck
To see (to see is their great bargain);
The black humps of their cattle speak

More forcefully than ever words or hands.
A settled people, whose good eye
Is closed to all but lechery,
Who spare neither the great nor young,
Who hate what the body understands,
Whose food is grass, whose wealth is dung.

Therefore, as in a painter's heavy line,
I feel the scene as it was once:
The men quarrelsome in bronze,
The thieves bustling and sweating there,
The driven beasts, the dull horsemen,
Contemptuous of the living air.

from *Stroke*

In the faint blue light
We are both strangers; so I'm forced to note
His stare that comes moulded from deep bone,
The full mouth pinched in too far, one hand
Climbing an aluminium bar.
Put, as though for the first time,
In a cot from which only a hand escapes,
He grasps at opposites, knowing
This room's a caricature of childhood.
"I'm done for."

"They're treating you all right?"
We talk from the corners of our mouths
Like old lags, while his body strains
To notice me, before he goes on watching
At the bed's foot
His flickering familiars,
Skehan, Wilson, Ellis, dead men, faces,
Bodies, paused in the aluminium light,
Submits his answer to his memories,
"Yes, I'm all right. But still it's terrible."

Words like a fever bring
The pillar of cloud, pillar of fire
Travelling the desert of the mind and face.
The deep-set, momentarily cunning eyes
Keep trying for a way to come
Through the bed's bars to his first home.
And almost find it. Going out I hear
Voices calling requiem, where the cars
Search out the fog and gritty snow,
Hushing its breathing under steady wheels.
Night shakes the seasonable ground.

from *Eleven Political Poems*

FOR BRIAN BUCKLEY

ELECTION SPEECH

Mottoes: words blown through a skull,
Programmes unwinding like a chain.
We listen, prurient and dull,
Each one bound by fear or gain
To the last ranting syllable.

Invented perils bring the sweat
Onto his practised lip. No doubt,
However, we shall live to eat
The meals that spin tomorrow out;
No doubt we'll lie in comfort yet

And drive each other to the polls.
Present and future weigh on us
Not as this glib voice recalls
But like a headless incubus,
Deaths, terrors that no vote controls.

He goes in quickly for the kill:
A fact, a promise, and a jibe.
I think of nothing; nothings fill
The image that his words inscribe,
My skull intoning from the hill.

NO NEW THING

No new thing under the sun:
The virtuous who prefer the dark;
Fools knighted; the brave undone;
The athletes at their killing work;
The tender-hearts who step in blood;
The sensitive paralysed in a mood;
The clerks who rubber-stamp our deaths,
Executors of death's estate;
Poets who count their dying breaths;
Lovers who pledge undying hate;
The self-made and self-ruined men;
The envious with the strength of ten.

They crowd in nightmares to my side,
Enlisting even private pain
In some world-plan of suicide:
Man, gutted and obedient man,
Who turns his coat when he is told,
Faithless to our shining world.
And hard-faced men, who beat the drum
To call me to this Cause or that,
Those heirs of someone else's tomb,
Can't see the sweeter work I'm at,
The building of the honeycomb.

A Summer Like This

FROM *LIGHTNING AND WATER*

You opening a gate
                    in a white wall
black latch on white-roughened stone
your hand
closing the trees
behind me   as I go
into the sun speeding at corners

and all down Hawthorn Road
                    cicadas shrilled up and sank
house after house
                    breaking the skin of each garden

speeding leaving my love
        my love-city
                in a summer like this

Robert
Clark

On Growing Old

1

The grim surprise of growing old
Is not the driftwood heap of years,
Nor dreariness when limbs go slow,
When aging flesh no longer rears,

Nor in the weary frequency
With which the body needs repairs,
Nor joys gone flat, nor any thing
But this — the heart no longer cares:

Can gaze with strange indifference on
The shapes that once absorbed the hours,
Can take with equal unconcern
The sunshine, moonlight, wind and showers.

2

A gentle providence ordains
The heart should not endure desires
The body can no longer serve.
To put ashore a man requires

So little gear. The fear of land
That haunts all seamen and ensures
The offing where their safety lies
Haunts him no more. The land wind lures

Him now with warmth of herb and scrub.
Alone, approaching untried shores,
His dinghy poised to catch the flood,
He waits there, resting on his oars.

The Dogman

The dogman dangles from the clouds,
Astride a beam of swinging air,
Unrealized hero of the crowds,
Whose upturned faces dimly stare

Like daisies watching from the ground,
Arrayed in far-off random files.
Their homage rises without sound
In grave content or drifting smiles.

The earth is open to his eye,
Spreading before him like a chart
From the blue-washed blind of sea and sky
To where the mountains lie apart.

Beneath his feet the city falls
In patterns of great blocks and spires,
A sumptuous Gulliver who sprawls
In bond to man's minute desires.

He is immune, a bird, a song,
A shaft of light, a glowing sun,
A god who ploughs above the throng,
A man reflecting all in one.

Propelled by joy, his love in spate,
He rides the climbing sky, and sings.
Another lark at heaven's gate
To another world his aubade brings.

It sends the mind down flues of time
To where all men in memory meet,
A hunter's song, a song to climb
The dawn, uncouth, yet wild and sweet.

Spent eyes revive and spill delight.
Dead hearts resolve to live again.
Once more a man upon a height
Recalls their dignity to men.

Frank
Hardy

The Great Australian Larrikin

As told by Billy Borker in the Albion Hotel, Parramatta

WHAT WOULD BE the best Australian story you ever heard, Billy?

The Great Australian Larrikin, as my father called it, is one of the best, I'd reckon, Jerome.

Have another drink and tell me about him.

Don't mind if I do. This fella's name was Dooley Franks. A real knockabout man. Lived here in Parramatta. Ran a double, did a bit of urging at the races, sold smuggled transistors. One night he went to Tommo's two-up school and won five hundred quid backing the tail. So he decided to join the Tattersall's Club. Up he choofs to the uniformed flunkey at the club door, wearing a polo neck jumper, suede shoes, and one of them small brimmed hats with a yellow feather in it. "Here, fill in this form," the flunkey says dubiously; "the committee will consider your application and let you know in due course." When the committee meets, the secretary says: "This Dooley Franks is an urger. We can't have him in the club." The committee members could not have agreed more: most of them *used* to be urgers, see. "Dooley Franks hasn't got two pennies to clink together. Just tell him the joining fee — a hundred pounds — and that'll be the end of it." So they write Dooley a letter and he bounces back and slams a bundle of tenners on the counter in front of the flunkey. Well, the committee got really worried. The secretary says: "Tell him he has to have three sponsors, famous people, not Australians. The furthest he's ever been from Parramatta is to the Kembla Grange racecourse." They think they've got old Dooley Franks beat, see. So the flunkey tells him: "Three famous people, not Australians." "Why didn't you say so in the first place?" Dooley says, "would have saved time and trouble. Eisenhower (he was President at that time), Khrushchev and the Pope. Just tell 'em Dooley Franks from Parramatta wants a reference."

He was joking, of course?

Wait till I tell yer. Don't spoil the story, mate, one of the best Australian stories ever told. Well, the committee got a shock, needless to say. Now, the secretary was a hard case, so he says: "Listen, this here Dooley Franks couldn't know Eisenhower, Khrushchev or the Pope. Tell you what we'll do. We'll offer to take him over to Washington, Moscow and Rome, in person. Then we'll hear no more about it." They write to Dooley Franks and he says: "All right with me. Air letters would be cheaper, but if you insist." The secretary says: "We're stuck with it now. We'll put in a hundred quid each and I'll go with him. It'll be the joke of the century." Away they go by air to Washington, up the steps to the White House. They wait around in corridors for about three days and eventually they get an appointment with one of Eisenhower's side-kicks. "I'm from Tattersall's Club, Sydney," the secretary says. The Yank is puzzled. "Sydney?" he asks. "Where's that?" "Australia," the secretary tells him. "Ah, yeah," the Yank replies. "That's where we sell all our old films to the television stations." "We want to see President Eisenhower," the secretary says. "You can't just come here and see the President. You have to have an appointment." Well, Dooley Franks is getting a bit impatient, see, so he says: "Listen, just tell Ike Dooley Franks wants to see him. The bloke who pinched six tins of petrol for him when his car ran out on the road to Paris. Dooley Franks from Parramatta." Well, the Yank goes away and comes back. "Mister Franks," he says, "why didn't you say so in the first place? President Eisenhower will see you right away." "Can I come too?" the secretary says. "No, the President wants to have a private chat with Mister Franks."

Surely he didn't actually know Eisenhower?

Well, he came back six hours later high as a kite. "Sorry to keep you waiting," he tells the secretary. "Me and Ike got talking old times over a few drinks and lost track of time." So they head off for Moscow.

Ah, don't tell me . . .

Up to the Kremlin gates with an interpreter they go. Freezing cold night, thirty-eight below. The secretary puts over a spiel about the Tattersall's Club and Dooley tells the bloke on the gate: "Just tell Nikita that Dooley Franks from Parramatta wants to see him. Was treasurer of the Sheepskins For Russia appeal during the war, sailed on the North Sea convoys and sold Russian magazines on the Sydney waterfront." Well, to make a long story short, the same thing happens: Khrushchev wants to see Comrade Franks, and the secretary of the Tattersall's Club is left freezing in the Red Square. Dooley comes out eventually, and next day they head for Rome. And the secretary is thinking: What will I tell the committee when I get back? They'll never believe me. If he gets in to see the Pope, I'm going with him.

And did he?

Well, they see a cardinal, but he says you have to make an appointment for an audience with the Pope. So Dooley tells him: "Just say Dooley Franks from

Parramatta; was an altar boy at St Patrick's Cathedral, got a brother a priest and a sister a nun.'' The cardinal comes back — if you don't believe me you can ask old Dooley himself — he says the Pope will grant a private audience to Mister Franks. The secretary begs to be let in. "I must see them together," he says. "His Holiness wishes to see only Mister Franks. But if you want to see them together you can stand down in the square. His Holiness will appear on the balcony at one o'clock and I'll arrange for Mister Franks to stand with him." Well, the secretary is desperate: what's he going to tell the committee? He goes away and comes back at one o'clock. The square is packed with fifty thousand people. The secretary is so far away he can't even see the balcony. The crowd cheers. There's a Yankee tourist standing near by with a pair of field-glasses. The secretary begs him: "Lend me your field-glasses." The Yank says: "They're not field-glasses, they're binoculars. And you can't borrow them. I've come ten thousand miles to see the Vatican . . ." The secretary says: "Well, what can you see?" "Two men standing on the balcony," the Yank tells him. The secretary tugs his arm. "Can you recognise them? Who are they?" The Yank takes a good look through his binoculars: "Well, I can't place the guy in the funny hat but the other guy is definitely Dooley Franks from Parramatta."

Now I've heard everything.

Francis
Webb

Cap and Bells

Tonight the stars are yellow sparks
Dashed out from the moon's hot steel;
And for me, now, no menace lurks
In this darkness crannied by lights; nor do I feel
A trace of the old loneliness here in this crowded train;
While, far below me, each naked light trails a sabre
Of blue steel over the grave great peace of the harbour.

To know this peace is to have outgrown
Thoughts of despair, of some driving crank of fate,
Of corroded tissues in the bleak shell of a town:
Darkness, lights, happiness — all are right,
All bear messages of the hidden heart;
And for me always the grave great peace is stronger
In flaring colours, and a laugh, and a careless singer.

Die in the blood and salt of your thoughts; and die
When the columns of your sun are thrust aside and broken;
But I have chosen the little, obscure way
In the dim, shouting vortex; I have taken
A fool's power in his cap and bells
And know that in my time the haggard Prince will discover
A blunt shell of Yorick, that laughs for ever and ever.

from *Disaster Bay*

The barque *Jane Spiers*,
Little clutter of forgotten timbers
Under the tea-tree, buried in sand,
Keel and ribs and spars
Drowning in the yellow clutch
Of Stephen's Beach.

Only a twisted shank,
Oddity of time, like a fossil
Curls up out of the sand:
Only the seabirds think
And the hopping land-birds watch
On Stephen's Beach.

Minutes tick past. Cape Howe slips far behind;
What cause for fear? No one may trust the night
That plucks response from things lodged deep in the mind,
Omens, unreason. While the wake skims level and white,

Churned away from the blade of the steady bows,
And steady's the course, untroubled the drowsy guide,
You know that this wraith of a ship must safely browse
Home in the roadstead, nudged by a leisurely tide.

And now as a cloud topples from the moon like a leech
The seaway eases and flakes into brilliant caves,
A gully of pearl loops out on the distant beach
And oars of silver lick at the turning waves.

Midnight stuns the air. The piano stops playing,
The shuttle of voices drops, screws muffled in the hull,
The flimsy envelope of water tears with a fraying
Rustle like a whisper, the wind flags in a lull.

Yet there's no danger at all where moonlight carves
The course to follow, a blazing, narrowing scar,
And the fine thread of the forestay cleanly halves
The Green Cape Light pinpointed like a low star,

A star of assurance. Nadgee thrashes by:
Here the seaboard withdraws to a giant bay
And craning hills sheer off to become the sky,
Each furlong pulls the shore further away.

Bells pattern the air: growing less real,
The *Ly-ee-moon*, and your thoughts wavering too,
Blinded by that vanishing hour, weary of the steel
Flick-over of the wake, buzz and gride of the screw.

But worlds are back in the wheelhouse, where lamps connive
At a thousand conspiracies of shadow and glare;
Hunched over his wheel the steersman looks alive
Though silence lies on him like dust, lies everywhere.

Minutes leap. On the hour's towering ascent
A blue, dead sailor jerks out of the sea,
Netted in phosphorescence, head slumped and bent,
Stone mouth leaking peril and prophecy.

His fingers on the bollard glitter, pale and stark
As the limp rays of a starfish, leave traces of frost
When he sinks back and his arm slews out in an arc:
Ghost salutes coming ghost.

Minutes leap. Another hour gathers with the roar
Of surf looming up with the returning line of shore,
And here the *City of Sydney* went aground
In a gibbering riot of sirens, while fog closed round.

But the Light flashes clearly, whirls on the hump of the Cape
Its spattering disk of warning, a sign known well;
Breakers hurl guttural bewares about the shape
Of table-topped rocks, close at hand and visible —

Full speed. Eyes sharp with terror. Hands that pluck
Vainly at the wheel. Too late the sudden spin.
The cry of a ghost, weakening — Christ, we've struck!
As lights snap out and darkness flounders in.

Bells of St Peter Mancroft

Gay golden volleys of banter
Bombard the clockwork grief;
A frisson of gold at the centre
Of prayer, bright core of life.

Who knew the old lofty tower,
The ancient holy eye,
To come open like a flower,
To roll and wink with joy?

Townspeople, who wear
Shrewd colours and know the move,
Now blunder and wander, I swear,
In a transport of love.

And the belfry, hale and blest:
Picture the jolly hand
Milking each swinging breast
Of its laughing golden sound.

For My Grandfather

When the ropes droop and loosen, and the gust
Piecemeal upon a widening quietness fails,
Fail breath and spirit; against the bony mast
Work in like skin the frayed and slackened sails.
In the green lull where ribs and keel lie wrecked,
Wrapped in the sodden, enigmatic sand,
Things that ache sunward, seaward, with him locked,
Tug at the rigging of the dead ship-lover's hand.
Though no wind's whitening eloquence may fill
Drowned canvas with the steady bulge of breath,
Doubling for past, for future, are never still
The bones ambiguous with life and death.

Dusk over Bradley's Head: a feeble gull
Whose sinking body is the past at edge
Of form and nothing; here the beautiful
Letona gybes, off the spray-shaken ledge.
And to those years dusk comes but as a rift
In the flesh of sunlight, closed by memory;
Shells stir in the pull of water, lift
Fragile and holy faces to the sky.
My years and yours are scrawled upon this air
Rapped by the gavel of my living breath:
Rather than time upon my wrist I wear
The dial, the four quarters, of your death.

End of the Picnic

When that humble-headed elder, the sea, gave his wide
Strenuous arm to a blasphemy, hauling the girth
And the sail and the black yard
Of unknown *Endeavour* towards this holy beach,
Heaven would be watching. And the two men. And the earth,
Immaculate, illuminant, out of reach.

It must break — on sacred water this swindle of a wave.
Thick canvas flogged the sticks. Hell lay hove-to.
Heaven did not move.
Two men stood safe: even when the prying, peering
Longboat, the devil's totem, cast off and grew,
No god shifted an inch to take a bearing.

It was Heaven-and-earth's jolting out of them shook the men.
It was uninitiate scurf and bone that fled.
Cook's column holds here.
Our ferry is homesick, whistling again and again;
But still I see how the myth of a daylight bled
Standing in ribbons, over our heads, for an hour.

A Tip for Saturday

I met Jack on a Friday night,
Headway was medium, in spite
Of lurching walls in the spinning town,
Taxis that sought to mow him down,
Strange girls that dashed into his arms,
Then cursed him in no uncertain terms.
The air was still, the sky was grey.
I thought of tips for Saturday.

The navigator's task affords
Small safety from a spate of words.
He pointed me to starry skies
On stilts of queer philosophies,
While oaths made rapid cubic gain,
Like roly-poly on the plain.

I quote one mighty thought on wars:
There'd be some friction if the stars
Were like us, macrocosms jammed
Edgeways like sardines on this damned
Insignificant little planet:
Figuratively, literally, he spat on it.

Meekly surrendering to the shocks
Of war, religion, politics,
My voice could not attempt a breach.
Jack filled the road with noisy speech,
With gusto, verve, and animation
From Windsor pub to Town Hall station.

The air was still, the sky was grey.
Reluctantly I turned away
Without a tip for Saturday.

Five Days Old

FOR CHRISTOPHER JOHN

Christmas is in the air.
You are given into my hands
Out of quietest, loneliest lands.
My trembling is all my prayer.
To blown straw was given
All the fullness of Heaven.

The tiny, not the immense,
Will teach our groping eyes.
So the absorbed skies
Bleed stars of innocence.
So cloud-voice in war and trouble
Is at last Christ in the stable.

Now wonderingly engrossed
In your fearless delicacies,
I am launched upon sacred seas,
Humbly and utterly lost
In the mystery of creation,
Bells, bells of ocean.

Too pure for my tongue to praise,
That sober, exquisite yawn
Or the gradual, generous dawn
At an eyelid, maker of days:
To shrive my thought for perfection
I must breathe old tempests of action

For the snowflake and face of love,
Windfall and word of truth,
Honour close to death.
O eternal truthfulness, Dove,
Tell me what I hold —
Myrrh? Frankincense? Gold?

If this is man, then the danger
And fear are as lights of the inn,
Faint and remote as sin
Out here by the manger.
In the sleeping, weeping weather
We shall all kneel down together.

Peter
Porter

Phar Lap in the Melbourne Museum

A masterpiece of the taxidermist's art,
Australia's top patrician stares
Gravely ahead at crowded emptiness.
As if alive, the lustre of dead hairs,
Lozenged liquid eyes, black nostrils
Gently flared, otter-satin coat declares
That death cannot visit in this thin perfection.

The democratic hero full of guile,
Noble, handsome, gentle Houyhnhnm
(In both Paddock and St Leger difference is
Lost in the welter of money) — to see him win
Men sold farms, rode miles in floods,
Stole money, locked up wives, somehow got in:
First away, he led the field and easily won.

It was his simple excellence to be best.
Tough men owned him, their minds beset
By stakes, bookies' doubles, crooked jocks.
He soon became a byword, public asset,
A horse with a nation's soul upon his back —
Australia's Ark of the Covenant, set
Before the people, perfect, loved like God.

And like God to be betrayed by friends,
Sent to America, he died of poisoned food.
In Australia children cried to hear the news
(This Prince of Orange knew no bad or good).
It was, as people knew, a plot of life:
To live in strength, to excel and die too soon,
So they drained his body and they stuffed his skin.

Twenty years later on Sunday afternoons
You still can't see him for the rubbing crowds.
He shares with Bradman and Ned Kelly some
Of the dirty jokes you still can't say out loud.
It is Australian innocence to love
The naturally excessive and be proud
Of a thoroughbred bay gelding who ran fast.

R. A.
Simpson

The Departure of Governor Macquarie

Sydney, 1822

Waiting to leave, not wanting to leave like this,
His wife and son beside him in the boat,
The Governor is still imperious.
Oars are upright.

      Across the harbour, masts
As thin as needles, sway, provoke the sky,
Recall for him the pin-pricks he has known:
Hating their exile, men have hated him,
A Scot as humourless as depths in stone.

The future is words. The work is left back there —
Each name left tenderly on what was once
Rubble and rock, trees lacking distinction.
If he was kind to convicts (perhaps unwise)
The rulings have all waxed to order now.

Surrender meant blending with the dolts,
Making corruption his friend, and so he planned
Apart — an exile day by day preserving
Pride and courage for his last eclipse
And that applause heard only in himself.

The continent he leaves remains with him
Like so much of the self that stays unknown.
Over all regret prevails and burns;
It melts convictions and it will not set.

Bystander: Anzac Day

At dawn they come and stand,
Thinking about the dead,
And talk of wars that he
Has never known. Instead

Of soldiers he finds rows
Of medals, meaningless
To him, and not one ghost
Arrives like the day on grass

To speak of history
Until the bugle sounds
For hatless men, blares down
The cratered years in minds:

Then he finds the dead
No longer lost or scorned . . .
They stand in the rain and sing;
The mourners are the mourned.

Discoveries

Across long wastes as if in search of love
The Dutchmen sailed toward this coast;
What cliffs they saw were primitive and cruel —
And so they went the way they came:
Time was deceived and shut its eyes once more.
We could not love till now; but love
Is found like islands lost, though seen with fear —
And words have made this country clear.

And yet to hold our love we never explore
The central dark, the mystery,
Because we know what deserts wait for those
Who seek; and though we seem to move
In time, there are no islands when we love.

Randolph
Stow

The Ghost at Anlaby

FOR GEOFFREY AND NINETTE DUTTON

Now sulkies come haunting softwheeled down the
leaves; on the cool veranda, over
whisky, wistaria, gentlemen admire
antwaisted, hamsleeved, bellskirted ladies
crossing the lawns with fishtailed racquets
intent on tennis. Heart, unlearn your fire.

Forget now, forget. Below the willows
Tom Roberts squatters, George Lambert ladies,
whose boats and fancy made this dam a lake,
speak of, remember, no visitant stranger.
Once time was a sportsman, and I the quarry,
who now would sleep with death, for sleep's kind sake.

But O whose fingers, soft as wistaria,
played with my watch-chain, under the crabapples;
under the lilacs in October flower
whose fingers like lingering tendrils twined in
my hair, my beard? What phantom remembers
that wicked, warm, Edwardian midday hour?

Rosella-plumed sun, go quickly down on
my afternoon ghosts. Let purple night that
brings all lovers to their billiard-rooms descend.
Click of the balls. Among wraiths of cigar-smoke,
with rib-nudging stories I died before telling,
I shall go haunting in search of a friend, a friend.

The Land's Meaning

FOR SIDNEY NOLAN

The love of man is a weed of the waste places.
One may think of it as the spinifex of dry souls.

I have not, it is true, made the trek to the difficult country
where it is said to grow; but signs come back,
reports come back, of continuing exploration
in that terrain. And certain of our young men,
who turned in despair from the bar, upsetting a glass,
and swore: "No more" (for the tin rooms stank of flyspray)
are sending word that the mastery of silence
alone is empire. What is God, they say,
but a man unwounded in his loneliness?

And the question (applauded, derided) falls like dust
on veranda and bar; and in pauses, when thinking ceases,
the footprints of the recently departed
march to the mind's horizons, and endure.

And often enough as we turn again, and laugh,
cloud, hide away the tracks with an acid word,
there is one or more gone past the door to stand
(wondering, debating) in the iron street,
and toss a coin, and pass, to the township's end,
where one-eyed 'Mat, eternal dealer in camels,
grins in his dusty yard like a split fruit.

But one who has returned, his eyes blurred maps
of landscapes still unmapped, gives this account:

"The third day, cockatoos dropped dead in the air.
Then the crows turned back, the camels knelt down and stayed there,
and a skin-coloured surf of sandhills jumped the horizon
and swamped me. I was bushed for forty years.

"And I came to a bloke all alone like a kurrajong tree.
And I said to him: 'Mate — I don't need to know your name —
Let me camp in your shade, let me sleep, till the sun goes down.' "

Dust

"Enough," she said. But the dust still rained around her;
over her living room (hideous, autumnal)
dropping its small defiance.
                                    The clock turned green.
She spurned her broom and took a train. The neighbours
have heard nothing.

Jungles, deserts, stars — the six days of creation —
came floating in, gold on a chute of light.
In May, grudging farmers admired the carpet
and foretold a rich year.

Miraculous August! What shelves of yellow capeweed,
what pouffes of everlastings. We worship nature
in my country.

Never such heath as flowered on the virgin slopes
of the terrible armchairs. Never convolvulus
brighter than that which choked the china dogs.
Bushwalkers' Clubs boiled their billies with humility
in chimneys where orchids and treesnakes
luxuriantly intertwined.

A photographer came from *The West Australian*, and ten
teenage reportresses. Teachers of botany
overflowed to the garden.

Indeed, trains were run from Yalgoo and Oodnadatta.
But the neighbours slept behind sealed doors, with feather
dusters beside their beds.

The Singing Bones

"Out where the dead men lie."
                                    Barcroft Boake

Out there, beyond the boundary fence, beyond
the scrub-dark flat horizon that the crows
returned from, evenings, days of rusty wind
raised from the bones a stiff lament, whose sound
netted my childhood round, and even here still blows.

My country's heart is ash in the market-place,
is aftermath of martyrdom. Out there
its sand-enshrined lay saints lie piece by piece,
Leichhardt by Gibson, stealing the wind's voice,
And Lawson's tramps, by choice made mummia and air.

No pilgrims leave, no holy-days are kept
for these who died of landscape. Who can find,
even, the camp-sites where the saints last slept?
Out there their place is, where the charts are gapped,
unreachable, unmapped, and mainly in the mind.

They were all poets, so the poets said,
who kept their end in mind in all they wrote
and hymned their bones, and joined them. Gordon died
happy, one surf-loud dawn, shot through the head,
and Boake astonished, dead, his stockwhip round his throat.

Time, time and again, when the inland wind
beats over myall from the dunes, I hear
the singing bones, their glum Victorian strain.
A ritual manliness, embracing pain
to know; to taste terrain their heirs need not draw near.

Landscapes

A crow cries: and the world unrolls like a blanket;
like a worn bush blanket, charred at the horizons.

But the butcherbird draws all in; that voice is a builder
of roofless cathedrals and claustrophobic forests
— and one need not notice walls, so huge is the sky.

In the morning, waking, one is most in love.
It is then that the cool convection of song and echo
wells in the clearings, and all is possible.

It is then you are not there. We meet after noon.
In the wrack of the crow. In a desert of broken quartz.

Hal
Porter

At the Galahad

FINALLY, BORED with the higgledy-piggledy autumn beach, the now-on now-off sunshine and the hard-eyed importunities of seagulls, I walked to the Galahad Hotel for a drink. There, risking a fractured pelvis on the immensity of the black-and-white-tiled foyer, I ran into Rupert Gaar-Smith. About us bronze nudes upheld spheres lit by forty-watt globes. Garr-Smith had an air of distracted importance; his large eyes rolled like a gelding's.

We were of an age, and old acquaintances; thirty-odd years before we had lived opposite in a Gippsland country town. Boyhood proximity and many accidental encounters such as this one had produced a seeming-friendship, though now we were older we hardly liked each other. We were not friendly enough to quarrel, but were always titillated by the way our paths kept interlocking at odd places.

My career had been patchwork; so had his. But our planes of experiment were well separated. He had been a Wurlitzer-organist, an actor, a radio-announcer, a dress-material salesman; once he had run a Collins Street *coffee shoppe* hung with Klee and Miró prints. God knows what else he'd done or would finish up doing, but I was surprised to find him assistant manager of a hotel, and such a hotel, and in that place.

That place was the seaside suburb where I had been skulking past the film-set scaffolding of Big Dippers and shuttered ice-cream kiosks. It was a suburb that had sledded downhill from fashionable elegance in late-Victorian and Edwardian years to the tawdry and the downright criminal: it was now a Cannes to spiv, cat-burglar, confidence-man, petty gangster's moll, pervert and juvenile delinquent. Port Phillip waters nudging oranges and fishing-net corks onto the beach exhaled that smell of decaying seaweed Edwardians called ozone.

The suburb, built-up as a sundae, breathed back the stench of hamburger, espresso, and fish-and-chip shops. Time had added some pseudo-Gropius flats, tiled bus-stop shelters, an outlining of neon, a glaciarium like a hangar, and a multi-coloured coating of paint. This covered everything: balustrade, roof,

Greek Revival, Belgian Gothic, Florentine Renaissance, stucco faces of rams and Minervas, moulded-iron parapets and Moorish arches.

Only the Pompeiian tiles, leading to basalt steps still edged with blackout-white, had missed this symbolic mid-century veneer. Only these and the Galahad Hotel.

The Galahad retained much of the top-heavy grandeur of its prime when Sarah Bernhardt had stayed there, Rudyard Kipling, Henry Handel Richardson, and squatters' broods with their immigrant nursemaids. Framed menus of Derby Day meals at Windsor Castle hung in the vast dining-room, with its Carrara fireplaces, stained-glass windows of Malory knights and ladies, its life-size Majolica swans. It was one of those mansarded hotels in which marble statues of the Seasons and Virtues stood below huge oil-paintings — *Sunset in Egypt, Dawn at Ronda* — and prints of setters by Thomas Blinks. There were pillars of liver-coloured stone; corridors ended at looking-glass walls in which one sidestepped oneself just before the crash.

Rupert Gaar-Smith, theatrical of voice, jowly, in charcoal-grey and handmade shoes, too greenish-gold of hair for — forty-one? forty-two? — seemed pleased to see me: "You are manna," he said, as though to the gallery. "Manna! Your ear I must have. I must unburden ere I go quite em, ay, dee."

His manner *was* odd; the dressing-room affectations I'd heard before, but there was intensity in his wheedlings. "Spare me a scant half-hour. For the sake of our in-no-cent boyhood. My washstand, dear man, groans with expensive strong waters."

"Don't be a fool," I said. "I'd enjoy a natter. And free drinks."

"Oh, *good*," he said. Ringingly he called towards the reception-desk, "Laura, my ducks . . . oh, it's you, Miss Daly. Miss Daly, I am now off duty. Mr Rockleigh is on. You'll find him in . . . well, *you* know where."

Gesturing me on rather in the manner of the ghost in *Hamlet*, he said from the corner of his mouth, "In the saloon-bar is Brother Rockleigh", and led me to his room by corridors at first thickly wall-to-walled, next runner-carpeted, finally of linoleum glossy as a sergeant-major's boot.

His room, in the oldest part of the hotel, was large: marble fireplace, cedar armchairs, brass double-bed like Salvador Dali's, tiled washstand serving as a cocktail-bar. He poured drinks, chattering on.

"Gin and tonic? Thank God *you* turned up. I can tell someone; get the thing off my chest. Two of the old girls. And each time I was on duty. Enough tonic? On duty *both* times, wot you. Very *sinister*. And all so . . . so . . ." He handed me my drink.

"How about," I said, "starting at point A?"

"Murder," he said.

"Go hon!"

"Murder most foul. Suicide. Jealousy, lunacy, the *lot*."

"The suspense," I said, "is killing me."

"Sit *down*," he said. "Do you know that five minutes before I met you I'd just seen-off the second old witch to the morgue? Discreetly. Back-alley job: past the coke-heaps."

I felt I had raised an eyebrow.

"All right, all right. Toss that down." He poured more drinks. "I," he said, "am the only one who knows."

"Knows what?"

"Oh don't be tah-some! I'll start at point A; just give me a burl." He sat down. I could see him arranging his thoughts like a Conrad character; he drank; he began.

"This place is a madhouse — not just my opinion. In the hotel-racket it's called Worthington's Circus. Papa Worthington owns it, lock, stock, fire-extinguisher to cellar, every cockroach behind the *bain marie*, every souvenired liqueur-glass. Inherited in the twenties before this suburb got seedy. At least before the seediness started to show. He was the only son, spoiled — Little Lord Fauntleroy. He's an old maid now; married to an old maid. Not pub-types like his mum and dad, who ran a pretty dazzling show.

"He's got plenty of loot; has shares in everything from here to Perth and is just not interested in being Mr Ritz. The Galahad is merely home to him. So long as everything is as dear mum and dad left it, he's as happy as Larry. Who *is* Larry? All he and Mrs W. do is travel and buy appalling *objets d'art*; their suite is the sort you'd expect Boris Karloff to live in. Don't worry me, is his idea, just keep on as Mum did.

"Perhaps he's right. It certainly means good food, linen sheets, cedar furniture and no nasty questions about expense so long as it's nothing to do with Americanization, chromium, public-address systems, wireless, all that sort of thing. But he won't throw anything away: you know how the rich always break their fingernails undoing the string on parcels?

"Afterwards I'll show you disused nurseries, smoking-rooms and music-rooms all chockablock with Sheffield-plate teapots, Venetian-glass finger-bowls, Waterford jugs, candlesticks, hundreds of marble clocks, cruets and tureens. One old writing-room is packed to the ceiling with chamber-pots. And the patching and mending goes on all the time: lino., carpets, sheets, blankets, loose-covers. There's a carpenter-johnny wearing one of those baize apron-things who's been patch, patch, patching for forty years. Look!"

He rose, opened the door to his bathroom: a deep bath set in mahogany, a washhand-basin and lavatory-bowl with a design in Willow-Pattern blue.

"Early Doulton," he said. "Now look at the floor."

It was gleaming sheet-lead patched in twenty places with exquisite squares and rectangles of new lead.

"See? Papa Worthington doesn't *want* new things. Or new ideas. Why has he got Rockleigh, the near-dipso., as manager? And me as assistant? Because we're mild bunnies willing to jog along in the old way. A bright and shiny boy from the Hotel Managers' High School in Michigan or wherever would be out on his bee, you, em at the first peep about laminated wood or shilling-in-the-slot wireless-sets."

"Point A yet?" I said.

"Have another drink, *paysan*, and don't . . . be . . . tah-some! I'm explaining the kind of hotel it is. Certain sorts of pubs attract certain sorts of guests." He was pouring drinks again. "This one's a leftover from what the *Readers' Digest* would call 'more spacious days'. So are the cruets and marble virgins. All leftovers." He sat. The drinks were strong. His voice had lost much of its back-row-of-the-gods pitch. "So are its permanent guests."

He drank again. "Leftovers! The place has about thirty of these permanents — like a . . . a home for retired gentlewomen. Bishops' spinster daughters, Anglo-Indian widows, superannuated deaconesses — *you* know the type: eking out allowances, savings or legacies, bitching at the waitresses and chambermaids, always shooting the roller-blinds *right* up. Something's always too hot or too cold. Or not early enough. Or late again. . . ."

I saw what he meant. I knew them: gunmetal-grey stockings; long, narrow shoes; crocodile-skin handbag containing scraps of a richer past; the brown snapshots of the 1920 tennis-party at Kuala Lumpur; the juiceless voices:

"Oh, Mr Gaar-Smith, Ai don't want to make trouble for the gels. Yet Ai do feel that the gel on mai teble is not quaite . . . well, frenkly, she's *vedy* sleck. Mai toast this morning was barely . . ."

I could see the obsessive glitter in ageing eyes: Food, the god of the lonely, the god of many communions. Tea in bed. Breakfast. Morning-tea. Luncheon. Afternoon-tea. Dinner. Supper.

"Some of the old bags," he said, "eat more than a stevedore father-of-nine. Imagine a silvery-haired little-old-lady-passing-by." His voice became maliciously falsetto, he peered at an imaginary menu:

" 'Now, wetress, let me see. Ai'm not vedy hungry this morning. But breakfast is such an important meal; Ai'd better trai end nibble something. Cereals . . . end fruit. What is the fruit? Oh, I'm vedy fond of pears; bring me three . . . no . . . *four* pieces. Kedgeree, this morning! Oh, Ai adore it. Kedgeree then — end on buttered toast, not drai. Perhaps, too, a steak, end tomatoes. Waitress, tel chef it's for me; he knows Ai laike it medium. Not too rare. Not all draid up. End I'll hev a fraid egg with thet . . .' Never fear my boy, Mother Macree will get through the lot like a grey-nurse. She'll sit frail and fretting till morning-tea.

"Then she'll be ready to wait for tiffin. My God, they've got *me* saying it. That's what half of them call it: 'Ai thought the tiffin-gong was a little leet. Mai watch says three minutes past.' Tiffin! In this little Chicago, in 1956, with bodgies and widgies about to batter through the revolving doors with Coca Cola bottles! I need another drink."

I was beginning to understand how he felt as keeper of this genteel zoo of women with nothing to do except read Frances Parkinson Keyes, gossip, vilify, take purgatives and eat.

It was in the dining-room, beneath the stained-glass Burne-Jones Galahads, Geraints, Gareths and Guineveres, that trouble began.

At a dominating table, attended by a waitress who served no one else, Mr and Mrs Worthington royally disregarded the world from behind an elaborate epergne. They were sacrosanct; the year could have been 1913. Almost equally sacrosanct were the spinsters and widows whose tables lined the walls so that intruding fly-by-nights, the mobile Present, occupying central tables, were hemmed-in by the static and withering Past, each with her still-life on the cloth before her of bottles of digestive-tablets, jars of anchovy-paste, chutney, marmalade or Dusseldorf mustard.

Some had sat at one table for twenty years. Solitary, with the unwinking eyes of barracoota, they assessed the intransigents from the vulgar world of nylon, jet-planes and divorce. I felt the pathos of these macabre spectators; how many hundreds — thousands — had they silently rejected beneath the lofty ceiling, with its double row of moulded acanthus-wheels from which depended involved electroliers?

Most ghastly was his description of the corridor outside the dining-room. It was customary for the manager on duty to unlock the twelve-foot-high double-doors of plate-glass, sand-blasted and gold-leafed with *art nouveau* floridities, and with *art nouveau* handles. This happened when the gong had been beaten to silence.

But, long before, Gaar-Smith's old hags, bats, trouts, and faggots, the colonels' widows, and the daughters of judges who had died younger than their old-maid survivors, with powdered froglike throats, waited, spitefully examining the *cloisonné* watches pinned to their sapless breasts. This elderly queuing for food had, in that setting, a taint of unbalance. What were they really waiting for?

The stiff drinks were having effect: impartiality and objectivity were losing ground.

"Note and note well," said Gaar-Smith, pouring out the fifth — or was it the sixth? — gin and tonic, "that gent.-on-duty unlocks door." His accent had lost its drama-school succulence, was down-to-earth and re-Gippslandized.

"Press on," I said. "You interest me, Mr Gaar-Smith, sir."

"We-e-ell," he sucked at his drink, "some of the crazed old harpies get into

346

their skulls the idea that certain tables are in better possies than others. Quite arbitrarily. Or because they hate someone. Then they'll scheme and lie like Lucifer. They'll do . . . anything.'' He drank again, glared at nothing. ''Anything,'' he repeated. He went on:

''About three months ago one of them went off to foist herself on a nephew in South Aussie for a couple of months —''

''Foist?'' I said. ''Don't be too tough. She may have been asked. Aunts are.''

He fixed me with tipsy severity: ''You don't know 'em. Tough as mallee-roots, a bite like a tiger-snake. No relative could put up with any of 'em for two *hours*. Why are they all here? Because none of their families can bear them. People don't hurl helpless old girls into the hard world. These aren't helpless. Far from it. They have the money; Worthington's mad; they're mad, and there's lots of lovely food. I wouldn't trust one of those . . .''

''Go on, go on,'' I said. ''Very sorry. Go on.''

''O.K. This old aunt, Beaufort by name, is — *was* — like something out of Barrie; all blue eyes, lavender-water and bunions. So sweet; such pink little cheeks: 'Oh, Mr Gaar-Smith, Ai'm so sorry to bother you, but you know Ai'm going away for two months. Now, about mai little teble. Ai've had it for faive years, end Ai'm most etteched to it. Ai expect it when Ai return. Ai'm certain you'll keep it for me.' And she gave me an envelope with four-bob in it and — off to upset things in Adelaide.

''I, dear man, would have kept her table for her; the here-today-and-gone-tomorrows could have used it when we were in a hole, but only for lends, not for keepies. Yes, I'd have kept her bloody four-bob table for her — I'm no neck-sticker-outer. But I'm ess, ell, oh, double-you; and just a Gippsland moron; these dolls are supersonic. No sooner had Beaufort, frail as a leopard, tottered to her taxi than another old tartar was after me — *pounce*. The taxi hadn't even started. 'Oh, Mr Gaar-Smith, *so* sorry to bother you but . . .'

''This killer's name was Carlyle, and she was after Beaufort's table.

''I can *so-sorry* with the best of them: 'I'm *so* sorry, Mrs Carlyle, but Miss Beaufort will only be away for a time and we've already arranged,' etcetera, etcetera, 'and I'm *so* sorry and I'm sure you understand.' Of course she was so sorry, too, but she understood, she quaite quaite understood. It was just that with her rheumatism, and her table was in such a shocking draught. . . . Draught! You couldn't get a draught into that dining-room if you were paid to. But we'd played our little scene and I — poor deluded rustic — heaved a sigh of relief.

''As you observe, I have no illusions about these old cows, but I knew they didn't break the rules, at least not in such a way as to lay themselves open to rebuke or even comment. Cold war's the shot; they work underground, like ferrets; no loss of face, all decencies preserved on the surface. They'll commit hair-raising bitcheries, but protocol is observed and there'll be a foolproof justification; they'll refer you back to the nod they've been given with the speed of light.

"The next time I was on duty there was Underground Agent Carlyle at the Beaufort's table. She saw me gaping like a Tassie shepherd who's just seen his baa-lamb gnawing away at a fox. She beckoned me over. Archly is the word, as archly as Clytemnestra: 'Ai expect you think Ai'm being a notty gel. Ai'm not, really.' She sipped some *consommé*, and I waited for revelation as she intended I should. Then, 'Ai heppened to see Mr Worthington.' More *consommé*. Like hell *heppened to see*. Lay in wait like fly-paper. 'Mr Worthington was asking after mai rheumatism. Ai explained about the draught. He ebsolutely insisted thet Ai hev Miss Beaufort's teble. Ai'm sure you understand.'

"I understood. I'm paid for just that. I didn't utter a peep. How could I? Worthington's so-and-so Circus, and Papa W. cracking his whip in fine confusion. 'Nother snort, old boy? All little Rupert Gaar-Smith had to do was await La Beaufort's return. That's all: the tumbril was on its way — look, lil' Rupe, there's pretty guillotine sparkling in the morning sunshine. . . ."

He was getting drunk. I too. Nevertheless, I could see the humiliation brewing, the maddening impotency.

Miss Beaufort came back. Mrs Carlyle, in legalizing her own action, had also legalized his defection. She had presented Worthington's fiat to him; he did the same to Miss Beaufort. She went an unusual colour; he thought she was about to faint. He hoped she would carry the squabble to Olympus, go raging to Worthington. She did nothing but control herself to say flatly and softly:

"So thet woman is to hev mai table. After faive years . . . faive years. *Thet* woman." She closed her eyes — *was* she going to faint? She opened them again.

"We shell see," she said.

Next she began to walk away down the long corridor doubly reflected and lengthened to infinity in the walls of looking-glass at each end. He could see their two selves repeated there endlessly, diminishing away for ever, the golden fence of brass standard-ashtrays vanishing to nothing. A few paces and she turned, came back to him — lavender water, blue eyes.

"They all seem to wear those blue eyes," he said thickly, "with a whitish ring at the edge of the iris, like . . . like . . ." But gin had drowned the simile.

She looked at him with those imperfect eyes:

"Mr Gaar-Smith, Ai feel you hev let me down bedly. It is only raight for me to ask you return the gretuity you hev decaidedly done nothing to earn."

Gratuity? Gratuity?

At first he did not understand, and then did. While she waited he groped in his pockets: no silver. The smallest money he had was a ten-shilling-note which, as he held it oafishly, she took. "Ai hev no chenge," she said. "Ai shell send it down to you." At the next mealtime a waitress brought him six shillings neatly enclosed — not in an envelope; in a square of brown-paper.

A week later Mrs Carlyle was found dead on the tiles at the bottom of a stair well.

She had apparently fallen from five floors up through the worm-eaten balustrade.

"I wash . . . I *was* on duty." He was getting very drunk. "About an hour before tiffin — luncheon — was correcting error in French on all the menus when housekeeper told me. Now 'member . . . *re*-member this: housekeeper, carpenter and I were the only ones in Galahad who knew until hours-'n'-hours later what had happened. Hotels smother these sorts of things quick-smart. No fuss, no scandal, nothing nasty in woodshed. Doctor, police, morgue-blokes all teed-up pronto. Body whipped out back way! Ultimate verdict — accidental death."

He drank. His funny-man's goo-goo eyes were ludicrously tragic: "I know it wasn't. I know, boy, it was *not* accidental. No one could imagine what sixty-year-old woman doing up there in forbidden, disused section, rooms filled with left umbrellas and portmanteaux and furs. But old girls bit odd, eh? they said. Odd!

"So Carlyle's smuggled out like a load of dirty laundry; I wash shaky little paws, comb hair, down tiny brandy and — *Boom! Boom! Boom!* — the lunch-gong. Got it? See it? See it all? Old faggots in clean pinnies lined up like orphans outside e-nor-mous glass doors, waitresses inside fiddling with apron-bows and butter-knives, me advancing *avec* poise with key to holy door . . . walk, walk. You know, long way, like Valli at end of 'The Third Man' . . . walk, walk, walk. Show mush go on! Reach door. Turn key. Hostess inside swings doors open . . . smile, smile. In the old otters file. In files Beaufort."

He stopped. While I waited he drained his glass and yet seemed to regain clarity and sobriety.

"Honest to God I wasn't even thinking of her. But I seemed to notice her specially; don't know why.

"She walked to the table she'd been using, walked firmly like — like Lady Hamlet. No, no; like Lady Macbeth and the dagger things. *You* know. She gathered her collection of bicarb. and doodads — and her table-napkin, and went straight as a die to her old table; Carlyle's table. She sat down, arranged her paraphernalia, and began to read the menu. It wasn't until she was through her *entrée* that I realized what was wrong.

"I was shattered. I couldn't think what I ought to do. My hands started to shake again. Not hers, bruvver. She ate through four courses."

Then, fiercely, at me: "Get it? Get it?"

I got it. I was willing to half-believe what he fully believed: she had known, before entering the dining-room, that her old table would be empty, would be hers again and till the end of time if she and her money and the Galahad could last so long. However, it seemed common sense to suggest, even if it did make her behaviour still pretty cold-blooded:

"Someone could have told her."

"No! Who? Who, man? Housekeeper? Carpenter? Not *them*. And no one else knew."

"Somebody who saw the body being whipped out; a kitchen-boy lurking behind the coke-bunkers."

"*No*. Nobody. Anyway, covered up — head to foot. Oh, I knew there'd be explanations like yours. 'S why I kept my trap shut. No one else noticed Beaufort back at her own table. I *practically* convinced me I was loco. Prac-tic-ally. Not any more. Not after today."

"Today?"

"I *told* you, child, there were two stiff-uns. Beaufort deadibones in bed this morning. You should have heard the Latvian chambermaid screaming like an ambulance! No note on pillow. Overdose sleeping-pills. Accident! Of *course*. Why should shweet, lavender-scented, well-heeled old bod commit suicide?"

He began to giggle drunkenly. "Accident my truss! Must have had conscience after all . . . conscience, eh . . .? Believe now?"

It didn't matter if I did. I'd served my purpose: the parcel of unwanted knowledge had been divided in two.

Before I could answer him a gong began, primitively, reverberating through rooms of leftovers: umbrellas lost for decades, candlesticks no one used, clocks that had stopped on some sunny day a long time ago.

"Dressing-gong!" said Gaar-Smith, and stumbled to the washstand for another drink.

As the gong thudded like drums of death, I imagined puckered fingers lifting rings from china ring-trees, pinning on brooches of opals, lightly powdering collapsed cheeks.

Gaar-Smith was giggling, giggling and horridly mincing about:

"Reahlly don't feel laike dressing tonaight . . . not going to hev any dinnah tonaight . . . someone else cen hev mai teble. . . ."

I understood.

Fiend and Friend

PERROT WAS young enough, at twenty-four, to be enthusiastic, energetic, sympathetic, to have all the softie bents of an inexperienced junior master in a Public School — doesn't matter where. He was hopeless; the boys offhandedly disliked him. That was the year — oh, long enough ago for *Cappuccino* to suggest a monk, Zen Buddhism to be a zealot's study rather than a fad; the Windsor Knot was just making Australia and Perrot and, while a cannery was a cannery, canned peaches were tinned peaches. Television was years off; people therefore sometimes looked at sunsets as though they were living in the nineteenth century. Perrot even, now and then, after cricket practice, blinked at Turner, Harrow-on-the-Hill sunsets from the disproportionately grandiose Italianate portico of The School which, on its last Victorian legs, nevertheless still took charge of a view that sloped down for miles, and was open to the common-cold- or hayfever-bringing gusts from . . . from an ocean needless to name. The School prospectus, sprinkled with Hollandse Medieval initials, used *panorama* and *ozone*, and extolled as *healthful zephyrs* largely southerly and often refrigeratingly antarctic winds.

The School's heyday had been also the bicycle's, Brittania's and Beardsley's; in Perrot's time all was flaking, cracked, sutured by Virginia Creeper, down-at-heel but not seedy. The place had *cachet* though doors would not lock, windows would not open, floorboards were so worn that knots stood up like carbuncles. Glass cases of stuffed hawks and unglittering geological samples stood in subfusc corridors. It was draughty as the Parthenon; the flywire screens of kitchens, sculleries and dining-hall were more ragged than the Bayeux tapestry.

The Head, the Common Room, Matron, Sister, the Housekeeper, the ex-Test-bowler cricket coach all intimated or brazenly kept on indicating that they had come from — how long ago? — somewhere better. *Somewhere better*, of course, meant *youth* and was the answer; jobs had been no better; they had been younger. While too intelligent, educated or experienced for hope, and aware they could be on their way nowhere else, they were not resigned to their own unhappiness though, the easy sagacity, they were to each other's. Fretfully they droned like senile bees; there was an atmosphere of Eventide Home. In the Common Room hung academic gowns like attire Villon might have worn. Perrot's gown alone seemed Byronic. It was new. Perrot, the one young master, alone represented the generation between boys and ageing staff. Perrot alone of the adults was on his way somewhere else. For others this was the last year because, after seventy years of lathing out judges, knights, diplomats, dipsomaniacs, professional bores and one undramatic murderer, The School was to close. Next year the desks incised with unthinkable dates, the FOO-haunted changing-rooms, The School barber like someone out of Jerome K. Jerome, the music master who affected a velvet-collared overcoat and Lisztian hair, all, everyone, would be gone, the boys doubly so.

Doubly? Gone as schoolboys of that School, gone irrevocably as boys for, turn one's back and temperamental tennis professionals took their places, quick-gnawing sub-deans, shy graziers, terse shire engineers, turners-and-fitters, tally-clerks, journalists, *divorcés*, no-hopers garnet-eyed and bender-skinny quavering, "Two bob, dig", in a Russell Drysdale town. But, fleetingly, boys. Conventional as cannibals, secretive as stool pigeons, shrewish as little girls, sensitive, six inches above the footpaths of common sense, a rabble with its own two-up school protocol, they missed nostalgia, wistfulness, the end-of-an-era atmosphere. They acted *Boys will be Boys* with *éclat*. No one, indeed, can act a boy as well as a boy.

Except for Rymill. He overacted, at least for Perrot and largely for Perrot.

Rymill seemed the scandalous boy from nowhere. He was spare as if his spirit abhorred the luxury of flesh, Murillo-eyed changeling, the unsmiling gipsy at the manor gates. He travelled south from some unimaginable part of Queensland — hinterland, borderland, Goblin Market, God knew! — by shattered buses to board other shattered buses on teeth-splintering back roads, by trains with sand-paper seats through landscapes of glaring antagonism or where impermanent rivers, momentarily mad with seeming ginger beer, flushed like lavatories. End of term — abracadabra! — he disappeared. First day of term, while others were unpacking, there he was — whoosh! — as though riding it bareback to puncture, yoo-hooing about on someone else's bicycle. He was Perrot's Old Man of the Sea, his nigger in the woodpile, his *bête noire*, his . . . "I could give Dr Roget a hundred he hasn't thought of for *bane*," Perrot would cry. "A thousand! I'll disembowel the Rymill; I'll garotte him; I'll commit mayhem; I'll . . ." Perrot was thus desperately facetious as people are when they imitate Cockney at sticky moments. He hated Rymill. The Common Room smiled like a waiting-room of Mona Lisas, a club of Punches, a jury ardent to pronounce, "Guilty!"

"I shall cane the next boy who . . ." Perrot cried, deliberately dramatically for the little monsters, sweeping about so that his gown was Hamlet's cloak on the swirl. Rymill was the next boy.

"Who said that?" called Perrot, spooning out rissoles at table. "Who said 'compost'? Ah, I might have known! See me after luncheon, Rymill."

Perrot, looking up in prep., impelled to look up, met the intense and shocking gaze of a little man with an enormous *papier-mâché* Jewish nose and horn-rimmed spectacles who was sitting in Rymill's desk. "Out here, Rymill!" he shouted.

"Hell!" yelled Perrot leaping like Buster Keaton from the thistle on his chair. He knew at whom to direct his outrage. Rubbing his behind, Rymill was already on his way, face bleak as a saint's.

Rymill's misdemeanours had the dreary innocence of japes and merry pranks conned from a 1913 *Boy's Own Paper*; they smelt of the lamp, of Baden-Powell and Goodnatured Boyish Fun: there were crackers, treacle in the inkwell, sewn-up pyjama legs, vile stenches, tin blots on pages, lizards in desks . . . It was persistence and repetition, impenitence and intensity that marked Rymill eccentric. Perrot was the target.

In choice of friend Rymill carried eccentricity further. He had screened The School to find an *alter ego* as like himself in appearance but as unlike in behaviour. Van der Velde, a Dutch consul's son, was the choice, a boy of his height, age, curls and colouring but bland, cautious and smilingly courteous. War and Peace, thought Perrot in distracted moments, Whisky and Water, Mad Hatter and Dormouse, Fiend and Friend. Van der Velde spent much of his time eating, an exercise Rymill seemed to like little, gorged as he was, Perrot thought, by plottings, plannings, and venom. The consul's son always ate Rymill's pudding; as left-handed as the King of Spades he was rarely seen without a bag of *éclairs* or grapes into which he south-paw dipped and dipped. He was affable and godly Rymill.

Tirelessly, sombre, with nicotine-stained fingers, skulls-and-crossbones inked on wrists, Rymill himself continued overacting Tom Sawyer, *Triumph* and *Stalky and Co.* until The School was bored to screeching, "Ow, chuckit, Rymill!" "Pipe down, Rymill!" "Go to *buggery*, Rymill!" Only his friend, left-handedly pecking into caramel cartons, laxly indulged him. Only Perrot was beyond the shallows of boredom or forbearance; Rymill was to him the seventh wave, the deadly bumper, the slug in the salad, as ever-present as Satan, as over-shadowing as a Doré one. Rymill was thirteen.

The older masters were invigorated, as with moral penicillin, by Perrot's distress; it graced their morose last year that he was rattled by a mere whipper-snapper; young-manhood, with its imperfections of disciplinary technique, seemed less worthy of regret.

Even the Head, as classical of profile and as remote as a Carrera Olympian topping an insurance building, said with dispassion, "My dear young man, Rymill is impermanent. Boys are, you know, quite." He paused; reflection from some high-flying pigeon of thought flicked his rigid handsomeness. "He's an only son, you know. And fatherless. Perhaps this campaign of terror is disguised affection, hero-worship. However, though I can't expel him *yet*, shall I cane him for you? Brutally?"

Cynical bastard, thought Perrot but, "Heavens, no," he said. "Heavens, *no*, sir. I'll learn to cope."

"Cope?" said the Head as though Perrot had used a four-letter obscenity.

"Manage . . . that is, handle the situation, sir."

"I'm certain you will. You — a vigorous, intelligent stripling. . . ." The Head looked at his knuckles as if they were new.

Perrot flushed. "It's just, sir, that his behaviour's so incredible."

"Nothing, Perrot, is incredible until one has said it is. And saying it . . . well, untruth, eh? I *myself* find it all credible."

"Thank you, sir," said Perrot as though imparting, after losing all toenails, the secret the Gestapo wanted.

The Head stared an unwinking four seconds at the air agitated by Perrot's exit, then returned with detachment to what he called a railway novel, a paperback James Hadley Chase, whose bloodhouse world seemed calmer much than the one he had long inhabited — bickering Board, backbiting masters, pregnant maids, parents with delusions, neurotic housekeepers, imperious Matrons, hyperbolizing tradesmen, drunken ground-keepers, domineering archbishops, conveyor belts of boys transparent and meretricious as Christmas stockings, and, above all, an ex-actress wife who felt herself gifted and young enough to retreat into the costly fantasy of fashion from the cut-rate indelicacy of having fallen, almost immediately after marriage, out of love with him.

Then came the absurd affair of the Music Room ceiling.

Perrot was on evening duty which usually, for him, resembled the French Revolution. However, prep., showers, lights-out had passed in such peace, as though another master were on duty, that he should have warned himself. Instead, he went gulled to bed to find himself stark awake at some deep hour: horizon askew, raft sinking, the moon turned over. God, he thought, resident masters are like mothers. There was a wrong weight of silence; an area of breathing and dreaming and stirring had been subtracted from the sum of boarding-house night. He switched on. Two-o'-bloody-clock, *ante meridiem*. He padded seeking with electric torch. Dormitory One — dead to the world. Dormitory Two — eight-year-old Bernstein, frail as Tiny Tim, snoring like a warthog. Dormitory Three — "I . . . might . . . have . . . known," said Perrot to the twelve beds and their bulges that neither twisted, snorted nor dreamed. Midnight feast! he thought. Rymill!

As though seeking Jesus's lambs, but fuming like Etna, Perrot stamped here and there. No one in the gymnasium except the vaulting horse grazing tan bark under the trapeze; no one in the cricket pavilion except Callaghan's cricket boots, and a singlet abandoned like an after-birth in one corner; no one in the old science theatre except the memory of useless lectures; no one in any custom-sacred place. Within twenty minutes Perrot began to suggest to himself the notion of being in nightmare, himself ranging the famous slope for a dozen Jack-o'-Lantern sub-adolescents, his torch springing junior Erl Kings under olive-trees and stabbing the head-hunter rustlers in canna plantations, barking, "Rymill! Rymill!" in the provoking darkness.

On the boil, he returned to his study and waited, gnawing at the smoke of cigarettes, and deciding to become a jackeroo with an English accent and a *fiancée* called Christine. What else to do except turn on the sun like an electric light?

At last he heard sibilances and graveside shufflings that should have been theme-musicked by Grieg. These approached; it was reminiscent of *Alice in Wonderland*, something about Bill the Lizard, "Hold up his head. . . . Brandy now. . . . Don't choke him. . . ." Ahead of the tissue-paper hubbub Van der Velde appeared first at the doorway, his dressing-gown pockets bulged with Chocolate Royals. His eyes were too starry, were lunatic's. "Oh, sir," he cried, "Oh, sir — Rymill's hurt!" Perrot disconcerted himself by stubbing the cigarette he had just lit.

And there, over-zealously supported by *all* the Lost Boys, everyone a finger in the pie, lying in a pansyish though awkwardly sustained pose, was Rymill. One leg, on deliberate foreground display, dripped blood and stained the pyjama-leg torn like a beachcomber's at a Fancy Dress Ball. Perrot transformed himself to a competent schoolmaster. There were cuts and more dramatic blood than seemed necessary. "I'm perfectly all right, sir," said Rymill. "I'm perfectly, perfectly all right. I'm perfectly, perfectly, *perfectly* . . ."

"Take him," said Perrot, suddenly raddled with a cutthroat's anger, "take him to the nearest bathroom. We'll see if we need disturb Sister or Matron." In a stimulating hush of doom Rymill's Caesar's body was borne to where his washed wounds were revealed as scarcely more than scrimshawing. Joy faded from the mob at this treacherous let-down. "Get to bed, all of you," said Perrot, angrier than they thought a dope could be. "Get out of my sight. Except Van der Velde. You'll tell me everything, if I have to use torture. And for God's sake stop eating," he said viciously. "Your whole life is a litter of banana peel and a trail of paper bags. Stop it." Ruthlessly, yet with a suffusion of paternal affection he had no cause to feel, did not care to harbour and certainly not to admit, Perrot iodined and sticking-plastered while Van der Velde, an undevilled version of the patient, told of the feast.

"It was my fault, sir," said Rymill with death-bed weariness. "I planned it. I am to blame. I . . ."

"Shut up," cried Perrot. "Do shut *up*. Don't come the noble, self-sacrificing schoolboy with me. I'm sick of you."

Planning had taken weeks. Climbing to get tennis-balls from rain-gutters Rymill had prowled the elaborate valleys and steeps of the roof, and had so loosened a sheet of corrugated iron that the caveland of rafters was opened to him. Perrot perceived the value of this to Rymill; even those fed-up with his *Schoolboy's Annual* pranks could not resist a beano in such a setting. Old mattresses were filched from the infirmary store-room, a catwalk of planks was made across the rafters, an electric light circuit tapped. "God, you little fools!" said Perrot and, bitterly, "Then, *then*, all you waited for was a night *I* was on duty, eh?" Rymill stared with luminous fixity. Van der Velde gushed, "Well, sir, not *really*. The day after tomorrow's end of term *and* . . ." Perrot disregarded him. "You are to blame, aren't you, Rymill?" he said. "Remember saying that? You waited until I was on duty, didn't you?" The stare, its quality untranslatable, continued. "Didn't you, Rymill?" Perrot could just control his voice. "Yes, sir," said Rymill as though he were lying to save some face or other. He closed his eyes. Van der Velde continued.

Feast over, the boys were returning when Rymill had fallen from the catwalk; his leg had gone through the Music Room ceiling.

"How do you know it was the Music Room?"

"We flashed torches through the hole," said Van der Velde. "There's plaster all over the grand. It looks frightful, sir. Tons and tons of it."

"Get to bed," said Perrot. "Get to your wretched beds. I shouldn't like to be in your shoes tomorrow when the Head sees all that mess."

Rymill opened his eyes, said with passionate earnestness, "Sir, couldn't we clean up the mess so that it won't look so bad, and then the Head wouldn't be so mad with us? *Please*, sir?"

Perrot could hardly speak; when he did he was astounded to hear, "Rymill . . . Rymill, I hate you. Hate *you*. I have never in my life . . . Get out!"

When the two had gone, Perrot, distressed at anger but still angry, walked to the Music Room. Tons and tons was right; the hole in the ceiling seemed too small for the wreckage below. I wonder, he thought, if there's blood up there and, remembering the torn leg which seemed younger, as though it belonged to a child, as though it had a mother and could be loved, Perrot cleaned up. It took a long time, and became a labour of fantasy for he could not tell himself why he was repaying months of torment with furtive dirty work.

He did not see Rymill until next term. At breakup, the boy had disappeared across horrors of scarcely inhabited space, and had returned bearing a gift. The fact of the gift astounded Perrot, the nature of it electrified him: eleven feet of swamp-python's skin. Eyeing gift and what he felt was Greek with distaste, Perrot listened to Rymill attempting to consecrate the musty tribute. "Belts, sir," he chattered desperately on, "and little pouches for money. Or combs. You *know*. Maybe a wallet or a portfolio. I know a bloke . . . a *man* who has shoes." Perrot was able, just, to say, "Thank you, Rymill." This meant, "O.K., I don't know what you're up to, but leave the repulsive thing and vamoose. I don't trust you. I don't like you." Rymill got the meaning, faded-out his chattering, looked paler and shocked. Then, "Is that all, sir?" he said, was it pleadingly? Is what all? thought Perrot. Should I burst into fireworks because he's sucking up to me? Run a hand over his curls and pretend that snake-skin shoes were what I wanted most in the world? "That's *all*," said Perrot. Rymill turned and left.

The final term was given over to ritual farewell: the last Old Boy's Cricket Match, the last Swimming Carnival, the last Knight-and-Bishop-studded Garden Party; bunting flapped continually; potted palms were always being borrowed from the City Hall. It was the *Titanic* sinking with lights ablaze, rag-time, and ornamental behaviour. The Head, distant behind railway novels, nevertheless conceived imperial notions, and sent the Second Master marathon-ing from him to Common Room like a Euripidean messenger — shields and silver cups were polished for the first time in memory; a six-fold School Maga-zine, gilt-embossed, and over-decorated with nineteenth-century fleurons, was distributed free and, *crescendo*, the messenger recited that *Peter Pan* was to be produced by the Head's wife who had been plucked, as it were, from the very sill of the Darling nursery for she had been being a notable Peter Pan almost till her wedding-day. Auditions happened as incontinently as nervous break-downs. Proud seniors, acne aflame like sprays of Cartier rubies, were returned from failing Hook or Smee to their degrading skill in the elementary properties of the parabola, whey-faced boys whose voices had not broken were pincered out of German classes to try for Wendy. Van der Velde — curls, slight build, Consular-Englishy voice — was Peter Pan. Since no expense, ardour and hard work were spared, the Head's wife was able, on the second last night of the last of all terms to bring off a technical and dramatic success.

One moment seemed to Perrot to have oblique poignancy. Peter Pan cried, "Look!" and rose on his invisible wires, cleaving the air with unforeseen grace. All fake, thought Perrot, and it's only Van der Velde and his smile on wires, someone who will be a molly-duked loud-mouth with false teeth and hairy ears. But, for a moment, a dream child flitted charmingly, Peter Pan, the dream no one should have. The show went on. The Indians stamped; the pirate cutlasses flashed; the show closed. The School closed. The School was pulled down and the appalling abode of a politician went up. The sloping view became sloping streets and crescents. The birds lost their Public School accents and, fidgeting in suburban birdbaths, acquired unsurer ones; the southerly "zephyrs" scattered largesse of hayfever on housewives in super-market head-scarves; the Head in retirement wrote a remaindered mystery novel containing five split infinitives, and died, and Perrot became an anodized schoolmaster no boy could faze. Rymill had taught him much, and not to let ells be taken, never to give an inch.

Eleven, twelve, thirteen years passed.

Perrot, ambitious, unlovable, cultivating loneliness, moved from school to school. As such schoolmasters are, he was often disconcerted by unplaceable men who fired at him their "Sir! Nice to see you!" These reunions with their hand-pumpings, post mortems and mediocre revelations had for him the garbled air of embraces at funerals. He did not know what to say to these strangers. But unwritten rules stated that schoolmasters were interested, and that the advancing unknown who might merely be wishing to ask where the next corner was, could not be repulsed when he cried, "Sir!" — that invocation to boyhood lost in the quicksands.

So there was Perrot mincing wine matters with his favourite Basque waiter at the Trattoria Triaca, when "Sir!" Two of them. Which school? Who? It was Rymill, they cried. It was Van der Velde, they cried. It was two men. It was two half-drunk men — one huge as Orson Welles, fleshed and flushed, the other slender and flashing smilelessly more teeth than a rajah. Perrot learnt with deep uninterest that Rymill and Van der Velde had bumped into each other, first time for years, below in Young and Jackson's Hotel. (Perrot: How did *they* recognize each other?) Now, to meet their schoolmaster (Perrot: Beloved? Revered? Respected? Disliked?) was coincidence worthy of over-drinking and unrelenting *brouhaha*. Perrot knew the grisly drill, resigned himself, drank quickly, arranged an expression and listened. It was necessary, as always, to submit to a depersonalizing and repersonalizing that made him feel that someone else had badly impersonated him years ago. Rymill and Van der Velde recalled what he knew nothing of, told an involved Perrot legend of a doing so contrary to his essential nature that he could not recognize himself. Did he remember this, and that, and the other? Oh, yes, he did, he did, he did, he lied, and shocked Leo the Basque by asking twice for double Scotch in the middle of claret. Did he remember one night, when Old Nodsy (who the hell was old Nodsy?), short-cutting through the basement, caught Halliburton (and who was *he*?) — did he remember Halliburton? ("Of course, of course. Old Halliburton, eh!") — well, Halliburton was in a pretty hot clinch with one of the sewing-maids in a niche, and nearly fainted, and all Old Nodsy said was, "Goodnight, goodnight. You should be in bed!"

They roared. Perrot mimed roaring, idiot on the rack, and tossed off another drink.

Did he remember . . .? *And* did he remember . . .?

By the third bottle of claret Perrot had scraped together his own scant memories. Peter Pan flying in the spotlight, he thought. And the Music Room ceiling! No wonder at all that Rymill had crashed through for, within the boy who had nearly driven him bats, had hibernated this double-chinned, gutsy hearty who had just knocked over his claret. So this was what happened to naughty boys; this was justice! It warmed Perrot but he also felt old hatred like a re-awakened indigestion. He'd always hated Rymill, hadn't he? Wasn't there some odd backblocks background? And something about a snake-skin?

Van der Velde had shed boyhood more effectively, his manners were gracious (consular background, Perrot recalled) — at least he hadn't knocked over two glasses of wine. Yes, Van der Velde hadn't turned out badly though he had been smug, always chewing at bits and pieces like a pregnant woman.

And then the fat man, the uncouth, the knocker-over, suddenly blundered to his feet. "I think," he said, "I'm going to perk . . ." and walked out.

"Look after that man, please, Leo," said Perrot. He had never spoken like a schoolmaster to the Basque before. I'm drunk, he thought. I hope Rymill is sick as a dog. I hope he crashes through the lavatory floor into Young and Jackson's. I hope . . .

"What are you thinking of, sir?"

"I don't think I was thinking. But I was before, you know, of the few things I do remember about the old School. Things you two wouldn't. The sunsets, the parklands sloping away. All gone — the big porch, the Virginia Creeper, the oak-trees. I'm drunk, you see . . . nostalgic flapdoodle. Hadn't thought of them for years. And you . . . Peter Panning away there. I'm not usually sentimental but I *am* drunk. And Rymill. I used to hate him. A fiend. I used to call you two fiend and friend, you know, war and peace. Absurd! You, of course, were peace and friend." Perrot giggled. "Rymill would plummet *right* through the ceiling now. . . ." He seemed to hear a Marx Brothers' crash into a grand piano.

"Sir?"

"For Pete's sake, don't tell me you don't remember that? I've listened to so much tonight that *I* didn't remember. . . ."

"Of course I remember, sir. I've still got scars. And I've never forgotten how kind you were."

Scars? Kind?

"I *thought* you'd got us muddled, sir. That's Van der Velde who tottered out to the dyke. I'm Rymill."

Perrot now observed that the man before him not only had a moustache like the Knave of Hearts' but that he held his wine-glass in his right hand as the Knave holds the nameless and baffling leaf. This was not the consul's left-handed son. This was the hellion who had vaccinated him against boys for ever. Here he was facing again in a restaurant smelling of *minestrone* and garlicked salad bowls, two untranslatable eyes set in luminous, unsmiling fixity. As once before, but drunkenly now, he was aware of something paternally unzippering: an *exeat* had to be given, an expiation made; words *had* to be said. Reluctantly Perrot said some, "I didn't really hate you, Rymill." But these were not right; they were, indeed, a lie.

Perrot frowned, closed his eyes, thinking: here — now — are two grog-soaked men who had nearly fought out something thirteen years ago, but merely nearly. Time's inevitable simplicity being revealed, it was easy to follow the paper-chase of greasy bags that led absolutely from Peter Pan to a fat man; it was difficult to chart what unfinished business, what trail of misgivings led to this overdue confrontation in the Trattoria Triaca. He heard Rymill saying (insolently? gratefully?), "Why, sir, did you clean up the mess in the Music Room?" The question left echoes in the soundbox of Perrot's conscience; fantastically he seemed to hear a dead man, the Head, intoning, "Only son . . . fatherless . . . hero-worship . . ."

Perrot's frown melted; he opened his eyes with conviction; he realized what should have been said years ago instead of "That's *all*." Revolted, unwilling, but as enthusiastically as possible, he therefore said it now, "Did you kill that enormous python yourself?" It was a confession of sin.

He saw Rymill smile *Yes, of course, silly sir* as he would have smiled thirteen years ago. Whether the smile was tinted sardonically or affectionately Perrot neither knew nor cared, but it was the appeased smile of one who has finished training his schoolmaster.

It was also, Perrot realized with horror, the first smile he had ever seen on Rymill's face.

Country Town

THIS, YOU must know, is less a story of people than of a country town. Australian? Unmistakably. Plot? Life? Yes. Love? Well — y-e-e-e-s. For example, I am put out to know that, in some windy part of my mind, *I* love this home town as one might inescapably love a hypocrite uncle as boring as immortality and with the points of view of a blowfly, or a recurring sweet dream one knows too well is a dream, or a cocktail that has a terrific lift though it tastes like the inside of a coffin. Love, you think? Eh?

I left the place thirty years ago. Absence did no more than qualify me to dispassion about *Before* and *After*, make me see more clearly what happened next, the new make-up and changed lighting after Intermission. All I learnt while out smoking the cigarettes too gaudily labelled *Experience* is — a safe cynicism — that civilization makes anything no less accidental, anything at all: living, lusting, dying and so on.

I return one sunset, accidental (you see!) — accidental nice timing — the town seems, for a thin slice of time, to be not one skerrick changed. It has the *High Noon* frontier town look Australian country towns have when horizontal rays stress that two storeys is the limit and in Main Street only, that the rest of the town is on one floor and mostly weatherboard. Those ridge-and-gulch acres of corrugated iron roofs! Those chimneys! — a functioning museum of bricklayer fashions: 1873, 1885, 1902, 1919, 1926, 1938, 1959 . . .

My nostalgic, just tearless eye strains to unfade on upper-floor brick side-walls words still there from my boyhood and earlier: *Bush's Family Grocer, Kyle's Cash Bakery, Mantles and Robes, Horse Bazaar — Omnibus Depôt — Wedding Carriages for Hire*. The tide of falsifying plastic paint, peg-board, and plate glass canted off the vertical does not rise to the first floor; above is the past; as well, in Main Street backyards Chic Sale privies loll spastically against tors of packing-cases. The two poplars still domineer, dead-centre of the town, like nervous Azraels; the aluminium-painted penny-farthing sits as ever on the roof-line of the bicycle-shop. Well, well! Are there, beneath these tongue-and-groove false fronts, still fruit-shops unaware of sweet-corn, canteloupes, milk-bars and juke-boxes but which display, as of old, their decay-velveted Valencias, flaccid rhubarb and firkin-sized ironbark pumpkins under fretwork arches and dusty witch-balls? Does artificial rain meander down the butcher's plate-glass in front of the parsley-eyed pig's head on its fly-corpse-curranted marble? Is the arc of enamelled letters BOURNVILLE COCOA (two letters always missing) stuck yet on grocers' shop-windows?

No; and for ever, no.

No the monumental mason's urns and scrolls poking through horehound and fennel; no the smithy, the saddler's, the doctors' red lamps, the Show Day procession, the elm avenues, the hitching-rings on shop-veranda posts; no the hickory golf clubs mashie and cleek, washerwomen, bullockies, knickerbockered boys in boots, girls in ribbed stockings, the hat on every outdoor head, the immodestly defining cotton bathers from which inky dye seeped into the white-edged sleevelets, and no no no the sound of hoofs on gravel roads. Gone cabby, rabbit-oh and fish-oh, John Chinaman green-grocer, the dago ice-cream cart and its bell, the Hindu old-iron man, the scissors-grinder, the Afghan pedlar, and all their clockwork nags which wore in midsummer their earholed equine mil-linery above wowserish William S. Hart faces; gone the medieval pageantry of hearse-horses, Black Prince plumes, the top-hatted undertakers in cutaway coats. Gone what was called the night-cart though it came, two-horsed, also in daylight, a zeppelin-grey tank-like machine, two storeys high, back to back terraces of dunnican cubicles that clanged shut as jails must clang. *That* was one of the town's sounds.

Early in December, one found a card on the lavatory seat:

Enjoy Christmas as best you can,
And don't forget the dunny man.

Did parents leave a Christian half-crown near the egg-shaped hole? Or, not breathing, waylay the burly untouchable with the top of his felt hat squashed so horizontal from reeking burdens that he appeared mathematically scalped, and present some gift with a gracious clause? I don't remember. One should know, but . . .

I knew lies, carnality, happiness, despair, even viciousness and *ennui*. I had heard of Rembrandt, Bach, Pavlova, Tutankhamen and Jack-the-Ripper but never of fish and chips, spaghetti or grape-fruit. Oh, a local, a yokel, a hick, a peasant, a simple boy from Woop Woop! Had I heard of wireless? There must have been crystal sets in the shire, but as I prowled back streets, criminally over-nonchalant, to steal quinces or blood-filled Satsumas, I heard only the melancholy of old-maid uprights behind fringed holland blinds. Fingers of unseen pale hands tinkling "*. . . I loved beside the Shalimar . . .*" where, indeed, are you now? Piano or pianola, just around the next picket-fence corner overhung by cassias lay — had I known it — the opening of Canberra, *The Jazz Singer*, the Depression, miniature golf, Club Sandwiches, and, for me, long pants, silk socks, Melbourne (The City!) and what I thought was Life. It took years, that last one.

So with Life dwindled to life, kings and kingdoms foundered, bombs dropped as frequently as bricks, the moon to be colonized by scientific dogs or mad Crusoes, I return, middle-aged and less *dégagé* than I thought, to another chain-store town. Fluorescent street-lights glare on the metallic venetians and desper-ately garish doors. Neons display their *tics* above all the pubs, the cinema, the drive-in, the ice-block automat, the auto-port, the self-service petrol bowser, the motel, the transport drivers' steak-and-egg road-houses, and the caravan park whose machicolated public lavatories like Disney castles have been built with municipal delicacy on the top of pioneer graves. Neons utter *Hamburgers, Fish and Chips, Milk Bar, All Night Café, Smokes, Snacks, Eats* — God-knows-what-else — and *Espresso*.

The shingled virgins in berets who tormented my adolescence, and Black-Bottomed or Parma-Waltzed in the Mechanics' Hall — chocolate stencilled dado, tangerine *crêpe* paper streamers looped into gas-less gasoliers under the pitch-pine ceiling — now sit beneath the Wandering Jew and other pendulant weeds of *Maxim's Espresso* smoking king-sized filter-tips, continentally rapping out, "Cappuccino!" and tempting the Providence of matronly zippers as they stretch to choose with plastic tongs another musty Jewish-Viennese cake from under the plastic cover. Forsworn the pottery teapot, the toasted ham sandwich and cheese cakes!

Coronetted sewer-poles pierce up in every direction but hoisted high above them like the Euclid problems of *ex-avant-garde* wire-sculpture or Woolworth potato-mashers are the symbols of a sinister craze — the H.P. T.V. aerials.

Had I foreseen all these? Nearly all, for they are everywhere else, the production-belt contrumpery, the wrought-iron knick-knackery, the Yankeefied barbecue furniture, cheap-jack self-service stores, cellophaned rubbish, grubbed-out street elms, municipal vandalism, pre-fab. schoolrooms, jerry-built Commission houses, "1984" public address systems, the arc-lit pennants and tubbed privets of the used car dealers, the labour-pains of a second Industrial Revolution — how could I not have foreseen? I had not foreseen that I should spend my first night in what, to me, was Mrs Topper's bedroom.

In days when tracks in the river-bank grass or across homestead paddocks were triple, two for wheels plus one for hoofs, and are now merely car-wheel double, in days when Christmas meant eucalypt saplings glorifying every veranda post of every shop, when Jew's Harps and German transfers could be bought, and cigarette cards were silk-covered, Topper was a schoolboy friend and what I considered rich. His parents' house with slate roof, wide tiled verandas, stables, orchard, tennis court, septic tank, even its palm lawn, arbutus and monkey puzzle had, for me, then, much elegance. Lorraine Lee roses sum it up: they were just in; Toppers had them. We played Mah Jongg, listened to *Horsy, Keep Your Tail Up* and *O, Katharina* on a Victrola inside, a portable Decca outside, ate the non-alcoholic almond-porcupined trifles left over from Mrs Topper's parties and, to make the bosomy housemaid bounce about screeching like a cockatoo, chewed mouthfuls of walnuts which we regurgitated in front of her, pretending we vomited.

One Saturday a charitable bazaar called a Garden Fête was held there. All I remember is one stall, lattice hung with home-made wistaria, and run by the cinema pianist, a fluting spinster beaked as, and now as dead as, Virginia Woolf.

A blue paper chrysanthemum at each temple, and hung with a kimono, she sold heart-shaped velveteen pin-cushions, shirt-flannel pen-wipers, gilded wheels made of matchbox drawers (what were they *for*?) and the first Turkish Delight I had tasted.

And once, as though destiny were showing me the other side of the medal first . . . the ornamental side, the side for romantic little boys, a side to remember . . . I was taken into Mrs Topper's bedroom when she had some *malaise* to say "Hullo", or even "Hello". Since my own bed was rather shame-makingly like the brass and enamelled iron death-bed of Pius XII at Castel Godolfo her wagon-sized one of fumed oak had a Cecil B. de Mille quality, and Mrs Topper, fragile and *eau-de-Cologned*, rather the air of Gloria Swanson. The room seemed to me enormous and was large; its lavender wallpaper was panelled with strips of what formed the terribly dainty black-and-silver frieze. Through the lace curtains of the bay window could be seen, far off behind the pergola of Dorothy Perkins roses, the morass where I waded for swans' and plovers' eggs, and learnt to smoke, having stolen three Britannia-embossed pennies for the packet from my mother's kitchen-purse, the shabby morocco one with the steel catch.

Now, here I was, more years later than seemed possible even to me who had enthusiastically used up or outrageously thrown away every hour of them, in Mrs Topper's bedroom for the second time — to sleep there for one night.

Topper's is now a boarding-house for men run as scrupulously as a hospital by Hungarians called New Australians; a hoarding under the monkey puzzle shouts Something-or-other Guest House. The property has been subdivided; women's magazine houses, architectural illiteracies of built-in plywood and man-made fibres, share out such Topper trees as remain. The house is also subdiv-ided, partitions bisecting rooms, fibro-plaster sleep-outs lining the verandas. Some garage hand or gas-works stoker is always removing Al Jolson under the shower; ironstone china clashes in the pantry; transistor wirelesses play con-stantly and from every direction, and — oh, that other side of the medal — Mrs Topper's bedroom, with aseptically white walls, contains four monk-cell beds, four gents' wardrobes, four bedside cupboards and reading-lamps, four vacuumed hideous scatter rugs. Cheek by jowl the men live like well-behaved butch dolls.

Since I was to sleep once only in this room — there was some one-day hitch about a promised bungalow outside — I was unpacking just enough to make a homing perch, and getting my eye in before going out to get anaesthetically drunk, for in no other way would I be able to sleep in this dormitory with three unknowns whose paraphernalia disposed strictly in each quarter-room advertised variously addicted men but undeniably young ones, young *blokes* and to be eluded: middle-aged men of my sort relish young men far less than old men do.

I was, however, not quickly enough unpacked to escape young men for, in acrobat vees, patently dewy from a shower, enter, *vigoroso*, on peanut-shaped toes, one of them. Say, rather, a young man made an entrance: chest out, belly in, a *pas seul* seemed imminent. Instantly, though it was impossible, I felt I knew him, had met him. He was somewhat above short, flaxen, pretty as a pretty ape with little electric-blue eyes which, in a crackle, assessed my suit and shoes and condoned his tooth-paste smile and knuckle-deforming handshake. My mind said, "Ouch!" He was pleased to meet me, man. I how-d'-y'-do'ed. He was Kurt Schmidt, man. He was now — ha, ha — a dinkum Aussie, man. He flexed.

Now he would examine *my* silver-mark.

His torso and arms were physical culture magazine, Mr Universe; he kept on wincing these upper wonders which tapered to skinny legs bandy as Rupert Brooke's and feet small as a girl's. Decidedly better kit-cat than full.

He strutted, he prattled, reluctant to obscure his top-heavy form, to enclose it in whatever usually contained it; he juggled two cut-in dimples as Sonja Henie used to — oh, he turned it on. His English was good though larded with bodgie-isms and low camp patter that were not *quite* right. Self-possessed as a musical comedy child he dealt questions like a Five Hundred hand. How long was I sojourning in this wierdsville burg, huh? What did I do for a crust? How had I got here? Did I have a car? Did I have a car, huh? When I told him that I could not drive one and had no desire to own one, it was as though I had stabbed him. "Oh, no!" he cried in agony. *So I was a weird-o! Really rat! Did I have any bread?* I saw him think that. I saw him jettison his first assessment, sensed his interest change direction; he became as busy and charming as a cat when the refrigerator is opened. But I *must* have a car, man, just for hacking round, like. For cruising, huh? He became fanatic as a missionary; his voice went off key with zeal. Daddy-O, a car was the *most*. A car had protein.

Behind the dimples, the stomach muscles like an active anatomical chart and the heliographing teeth I was aware of dead-pan evaluation: Daddy-O, oh, Daddy-O, how I could send you up! You're a double freak, a squarehead square, a fossil with your dullsville old hand-made brogues, but I dig you — I dig you, creep.

He could, he raved on, *he* could drive a car, but any, and neat-o. Cars fractured him, like. He was a car cat, yes, *man*. Drive! Z-e-e-o-o-oom! Here he unconsciously mimed, trance took him: hands and forearm on a steering-wheel, dimples flattened, he slitted eyes at some roadway flaring under at seventy, eighty, ninety . . . Then he came to, lit up, moved in selling hard, saying that a flip . . . a *gentleman* like me *should* have a car; I was a grool not to; listen, Daddy-O, he had a gasser of an idea, like — he'd drive for me, with pleasure, but definite *pleasure*. I must must must get a car. Next, intensifying his dimples and so suddenly so very offhandedly that I heard the gears grind, "What you doing tonight, Mac? Dolls, huh?"

It was a try-out subtle as evisceration. A naughty monkey, he looked slyer than he thought he looked wistful and charming.

"No," I said, "no — er — women."

He registered. He rippled muscles at me, smiled and smiled, tacked over me again with miss-nothing eyes. I exchanged jargons, "No dolls. I'm going to get full as a State School, whittled as a penguin, cacko, blind sleeping drunk."

"A booze cat, man!" He looked at nothing on the ceiling, and "By yourself, Jim?" he said.

"By myself." He waited bridally for the unless he'd like to join me. Background hi-fi should have been doing muted dog tunes for ickies — *Moonlight and Roses? Shine on, Harvest Moon?*

I let him ask. I let him thrust himself on me. Since I had long ago learnt to bypass the eccentricities of the innocent, to be beware of, to flee the naked heart, I was safe dallying here, for this was no simon-pure innocent, this was a shandy one, a pony-shandy and no trouble at all. So, I said, I'd be pleased to have a . . . but he was already at his dressing.

I waited while he got into a nylon singlet, a drip-dry non-iron nylo-poplin shirt, while he knotted in a manner new to me a lean strap of tinsel-threaded tie; I waited for the nylon-neon sockettes, the velvety royal blue shoon (they were scarcely shoes); I watched him tease his gilt pompadour with a pink plastic comb and breathe-on and polish his antiqued signet ring. Now — *now* — the suit!

Therefore, the first night back and out in the home town I had never drunk in was spent drinking in vinyl chairs on laminex table-tops with a suit of a colour and cut I had never drunk with before, sprayed by the dimples, and arch and ancient boyishness of a quarter-bodgie from a Berlin slum, a camp-fringee, New Australian railway fireman who thought that the answer at the end of the book was *The End Justifies the Means*, and that the use of a car to lure fiffies, chickies and sorts was worth Time Out from normality, was worth whatever might occur — the off-beat, the sordid, a gamut of distaste, recrimination, bitterness, any-bloody-thing. He was too young and tainted and foreign to know that my indifference to some conventions was boredom and vanity, and not the colour he thought; he mistook it for tolerance, *laisser-faire* and anything-goes. As we bumped shoulders back to the dormitory that night alternately singing *Die Dörf Musik* and wrangling patiently as father and son about cars, it came to me why he had seemed familiar — he was a later but other Otto Nowak from Isherwood's "Good-bye to Berlin". He was a boy of the Friedrichstrasse amusement-joints, corruption and simplicity pathetically balanced, his trained-animal tricks too orchidaceous for an Australian country town, his judgments impaired from a past in which he had sat nibbling sugar wafers, a *Puppenjunge* playing a pick-up in a Hallesches Tor *lokal*. Although a Beautiful Friendship blessed by a scarlet M.G.'ish sort of open-topped and souped-up car did not develop, Kurt Schmidt and I moved from Mister to Christian- to nick-names. I liked him because I did not like him enough to be moved by his desires and frustrations. There was not even a scrap-heap 1929 Chevrolet in sight for him. He could not imagine that I could see through his automobile bowings and scrapings which familiarity bred to nagging; he could not see that I might have pitied him because, to him, I was a rock-head he couldn't drive ape, I was as square as a butter-box and practically a primate. Nevertheless, from time to time, I for catharsis, he to employ doll-less desolation, we went on the scoot together. What he got from these outings except hangovers and grog-blossoms I do not know; I learnt the last verse of *Die Lorelei*.

The town is indeed more changed, or rather is changing more rapidly, than I first thought. It is also less changed, much less changeable. One hand of the clock races on, the other slackens, drags, is reluctant.

The unpainted virgins of my adolescence who handed Conversation Lollies — *Meet me at the Corner, Do you like kisses?* — in High School geography lessons now play the mother's part in the Drama Society's *Quiet Weekend*, rule the roost at Red Cross meetings, support hefty backsides on shooting-sticks at country race meetings, are avid Solo players, make Shepherd's Pie on Tuesday, sell for offshoot Christianity and too much on market-day street-stalls their no-egg Swiss Rolls, their sugar-bag peg-aprons, their jars of unsuccessful jams from which the mould has been skimmed, unbelievable jams — Green-Tomato-and-Passion-Fruit, Carrot-and-Grape. The Angelus rings the same pattern of threes on the same bell I heard as a boy but Pioneer buses now pull up outside St Pat's to let Protestant women holding gesture handkerchiefs on unsure heads and men stiff-legged as Don Juan's Commendatore go staring at the Heaven-and-Hell painted ceiling, while, aloft outside, the Virgin with daddies-long-legs up her marble sleeves holds dusty hands towards the neon-eiffel-scaffolding of Rash's Tyre Service. Seventy-year-old hawthorns still hedge the river-flat paddocks but the hop-kilns have gone, and it is not an Australian navvy or bank clerk who showily swallow-dives and jack-knives from the willows by the Rowing Club but a Berliner, brute-shouldered and maiden-footed, looking younger than he is, peacocking without hope in the minimum of baby-blue satin trunks, spying among the lunch-time shopgirls and Shire Hall typists for a sort, a bint, a woman, a wife, even a talkie-teener sweetheart. Changed, you see, yet unchanged: the Technical School and High School adolescents wear grey *mélange*, school-striped ties, crested caps; only a scattering of these acned androgynes become bejeaned and rug-headed Coca Cola boys when the lawn has been mowed and the morning-wood cut.

The gasometer is rustier; the water-tower is grubbier; the back-streets are blanker now the elms are torn out; but gasometer and water-tower yet, streets yet. And in those back-streets, their Coolgardies replaced by refrigerators, their outdoor coppers by washing machines, their supper-cloths embroidered with crinolined women by aboriginal *motif* ash-trays, those I knew years ago still live among saddle bag suites, music canterburies, Maxfield Parrish reproductions, Congoleum squares, and sideboards as elaborate as reredoses. They are those whose undeveloped beauties of being, whose immature cruelties, nobilities and magnanimities are scarcely used, rarely seen. All the powers of language and pleasures of communication are nil and nix-nought-nothing. Theirs the servile but deadly gestures of animals, the slogans of popular science, the monosyllables of news-items; when it is 103° in the shade, "Hot, eh?" they tender. Much besides charm is truant. Resignation veils all, or self-abnegation reeking of conceit, or the egotism, savagery and delusions of motherhood. My once-friends, those Oxford-Bags-and-Fair-Isle-Sweater youths are R.S.L. men bewitched to Brickhill fans, Masons with ulcers, Rotarians with moustached wives and clean-shaven sons, budgerigar- or delphinium-cranks, committee-men, vestrymen, aitchless speechmakers, Rechabites, beer-goitre boys, scout-masters with the morals of Lamas, saints in an air-lock, mute inglorious Casanovas, filleted Satans, half-cold or flyblown morsels on the plate of Time. I — haunted by such important unimportances as when to write *spirt* and when *spurt* — am irrevocably one of this mob. My once-friends? Perhaps friends yet, whom death will change to nothing but the dead, who see the lost sections of their and my boyhood town shining with false but blinding seduction through the overlayings of thirty years. There, we think, was the pine avenue, *that* garage was the joss-house for the settlement of Amoy Chinese from the gold-fields, there were the pioneer vineyards, the wharves for the river-steamers, the old convent, the row of giant mulberry-trees. Cook's Corner, we say, Balmer's Hill, the Tannies, the Cut, Russo's, the School of Mines — names that will go when we all go. Now is for them and me the transparencies *Now* and *Then* superimposed one on another. We walk two streets when we walk the one.

Not so the foreigners, the New Australians walking in the very heart now of our barbarians' luxury, rubbing shoulders with those who carry like a useless breviary the magic rubbish of *How to Win Friends and Influence People*; not the black-stockinged women all in black and their podgy, sullen daughters, their Latin male-children who switch from raucous boy to raucous Tennessee Williams man between one Saturday morning's Main Street gossiping and the next; not the Sicilians or Albanians or Greeks under 1911 street verandas and the click of changing neons, short-legged, rings on their dirty fingers, womanlessly engaged in melancholy or professional carping, their eyes meantime racing about like crickets to covet in side-glances the *cinemaromanzi* breasts of paper-back platinum blondes; not the Fire Brigade Dance refusee, purple-suited, smelling of Californian Poppy hair-oil, stale sweat and Latvian loneliness; not the gangling Dutchman chewing unwanted lips before the display, like circus machinery, of orange-coloured bale loaders and rotary hoes; not the side-burned pair, in tight trousers of nameless cloth and pointed shoes polka-dotted with punctures, dawdling, as through the mazes of homesickness, among the little girls' games drawn like aboriginal totems on the footpaths. One street only these walk; they inhabit an Ionesco stage-set, a province without memories, or memories only of the day before yesterday: the hysterical misunderstanding at the employment office, the fight behind the Greek Café, the night-out with drunken aborigines under the Wy Yung Bridge, the voice crying, "You bloody dago bastard, you!" the male tears and threatening knife in the shadow of the tannery.

Until my flat was ready, and flats are still as rare in country towns as ants' holidays, I stayed on at the Something-or-other Guest House occupying what the Hungarian proprietors called a bungalow, Kurt Schmidt *die Hütte* and I my cardboard box. It was a seven-foot cube of plaster-board and masonite under a Topper loquat-tree I had often climbed as a child. I fitted into it, just, Laika in Sputnik; a visitor meant a physical relationship. Entering the back gate, near the cave of shadow under the peppercorn, to reach this toy dwelling was, night after night, like turning to yet another illustration in a work by Goya or Hogarth. It was here, outside the gate, that boarders returning home went through a kind of ritual purification. It was partly the result of the stern commercial motherlinesses of the Hungarians, partly unwritten etiquette, to complete pre-sleep dirty work under the peppercorn, to remove all make-up before bedding down; once the gate slammed behind, the night was formally over. Consequently someone was always emptying himself of too much Ruby Port or bottled beer, or maudlinly mopping up the blood-nose he had given his bubbling china, or hooking arms for a surrealistic half an hour over the fence-top to auto-suggest legs strong and biddable for the walk across the yard, up the steps and down the dangerous corridor. Presently, night after night, it was obvious that the snowy-haired one of two bodies wrestling, mumbling and mewling amorously in the cavern of shadow was Kurt Schmidt. The other was the new kitchenmaid-waitress who occupied a cell simmering with cheap scent somewhere in the hive of the boarding-house. After Football Dance, Old Time Ball or cinema, this nightly rehearsal for the activity of consummation boiled down to merely male and female, Kurt Schmidt and Vi'let Smith, saying good night at the front gate, the same gate for both, and a back gate. Vi'let Smith, indeed, may never have had a front gate. For her, the kitchenmaid who was a pantrymaid's daughter, Kurt Schmidt might well be Cinderella's handsome foreigner from a Mills and Boon romance; for the German who had been exposed to more thousands of miles, more sharpening and hardening experiences, this too ordinary relationship was possibly a treachery of his own flesh — or was he astute enough to accept that no grazier's golfing daughter in a Humber would fall for his cute fireman's face, film-star-smutted, at the railway crossing? no doctor's widow (1958 Chrysler Royal) turn her hot eye himwards some enchanted morning outside the barber's? no crumb of country town woman fall to a New Australian from any table the subtlest class higher?

How time blows by gustily as the breaths of passion!

How time blew by! — mopping and mowing like a willy-willy past the plastic bracken in the butcher's Sunday shop-window, past the gravestone of my mother who died ten years younger than I am now, past the Gothic Boer War monument (imported marble), the towering 1914–18 Cenotaph (local granite) with its foot-note for the dead of World War II (cracked cement troughs of gazanias), past all sorts of lovers who thought they loved, past Vi'let Smith and her chewed finger-nails and engagement ring of three pin-head diamonds. Kurt Schmidt no longer deepened dimples to excite me to buy an M.G., a jinker or even pawn-shop roller-skates. He asked my advice, stern and dedicated, on the fundamen-tals of setting up house, on radiograms, wall-plaques, musical beer-steins and plastic salad-servers. He austerely dropped tailor-mades for the makings, drank porter-gaffs, put threepences in a milk-bottle, and finished mauling Vi'let good night at the first whistle of the midnight train.

Most evocative, most haunting of night noises is that cry of the late train — wearily exultant journey's-ending, a telescope of sound through which the eye in the ear sees the acres of moonlit paddocks surrounding the town, the never-ending net of post-and-rail, the golgothic slaughter-yards, the cemetery over-run with sparaxis, the rams or ghosts of rams, the mopoke-haunted wind-breaks, the windmills, the messmate hills and bell-bird gullies, the smaller towns beyond — tin and boards and silence broken only by a baby crying like a ewe, the suburbs half-country, the suburbs half-city, and, dirty as a potato, the faraway youth-luring city itself. Ah, the midnight train! — the train awash with fatigue, with abandoned magazines, crushed paper cups, lolling bodies, faces wearing eyes looped in shadows. It is bringing Auntie Ettie the common-as-dirt old age pen-sioner or Aunt Margaret the well-heeled whinger with her beloved papilloma, it is bringing the end-of-term school-girl boarder, grandpa with the shark's tooth on his watch-chain, Bruce from the Melbourne Show, mother and the new city-born baby, bringing Australians home again. Now it brings too the smell-of-an-oilrag escapees from tourist countries littered with the fabulous wreckage of pasts, the shrewd, the defeated, the go-getting, the horizon-chasing, the under-cutting, from Athens, Bethnal Green, Hamburg, Haarlem, Mammola and Vysoke Myto, the women in black with fate-like faces and dandruffy madonna coiffures, the runtish men reeking with garlic and grappa, the cockney with rotten teeth. Here come the sly eyes, the bare doggy eyes, the lips hemmed together, the cheeks twitching still from a life of unfulfilled ventures, the spiv hands, the beast hands with grimy knuckles, the foreign garments buttoned on savings folded as tightly in purses as fear is in the kernel of being.

In this story of a country town I must, reluctantly, imagine one scene only. One sentence, then, of invention: Kurt Schmidt sits, decorously disposed on the

370

green leather of a second-class smoker, dimples in abeyance, suitcases Teutonically buckled, his tiny cheap-brooch eyes glinting in appraisement of the miles of rich weeds and butter-factories and timber-mills through which he is in a few years to drive a train, perhaps the very one he is now driven in. You see him? . . . blond, clean as veal, exercising those emotions that work in pairs, ambition and self-distrust, curiosity and uneasiness, hope and alarm.

Do the sleepless, the wide-awake dying, the woman in labour, the telephone girl on night-duty, the late reader, the insomniac debtor, the youth entangled in prayer, the adulterers under the river-bank horse-chestnuts, the High School teacher correcting algebra, the saxophone player limping homewards, do they all really know, when they hear the whistle that bores the night like an enchanted gimlet, what travels in with their returning flesh-and-blood, with Auntie Ettie or the fourth generation Australian baby brother? Or what else tomorrow might bring besides an aunt's coarse gossip, and new nappies on the rotary-clothes-line by the unsatisfactory lemon-tree in the backyard?

Tomorrow is still, of course, the fancy dress football match, Thatcher's Summer Sale of Men's Wear, the C.W.A. raffia-work display, the Legacy dinner, the Chess Club final, the Buffaloes' booze-up, the Library Committee meeting, the C.A.E. Mozart evening at the Prince Regent, the rock-'n'-roll in the Mechanics' . . . tomorrow is still tomorrow and a repetition of customary yesterdays. The kilties sackdoodle, the band practises *Poet and Peasant* Overture, the trout-fishing opens, the duck-shooting closes, blackberrying is on, mushrooms are everywhere, there are frost, and thunderstorms, and north winds like Magog's breath . . . why not? Tomorrow has gone on thus for years.

Thus?

Have you seen the papers on the notice-board outside the police station headed FISCHEREI UND WILDEHOERDE and UFFICIO DELLA PESCA E DELLA CACCIAGIONE? Have you looked in the delicatessens that no longer call themselves Small Goods but sometimes Delikatessen and seen the tins of olive oil, the packets of poppy-seed and noodles, the tinned Dutch strawberries and spinach, the salami, the twenty kinds of cheeses, the sauerkraut, the spaghettini, vermicellini, sopra-capellini, fettucce, ziti and calzoni? Who are the once foreign, still foreign-looking, men with greased hair, *café noir* eyes, and sores on the corners of their mouths, whose photographs fill the photographer's display cases? And look! — in the cemetery where a headstone of Welsh slate under an actual yew ninety years old states *Sophia Ellen Knight, 1863*, there are now photographs behind glass cemented into the grave-edgings: this molten-eyed tot with the prissy half-smile and frizzy hair appears to have died here in 1956 somewhere in one of the streets named after pioneers, explorers or Great War brigadiers, *Mariarosa Serafina Tocchi, born 1951, Casalbuono, Italia*.

As country town people do, I know a lot about my country town in a common-

or-garden way; eyes and ears get information *gratis*, one breathes in facts, lies or legends effortlessly without needing to nosey-parker — to use the jargon — writer-wise.

I know that, tomorrow, if I am or you are by chance near St John's Church of England which looks over the river-willows, across the lucerne flats to the Old People's Village on the hill, it will amuse to cast a glance at the Rectory opposite. The front door will be hurled open. The Canon's fox-terrier will nimble about Grockishly, yapping like a heathen. The Canon will shoot, jet-propelled, out of the ecclesiastical front gate and come sprinting ex-athletically across the road, back just in time from blessing the fishing-fleet . . . just in time, for here comes the bridegroom's taxi containing Kurt Schmidt, the blond fireman from the gnawed core of Berlin, the up-and-coming engine-driver, in a black suit with, thank God, horizontal pockets. His face is brightly silly with nervousness. Now, just femininely late enough, here comes the bride in a nearly charming gown she can wear later at the Hospital Ball, here comes Vi'let Smith the waitress with Woolworth flowers in her hair and a Marilyn Monroe mouth painted over her mouse-trap one, the waitress-kitchenmaid whose mother was a pantrymaid and whose daughter will be, whose son will be, whose children will be . . . will be. . . .

I wrote that I knew much, but that is really all I know about my home town, a country town I am startled to discover that I love as one loves an ageing mother with dyed hair, slapdash lacquered finger-nails, and skirts too short for her varicose-veined legs. Or do I love it as one shudderingly does a cocktail tasting like the inside of a coffin but with a terrific lift? Anyway, some sort of cocktail is poured — whew! — and I, you, we, they must drink it. Not pronto, of course, for me . . . but certainly later. Oh, cer-tain-ly!

Party Forty-two and Mrs Brewer

I DON'T know Sydney very well. The daylight part of my fevered forays there are spent in an ague of traffic terror on a pedestrian-refuge I can't remember why I'm on, or soothing myself in the saloon bar of Aaron's Hotel. Otherwise, I inhabit taxi-cabs *en route* to yet another party . . . somewhere.

See me, then, about eightish on a Sunday summer evening so recent that I am surprised to be already de-alcoholized enough to control a pen, sliding out of a taxi-cab . . . somewhere, some suburb *somewhere*. There were three other men with me, though they seemed more because of Da-vid's banjo. We were just late. We had been lost, long enough for it to be droll, and almost long enough for it not to be, in vertically lofty streets swanking it as avenues. The house was so new that I felt paint-splashed shoes still to be in the garage; there could have been no time for corks and string to overrun kitchen-drawers; the frangipanis each side of the front door were infantile.

As we entered, I perceived, nearly not in time, that it was not a gathering to enter rather vividly with a dilly-bag of witticisms: the room — the *lounge-room* — self-consciously contemporary (one stubbornly wall-papered wall), was chock full of men and women jumbled together like general-store kitchenware. There was an air of bath-water . . . sub-tepid . . . gurgling down the plug-hole. On the wallpaper I could see, Belshazzar-like, intimations of the near speech-riddled future: "Ladies, and gents, and others! Now, let's have a little bit of shush . . .!''

Indicatively, the hostess, a doggedly brisk secretary when normal, was called Dot. She wore, of course, a pleated skirt that could not swish and whip about. Her husband, an s.-p. bookmaker, was — it goes without saying — called Frank.

There would be, I also instantly knew, a belt of husbands called Frank — the sort of Franks whose wives buy their shirts and ties. Over Dot's newly-bingled hair I saw these Franks in the glimmering worsted trousers with an abundance of buttoned pockets by which Australian men can be picked in Trafalgar Square or Montmartre. It was as patent as massacre that something supremely dreadful had happened, early, so early, too early: there was a surfeit of out-of-tune gaiety. Men, and the unmarried women with fingernails lacquered pallidly, were laughing *Ha, ha, ha!* with their eyes fixed. The married women, with fingernails lacquered darkly, talked with earthy verve, and immodest decisiveness, of detergents. I am, I thought, going to shrivel with boredom. I deserved, of course (I also thought), no more.

You see, I had been being off-the-chain (hang the expense!) for six weeks, in *Sydney*! This was my forty-second (you get it?) and final party. The next day I would be returning to South Gippsland, behind Wilson's Promontory, to be a sobersides among the peat, the grass trees, the black cockatoos always flying north with rain at their tails, the surely false-eyelashed Jerseys, and the high-heeled Berkshire piglets.

In my visitor's guise of Simple Country Boy I had over-enjoyed the six weeks. I had, among other things, spent four hours in Darlinghurst lock-up, punched a drama critic, broken a rib, told-off an editor, conversed with a negro, four Communists and a lesbian, drunk half a bottle of South Australian whisky during a rococo performance of *Love's Labour's Lost*, and been turfed with skill and taste out of the Journalists' Club.

I was staying in Elizabeth Bay, downstairs from King's Cross, in a sort of underground palace coated with *Ficus stipulata*. It contained chandeliers from Murano, a bathroom bigger than a kitchen, a kitchen smaller than a bathroom, and seeming acres of entertainment-inducing parquet like a shot-silk chessboard. Sky-high camphor-laurels, which once edged the drive of Elizabeth Bay House, fastidiously dropped an odd leaf or two to impel perfectly circular ripples, *à la* Disney, on the surface of the swimming-pool. One of my forbearing hosts was a psychic A.B.C. producer with the mien of an intellectual koala, a Whistler-esque tongue, all the Belafonte recordings, a cat called Mrs Woffington, and a 24-carat heart. The other host was a well-heeled, middle-aged playboy called Da-vid who twangled his little banjo in the only room I've known subdue a television-set. Life-sized Goddesses of Mercy closed their golden eyes with repulsion on the top of vast carved, lacquered and gilded chests and tall-boys.

We three, *plus* Laurence, an actor awash with a Sunday of gin-and-milk, were all discreetly middle-aged, two bachelors and two *divorcés*, and as disenchanted and potentially sparkling as a quartet of Bemelmanses. We had been driven to this forty-second party by a Singapore Chinese university student, driven to wherever the party was . . . Cammeray, Collaroy . . . some fairly perpendicular suburb with a view of other vertical suburbs' electric lights, and their reflections in an area of liquid — a lake, or harbour, or something.

This Oriental taxi-driver, with whom I had been coincidentally lost for an hour the night before (the forty-first) on similar perpendicularities near Beauty Point, was called Peng Chin.

Until we entered the house, I considered Peng Chin a sure-fire entrance topic. This topic, burgeoning like a Jacobean tapestry as we climbed a million concrete steps to the house, died its sudden death in the open door. Half a visual sniff, and one thought — I repeat — I am going to shrivel with boredom.

However and however, one had not foreseen — how could one? — Mrs Brewer, the hired help.

Hi-Jinx's Melbourne Cup win a week over. Dot was doing the grand on Frank's rake-off. A buffet meal, eighty-guest-sized for the forty in the living-room was set out more heart-rendingly and lavishly than in women's magazine illustrations. There was more than a touch of Mrs Beeton in the cairns of prawns and oysters, in the ham, the chickens, the turkey, and the subsidiary delicacies.

Mrs Brewer had been engaged, I later learned, to help prepare and arrange these succulences, to pass out plates and forks and, more brutally, to wash-up and clear away. She was *cachet*. After the cleaning-up she would put on a browbeaten hat of navy-blue felt and (surely) speed off on an old bicycle.

Not so.

By the time Peng, after consulting his map often on the brinks of precipices, had nosed out Dot and Frank's eyrie, Mrs Brewer had, as it were, dramatically rocketed from the sink to the height of Nazidom.

"God!" said Dot, wild-eyed parlourmaid at what she had considered her own door. "Oh, God, thank God, you've got here. I'll kill her; I'll *kill* her!"

We imagined she spoke thus impatiently of some time-honoured murderee: a mother-in-law or a busybody aunt.

"That woman. My *char*. She's drunk as a wheelbarrow. She's *let* us have two — *two* — drinks each before we eat. And no more. She's taken charge of the bar. *We can't move her.*"

She seemed to feel her neck scorching. She raised her voice, and swished her pleats as though she still possessed rights.

"Here they are, Mrs Brewer. They're *terribly* sorry to be so late. Their taxi-man got lost."

We had said not a word. Da-vid dropped his banjo and said, "Witch!"

"Shut *up*," hissed Dot. " 'Fyou want a snort, for God's sake, charm, charm, charm."

Then, "Come on, boys," she trilled with the most bogus jubilation, "and meet our Mrs Brewer."

She led us, like a cinema usherette, through and past the standing Franks, and the sitting wives and women, who gave us, long-entombed miners at sight of rescuers, glances of positive love.

We reached Mrs Brewer.

The long, Laminexed counter which cut off the kitchen from the living-room cut her off from the world of capricious mortals. Klytemnestra her very self, she was alone, fiercely imperious, sacrosanct. She and her domestic sanctuary were beyond rape of any kind.

In the manner of one sponsoring gormless serfs to a Celtic warrior-queen, Dot began a spirited, near-hysteric litany of introductions.

Mrs Brewer closed her eyes as against a silly willy-willy. I had a blood-curdling impression of inner eyelids moving horizontally across the eyeballs as the outer eyelids contemptuously descended.

Dot faltered.

Mrs Brewer spoke.

"One at a toime, love," she said nasally, malcontentedly, but with eyeless power. "One . . . at . . . a . . . toime. *Please*." Oh, the perfect lady. She vouchsafed her eyes. "Do you moind?"

The *Do you moind?*, despite its irrefutable Queensland accent, was delivered as offensively as the English deliver it, attended by a smile as false as her teeth. Mrs Brewer was drunk. Not wheelbarrow-drunk; but firmly drunk, at the *idée-fixe*, no-shenanigans stage where life was real, life was earnest, and administration was all.

She, Mrs Brewer, was logic's king-pin, and alone could save.

She was short, stocky-short — nuggety — and swart. All this suggested the fortune-telling gipsy, but she really resembled nothing so much, particularly about the eyes, as a middle-aged cocker-spaniel with an obsession. It was easy to suspect her face of, at that moment, much unused mobility.

Without delving, I can remember seeing only two other women with her cast of unhaggling directness. One was an Italian matron in a little bar in Cremona where an American millionaire's alcoholic son and I, doing Italy in a Fiat 500, were drinking grappa and avoiding buying veesky-sodah for a German prostitute in a dress of a houndstooth pattern so large that it blinked blackly and whitely as one looked.

The matron, who was perhaps the owner's passing-by sister or sister-in-law, was feeding one of those Belgian milkcart dogs with ice-cream to amuse us into spending more *lire* on more grappa, when a brawl began between two nasty little Italian men.

Nasty little eyes appeared — four.

Nasty little knives appeared — two.

Everyone scattered, jabbering operatically, knocking over chairs unnecessarily, for effect. The prostitute screamed with Teutonic verisimilitude.

Handing me the ice-cream and, so to speak, the dog, the matron reached a Michael Angelo arm over the counter for a broom. With the *handle* she chopped, she hacked — *crack! crack! crack-crack-crack! (da capo)*: Punch killing Judy.

The two men knifeless, she picked up and chucked the knives through the door, replaced the broom, and returned to dog and ice-cream with no more than a draughty brief smile which said, in effect, "Thank you for looking after Toto while I was busy."

The other woman, I remember, was called Bunny Something and, dressed in cheesecloth and beads as Cleopatra at an Artists' Ball in the St Kilda Town Hall, some summer in the 'thirties, lifted a helmet from a policeman's head, sauntered the length of the hall with it, and disappeared, and for ever.

The third was Mrs Brewer, to whose leery and alarming façade Laurence, the actor, was the first of us to be (the word is hand-picked) presented.

She absorbed Laurence's status, and him, with a damp and dampening gaze. He gave her, steadily, a famous look. The suspense was killing. No one would have been surprised if she had barked — or bitten.

After three years: "Wotillut be, love?" she said, unsmiling, but mollified to melting-point.

"Gin-and-tonic. If I *may*. If you will be so kind. *Please*. My *dear*," said Laurence, as on carnal knowledge bent, throbbing like a motor-launch, and unleashing a smile of some brilliance.

"May I beg a fairly *strong* one?"

He augmented the smile from sufficiently to quite brilliant.

"My ticker . . . a little dicky," he improvised, setting his fingers (slender, sensitive, *et cetera*) on his dove-grey waistcoat, and releasing a light cough.

"Wotchew want, love, is a noice great big brandy," said Mrs Brewer, her spaniel eyes having appraised and estimated. She had put her right hand on the Laminex, and was judicially tapping on this member's glazed and toad-back mottlings with stubby left-hand fingers, in the proper one of which was embedded a time-smoothed wedding-ring, vintage 1921.

"Brandy!" Laurence's voice sounded as if it wore a muzzle, and the pouches beneath his eyes momentarily sagged in dismay.

"Laurence, *honey*," said Dot, toothily, showing strain and an inclination towards hysteria even though in a model lacy blouse and too much mascara. "Do listen to Mrs Brewer. She *knows. Have* a brandy."

For God's sake, let's get it over! was understood.

"Huh!" said Mrs Brewer instantly scuppering the idea of brandy. "Huh! Women! Stuck-up! Ear-rings too toight. *And* nag, nag, nag."

As abstractedly and confidently as a blindfold knife-thrower she whizzed a curare-dart glance, bull's-eye, at Dot, and reached for the gin-bottle, meantime tossing sidelong, "You better get those ear-rings off, me girl."

No one, but no one, had ever called Laurence anything except Laurence, yet: "Oi seenya on the telly, Laurie, love," said Mrs Brewer sloshing out three-quarters of a goblet of gin. "Oi seenya. You're a gennulmun."

She poured, negligently competent, about a teaspoon of lemonade on the surface of the gin.

"Drinkitup, love. It'll warm the cockles. But don't . . ." She began to act conspiratorially, leaning forward to give the impression of whispering, but declaiming loudly: ". . . don't give none to that thing in the green. Him all mockered-up in his corjaroy pants!"

The mild young man, with his green cumbering pullover and medievally-pointed shoes, simulated deafness but went paeony-pink under his organized fringe of bull's-wool, sipped in a poised way at his empty tumbler, and dropped a sophisticated *mot* into the grassy coiffure of the skittish widow perched like an imp on a Port Said pouffe.

"Corjaroy, but! A tonk, that's what. If me hubby was aloive . . ."

"Mrs Brewer," said Dot, just able to keep to the social rails, and schismlessly

377

gracious, "please excuse. I'd like you to meet Mr Jack, of the A.B.C. who . . ."

"Some people, Laurie," said Mrs Brewer, sparing no more than an oblique though envenomed dart, "some people are prolly so drunk that they don't know no better. Manners! Interrupting, but! *And* won't take advice about ear-rings and *im*flamed lobes and cancer. Drinkitup, Laurie, love."

"Mrs Brewer," said Laurence, perceiving his duty, and smiling back as far as wisdom-teeth. It was the best acting or, at least, the most magnetic I've seen him do. It approached the classic. A second before, he had started from his devil's nostrum of gin as from a bowl of hemlock. Now, his eyes were melting with ardour in the direction of Mrs Brewer's three-haired mole, and his voice was saccharine as a chocolate laxative: "*Dear* Mrs Brewer . . ."

"Reet," said Mrs Brewer, licking a finger to wipe along one tousled eyebrow. "Call me Reet. Rita Jessica's me full name. But friends call me Reet, but. You call me Reet, Laurie love. Me late mister useta call me Reet."

She licked an opposite forefinger, and spittled the other and higher eyebrow.

"The old basket, me late," she said ruminatively, with a tincture of dislike.

"Reet," said Laurence in the tone of one deeply purring, *Do-lor-es, my be-lov-ed*, "Reet, *ducks*."

Was he getting too far into character?

"My *friend* Mr Jack — of the A.B.C. — is dying to meet you. Reet." And he added, for better measure, "But!"

Mrs Brewer emitted a clear and involuntary hiccough. It surprised her.

"Beg yours, love," she said. "Gherkins!"

Brandy, being gherkins, revealed her unfaltering grasp of the situation, and: "Any friend of yours, love," she said and turned her mole, her dog-eyed gipsy face and groomed eyebrows towards her waiting subject.

"Pleastameetcha," she said. "Oi lissen to 'Green Paddocks' on the woireless. It's . . ."

She considered.

She admitted.

". . . It's very true to loife. You're a gennulmun. Wotillut be, Jacko, love?"

It was in this manner that the four of us — Laurie (love), Jacko (love), Davie (boy) and Hal (-pal) — received each our ration of two terrifying drinks. As we got them down (mine was a quadruple whisky with an accidental addition of gin) we could not have fawned more on wicked duchesses than on Mrs Brewer.

The world awaited us and its buffet meal.

The women had dropped detergents for children drinking kerosene.

The men seemed to have got into a stalag-prisoners' huddle, perhaps planning a tunnel under the counter, perhaps lynching.

Dot had gone, with brave straight back and subdued skirt-pleats, to the lavatory, to forestall cancerous lobes, to cry, to restore cried-off mascara, and purge herself of filthy language.

"And don't, moind you," we were warned, "give nothing to that thing in the green. Or" — her eyes became small as sweet-pea seeds as they sighted another enemy — "to that bit he's earbashing. Deliquids! Lairs!"

That Bit wore a quantity of black hair arranged like a busby from beneath which a diminished, floury poker-face confronted humanity with unmoving Japanese eyes.

"If me late hubby was aloive, he'd *do* him, but, the little tonk."

"What," I said (oh, brightly, subject-changing) "was your husband's name, Mrs Br . . . Reet?"

I hoped for *Frank*, to prove something my second drink was making me think I thought.

She didn't quite turn on me.

"*Mis-ter* Brewer," she said, non-committal, with sinister flatness. Her eyes performed some female insincerity, a side-glance mentally and visibly: she hadn't *liked* Mr Brewer.

"He's passed on. Old basket. Trouble with his tubes."

Tubes?

We put our brows into furrows.

Jacko, love, told me later that he saw a very involved ants'-nest in section, I favoured the disembowelment of a dead horse I'd witnessed as a boy at Seaspray in Easter, 1930.

"Oh, nod t' worry, nod t' worry," said Mrs Brewer as one saying, "Hiroshima! A bagatelle!" and as though we looked, we and our furrows, as if we *were* unduly, unnecessarily and neurotically worrying.

The widow of the late *Mis-ter* Brewer stimulated herself: her inner clock had struck a serious hour.

"Drinkitup!" she said, addressing us each severally and with maternal severity. "Drinkitup! Drinkitup! And you, too, bozo, drinkitup. Quick-smart! That woman's left it all to Reet. Cancer of the lobes, that's what the poor liddle thing'll finish up with."

To our fascination she began to pound on the Laminex with a soda-siphon. The hubbub of factitious joy faded. Into this abatement she shouted, as from a far-off hilltop, "Come and get it!"

They came to get it, shuffling rather, laughing somewhat and somewhat showily and with much ease, and mingling in a sort of factory-canteen queue.

Mrs Brewer regarded this immoral pattern with deep distaste.

She bided her time.

She struck.

"Ladies first!" she cried. "Think you're Russians, eh? Ladies first! Do you moind . . . *gennulmun*?"

The brutes, the roughnecks, the animals, the bronzed Anzacs who'd forgotten their courting-days, sidestepped, sincerely abashed though wishing not to show it; the women became unnecessarily elated and decidedly showed it.

Mrs Brewer took up a handful of forks, and then remembered that she was, after all, a general.

"Me heart," she said, attempting faintness, and placing the handful of forks on her Roman matron bosom. "Davie, boy . . . Jacko, love . . . Hal-pal . . . You come around here with me. You're gennulmen. The plates and forks. Me heart! Where's me brandy? A noice quiet liddle brandy'll set me to roights."

She began, the ghost of Hamlet's father, to drift off. She sat on a low stool by the refrigerator, screening her goddessliness from the common gaze with an open cupboard-door. As we turned to our task of handing over plates and forks, there was the sound of fluid descending from bottle to tumbler, and the voice of the all-knowing and ever-watchful: "One plate per person. One fork per person. Oyster-shells to go in the . . ." Brandy washed that one out of hearing.

While we handed over plates and forks, as it were from the altar, we and the guests exchanged many a merry quip. But how censored! How underlined with winkings and shruggings and smiles of a certain sort! How censored even these voiceless gestures!

Dot appeared again, bereft of tears and with cold-cream-shiny lobes, having learned of life, as her guests had, that no matter how closely they had electric-shaved, or how constricting their new girdles were, no matter how heedfully they walked on social eggs, they were, right there and then, no more than visitors in a world of runaway pantechnicons bull-dozing into the bird's-eye maple bed-room, a world of burning toast, enamel bed-pans, hangnails, influenza, and unsuccessful permanent waves.

Mrs Brewer, heart or no heart, brandy or no brandy, was the objectification of this intrusive world, the bitch goddess, the schoolmistress with sour stomach, the rude salesgirl, the malicious mother-in-law, the tram-conductress handing on her headache, the one who hamstrung you when you were about to caper to *The Spring Song*. Even in her retirement Mrs Brewer was a force; gurglings and glassy clinkings from behind the cupboard-door testified to her reality.

She was, moreover, resurrectible.

Indeed, just as the young man in the green jumper was about to take his plate, Mrs Brewer slammed the cupboard-door shut, and revealed herself.

She was now immortally shicker.

She swayed like a more squat foxglove, sadder and swarthier.

She doubtless saw more of each of us than each was.

The young man, disposed too centrally, retracted the guilty leprous hand that had been about to tarnish the rim of a plate.

"You!" croaked Mrs Brewer.

Facing the Angel of Death the young man was courageously steady, but his pullover seemed suddenly bluer than green.

"You!" She appeared to wish to have the refrigerator-handle let go her hand. Tears suddenly flowed down her cheeks. She was understood to say, "Shorry, love . . . shorry . . . Call me Reet. Odly a boy. Odly a chuvenile deliquid. Reetie's been rude. Oh, Oi been thinking . . . Laurie, love . . ." she said, uprooting herself to take, like a toddler, a few bowlegged steps towards Mr Jack, producer, A.B.C., and, laying hands upon his Harris-tweed sleeves, to implore: "Laurie, love, givim a noice liddle brandy, the poor boy. Letum allhava noice . . . lid-dle . . ."

In a manner gymnastic and stylized, with some flexibility, no noise, a bottle clasped to her diaphragm, Mrs Brewer descended towards, sank to, the highly-coloured floor, and passed out.

As in a republic founded on the assassination of a despot, there were immediate and disgraceful confusions, there was undisciplined and pointless drama. There were cries, bumpings-into-others, orders and counter-orders, even some immediately-rebuked incivilities of gloating.

"Oh, poor old *dear!*" cried Dot and a number of women with chicken-greasy mouth-corners, and they entered the temple where the priestess lay, the brandy-bottle welded to her hands, curled up like a crayfish.

With conscious tenderness, and a clattering display of warm humanity, and a sense of burying and praising Caesar in one, she and the undetachable bottle were carried to the bedroom, laid on the candlewick quilt and, when her worn little bunion-moulded shoes were removed, concealed beneath an eiderdown. The bobble-edged bedside-lamp was turned out. The queen was dead. The war was over. The drought had broken.

The party now adopted shapelessness.

We four were thrown out of the kitchen.

Frank recaptured manliness, and poured drinks competently as though that were the thing.

Owners of orchid-coloured fingernails began asking for drinks that needed slices of things in them.

Owners of ox-blood fingernails washed plates or one-upped each other's tales of hepatitis, fibrositis, tonsilitis, appendicitis.

Dot, renewed into hostess, showed guests who lived in *old* houses how doors opened (and shut), how drawers slid out and slid back, how cupboards worked, and what shelves were for.

Presently, a young man who could have been Ern, for people called him so, a man young enough to wear a bandeau of blackheads on his inch-and-a-quarter of brow, professionally remotely exercised a concertina below his dreamy but disdainful grimace. One felt that, should the listeners' wariness have faltered, he would have executed, masterfully and brilliantly, *The Warsaw Concerto* and, to astounded and oceanic applause, torn off his lubricated wig and unsatisfactory Ern-mask.

The mood was, however, otherwise. Voices implored for sadder music. And sadder. The yearning melodies of thirty years before were wailed with much attention to melancholy. Loneliness, broken dreams and hearts and vows, depressed their spirits and discouraged drinking.

Two reckless creatures, man and wife, who had won a Charleston competition in 1927, shamelessly called for madder music. His bald head and glossy, huge, silver-grey behind, and her legs of sinew and bone spastically flailing, did nothing except recall *I Wonder Who's Kissing Her Now?* and *All Alone* and *Melancholy Baby*.

Everyone was well on the way to asking Ern for *Won't You Buy My Pretty Flowers?*, *The Letter Edged in Black*, and *It's Only a Beautiful Picture in a Beautiful Golden Frame*.

"All passion spent," said Da-vid from a corner of his mouth.

"All dreaming done," said Mr Jack from a corner of his.

"Let us telephone for a taxi-cab," said Laurence, ventriloquistically not moving a muscle.

"Peng Chin!" I said. "The ball is over. Let's get lost outside rather than here."

I knew that, somewhere in the cigarette smoke and melodious dirges lurked the man with more eyebrows than hair who was aching to spring into prominence through the merest second's gap and . . .

He sprang.

Little Grey Home in the West had sadly guttered out; there was a pause; *there* was the tiny sandy man like a football-club secretary.

"Hey!" he roared. "Hey, ladies and gents. And *others*." No one did anything. "Now, let's have a little bit of shush. I would like . . ."

We had our hands on the telephone.

"Aw, don't be auntie," crowed a hoarse and heavenly voice. "No bloody speeches, but. Do you moind?"

I seemed to hear *High School Cadets* being played, masterfully and brilliantly *and* loudly, by six angelic brass bands.

It was Madame Lazarus. It was dat ol' devil She. It was life. It was Mrs Brewer.

She blinked at the door. She surveyed disorganization. Her geiger worked. She licked two forefingers and burnished her eyebrows.

"Gawd, you're a broight lot of so-and-so's," she said.

Slowly, very slowly, she crossed her eyes and said, "Poor Old Reet can't get her shoes on, but."

It was royalty proclaiming, "Our crown has shrunk. So sorry. Nevertheless, on with the *levée*."

She uncrossed her eyes, cried out, "Drinks on the house!" raised her skirts above the knees of her lady-harrier's legs with hairs flattened like scales beneath the nylon, and began a delirious witchdoctor's prancing while she shrilly sang "Kneesup, Mother Brown! Kneesup, Mother Brown . . .!"

Her face, as it bounced, was radiant rubber with enough permutations and combinations of expression to outlast anyone anywhere. I'll swear her ears moved contrapuntally but wittily.

Da-vid grabbed his banjo.

Mrs Brewer's warped suspenders were more exhilarating than skiing.

We forgot telephones and Peng Chins.

At last, with a roar, the party began.

Ern dropped his disdain; his brow shot up an inch.

That Bit opened her eyes, which flashed like . . . like stars! She smiled! She had teeth! White!

The thing, the tonk, the mild young man in the green pullover, advanced at a canter towards Mrs Brewer.

"Knees Up, Mothah Brahoon!" he sang. "Knees Up, Mothah Brahoon . . .!"

It was a gaudy, a lively, an orgy, a bawdy, a rort. It was far and away the best of forty-two.

I cannot clearly understand how Reet (bull) and Hal-pal (toreador) and Hal-pal (terrified spinster) and Reet (bottom-pinching Latin) managed to break three Noritake bread-and-butter plates by 4.16 a.m., when one would have been more than enough. Since I've had to buy six to replace the three, Dot and Frank are three plates, two hangovers and a successful party up.

That's only natural.

It was Mrs Brewer's party.

Mountain Farm

FROM *PIECES FOR AN ALBUM*

Fractured ranges; sky-height gale!
Hog's-back orchards fed on hail
their quinces hurl and stony pears
a thousand feet down stony stairs.

Boxthorn hedge — a barbed-wire guard —
breaks the squall and girds the yard:
unruffled sculptures, things of rock
are duck, drake, kelpie, cat and cock.

While his granite garments grip
granite torso, granite hip,
farmer's statue eyes admire
his leaves cut by with veins of wire.

His pasture's stern: the very buds
confront the sleet as iron studs;
his chimney's horizontal smoke
turns on the wind an iron spoke.

Rigid man. Terrain severe.
Moss or mould must not appear.
One soft *faux pas*, one touch of spring,
would mar and murder everything.

Cocky Farmer

He, on the barebones bankrupt slope,
a crow-girt scarecrow, stares and stands.
His leafless lips and grassless hope,
his husk of hide, his sun-split hands,
mimic the cracked and cankered lands.

A dome of flame contains his night.
Sky has no tears, and he has none.
The whirlwinds wild and blind with light,
mopping and mowing, reel and run.
Hell's neap is full. It laps the sun.

His X-ray of mortality:
the useless fence, the useless gate,
the paralysed and bloodless tree.
Parched are his ponds and dams of hate.
Long and late, dog yelps, "Too late!"

The parrots curse the creek of stones.
The beaked and hollow heelers bark,
but will not wake the flock of bones.
No star of pain breaks from his dark.
He's Drought's own groom. He'll leave no mark

except the eddies weaving dust,
sun that no creature dares indict,
planets no chiliads can rust,
remorseless fans of day and night
that winnow all save selves from sight.

In an Australian Country Graveyard

All hereabout anachronism's rife:
The landscape plays at Constable and Gray
With hedgerow, hawthorn, far-off farm-house roof;
A lowing herd to wind its text-book way;
A ballad graveyard, hackneyed rhymes of yew,
Headstones set elegiacally askew.

Not astronauts but Abels, men of earth
Have gone to earth here in an earth so rich
The jonquils reel and reek on plot and path;
The moss, in blisters like a pine-green pitch,
Leaks through the fissured slabs that lid them down
Who've slipped life's leash for this pacific town.

These sketchy cellar-citizens of bone
Need no police to frisk the Celtic cross
Or flash a glim on Church of England urn:
Fin de siècle sentry angels toss
A stone-pale hand aloft as if to thumb
Hay-wain or hansom that will never come.

No wheels; no clock a wheel of rights and wrongs
To turn and chime an hour of kill or kiss;
Only the footless wind on footloose wings
Wheels hissing through the thistles: "Look on this!
Here's grief gone dry; here's craft and thrift blown out;
Here's not a word; here's what it's all about!"

Behind that Sun-splashed Tourist Poster

To Shelly Beach the painted fingers point.
    No point in this: the season's over.
Dunes are bald and loutless; summer's spayed;
    the furled and salt-starched ice-cream awnings fade;
and now no bed-and-bawed-bent tripper ever
    hunts pick-ups on the drizzling Esplanade —
all's
    out of
        joint.

    No one to litter, loiter, swindle, spend.
No juke-box keens. No carnies gabble.
    One yacht, turned turtle, silly in the sand . . .
One gap-toothed neon for night's no-man's-land:
    one ISH & IPS on Nick the Greek's tin gable . . .
One guest, a leftist vicar, at the Grand —
    he's
        round
            the bend.

Each kiosk's rusted shut. The tide-line's fringed
    with kelp, wrack, trawler muck. It's later
than he thinks, the one-eyed odd-job man
    who, wine-hot in the rain-wet caravan,
awaits his abo, skin-and-bone Lolita.
    The tide's today run wryer than they ran —
the
    time's
        unhinged.

    So's the beach-combing spinster at her sport:
the Furies are her dotty sisters.
    She squeaks with glee to find the drowned girl there
with crab-torn thighs, and sea-lice-beaded hair
    (unmissed though missing, NIL in known disasters),
and reads an answer in the sockets' stare —
    x
      equals
         nought.

Brett

WHEN BENITO MUSSOLINI was Il Duce the Milan railway station was built.

Architecture without much conscience, it is edificial, colossal, and not unfittingly dictatorial. It is also very dreary: an intention to grandeur of the sublime kind doesn't at all come off. A façade of would-be triumphal arches leads into a succession of vast, austere lobbies, seemingly limitless, and far too lofty. Here, misshapen echoes vault cumbrously and forlornly about like headaches with nowhere to settle.

Once through the first dolorous arcade the traveller is confronted and affronted by a cyclopean alp of stairs which suggests by its mathematical cruelty the incline of an Aztec ziggurat. This scarp of livid stone depresses rather than overawes: it must be toiled up to attain the platforms from one of which *l'accelerato* starts south to run through Lombardy towards Parma, Bologna, Florence, and the ever-flowing, ever-cold fountains of Rome.

On a bleak afternoon in late November, a day of drizzle from a steel-grey sky onto a seal-grey city, Jean D. and I were being farewelled at the station by the Australian Consul-General's wife with whom we had lunched. Afterwards she had come with us to a refrigerated Santa Maria della Grazie while, as our planned last sight-seeing in Milan, we looked again at Leonardo da Vinci's *The Last Supper*.

We were both wary again-lookers drifting through the Old World in the direction of the equator, and back to Australia. Middle-aged, unpassionate but firm friends, hard-bitten tourists, we were revisiting together what we had, when younger, separately visited before. To sum up our itinerary — a Harry's Bar or a Trader Vic's was as much part of it as any Gothic polyptych, Byzantine mosaic or Bernini triton.

Somewhat chastened by *The Last Supper*, we were to catch the two-fifty for Florence.

The three of us stood flinching in the maelstrom of draughts at the foot of the grim cliff of stairs while Mario the consular chauffeur unloaded our baggage from the consular Fiat.

It was I perhaps who first noticed the young woman: her face. It was the Consul-General's wife who first spoke of her.

"Now *that*," she said, "is what I should be wearing." She added, "With my impossible legs."

Jean D. and I, prudent cowards, looked neither at each other nor the legs we'd already noted as misproportionately strapping beneath the Consul-General's wife's svelte upper, and her delicately hollow face. We gave instead the keenest attention to what the young woman wore, the back-view as she ascended with much grace the Teotihuacán-like steep.

It was the year when the pitiless fashion of the mini-skirt was just giving way to a more humane one; freakish legs were returning to the seductive obscurity of longer skirts. In England, Germany, and France we had already seen numbers of women wearing the new style. The one before our eyes was the first we'd seen in Italy. A maxi-coat recalling a Ukrainian Cossack's, and worn with Russian boots, it was not only fitting wear for the untender wintriness of the day but strikingly set off its wearer's tallness and litheness. The flared skirt and its border of fur lilted romantically as she mounted the steps with all the stylish bravado of a *jeune premier* in a Graustarkian operetta. The two women with me went into analytical raptures which I did not interrupt with:

"But did you see her face?"

Useless to interrupt: had they seen it they would by then have forgotten: the Cossackian coat had become headless to them.

It was clear that what had caught my eye had not caught theirs: a face so like Eleanor da Toledo's in the Angelo Bronzino portrait that I felt myself go actually open-mouthed with amazement. It was, in effect, double amazement. There I was, about to board *l'accelerato* for Florence where one of the reasons for a proposed trek through the endless little salons of the Uffizi Gallery was to moon yet again, for the fifth or sixth time, in front of that very portrait with its sealed, cool countenance, its eyes depthless with indifference. Extraordinarily alike, portrait and passer-by: for an absurd moment it seemed reasonable to accept that Eleanor da Toledo could be a sixteenth-century ancestress of the supple stranger whose face was not only also impassive and impenetrable, a courtly mask, but whose hatless black hair was arranged much as the woman in the painting had arranged hers — was that looking-glass still alive? — more than three centuries ago.

Reason alone, I knew, is too fallible. That glimpse of her, fleeting yet charged, was no more than one from which a poem might be made, taut with regret because both the world and the Milan railway station were boundless enough for me and Eleanor da Toledo's reincarnation never to be breathing again at the same time the same freezing air with its odour of damp metal.

Jean D. and I said good-bye to the Consul-General's wife at the bottom of the steps, and climbed — how much less buoyantly than the tall girl with the still face and swashbuckling coat! — up and up into the skirmish of echoes, and the arctic cross-currents of inexplicable little indoor winds.

It would have matched my mood of Baudelairian spleen to find every seat in the train taken, and the corridor jammed with a rain-soaked herd of pilgrims on their way to Rome. The train was far from crowded. In the eight-seater *seconda classe* compartment where we settled five minutes before departure there were only three passengers.

In one window-seat was a very fat Italian woman, fiftyish, high-bosomed, with an adolescent moustache.

Opposite her sat a stocky young man brutally handsome as a brigand.

Their attire announced that they were possibly of the lower middle class, in any country the most conventional, and therefore the most easily identified. They wore the sort of clothes seen behind the plate-glass of smaller department stores, the uniform of the hide-bound and frugal, unemphatic wear, factory-made of artificial materials. The one thing about them not ersatz was their behaviour; but even that, taking into consideration the melodramatic country we were in, was orthodox enough.

They were patently mother and son: a family profile jutted out of her blubber and his sullenness, and they were so engrossed in a generation tiff that they neither spared us a side-glance nor lost an impassioned syllable when we came in. They were both holding forth at the one time; her soprano railing went volubly on above his fierce baritone declaiming over and over again:

"Non è stata colpa mia!" — whatever it was it wasn't his fault — *"Non è stata colpa mia, mamma! Non . . . è . . . stata . . . colpa . . . mia!"*

On the badgered son's side of the compartment, plumb in the middle, the half-clock-face of the air-conditioning switch directly above his hair which was like goffered iron, sat another Italian, perhaps seventy, perhaps only sixty: it was hard to tell. Not once in the two-and-a-half hours he was with us did we hear him speak, or catch his eye.

He sat monolithically upright as a stone Rameses, contentedly withdrawn, his scoured, sun-darkened hands inactively set on his hams. The contours and rich rustic colouring of his face reminded me of an Arcimboldi one, a composition of corn-cobs, pomegranates, chestnuts, and onions. He seemed so much of the earth that we'd have to be, one felt, famished oxen or ailing vines, before his attention would turn to us, and his unreflective eyes come to life. He could, of course, have been a rugged solitary who despised the vile world, and played Ravel exquisitely.

I sat on the so-to-speak masculine side of the compartment, in the corner next to the corridor. Jean arranged herself opposite and, as we usually did on train journeys, we began the process of retracting somewhat from each other. She opened her guidebook at, I had no doubt, the chapter on Florence. A loud-speaker voice gabbling truculently against its own several echoes announced that our train was about to leave. I experienced that sensation of feline well-being mingled with here-we-go-again boredom the experienced traveller is apt to experience at such times.

Then, at the last moment, mere seconds before the wheels turned, the young woman in the Cossack coat flashed radiantly into sight at the doorway, scanned the compartment with lustrous heartless eyes, and appeared to find it worthy of her. From where she stood, and deftly as a basketball player throwing a goal, she tossed her valise onto the rack.

This *coup de théâtre* accomplished, she moved in, and sat with decisive aplomb between Jean D. and the fat mother who, at a climax of son-baiting, her wattles aquiver, spat out a scalding babble of insult. The victim had had enough. Harshly crying, "*Non l'ho fatto apposta!*" — I didn't do it on purpose! — he folded his arms as though barricading himself behind them, set his jaws, and closed his eyes. A door had been slammed in a face.

Furtively, as if sidling from an unhallowed cathedral, the train slipped between the soaring nave piers, through a rood screen of grimy girders, over the no-altar, and out into the Milanese rain so like all other rains, the dejected industrial outskirts that could have been anywhere.

All this, and a funereal burden of smoke lowering above a palisade of chimney-stacks, I took in from the corner of my senses. For the rest I was covertly but wholly taking in the unbelievable late arrival.

She was, I saw, years younger than Bronzino's Eleanor, but twentieth-century experiences had given her an additional gloss of age in a dimension beyond years. Self-possession's self, she lit a cigarette, and opened a Penguin. The nails of the ringless, long long Renaissance fingers were bitten. That was a touch jarringly too human and modern, and stopped me in my tracks on the poetic by-path I'd taken. The Penguin was Elizabeth Bowen's *To the North*.

So, as well as being a nail-biter, she wasn't a Latin after all! This reversed sign-post was more than intriguing: I contemplated a remark about Elizabeth Bowen. Jean D. was ahead of me.

The proximity of the fur-trimmed Cossack sleeve to her Scotch tweed one generated some electricity of intuition. My friend closed the guidebook in a final way and, with the certainty that the animal in the cage she was entering was of a familiar species, spoke to the young woman. The species certainly was familiar; the animal ready to play, and without reserve. She was also Australian. She had been working for three months, *au pair* but with a small salary, as nursemaid to the baby twins of a Signor and Signora Russo, at Parma. Oh, she was absolutely without reserve. She abhorred Parma, she said, loathed the Signor who was, like all Dago men, sly and a sex maniac; scorned the Signora; and couldn't stand babies. And the meals! *Pasta*, no matter what shape or colour, she hated. Veal too, and sausages containing God knows what. As for the continental breakfast, that was hardly food at all, or at most:

"*Slum* food, actually. Bread-and-jam and cocoa — and I *detest* crusts!"

She was twenty going on twenty-one. Her name was Brett Something-or-Other. Had her mother been reading Hemingway when she was pregnant? I didn't ask although dying to. Maybe, as people do to lighten the hard work of travel, she would come to telling.

Travellers, imprisoned with strangers in foreign trains, ships' bars, air-terminal waiting-rooms, chartered tourist buses lunging through Turkey or Afghanistan, are inclined to foil *ennui* by being as unreticent about themselves as characters in a Chekhov play.

About themselves: how else keep their identity in places they do not belong to?

About themselves: even though the impression they more often than not create is of eccentricity, recklessness, animal cunning, of an incredible toughness shot through with peculiar snobberies and almost-idiot simplicities. Perhaps Brett would later clear up why she had been named Brett. As I listened to her talking to Jean D. in an educated, extrovert voice, it was manifest she had no thought of hiding anything.

I am, her manner said, what I am: lump it or leave it.

While exchanging *dragées* and peppermints and cigarettes, the women exchanged more and more of themselves, admitting me to their confidences but offhandedly, as though I were scarcely human, a dummy on the side-line. For all her poise (the panache, for example, with which she'd entered the compartment) she seemed to live in perpetual suspense. Her version of herself was hounded and harassed, a chronic Victim of Fate. It was done humorously, yet, as I laughed, I felt alarm at what catastrophe might be just ahead: some of the past catastrophes, however hilariously she presented them, seemed to me hair-raising, rape or murder an inch off.

She was always losing things, her passport, traveller's cheques, a camera, or leaving her purse with the last of her money in it at some place so disreputable that there was no hope of its being returned. She missed trains or buses to find herself stranded among near-cutthroats at unhealthy hours, drifted solo into the back-alley haunts of criminals and prostitutes; found herself fighting off inflamed lechers in places so out-of-the-way that no Good Samaritan would have heard her scream. Once she and an Australian girl-friend, speeding through Germany in a rented car had run down a deer on the outskirts of East Berlin at three o'clock in the morning, and had spent three days and nights in a lock-up.

"The food," she said, "was miraculous — *Kaffee mit Sahne*, yet!"

She was, she said, in trouble at the moment, with not a brass razoo to her name, down to her last unbroached packet of cigarettes, and nearly three days late in getting back from the week-end she had nagged Signora Russo into letting her spend in Milan.

"Everything, but everything, happens to poor Brett," she said complacently.

Meantime, outside, a landscape like a rain-botched *grisaille*, sodden Lombardy slid murkily by between the profiles of mother and son. He had been permitted a length of sanctuary behind the barrier of his folded arms and shuttered eyes while she dipped at mechanic intervals into a black plastic carry-all for titbits she chewed with the engrossed mien of a plot-hatcher. A moment arrived when she was sated, and had ruminated her next move into shape. She attacked again, sharply: "Carlo!"

No response so, more sharply, louder: "Car-lo, Car-lo!"

Once more, no response.

The jelly of her face stiffened: she knew he heard within the fort. From among the chattels banked up around her she groped out a chubby umbrella, and tapped his knee with the blunt ferrule. He still kept to his asylum; one felt he had his back to the door, hard. A muscle flickered on his cheek.

"Car-*lo!*"

This time she tapped viciously enough to hurt. He didn't wince but his eyes, as inexpressive as all brown eyes are, shot wide open, then immediately became slits. Politely enough, yet gratingly, threateningly, he asked what she wanted, "*Che cosa desidera?*"

She beat on the seat beside her with a fat little hand, and trilled:

"*È troppo duro; è troppo duro.*"

It wasn't hard at all; on this tourist-ridden line even the second class catered for spoiled foreigners. Anyway, had it been brown sienna marble instead of brown leatherette padded with foam rubber, Carlo's mother was her own luxurious cushions. Marble, fakir's spikes, fire-walker's coals, what could her child have done? Nurse her? Advise her to stand, or swing like a larger marmoset from the luggage-rack? He didn't even bother to answer, shut his eyes, and contemptuously, as though to exclude someone crazy.

Unbearable! Unfilial! Humiliating! — the ferrule prodding maliciously at his entwined fore-arms expressed these for her. He came to angry life, and grabbed the ferrule, far from playfully.

"*Carlo, ma no!*"

She squealed as if we other four were not there, tug-of-warring frantically as with a real snatch-thief, both hands in use. A new line, femininity, was jolted into being.

"*Fa freddo,*" she wailed, piping, frail and helpless.

"*Fa freddo, Car-lo mi-o!*" and pounded her patent-leather trotters girlishly on the floor to indicate their being violet with cold. Suddenly he let go and, as she bounced back with a squeak, stretched out for the air-conditioner switch above the hair of the Rameses man who didn't even slope his head automatically to one side but remained static and sequestered as a private image. Carlo pushed the pointer to its heat limit, *Caldo*, and, as one saying, "There, boil to death, dear mother, and leave me in peace", again immured himself behind his arms and eyelids.

Brett said very clearly, "The perverse old bitch! What that overweight madam needs is a back-hander across the chops!"

It was fascinating. Edged with indictment as her voice was, her face remained serene. She might have been praising or blessing the brawlers. They had, however, aroused a sleeping dog. She began again to denigrate Signora Russo and all living Italians. Because of the crystal pitch of her voice, she was as embarrassing as a cruel child. It disordered me. How could she know that the Italians didn't understand English, that she wasn't committing a social atrocity? I suppose, in fact, that she didn't care if every word were intelligible, and that she looked on them as being as culpable as the next Italian.

She hadn't come to Italy to dislike it; its inhabitants had taught her to. She felt blameless: she'd earned her fare over; was paying her way, working her way, conning her way when all else failed, through an Old World she'd been lured into visiting by gilded legends, propaganda ablaze with seductive adjectives. She'd been taken in by a mirage of civilizations accounted superior to her own country's, of breathtaking landscapes strewn with gorgeous cities and enchanting villages alive with diverting and decorative people.

She had been too ingenuous to believe, had not lived long enough to learn, that the Utopias of the pamphlet are what one does one's best to avoid. Now, behind her happy-go-lucky cynicism and audacious front, disillusion stirred like Polonius behind the arras. She spared nothing: Italy was a fifth-rate vaudeville show, the Italians cheap and nasty buffoons. She was revolted by the showy clothes hiding the dismal secrets of uncleanliness; sick of the untrustworthiness, the emotionalism, and jealous pride; infuriated by the sensual, over-confident faces of those who accosted her.

"Brett's *virgo intacta*, and proud of it," she said almost ringingly. "But a wise virgin, and not a timid one."

The terrors of the flesh she held at bay: she had, it seemed, learnt well the perilous lessons of modesty and love but didn't think them shield enough.

"See here!"

She took from her hand-bag a pair of wickedly pointed little scissors.

"They're silver. My great-grandmother used them for embroidery. She'd die again if she knew, poor lamb, what I use them for."

In queues, crowded trains and trams, cinemas, and public gardens, she carried them in her hand ready to stab into men who touched her. Her intolerance was flawless. Cheek by jowl with Italians in the compartment of *l'accelerato* she was separated from them by an abyss of the spirit. The Italian woman and her son shocked her: she *hated* them, she said, her face as expressionless as a camellia — yet it might have been a serpent speaking.

Curiously, despite a force and stringency in her conversation, one became also aware of odd slacknesses, bewildering non sequiturs. The link between thought and thought seemed especially to dissolve at a direct question. At first I thought she was letting down a safety-curtain on some of Jean D.'s feelers, but her whole-hearted candour made that unlikely. It was just that, with one foot in sophistication, the other in naïveté, dislocations occurred. She was, for example, denouncing Signora Russo for always being underfoot, always hanging over her own babies:

"I don't know why she bothers with a nanny. I might just as well be in Saudi-Arabia. Sometimes I'd like to hit her."

Jean D., who thinks kindly of most Italians and all babies, said, "Oh, you can't mean that, Brett. She treats you very well. You have plenty of time off. After all, why shouldn't she dote on her own babies?"

"Because she'll ruin them. Besotted woman — tying and untying their ribbons all the time as if they were dolls."

"But she's their *mother*," Jean D., childless, was becoming fervent and stubborn.

"Yes, I suppose the creature is." To my surprise she spoke mildly, as if she had of a sudden seen the Signora in a new light, a kind of Crivelli Madonna dandling two Holy Children in front of an oriel window-sill crowded with porcelain-like fruit, enamelled-looking flowers, and highly glazed cucumbers.

"Then, surely," asked Jean D. more in the manner of a sentimental deaconess than I'd have believed possible, "she can be forgiven, or at least understood?"

"I . . . don't . . . think . . . so." Brett answered lingeringly, apparently in thought. It couldn't have been thought, for she added, "No, I *don't* think so. She's far too pretty, and has varicose veins." She paused. "Anyway, she's a bank-manager's wife."

Jean D. was flummoxed enough to say, "What difference does that make?"

"My father's one, too."

On the subject of returning to Parma three days later after racketing about Milan with wanderer Australian friends on their way to Venice her thoughts were equally random and unmarried to each other.

"What on earth," Jean D. had asked, "will your Signora say?"

"I don't care a damn what she says. Or does. She can rave on like that obese dolly in the window-seat if it gives her a kick. I'll make up some taradiddle or other — tell her I ran out of lire."

While I was still trying to spot what was askew about this, Jean D. said, "Heavens, girl, *that's* hardly a convincing lie. If you'd no money how could you afford three extra days?"

"It's not a lie." How calm she was. From the handbag containing scissors but no money she languidly took her last packet of cigarettes. "I told you I hadn't a brass razoo." Finically as a good little girl, she began opening the packet. "But this morning I had lashings of lucre."

"You haven't lost your purse again?" Jean D. was getting motherly.

"No. I can't imagine why — but no, the money's not lost this time. I lent it to two blokes who were skint."

"You *lent* it!" Jean D. was maternally severe. "So now you're skint. Who were they?'' She doubtless pictured a brace of confidence men from Naples pretending to be Veronese counts who'd left their wallets in other suits.

"One was an Australian.''

"I see." Jean D. was now absolute mother. "And the other?''

Brett languidly lit a cigarette, languidly exhaled. "Oh, he was an Australian.''

A silence had to fall. There was nothing to say. Jean D. looked at me, I at her, our eyes as it were shrugging. There was nothing else to do.

At that moment the mother in her discreet production-belt hat animated herself, and intoned with tragic intensity, "*Carlo mio, fa troppo caldo.*''

The son, perhaps truly, like a disciple at Gethsemane, slept on.

"*Io sudo,*" she whined, dabbing a pink handkerchief on her moustache which was indeed beaded with sweat. "*Io sudo, Carlo. Non posso sopportare il calda.*''

"She can't bear the bloody heat!''

Brett rose up, breathing authentic cigarette smoke, and metaphorical flame. "Neither can I. Excuse me, talkative," she said down in the coiffure of the living idol whose self-absorption remained unruffled as she abruptly turned the air-conditioning pointer right back to *Freddo*. "And I sincerely hope, Mother Macree, that you freeze to death.''

Whatever the words conveyed to us Australians, the tone cannot have conveyed anything to the Italians, particularly as she uttered without a side-glance at them, and had moved to perform her ostensibly gracious act like a well-bred and mobile caryatid on whose carven tresses an invisible burden of marble acanthus leaves and a ton of architrave were being perfectly balanced. Reseating herself, her visage politely neutral, "God, I *hate* them," she said.

Beyond the windows a drenched Lombardy was running out; before many minutes *l'accelerato* would be in drenched Emilia.

Sky-scraper crags, bottomless primeval lakes, cascades frothing soapily down gorges, leagues of blue-and-white snow-dunes, unemployed nature in any guise is not to my taste. It would have pleased me, however, had the plains docile from centuries of cultivation not been veiled in vertical water, to look out at them, at the tamed rivers, the food-bearing trees and drink-bearing vines, the wounded towers and castles far-off on their hill-top aeries, the farther-off mountains like penitentiary walls still keeping in something mediaeval and feudal, the fumes of vendetta and foray and, in the veins of the last of the vine-leaves, the blood of battle-axed mercenaries, of war-horses and lords, which had long ago extravagantly irrigated the soil. Since I was unable to see what lay outside, the beauty that is feud's aftermath, I had to make do with the feud in the compartment, and await its aftermath.

It wasn't a situation about which to be flinty. Brett's naïveté was too engaging for that, and her fearlessness rather moving because what was callous in it was not inborn but a culture: necessity its spore. Her fury was, I felt, only that of the displaced and disappointed, transient enough for air to have wafted it into her mind. The faintest movement of the weathervane, and a breath would puff it out.

Perhaps, now, she could never cry, "Open, sesame!" with the old wide-eyed expectation — she had learnt too much to want to, but she could still cry, "Open, wheat!", "Open, barley!" and not be let down. The consequences of her impercipience meant nothing to her, nothing: it proved nothing except the immeasurable distance between two national minds. She had arrived at the point where civilization (as she recognized it) was seen, by its absence, to have existed where she came from, not where she had come to. Homesickness can calcify the heart and buckle the vision as quickly and easily as vice.

The train advanced into Emilia and the melancholy border-land of twilight. Perhaps because abhorred Parma, amorous Signor Russo, the doting Signora and her beribboned twins, tomorrow and tomorrow, all swam nearer and nearer through the darkening rain, she fell silent, closed her eyes, and did not sleep.

Her face! — behind its composure an engagement with emotion could be guessed at, but the ivory surface, the Goddess of Mercy blankness admitted nothing: her hands with their bitten nails now and then shifted restlessly on her fashionable lap.

Jean D. opened her guidebook. Would it inform her that for nearly five centuries Florence had been, like Rome and Vienna, Madrid and Paris, a centre of fake antiquities and forged masterpieces?

Night's tide was in when Brett opened her eyes.

"Forgive me, Jean. I was out on business. Really! I've been desperately trying to think of something heart-breaking. Hopeless!"

She gave no explanation, but went on, "I must have some money. Must. *Must.*"

She was talking to Jean D. rather than to both of us but her wantonly clear voice could no doubt be heard in the next compartment if not farther off.

"Oh, dear, it's maddening. In three weeks' time I want to be out of Parma. You see, there's a promise I've got to keep. Two girl-friends are coming down from Norway. We'll join up at Milan, go down to Rome and Naples, then to Brindisi where we'll get a ship across the Adriatic to Greece. I've been there before, and *loathed* it, but a promise is a promise. Even if I have to sleep in the Parthenon, and get my Vitamin C from those sour oranges that grow on the street-trees in Athens, I'll need *real* money to get there. I was certain I'd have it by now, but everything's gone wrong. Me all over, of course. Time's running out. Poor little Brett's on the horns of a whatsis. No matter how much I try and try, I can't get my suit-case stolen. What would you do?"

"To . . . to get my suit-case stolen?" Jean D. spoke out of a fog. Suddenly it cleared: "Oh, I see. For the insurance, you mean?"

"Yes. It's money for jam. Or so I thought."

She had heavily insured everything she'd brought with her from Australia, and losing her expensive camera at a time when she was on the rocks had found the insurance money a god-send. The camera's loss had been an accident; the loss she was now set on was to be deliberate. The case she hoped to collect on was, she said, a costly monster so large that it had to be wheeled on an also-costly fold-up trolley. For the sort of bread-line travelling she and her young friends now did, invaders' skimpily-accoutred Blitzkriegs, the monster, with its attendant contraption, was a hindrance. It was also potential capital.

Her account of attempts to abandon it was very funny, illegal though her intentions. She'd done everything possible to contrive situations in which her head was morally above water, even if only just. Usually she left it on railway platforms next to the most criminal-looking people in sight while she walked conspicuously away, not looking back, to dally in station bars or waiting-rooms or buffets. Time after time she returned to find it, despised loot, exactly as she'd left it. Twice she had deserted it on buses. Once a group of men who resembled the denizens of a thieves' kitchen had yelled and whistled her back; once a wizened old man with a squint had scorched after her on a new-fangled bicycle.

"I suppose," she said, "the costly bloody monster *and* its costly trolley are too conspicuous to steal. And —" She smiled faintly. — "I'm too conspicuous to be stolen from. It bugs me. Either they're all daft, or I'm fated, or both."

In a Europe she regarded as an elaborate piece of machinery set up to bilk and pillage the tourist, an honesty she regarded as perverse dogged her.

"I'd contemplated defying the fates, and trying again in Milan, but decided no-no-*no*: better to enjoy myself than have the worry of not losing it again. I've got a better plan. When I get off at Parma . . . *hell*, where are we?"

The train was decelerating, running over points. She recognized, through the streaming panes, some reassuring combination of lights and outlines.

"Ah, thank God this isn't for me."

It was for Signor Rameses-Arcimboldi who unfolded into an unexpectedly squat man, took an old-fashioned kit-bag from the rack, slid open the door, and wordlessly, on his too-short legs, went out to wait in the corridor.

"*Carlo! Che ora è? Quanto ci fermiano qui? Ho sete, Carlo. Ho appetito!*" keened the mother.

Carlo, eyes balefully open, said cruelly that he wasn't thirsty or hungry: "*Non ho sete. Non ho appetito.*" Outraged, detonated, she released a torrent of melodious abuse. Like a lip-reader, or someone at a *film muto*, he watched, one felt, rather than heard.

The train stopped. The full-dress tirade didn't. The little platform was bare except for the silent man and his kit-bag jogging through the rain. A dog committing a dire aria could be heard. The train started.

"Oh, do shut up, you neurotic old sow," said Brett looking at the palm of one hand. "You know, it's a wonder he doesn't knife the whingeing hag. I'd like to see Signora Giovanni Russo try to bully me like that."

Right then, it came to me that for all the mother's malicious caterwauling and the son's churlishness, all the domestic discord, the two Italians with their passion-afflicted faces had quieter nerves than Brett with her unmarked brow and tender mouth. Theirs might well have been a happy partnership of hate, for hate has as many allegiances as love, and far less fallible ones. If their faces were, so to speak, chewed, their finger-nails weren't.

"You were saying," said Jean D., the orchestra-conductor tapping with the baton, "that when you get off at Parma . . ."

"I'll show them."

Brett flicked her compact open, reviewed her lips and eyes in the glass, did nothing to them.

"I used to have lovely nails until I took to feasting on them."

She put away the compact, and gazed tranquilly at her fingers.

"They really are repulsive. It makes me shudder to look at them."

"Show whom what?" Jean D. was pedantic but persistent. Curiosity gnawed at her like the Spartan youth's fox: she had no intention of letting Brett's riven mind remain unwelded.

"The insurance people, of course. When I get to Parma my new plan goes straight into action." She inhaled a sighing breath. "I'm going to report to the Dago station-master that I've lost the monster."

We said nothing.

"Have I shocked you? Everyone does it. *Have* I?"

Neither of us answered. I saw Jean D.'s face — and felt mine — congeal at non-committal. I said, "Will they believe you?"

"Oh, don't say that! They'll *have* to believe me. I'll make them. I used to be quite an actress at school; Portia, you know — 'it droppeth as the gentle rain', and so on."

She went into a kind of trance, enacting what she'd devised, running over her pathetic script.

"I'll tell them that the case was so enormous it couldn't fit on the mingy little second-class rack, so I left it in the corridor. What else could I do? Why didn't I book it through in the luggage-van? Because, poor maiden, I didn't get to the station in time." She dropped the mediumistic manner, and absurdly pleaded, "You saw that, didn't you, Jean, my leaping on just as the train was moving out?" Then she returned to her other fiction. "I was desperate. I'd been lost for *hours* in Milan, all all alone, and was worried frantic about getting back to the dear, sweet, lovely *bambini*. In the train I was so exhausted from trailing around Milan in the downpour that I fell asleep, and didn't wake up until we arrived at Parma. When I went out into the corridor to get my case — *mamma mia! il mio bello, bello bagaglio* — gone! I'll burst into tears. '*Mamma mia, mamma mia,*' I'll sob, '*Oh, mamma mia, il mio bagaglio!*' ''

The snatches of Italian interrupted the bickering in the window-seats; mother and son turned their simmering, feral eyes on the elegant foreigner. She sensed their attention. Without deigning to look at them, she said, "Stare, stare, monkey bear! Mind your own bloody business, slobs!"

I think Jean D. and I thought that, surely this time, some Mediterranean extra-sensory gift might have been at last brought into play, and the rudeness understood, for we both quickly spoke.

"Will it work?" was hers; "It won't work," was mine.

"It has to. I promised the girls I'd meet them outside the Milan cathedral at midday on the fifteenth of next month, traveller's cheques and all. I couldn't let them down. I've got to be a get-rich-quick maiden this time. All this mess wouldn't have happened if one of the nit-wits had had the nous to pinch the case instead of trying to pinch my you-know-what. Imagine poor Brett weeping and wailing in front of a lecherous gang of porters! '*Ah, poverina, poverina,*' they'll croon, and pat me, and I won't be able to use my scissors. And then there'll be the police, and I'll have to repeat the entire *mamma mia* performance."

She inhaled another, deeper sighing breath.

"One must martyr oneself for oneself," she said blandly.

Jean D. was near tears. It wouldn't have surprised me if she'd drawn the regal head down to her bosom.

"But aren't you worried, Brett?"

Did she really mean morally worried? Did she mean, on a lower plane, worried about attempting blatant perjury without any of the technique of the Duse it would require to make it work? Did she, on the lowest plane, mean worried at the possibility of being not believed? Which sort of worried did she mean?

"Worried! Of course. I spent my last lire in that clinical buffet on the Milan station to mop up a few fortifying vinos. I'm worried *stiff.*"

She — which sort of worried did she mean? She consulted the compact again, this time using a lipstick, wiping powder on, fussing with her scarf, touching up the leading lady or preparing the victim. Worried? The touched-up face was as pacific as a tarn nothing is reflected in.

She put a cigarette between her lips, and struck a match. The quivering of the tiny flame made it clear that her hand was unsteady.

"Oh dear," she said, "poor Brett."

She blew out the match without lighting the cigarette, and admonished herself: "Stop that instantly, you silly maiden. Stop, right now."

The aristocratic hands with their gnawed nails, held out before her,

Noel Counihan *Pub Talk* 1962
Oil on composition board 91.5 × 137.2 cm
Queensland Art Gallery

Jeffrey Smart *Cahill Expressway* 1962
Oil on plywood 81.2 × 111.7 cm
National Gallery of Victoria

became still.

"Anyway," she said, putting the cigarette back in the packet, "there's no time."

She stood, reached for her valise, put it on the seat, and sat again, tilting her head back, closing her eyes. She kept them closed for five minutes, ten minutes, until the train, jerking over points, passing through a lighted suburb, came to Parma, and stopped.

She opened her eyes. "Yes, Jean," she said, rising, and taking up her valise. "I'm *very* worried. I've been trying to think of something sad so that I can cry for those galoots out there. Good-bye."

At the door she spoke once again, and then went. The train started. We passed her, pliant and untouchable in the Cossack coat, moving over the brilliant reflections on the wet platform. The rain had gone. Her last words had not: we kept on hearing them.

"I'm terrified. What's going to happen now? All I need is tears, and I can't think of a single unhappy incident in my whole life."

The Clairvoyant Goat

THE SEAFRONT pub was old-fashioned. So was its bar. So were the flames munching away at offcuts in the bar's open fireplace.

So was the *tick-tock tick-tock tick-tock* of the outsize clock, a station-master's one, on the chimney-piece above the fire.

Big hand flicked dead upright; asserted eight to an accompaniment of the proper number of grave twangs; and instantly set off downhill pursuing nine.

Decades of downhill; decades of uphill; what a life!

Outside: a freezing night unfit for brass monkeys who cared about completeness.

Inside: customers enough for one barman.

The barman's hair was deeply corrugated, and has been said to be white as driven snow.

The customers were four fishermen with heads mollycoddled, if you please, in apparent tea-cosies, missus-knitted; and a baker's dozen of other assorted characters, locals all, two of them fake-beatniks.

Darts were being played by some of the sprightlier.

The varnish-glazed husk of a super-crab in spreadeagle above the fireplace and underneath the clock had its back to the topers. A microscopic spider who had spent all day engineering a secret and *de luxe* web between the crab's out-of-order chelae unremorsefully chucked it in at eight past eight.

At precisely this moment, and with somewhat the air of refugees from a terrain overrun with yetis and other hostiles, a man and a woman came . . . burst . . . in. Unlocal to a degree, they were, as it were, much creased from too long in the tin. It was parked outside, mini, and about to be deep-frozen by an unwavering Ice Age draught from Bass Strait, an untrustworthy geographical feature of which neither littoral teemed with orchids, humming-birds, bread-fruit trees, or boa-constrictors.

They dallied not on the way to the bar counter where, agile as toadstool pixies, they hoisted their backsides, hers vivid, his houndstooth, on to non-old-fashioned stools.

"Usual?" said the man to the woman.

The woman nodded, de-ashed a filter-tip in a brandy-extolling ashtray, and said:

"I must give up smoking."

"She said for the enth time," said the man and, to the barman who confronted him without revealing fervour or stimulation, "Two double brandies. Ginger ale. No ice."

"That's so," said the barman, plucking up two glasses one-hand, just . . . like . . . *that*!

"What's so?" said the man.

"There is no ice."

It was clear the barman firmly endorsed the theory that the lives of most people are not novels but cautionary tales or downright dirty yarns. Poker-faced, no smile to fritter away on blow-ins, he surgically dealt with up-to-date doovers, put the injected glasses and a circumcised ginger-ale bottle on the counter, and mentioned a price.

Planking some delved-out coins down, the man uttered information of a sort.

"Nippy out," was the contribution. "Very nippy, old boy."

"Another twenty cents, if you please," said the barman. "This is 1976. And . . . don't call me old boy."

"Baboon," the man said to the woman. "Yahoo! Ape! *An*-imal!"

Cowardy Custard, he said them unloudly, and the barman was about his business elsewhere.

The bogus hippies, zonked on eccentric and costly mixed drinks, had fed the juke-box lavishly. It was, for the seventh time in succession, exuding "Tie a Yellow Ribbon Round the Old Oak Tree", but discreetly, *sotto voce*. Robust playing was taboo. Indeed, the machine had been in a fashion spayed.

"Ah, the *bella musica*!" said the woman.

Perhaps in a mood to dance swoopingly about until some pale mad hour, the woman swayed a little in time, her ear-rings too, though contrariwise. "You know, it puts me in mind of . . ."

Some voicelessness took place.

The man then gave voice.

"Well?" he said.

She persisted mute, although she went on gently swaying, smoking, sip-sipping.

"Well?"

The man was trying again, more mustard this time.

"Well? Shall we press on to Mount Gambier tonight, or . . .?"

He drained his glass.

So did she hers, brusquely but abstractedly.

The man, upon whose lower face a grim grin was starting to manifest itself like a muzzle, was compelled by circumstance to order refills from the barman's yellow-pullovered shoulder-blades. Their owner was knocking back, publicly private but not unlanguidly, a dirty-big neat gin. It was only in his own good time, dumb as a viper and expressionless as junket, he executed the order.

Glass in hand, and picky now, the man again said:

"Well?"

This time the woman deigned to reply, but not at all silkily, and grimacing with disgust as though the villain in houndstooth had offered her a porringer of cold stewed child.

"I'll say it again, and I hope for the last time. I'll say it again. It's up to you, Bozo. You know I loathe Della, and you know that Della loathes the very thought of yours truly. So, why in the name of . . ."

"But we promised."

"We! What's this talk of we? *You* promised, you alone. Or say you did. Did you?"

She lit a new cigarette from the butt of the one before, and said:

"I must . . ."

"Give up smoking," cut in the man, nasty now. "You and Mount Etna."

They were both, his nibs and her ladyship, well supplied with neuroses of the most up-to-date sort.

Another interval of voicelessness took place. It was briefer. This time she gave voice first, and plangently.

"You're the driver, are you not? It's up to you, is it not? And, after all's said and done, she's your aunt, i'n't she? I, personally, couldn't care if the old faggot . . ."

"All right," he said. "All right. All right. All right. All *right*."

He drank.

She drank.

The quartet of fishermen was having a high old time gossiping about another fisherman who had the double distinction of absence and brand-new cancer. Doom-riddled instances were called to mind and joyfully recounted. Profound and forlorn platitudes were unselfishly exchanged.

"Wonder if they're sewn on," said the woman.

"Come again," said the man.

He had put on a cigar. It was not from Havana; and looked like the sort of cigar a chimpanzee could relish.

"Come again. What sewn on what?"

"The fish scales. On their dinky little woollen skull-caps."

"Oh."

The man took a look. He had unlucent circular eyes the colour of pewter.

"Local colour, it's called. They're being salty and folksy. That'll be the oldest inhabitant crooning by the hearth."

A rumpled great-grandpa was indeed minding his own business in front of the fire. He was slumped asleep in a stalwart but veteran armchair. Drunk as a skunk, he burbled consolingly to himself, was decades away, warm and drowsy in a cot.

One of the pseudo-beatniks, the one with dried hamburger sauce in his beard, loped neanderthally to the counter. He was understood to request two double vodka-and-*crème-de-menthes* with lemonade.

" 'N' change f' t' bahx," he also managed.

He proffered a ten-dollar note much cleaner than he.

The barman, eyeing it with contumely, did not spring into action. For some reason — probably a sense of theatre — he arranged himself arms akimbo.

"And for which box, sir?" he said. "That one?"

He levelled a sign-post forefinger at a collection box for spastic children.

"Or that?"

The finger now took aim at a large bottle in which lay a sediment of drunks' change.

The unsavoury youth, no Einstein he, was bemused and unhinged enough to snarl:

"*Juke* bahx, creep."

The barman's eyes instantly changed colour. Once more his arms went akimbo. There was an abatement of genial hubbub. He spoke.

"Out," he said dulcetly. "You have now done it, Sheamus Murphy. You have blotted your nasty little copy-book. Out! Take your dole money I and these gentlemen here are wickedly overtaxed for. And your freak mate. And out!"

He cleared his throat. He continued, soothingly as a pigeon babbling *I love you, Lulu*, to address the stripling:

"Or I'll deep-six the two of you."

"We gaht bread in that machine there, man," cavilled the primate. "Three-four replays yet."

"Out!"

Oh, soft and sweet; sweet and low!

"Democracy. Civil rights, man. We gaht 'em, y' know."

"I don't know. Out!"

This time the barman spoke loud and clear and, a large creature, waxed larger, and moved into central display his large hands.

They went.

One or other squawked "Fascist!" as the door swung to behind them. On the door were drawing-pinned a garish rodeo poster, and a homemade advertisement for a fifty-fifty dance in aid of a new dressing-shed for the football club.

As the door closed one of the darts-players perpetrated a miracle, and began to caper about making joyful and self-glorifying noise. He fell smack on his middle-aged bottom. His co-mates thereupon made more joyful noise.

Great-grandpa, deep in the heart of dreamland, murmured contentedly on.

The fire now and then starrily burped.

The well-fed juke-box continued to emit "Tie a Yellow Ribbon" in a moderate and not-yet-maddening manner.

"At least," said the woman, "the place has atmosphere."

"So," said the man — carper, knocker, model bore, "has a zoo."

He raised his voice Neroically:

"Another round here."

"Please," said the woman to the barman. "Please. Disregard my ill-bred chauffeur. Anyway, it's time I shouted."

"Too late," said the man, subtracting paper money from a wallet made in Hong Kong from the pelt of some oriental *lusus naturae*.

Putting on his muzzle grin the man attempted, God help him, to soft-soap the barman.

"Good show, old b . . . , good *show*. The damn' kids today, nothing more than animals. Your treatment: just what the silly goats need."

Freeze!

Then, quite unlovingly, woman and barman snapped in unison.

He:

"Watch it, mister, or . . ."

She:

"Have a little tact . . ."

A goat happened to have been subduedly toying with drinks on a stool two stools away from the woman, subduedly, as if in sackcloth and ashes, and too debilitated by melancholy to whimper "Oh, woe is me! Alack the day!"

Now, of a sudden, his dejection seemed at an end, and, although not exulting with cries of "Huzza!" and "Tol de rol!" and "Come to the fair!", he did indicate that he was no longer bowed down.

He turned a noble head towards the woman, and gave speech. It was a cultured voice, liquid and well modulated. There was the hint of some accent, probably European.

"We need hardly regret the departure of those two young . . ."

He paused, delicately choosing. Having chosen, he went on:

"Those two unripe persons. Otherwise. That agreeable melody, for instance. They have bequeathed it to us. Gratis, and thrice more. Based, it is said, on a song popular during the American Civil War."

"What's he going on about?" said the man to the woman. "What's he saying?"

"Something intelligent," said the barman sideways as he bustled towards the goat to whom he delivered a splendid smile, and jubilantly cried:

"At last! Welcome back to the land of the living! Thought you'd never make it. Not a squeak out of you for nearly two hours."

"It is the most complicated and fearsome hangover I've ever had," said the goat, "but it has abated, and continues to abate."

His jacket, Isle of Bute, was beautifully tailored, and newly dry-cleaned and pressed.

"Another whisky-Mac will do the deed. And I'd better have a fresh straw, please, Chris. Have one yourself."

"A fresh straw?"

Goat and barman laughed — but just enough, just enough.

Both had these television toothpaste teeth.

The man viewed this exchange with anything but love, anything but levity. The glance his pewter eyes flicked across the waggish two was one so opaque as to be ophidian. It cost him no effort at all almost to bark:

"Same again here."

The barman the goat had called Chris had ink-black eyebrows. He raised them, and opened to their widest his water-blue eyes; and slowly, nearly insolently, said:

"Similar, you mean."

The woman seemed to deem it wise to do something. First of all, she became pretty and charming, and spoke of her escort, sparring partner or whatever he was, as though he were from a far-off land, and could not yet be trusted to use the Australian patois:

"He means the same *sorts* of drinks."

She next contrived to become prettier still, all vivacity and zest: "My turn to buy. Must let the moths out", and — all in a flash! — downed the drink she had in hand; got the exact money smelling of make-up out of a weeny purse out of a fold-over handbag out of a soldierly shoulder-bag; and lit a cigarette. With a solid gold Ronson lighter at that.

The goat was much impressed.

"The first shots were fired by the Confederate troops on Port Sunter, April the twelfth, eighteen-sixty-one," he said, eyes aglow.

The eyes were oval and tar-black. His beard was trimmed with all the care of an Edwardian diplomat's. This distinguished-looking mortal added:

"By the way, my name . . ."

"Is spelt ay ell pee aitch," said the barman looming up to present the whisky-Mac and straw with some reverence, and the double brandies — one of them, anyway — with striking disinclination.

There was merry clamour from another part of the bar.

"Step on it, Snow!" cried the fishermen, impassioned by their intimacy with an accredited cancer subject. "Service! Shop! Battle stations, Snow! Pull the finger out!"

"Verily, as Christopher says, ay ell pee aitch. As, of course, in Coleridge's strange but unforgettable poem," said the goat to the woman. "Excuse me, please."

His profile prayerfully descended to the top of the straw protruding from the drink. Half the whisky-Mac ascended. He went on:

" 'Where Alph the sacred river ran' *et cetera*. You know the line, of course."

The woman and the man did not commit themselves.

"My lamented mama was the well-known Madame Rivière."

The goat chuckled.

"Rivière . . . you get it?"

The man and the woman did not commit themselves.

Purling now and then, dribbling a little, the aged soak in the fireside armchair continued his infantile snooze.

The fattest darts-player, bearing the emptied glass jug, waddled towards the counter for another litre of draught.

The spider, off-duty and frivolous, played lift-driver on the loose, sliding up and down its personal thread.

"A hundred yellow ribbons . . ." sang the juke-box for a final time — the mock-hippies' endowment was nearly swallowed up.

"Well?" said the man. His hairline moustache was askew, and his manner fretful. "Made up your mind yet? Mount Gambier?"

The woman seemed prepared to listen to the goat with the indiscriminate zest of a model prisoner.

"He's a charmer," she said.

She was by now not untipsy.

"He's shicker. And dingbats," hissed the man. "Use your wits, and stop evading the issue."

"Oh, catch . . . catch leprosy! Di'n't I say, 'It's up to you'? Di'n't I now? *I'm* not the one after your Auntie bloody Della's crummy old Wedgwood and silver."

"But I promised her. . . ."

"You're a liar, a crimson liar."

She began butt-lighting another cigarette, and unimpassionedly saying:

"I mus', I reelly mus' give up smoking."

"Please, do forgive this intrusion, Elsie," said the goat graciously inclining towards her, "but I feel I should . . ."

The woman was startled, very. Her eyes for a moment raced about like earwigs. Some inner liar of a female drew herself up haughtily.

"Elise," she said, most cannily. "It's E-*lise*."

Her manner added *You, varlet, are in grave error.*

"So? So . . . The error is mine. Perhaps because of excessive champagne yesterday. Christopher's twenty-ninth birthday celebration. Oh, don't be side-tracked by the snowy locks. Look at those black eyebrows. He's had white hair since boyhood. A family trait he's inherited just as I've inherited . . ."

"My name," began the woman, as intrigued as anything, "how did . . .?"

"I'll come to that," the goat said gently. He touched his Christian Dior cravat with a boulevardier's finical gesture.

"Notice my accent? It's faint, yes. But it's there." He permitted himself a Gallic shrug. "Mama was near enough to Provencal; papa was undefiled Swiss. He — well, you know the Swiss."

"Cuckoo clocks and condensed milk," grunted the man from the corner of his mouth. What he implied — something unseemly — was not clear, but he was staring bitterly at a Schweppes Soda advertisement, and looking overharried and underprivileged.

The goat disregarded his remark, cryptic though true enough.

"Switzers are notoriously unskittish. Thus papa. His ties were always lead-gray. Ah, attraction of opposites! Mama was an effervescent little thing, pretty as a doll but intelligent. Fey and famous sums her up. Yes, she was famous enough to be painted by Dame Laura Knight."

The goat's liveliness suddenly shrank.

Do you think the woman was put off?

No.

She had, in fact, changed from mere indiscriminate model prisoner to apparently drug-soused *guru*-worshipper; and hung on.

The spider, ready to call it a day, gave itself a farewell trip, basement to penthouse, and retired.

As suddenly as he had deflated the goat perked up. His eyes brillianted. He began to rattle on:

"My dear mama . . . Madame Angèle Rivière, Clairvoyante Extraordinaire . . . what a bobby-dazzler! Packed houses, crowned heads, exalted friends, all that sort of thing. I am heir to her eyes, the colour of them, and some of her gift for clairvoyance. A smidgin only but, when the circumstances are right, I can foretell . . . oh!"

He broke off and — in exact duet with the man — said:

"What's my name then?"

He added, "Oswald Truscott Bumleigh."

The man dropped the stub of his regrettable cigar.

The woman squealed.

The barman, picking up something from the corner of eye and ear, so abruptly deserted a sawn-off customer at the other end of the counter that, though his audience had gone, the little bloke still chattered on, and still held out a meagre forearm bared to display, certainly not rippling muscles, some cherished scorpion of surgeon's embroidery perhaps, or an indigo and indelicate tattoo.

"Okay here?" said the barman, hovering guardian-angelically opposite the goat, and suspiciously looking at — at Oswald Truscott Bumleigh.

The goat indicated his glass with a jet-black, perfectly manicured hoof and, smiling somewhat dreamily, murmured:

"Please, Chris, a double this time."

"And," said the man, too loudly, in the voice of one behind a door slammed in the face, "the same again, here, quick-smart."

Still too loudly, he addressed the woman:

"This, madam, is for the road. Bottoms up; and we're off!"

He slapped down a fistful of white money.

Once more the barman's eyes changed colour, and his arms went akimbo.

"Count ten," said the goat, looking patrician and wise. "One. Two. Three . . ."

"I am no madam, thank you for nothing, Ossie Bumleigh," said the woman, flicking away at her Ronson, and lighting the filter end.

"You know," her voice was fruity with dislike, "I've neverever taken a liking to Woodgewed, neverever . . . 'll tell her so. . . ."

"My pleas-ure . . . sir," said the barman to the man with brazen insincerity, and freely . . . too freely? . . . selecting coins from the slapped-down fistful.

He unnecessarily wiped the counter in front of the goat, set down his double on an unsullied coaster, said, "On the house!" and, before returning to the patient forearm, filled the goat in:

"Hughie's showing me where he had his acupuncture. Won't be long but, 'fyou need me . . ."

After a sup or two of her drink the woman got sad.

She had something to divulge to the goat.

"You were correc'. I know I've been E-lise f'reverunever but I was . . ."

"Christened Elsie," said the goat benignly. "And a very sweet name, too."

He gave a sort of tuneful giggle, and cleared his throat.

"My confession now. All that about Coleridge . . . a joke, a leetle *jeu d'esprit*. I wasn't named after the sacred river at all. Actually, mama named me after a French poet and journalist who once lived near her birthplace. She was born at Saint Maxime. He lived at Saint Raphaël. His name was Alphonse Karr, so Alph is short for . . ."

She raised her glass, and cried loud for all the bar to hear:

"To nicest clair-voy-ant in whole wide worl'."

"Hear, hear!"

This was the barman calling from afar.

Others, some catching on, some lost in the mists, vaguely yet fervently echoed him.

The goat, *comme il faut* as ever, crossed hoofs above his head in the manner of victorious pugilists or elected and not-yet-assassinated presidents of the United States of America.

"The stone end," said the man, Mr Bumleigh. He stood up. "Come on, come on. Leave that drink.''

"In the while ode whirl," said the woman; and polished off that drink.

Not at all in the manner of an expensive gigolo giving due service to a filthy-rich beldam, much more in the manner of a surly bus-conductor ridding his vehicle of a fractious octogenarian, he helped the woman dismount.

Her joints had become molten.

"Oops-a-daisy, Else," she admonished herself. "Wa'ch it, my girl, wa'ch it."

He, grimly resisting gravity on her behalf, prevented her downfall, and began superintending a progress across the room.

"Where off to, Bo-zo?"

"Have a bit of sense. Pull yourself together. You know damn' well where. Mount Gambier. Auntie Della."

They got to the rodeo poster.

Big hand was doing a head-stand at nine-thirty.

They overcame the swinging door.

Outside were the nickel-plated furrows of the winter sea, a fierce little bald moon, the gelid mini-car, and the road to Auntie Della's.

"Foiled! Left in the lurch!"

The goat was maundering on while the barman fabricated stiffies for him and himself.

"All is lost! Auntie Della's hideous late-Victorian villa is locked and barred, silent as the tomb. She left for Sydney, Flight Fifty-nine, at eight-fifty this morning. I do not envy in the slightest the next few hours of that ungentleman. Zoo! Apes and baboons! Animals! Kids and goats, indeed! He's got carburettor trouble, *serious* carburettor trouble, coming up. Three miles from the nearest telephone. He'll have to walk it. It'll be freezing, and pitch dark. One really shouldn't feel pleased."

"This one does. You're too much of a gentleman; too soft-hearted," said the barman. "Ginks like him get on my quince. She wasn't a bad sort of sheila. What she sees in an oaf like that . . . !"

"I intended telling her about my ancestors, the maternal ones, but . . ."

"Those satires?"

"Satyrs," said the goat. "Perhaps better I didn't get around to it. People, especially ladies a little relaxed by drink, get ideas, and expect too much. Ah, Auntie Della again!"

He closed his eyes.

The barman was all ears.

"Yes. In Fletcher Street, Woollahra, with the call-girl niece she'll leave all her crummy Wedgwood to."

He faded out, opened his eyes.

The barman waited for a while and then, like a fascinated child, pleaded:
"Oh, do go on, please, Alf."

"Alph," gently reproached the goat.

"Sorry, chief, but I'm still a bit frail after last night. I didn't hit the cot till five," said the barman. "And I had to be on the ball, all bright-eyed and bushy-tailed, at nine. Please go on . . ." he made it ". . . Alph."

"Sheamus Murphy's now been kicked out of the Commercial, too."

"Good."

"At this very moment he's being awfully sick."

"Good."

"In that little lane behind the post office."

He applied his lips to the straw, and absorbed a dose of whisky-Mac. Then he closed his eyes again.

"Ah, yes! Mr Bumleigh's vehicle is about to crack up. There isn't a house for miles. Big black clouds are covering up the moon. Elsie, poor dear, unaware of approaching catastrophe is attempting to sing that agreeable melody about yellow ribbons. Not wise. She's no golden-voiced songstress. Pity. It's a nice song."

"Like it played, squire?"

"Too kind, Christ-o-pher," said the goat, a shade drowsily. "Too kind. Press buttons N and 12."

"No worries."

The barman hand-vaulted the counter.

"Up there, Cazaly!" cried the older boozers, milling about. Among them were now the ex-darts-players.

"Tie a Yellow Ribbon" streamed forth.

The spider slumbered on.

Great-grandpa was being tempted from slumber by a sixty-three-year-old son croaking, "Rise and shine, captain", and ready with a porter-gaff.

The barman lifted the counter-flap, and was back.

"Chris," said the goat, "save your breath. You're on the point of saying, 'Hang about, chief, and I'll drive you home sweet home.' I'll say, 'Too kind, Chris, but I really do need a brisk walk, and some cold fresh air. So, if you don't mind, not tonight. Anyway, Sally Ann expects you tonight.' You'll pick up the departed Mr Oswald Truscott Bumleigh's sodden coaster, and say . . ."

"Sally Ann can wait," said Chris the yellow-pullovered, black-eyebrowed, snow-white-haired, twenty-nine-year-old barman picking up the sodden coaster used by the departed Mr Oswald Truscott Bumleigh.

"No, Sally Ann can't," said the goat, "and you shouldn't expect her to."

He finished his drink, and put on his beret.

"Don't keep her waiting, Chris. And," said the goat, "don't be a goat, you

goat. See you tomorrow.''
    Tipped his beret, smiled, hopped off the stool as nimbly as a . . . as a . . .
and
went out looking sober as a judge.
Big hand went on toiling uphill towards ten, and closing time.
No closing time, of course, for big hand.
Uphill . . . downhill.
Uphill . . . downhill.
Uphill . . . downhill.
What a life!

Chris
Wallace-Crabbe

Melbourne

Not on the ocean, on a muted bay
Where the broad rays drift slowly over mud
And flathead loll on sand, a city bloats
Between the plains of water and of loam.
If surf beats, it is faint and far away;
If slogans blow around, we stay at home.

And, like the bay, our blood flows easily,
Not warm, not cold (in all things moderate),
Following our familiar tides. Elsewhere
Victims are bleeding, sun is beating down
On patriot, guerrilla, refugee.
We see the newsreels when we dine in town.

Ideas are grown in other gardens while
This chocolate soil throws up its harvest of
Imported and deciduous platitudes,
None of them flowering boldly or for long;
And we, the gardeners, securely smile
Humming a bar or two of rusty song.

Old tunes are good enough if sing we must;
Old images, re-vamped *ad nauseam*,
Will sate the burgher's eye and keep him quiet
As the great wheels run on, and should he seek
Variety, there's wind, there's heat, there's frost
To feed his conversation all the week.

Highway by highway the remorseless cars
Strangle the city, put it out of pain,
Its limbs still kicking feebly on the hills.
Nobody cares. The artists sail at dawn
For brisker ports, or rot in public bars.
Though much has died here, little has been born.

Terra Australis

Here, and here only in an age of iron,
  The dreamers are proved right;
No armies underlie these rolling fields,
  No lost loves haunt the night,
Nor can the farmer, turning with his spade,
  Bring shard or helm to light.

Innocence clad in brown and faded gold
  Walks up and down these hills
Where unobtrusive flickering flowers rebuke
  The show of daffodils:
With sombre colours and with sparse designs
  Acre on acre fills.

Paradise lingers like a tapestry;
  The web has not been torn,
Luther and Cromwell, Socrates and Marx
  Have never yet been born,
Nor did a glowing Florence rise to shape
  The European dawn.

We are the final children of the earth
  Whom knowledge has not scarred,
Delighting still in sunlight and green grass
  Back in our own backyard:
Gaping, we hear the tales of adulthood
  Where life is dour and hard,
Far, far away, beyond some wicked wood.

December

I came at random
To a papery wind blowing
And rivers of darkness flowing through the market
Between deserted stalls,
And I turned at a random scent
To see the trucks that loomed along the kerb
Each in turn heavy with Christmas trees

And no one around to buy
Nobody here to sell,
But a resinous wind blowing.

Dorothy
Hewett

In Midland where the Trains Go By

In Midland still the trains go by,
The black smoke thunders on the sky,
Still in the grass the lovers lie.
And cheek on cheek and sigh on sigh
They dream and weep as you and I,
In Midland where the trains go by.

Across the bridge, across the town,
The workers hurry up and down.
The pub still stands, the publican
Is still a gross, corrupted man.
And bottles clinking in the park
Make symphonies of summer dark.

Across the bridge the stars go down,
Our two ghosts meet across the town.
Who dared so much must surely creep
Between young lovers lips, asleep,
Who dared so much must surely live
In train-smoke off the Midland bridge.

In Midland, in the railway yards,
They shuffle time like packs of cards
And kings and queens and jacks go down,
But we come up in Midland town.
O factory girls in cotton slips
And men with grease across your lips,
Let kings and queens and jacks go down
But we'll still kiss in Midland town.

An oath, a whisper and a laugh,
Will make our better epitaph.
We'll share a noggin in the park
And whistle songs against the dark.
There is no death that we can die
In Midland, where the trains go by.

Country Idyll

A glittering girl went out one day
On a dappled horse through the meadow hay,
And the quail rose clumsily, freckled brown,
In the morning light he rose up high
                              and then dropped down.
And "Sweet, sweet, we all must die"
Sang the glittering girl on the louring sky.

O she rode down to the gliding river
And the water covered her face forever,
And she prayed on horseback all of the way,
Crying, "This is the judge of all the days,
                              this is the master day."
And the sun rose up in a dusty haze,
And the plover sank in his song of praise.

O the girl went out on the gladsome water,
And the farmer searched for that whore, his daughter.
He smashed the haycocks, rattled the barn.
He said he'd find where the slut was laid
                              if he wrecked the farm.
While her lovers squatted in dust and played
Two-up under the peppermint shade.

And the river hid that she'd never been married,
And the river hid the child she carried
From the tea-cup tongues of the town.
It hid her breasts and her round high belly
                              as she floated down.
But her lovers never came out to see,
Playing two-up under the peppermint tree.

Once I Rode with Clancy...

Once I rode with Clancy through the wet hills of Wickepin,
By Kunjin and Corrigin with moonlight on the roofs,
And the iron shone faint and ghostly on the lonely moonlit siding
And the salt earth rang like crystal underneath our flying hoofs.

O once I rode with Clancy when my white flesh was tender,
And my hair a golden cloud along the wind,
Among the hills of Wickepin, the dry salt plains of Corrigin,
Where all my Quaker forebears strove and sinned.

Their black hats went bobbing through the Kunjin churchyard,
With great rapacious noses, sombre-eyed,
Ringbarked gums and planted pine trees, built a raw church
In a clearing, made it consecrated ground because they died.

From this seed I spring — the dour and sardonic Quaker men,
The women with hooked noses, baking bread,
Breeding, hymning, sowing, fencing off the stony earth,
That salts their bones for thanksgiving when they're dead.

It's a country full of old men, with thumbscrews on their hunger,
Their crosses leaning sideways in the scrub.
My cousins spit to windward, great noses blue with moonlight,
Their shoulders propping up the Kunjin pub.

O once I rode with Clancy through the wet hills of Wickepin,
By Kunjin and Corrigin with moonlight on the roofs,
And the iron shone faint and ghostly on the lonely, moonlit siding
And the salt earth rang like crystal underneath our flying hoofs.

And the old men rose muttering and cursed us from the graveyard
When they saw our wild white hoofs go flashing by,
For I ride with landless Clancy and their prayers are at my back,
They can shout out strings of curses on the sky.

By Wickepin, by Corrigin, by Kunjin's flinty hills,
On wild white hoofs that kindle into flame,
The river is my mirror, the wattle tree our roof,
Adrift across our bed like golden rain.

Let the old men clack and mutter, let their dead eyes run with rain.
I hear the crack of doom across the scrub,
For though I ride with Clancy there is much of me remains,
In that moonlit dust outside the Kunjin pub.

My golden hair has faded, my tender flesh is dark,
My voice has learned a wet and windy sigh
And I lean above the creekbed, catch my breath upon a ghost,
With a great rapacious nose and sombre eye.

Who Goes round my House by Night?

It's late at night poor Jackstraw visits me
To stick derisive fingers in my eyes;
The neighbours turn their backs and soundly snore
Pretending they're committed otherwise.

Here on the periphery of dawn and dark
He stands with all his tragedy intact.
I am intent on weeping for my needs;
Seeing myself, against the stars, hunchbacked.

Like children's nightmares he goes round the house.
He's poor old Tom, old Tom of Bedlam out
Screening the moon, and all the dogs will bark
Our conscience shut to hear his witless shout.

Uneasy thing the conjur man brings up
Out of the dark to grin and beckon me,
Conceived immaculate within this bed
To walk, and question my hypocrisy.

He stands in the closed doorways of the city,
God's fool in shabby coat and whispering voice,
Asking eternal questions of the world,
And I, who saw once, whole, am blind by choice.

Nail the spreadeagled shadow at my door,
Hammer the bloody imprint of his skin,
And though the sunlight grows across the floor,
I cannot let that tell-tale door swing in.

Then must I carry Jackstraw all my days,
The humpbacked victim of a childish sin,
How far . . . how far? . . . and the voice answers me:
"As far as love you'll carry him."

Bagman's Ballad

The boozy ballads are all sung,
The deeds are done, the ghosts are laid,
But look! around that river bend
Some bagman stretches in the shade.

And the immortal swagman goes
Singing down the centuries,
His jumbuck in his tucker bag,
His shadow on the blue-gum trees.

The low grey curtain of the scrub,
Shakes to the mythic bunyip's scream,
The burn of sun, of frost, of rum,
Palsies him in some hatter's dream.

Where is he running through the bush,
Tolling his bell of billycan,
The ballad, like a Bathurst burr,
Sticks to his back, poor witless man.

And when he drops, that dusty swag
Stands up and fights him on the road.
Where can he go? Matilda is
An awkward archetypal load.

We see him sometimes just at dusk,
But know him now for what he is,
Hiding in stolen overcoat,
Nightmare and dream that once were his.

The shadow of himself grows big,
Big as Mephistopheles,
He dodges through the stringybarks,
Playing Ned Kelly in the trees.

Do not disturb him, let him go.
He'll build a campfire by the creek,
The ashes of his glory will
Be cold and desolate next week.

Some ghostly town, some spindly pub,
Will quiet the torment in his brain,
Sweeney by the verandah post
Tipping his bottle at the rain.

There's Jimmy Woodsers in the bar,
And whisky, beers and shearers' rums,
While Kelly's ghostly armour gleams
Like sunlight, sliding through the gums.

And the immortal swagman goes,
Singing down the centuries,
He hangs on a sheepskin on the fence,
A shadow on the blue-gum trees.

Last Summer

In the little house with the sparrows,
The heavenly dew descends,
The wind-bells chime in the jacaranda,
Is this how the world ends?

The air is so thin and fragile,
We can hear spiders spin,
Shut up the house this summer,
Let nobody in.

A shadow hops in the garden,
The small sparrow sings,
Time spreads, the sun drops suddenly
And clips his wings.

A flurry and fall of sparrows,
Dropping into the sea,
What old man sits on the seashore
And counts and counts for me?

The grasshopper flicks and stumbles,
Hesitant in the grass,
The sea pounds and the rain pours,
On this dark house of glass.

I lie so still at midnight
You cannot hear me weep,
And who is there to tell you,
You cry all night, in your sleep.

John
Blight

The Island

The island is lost ground; an acre or two
in the realms of the sea. Is country
once loved of mother earth. Now, a whale's back
of wet mud, black, sliding back out of view
into the lost regions of a trackless sea;
and far, and farther away, as the tide's slack
takes up, is submerged, or part submerged
like a whale sounding in the shelving sea
— or could it be less noticed than a whale,
it is so small an island? Even the clouds have urged,
whipped it with rain, like spray, to go back to the sea;
crawl out the primeval monster, swishing a tail. . . .
There are such pleasures as becoming noticed, coming under the eye
of the lordly sun: an island becoming an ''I''.

Footprints

I am ever seeking the quieter beaches.
Do not believe, in Australia, there are miles
where at dawn you will not see the 'prints
— not on the East Coast, leastwise. Here, reaches
of sand are scarred from daybreak: the tiles
of footprints are laid down, the dents
made by feet in the sand are there — so stale to me,
such beaches seem no longer virgin to us few . . . to
people who do not want to meet each other, ever.
The lonely beach is for us, the lonely sea,
where we may commune with vast infinity.
But people mass down on the beach, and some are so clever,
no matter how early I rise, I despair
of finding a quiet beach, with no footprints there.

A Fisherman's Cottage

The glass floats from Jap fishing boats, like green jars,
lie in the marram grass, where bailer shells and sea stars
make one look up at the sky to feel
whether one's dry. If under a cloud's keel,
and dampened by rain, one can believe
one is submarine; for, perceive
— at the companionway of his front steps, clams,
and the saws of sawfish are his main door jambs.
There's a stuffed shark for a lintel, and
turtle shell spittoons filled with sand
on his deck-veranda. A fisherman's cottage
where a landlubber, in his dotage,
may fill his nostrils with the tang of salt
and dream he finds here Neptune's treasure vault.

Sea Beasts

The sea horse, of course, can't canter; the sea hare
never runs anywhere; while the sea cucumber
isn't a vegetable at all — but fable says
that men of China eat it for dinner, and there,
in China, along with sharks' fins and birds'-nests, number
it among delicacies; though it's a sea slug, no less!
All this topsyturvydom of the sea proves,
through such nomenclature, man moves
in a looking-glass world . . . all that he sees,
dreamed from the lees of some experience he suffers,
toping the heady bottle of the world's globe.
I do not think, if the seas were ink, these
records could be closed, with all that offers
as double proof his sea beasts need some scientist's probe.

Shells and Skulls

Death leaves them strewn on the shore, embedded in rocks
which were once mud of the sea floor.
Yet women and children gather shells. It never shocks
them to pick up shells. Skulls? Say no more!
Shells and skulls do not seem alike
except both may be white. On a background of black
shells look like gems, while skulls, bones, strike
terror in our hearts — insignia for no Union Jack,
but the Jolly Roger, pirates' flags! Why that
distinction of grace which death strangely saves
to bestow upon shells? Shells are the outlines of life,
its graceful shape; bones, like a hateful knife,
hide in the innards, sheathed in dissembling fat.
Shells tell us of life's pride — skulls, frightfully, of its graves.

Geoffrey
Lehmann

Pear Days in Queensland

FOR JAMES WANSFELL, ON WHOSE ARTICLE THIS IS BASED

Days of pear-madness, nights of pear-murder we spent
Digging and burning the prickly pear,
Poisoning, crushing with rollers drawn by bullocks,
Standing in pubs and swapping pear yarns,
Scraping the spines off with knives,
Sponging our thorn wounds with mustard,
Scratched brown and purple with Condy's and gentian violet,
While beyond the pressure lamp's wavering circle
The pear massed its nightmare armies by moonlight
And peered with balloon green faces over pub railings.

Our horses whinneyed with pain,
Fetlocks swollen to pumpkins where big thorns wedged.
Sometimes pear-happy our cattle romped through the cacti.
We hacked, we poisoned, we crushed, but the segments
Just split and sprouted again.
A tree grew from a burned green ear.
Munching amongst the yellow flowers a cow
Ate the soft red fruit and wandered five miles
And seeds passed with her stools became ten plants.
The pear flew in the stomachs of birds,
Breathed on the fur of bees, explored the night-wind.
A pad lived for three years hung in a room.

How could we fight what stuck to our boots and travelled
The red volcanic soil on our clothes and horses?
We sweated, were smeared with pear.
Pear cities covered millions and millions of acres,
Through a green Babylon we galloped flat out,
Pear leaves flying in all directions,
The roads just narrow tracks through walls of pear.
Mustering cattle we climbed up trees
To spot their heads amongst the plazas of cactus.

But we learned to live with pear-megalomania, these miles
Of green intestine digesting the world into pear.
We mashed the pads for feed,
Fermented them into alcohol
And extracted second grade dyes and oils.
We used the big yellow thorns for gramophone needles
And heard Enrico Caruso husky and faint
Sing from a thorn as we boiled in hot pear nights.

Then a moth came and Troy fell overnight.
The land was cleared, the arcades of pear collapsed.
The cactoblastis chewed its way through green cities
And we stood stunned in the pear-free open air,
Incredulous, a trifle uneasy
At the hemisphere of grassland tilting to the sea.

Now in winter we burn the sugarcane,
The hillside a honeycomb crumbling with fire
In blue indigo twilights blowing with orange smoke.
Our rivers and country daze us with largeness.
But at night we doze in mosquito nets
And smell ghost armies of cactus
In the heart of the rain forest, deeper than we can reach,
New resistant strains sending out clouds of pollen.

The Telescope at Siding Springs

The Warrumbungles loomed like derelict whales.
All night the whispering bush, dark, empty landscape
Gaunt mountains under shoals of browsing stars
Condensed their thoughts as lonely country does.
In woollen earmuffs, jackets firmly zipped
They moved in windless cold, boots sharp on concrete,
And the great mirror slowly turning followed
And drank a scratch of light their eyes were blind to.
Patiently magnified for hours through mirrors
A star chiselled a message on dark film,
A tentative diamond flickered in frail water.

A Girl Reading a Book in a Country Village

The shop is closed, the single street asleep.
Only a girl at dusk sits in a chair
And reads a book before her parents' house,
While trees hiss with the rush of passing traffic.

The yard in which she reads is small and bare,
The house is weathered brick, a workman's cottage,
But the town has ancient pepper trees and gums
For the green mind of a girl pleasing herself.

She smiles into her book while strangers pass,
Eyes cast down in her public reverie,
Is friendly in a light which has no shadows,
Facing the road and gazing at her page.

Patrick
White

Miss Slattery and Her Demon Lover

He stood holding the door just so far. A chain on it too.

"This," she said, "is Better Sales Pty. Ltd." Turning to a fresh page. "Market research," she explained. "We want you to help us, and hope, indirectly, to help you."

She moistened her mouth, easing a threat into an ethical compromise, technique pushed to the point where almost everyone was convinced. Only for herself the page on her pad would glare drearily blank.

Oh dear, do not be difficult, she would have said for choice to some old continental number whose afternoon sleep she had ruined.

"Faht do you vornt?" he asked.

"I want to ask you some questions," she said.

She could be very patient when paid.

"Kvestions?"

Was he going to close the door?

"Not you. Necessarily. The housewife."

She looked down the street, a good one, at the end of which the midday sun was waiting to deal her a blow.

"Housevife?"

At least he was slipping the chain.

"Nho! Nho! Nho!"

At least he was not going to grudge her a look.

"No lady?" she asked. "Of any kind?"

"Nho! Nefer! Nho! I vould not keep any vooman of a permanent description."

"That is frank," she answered. "You don't like them."

Her stilettoes were hurting.

"Oh, I *lihke*! How I *lihke*! Zet is *vhy*!"

"Let us get down to business?" she said, looking at her blank pad. "Since there is no lady, do you favour Priceless Pearl? Laundry starch. No. Kwik Kreem Breakfast Treat? Well," she said, "it's a kind of porridge that doesn't

428

get lumps.''

"Faht is porritch?''

"It is something the Scotch invented. It is, well, just *porridge*, Mr Tibor.''

"Szabo.''

"It is Tibor on the bell.''

"I am Hoongahrian,'' he said. "In Hoongary ze nimes are beck to front. Szabo Tibor. You onderstend?''

He could not enlist too much of himself, as if it were necessary to explain all such matters with passionate physical emphasis.

"Yes,'' she said. "I see. Now.''

He had those short, but white teeth. He was not all that old; rather, he had reached a phase where age becomes elastic. His shoes could have cost him a whole week's pay. Altogether, all over, he was rather suède, brown suède, not above her shoulder. And hips. He had hips!

But the hall looked lovely, behind him, in black and white.

"Vinyl tiles?'' Her toe pointed. "Or lino?''

After all, she was in business.

"Faht? Hoh! Nho! Zet is all from marble.''

"Like in a bank!''

"Yehs.''

"Well, now! Where did you find all that?''

"I brought it. Oh, yehs. I bring everysing. Here zere is nossing. Nossing!''

"Oh, come, Mr Tibor — Szabo — we Australians are not all that uncivilized. Not in 1961.''

"Civilahsed! I vill learn you faht is civilahsed!''

She had never believed intensely in the advantages of knowledge, so that it was too ridiculous to find herself walking through the marble halls of Tibor Szabo Tibor. But so cool. Hearing the door click, she remembered the women they saw into pieces, and leave in railway cloak-rooms, or dispose of in back yards, or simply dump in the Harbour.

There it was, too. For Szabo Tibor had bought a View. Though at that hour of day the water might have been cut out of zinc, or aluminium, which is sharper.

"You have got it good here,'' she said.

It was the kind of situation she had thought about, but never quite found herself in, and the strangeness of it made her languid, acting out a part she had seen others play, over life-size.

"Everysing I hef *mosst* be feuhrst class,'' Szabo Tibor was explaining. "Faht is your nime, please?''

"Oh,'' she said. "Slattery. Miss Slattery.''

"Zet is too match. Faht little nime else, please?''

Miss Slattery looked sad.

"I hate to tell you," she said. "I was christened Dimity. But my friends," she added, "call me Pete."

"Vitch is veuorse? Faht for a nime is zet? Pete!"

"It is better than going through life with Dimity attached."

"I vill call you nossing," Szabo Tibor announced.

Miss Slattery was walking around in someone else's room, with large, unlikely strides, but it made her feel better. The rugs were so easy, and so very white, she realized she hadn't taken her two-piece to the cleaner.

"A nime is not necessary," Szabo Tibor was saying. "Tike off your het, please; it is not necessary neither."

Miss Slattery did as she was told.

"I am not the hatty type, you know. They have us wear them for business reasons."

She shook out her hair, to which the bottle had contributed, not altogether successfully, though certain lights gave it a look of its own, she hoped: tawnier, luminous, dappled. There was the separate lock, too, which she had persuaded to hang in the way she wanted.

An Australian girl, he saw. Another Australian girl.

Oh dear, he was older perhaps than she had thought. But cuddly. By instinct she was kind. Only wanted to giggle. At some old teddy bear in suède.

Szabo Tibor said:

"Sit."

"Funny," she said, running her hands into the depths of the chair, a habit she always meant to get out of, "I have never mixed business and pleasure before."

But Szabo Tibor had brought something very small and sweet, which ran two fiery wires out of her throat and down her nose.

"It is goot. Nho?"

"I don't know about *that*" — she coughed — "Mr Szabo. Its effective, though!"

"In Australien," Mr Szabo said, and he was kneeling now, "peoples call me Tibby."

"Well! Have you a sense of humour!"

"Yehs! Yehs!" he said, and smiled. "*Witz*!"

When men started kneeling she wanted more than ever to giggle.

But Tibby Szabo was growing sterner.

"In Australien," he said, "no *Witz*. Nho! Novair!"

Shaking a forefinger at her. So that she became fascinated. It was so plump, for a finger, banana-coloured, with hackles of little black hairs.

"Do you onderstend?"

"Oh, yes, I understand all right. I am nossing."

She liked it, too.

"Then faht is it?" asked Tibby Szabo, looking at his finger.

"I am always surprised," she answered, "at the part texture plays."

"Are you intellectual girl?"

"My mind," she said re-crossing her legs, "turned to fudge at puberty. Isn't that delicious?"

"Faht is futch?"

"Oh dear," she said, "you're a whale for knowing. Aren't there the things you just accept?"

She made her lock hang, for this old number who wouldn't leave off kneeling by the chair. Not so very old, though. The little gaps between his white teeth left him looking sort of defenceless.

Then Tibby Szabo took her arm, as though it didn't belong to her. The whole thing was pretty peculiar, but not as peculiar as it should have been. He took her arm, as if it were, say, a cob of corn. As if he had been chewing on a cob of corn. She wanted to giggle, and did. Supposing Mum and Wendy had seen! They would have had a real good laugh.

"You have the funniest ways," she said, "Tib."

As Tibby Szabo kept on going up and down her arm.

When he started on the shoulder, she said:

"Stoput! What do you think I *am*?"

He heard enough to alter course.

A man's head in your lap always made you feel it was trying to fool itself — it looked so detached, improbable, and ridiculous.

He turned his eyes on then, as if knowing: here is the greatest sucker for eyes. Oh God, nothing ever went deeper than eyes. She was a goner.

"Oh God!" she said, "I am not like this!"

She was nothing like what she thought she was like. So she learned. She was the trampoline queen. She was an enormous, staggery spider. She was a rubber doll.

"You Austrahlian girls are visout *Temperament*," Tibby Szabo complained. "You are all gickle and talk. Passion is not to resist."

"I just about broke every bone in my body not resisting," Miss Slattery had to protest.

Her body that continued fluctuating overhead.

"Who ever heard of a glass ceiling!"

"Plenty glass ceiling. Zet is to see vis."

"Tibby," she asked, "this wouldn't be — mink?"

"Yehs. Yehs. Meenk beds are goot for ze body."

431

"I'll say!" she said.

She was so relaxed. She was half-dead. When it was possible to lift an arm, the long silken shudders took possession of her skin, and she realized the southerly had come, off the water, in at the window, giving her the goose-flesh.

"We're gunna catch a cold," she warned, and coughed.

"It is goot."

"I am glad to know that something is good," she said, sitting up, destroying the composition in the ceiling. "This sort of thing is all very well, but are you going to let me love you?"

Rounding on him. This fat and hairy man.

"Lof? Faht execkly do you mean?"

"Oh, Tibby!" she said.

Again he was fixing his eyes on her, extinct by now, but even in their dormancy they made her want to die. Or give. Or was it possible to give and live?

"Go to sleep," he ordered.

"Oh, Tibby!"

She fell back floppy whimpery but dozed. Once she looked sideways at his death-mask. She looked at the ceiling, too. It was not unlike those atrocity pictures she had always tried to avoid, in the papers, after the War.

It was incredible, but always had been.

By the time Miss Slattery stepped into the street, carrying her business hat, evening had drenched the good address with the mellower light of ripened pears. She trod through it, tilted, stilted, tentative. Her neck was horribly stiff.

After that there was the Providential, for she did not remain with Better Sales Pty Ltd; she was informed that her services would no longer be required. What was it, they asked, had made her so unreliable? She said she had become distracted.

In the circumstances she was fortunate to find the position with the Providential. There, too, she made friends with Phyllis Wimble.

"A Hungarian," Phyllis said, "I never met a Hungarian. Sometimes I think I will work through the nationalities like a girl I knew decided to go through the religions. But gave up at the Occultists."

"Why?"

"She simply got scared. They buried a man alive, one Saturday afternoon, over at Balmoral."

When old Huthnance came out of his office.

"Miss Slattery," he asked, "where is that Dewhurst policy?"

He was rather a sweetie really.

"Oh yes," Miss Slattery said. "I was checking."

"What is there to check?" Huthnance asked.

Ray Crooke *Sunrise, Albion Hotel, Normanton* 1962
Oil over tempera on composition board 76.5 × 121.7 cm
Queensland Art Gallery

Donald Friend *Explorers Surprising a Rare Bird* 1963
Acrylic with gold leaf on masonite 44 × 32 cm
Leslie Walford Collection

"Well," Miss Slattery said.

And Huthnance smiled. He was still at the smiling stage.

Thursday evenings Miss Slattery kept for Tibby Szabo. She would go there Saturdays too, usually staying over till Sunday, when they would breakfast in the continental style.

There was the Saturday Miss Slattery decided to give Tibby Szabo a treat. Domesticity jacked her up on her heels; she was full of secrecy and little ways.

When Tibby asked:

"Faht is zet?"

"What is what?"

"Zet stench! Zet blue *smoke* you are mecking in my kitchenette. Faht are you prepurring?"

"That is a baked dinner," Miss Slattery answered. "A leg of lamb, with pumpkin and two other veg."

"Lemb?" cried Tibby Szabo. "Lemb! It stinks. Nefer in Budapest did lemb so much as cross ze doorways."

And he opened the oven, and tossed the leg into the Harbour.

Miss Slattery cried then, or sat, rather, making her handkerchief into a ball.

Tibby Szabo prepared himself a snack. He had *Paprikawurst*, a breast of cold paprika chicken, paprikas in oil, paprika in cream cheese, and finally, she suspected, paprika.

"Eat!" he advised.

"A tiny crumb would choke me."

"You are not crying?" he asked through some remains of paprika.

"I was thinking," she replied.

"So! *Sink*-ing!"

Afterwards he made love to her, and because she had chosen love, she embraced it with a sad abandon, on the mink coverlet, under the glass sky.

Once, certainly, she sat up and said:

"It is all so *carnal*!"

"You use zeese intellectual veuords."

He had the paprika chicken in his teeth.

There was the telephone, too, with which Miss Slattery had to contend.

"Igen! *Igen*! IGEN!" Tibby Szabo would shout, and bash the receiver on somebody anonymous.

"All this *iggy* stuff!" she said.

It began to get on her nerves.

"Demn idiots!" Tibby Szabo complained.

"How do you make your money, Tib?" Miss Slattery asked, picking at the mink coverlet.

"I am Hoongahrian," he said. "It come to me over ze telephown."

Presently Szabo Tibor announced he was on his way to inspect several properties he owned around the city.

He had given her a key, at least, so that she might come and go.

"And you have had keys cut," she asked, "for all these other women, for
Monday, Tuesday, Wednesday, and Friday, in all these other flats?"

How he laughed.

"At least a real *Witz*! An Australian *Witz*!" he said on going.

It seemed no time before he returned.

"Faht," he said, "you are still here?"

"I am the passive type," she replied.

Indeed, she was so passive she had practically set in her own flesh beneath that
glass conscience of a ceiling. Although a mild evening was ready to soothe, she
shivered for her more than nakedness. When she stuck her head out the window,
there were the rhinestones of Sydney glittering on the neck of darkness. But it
was a splendour she saw could only dissolve.

"You Austrahlian girls," observed Tibby Szabo, "ven you are not all gickle,
you are all cry."

"Yes," she said. "I know," she said, "it makes things difficult. To be
Australian."

And when he popped inside her mouth a kiss like Turkish delight in action,
she was less than ever able to take herself in hand.

They drove around in Tibby's Jag. Because naturally Tibby Szabo had a Jag.

"Let us go to Manly," she said. "I have got to look at the Pacific Ocean."

Tibby drove, sometimes in short, disgusted bursts, at others in long, lovely
demonstrations of speed, or swooning swirls. His driving was so much the
expression of Tibby Szabo himself. He was wearing the little cigar-coloured hat.

"Of course," said Miss Slattery through her hair, "I know you well enough
to know that Manly is not Balaton."

"Balaton?"

Tibby jumped a pedestrian crossing.

"Faht do you know about Balaton?"

"I went to school," she said. "I saw it on the map. You had to look at
*some*thing. And there it was. A gap in the middle of Hungary."

She never tired of watching his hands. As he drove, the soft, cajoling palms
would whiten.

Afterwards when they were drawn up in comfort, inside the sounds of sea and
pines, and had bought the paper-bagful of prawns, and the prawn-coloured
people were squelching past, Tibby Szabo had to ask:

"Are you trying to spy on me viz all zese kvestions of Balaton?"

"All these questions? One bare mention!"

Prawn-shells tinkle as they hit the asphalt.

"I wouldn't open any drawer, not if I had the key. There's only one secret," she said, "I want to know the answer to."

"But Balaton!"

"So blue. Bluer than anything we've got. So everything," she said.

The sand-sprinkled people were going up and down. The soles of their feet were inured to it.

Tibby Szabo spat on the asphalt. It smoked.

"It isn't nice," she said, "to spit."

The tips of her fingers tasted of the salt-sweet prawns. The glassy rollers, uncurling on the sand, might have raked a little farther and swallowed her down, if she had not been engulfed already in deeper, glassier caverns.

"Faht is zis secret?" Tibby asked.

"Oh!"

She had to laugh.

"It is us," she said. "What does it add up to?"

"Faht it edds up to? I give you a hellofa good time. I pay ze electricity end ze gess. I put you in ze vay of cut-price frocks. You hef arranged sings pretty nice."

Suddenly too many prawn-shells were clinging to Miss Slattery's fingers.

"That is not what I mean," she choked. "When you love someone, I mean. I mean it's sort of difficult to put. When you could put your head in the gas-oven, and damn who's gunna pay the bill."

Because she did not have the words, she got out her lipstick, and began to persecute her mouth.

Ladies were looking by now into the expensive car. Their glass eyes expressed surprise.

"Lof!" Tibby Szabo laughed. "Lof is viz ze sahoul!" Then he grew very angry; he could have been throwing his hand away. "Faht do zay know of lof?" he shouted. "Here zere is only stike and bodies!"

Then they were looking into each other, each with an expression that suggested they might not arrive beyond a discovery just made.

Miss Slattery lobbed the paper-bag almost into the municipal bin.

"I am sursty," Tibby complained.

Indeed, salt formed in the corners of his mouth. Could it be that he was going to risk drinking deeper of the dregs?

"This Pacific Ocean," Miss Slattery said, or cried, "is all on the same note. Drive us home, Tibby," she said, "and make love to me."

As he released the brake, the prawn-coloured bodies on the asphalt continued to lumber up and down, regardless.

"Listen," Miss Slattery said, "a girl friend of Phyllis Wimble's called Apple is giving a party in Woolloomooloo. Saturday night, Phyllis says. It's going to be bohemian.''

Szabo Tibor drew his lower lip.

"Austrahlian-bohemian-proveenshul. Zere is nossing veuorse zan bohemian-proveenshul.''

"Try it and see," Miss Slattery advised, and bitterly added: "A lot was discovered only by mistake.''

"And faht is zis Epple?''

"She is an oxywelder.''

"A vooman? Faht does she oxyveld?''

"I dunno. Objects and things. Apple is an artist.''

Apple was a big girl in built-up hair and pixie glasses. The night of the party most of her objects had been removed, all except what she said was her major work.

"This is *Hypotenuse of Angst*," she explained. "It is considered very powerful.''
And smiled.

"Will you have claret?" Apple asked. "Or perhaps you prefer Scotch or gin. That will depend on whoever brings it along.''

Apple's party got under way. It was an old house, a large room running in many directions, walls full of Lovely Textures.

"Almost everybody here," Phyllis Wimble confided, "is doing something.''

"What have you brought, Phyl?" Miss Slattery asked.

"He is a grazier," Phyllis said, "that a nurse I know got tired of.''

"He is all body," Miss Slattery said, now that she had learnt.

"What do you expect?''

Those who had them were tuning their guitars.

"Those are the Spanish guitarists," Phyllis explained. "And these are English teddies off a liner. They are only the atmosphere. It's Apple's friends who are doing things.''

"Looks a bit," the grazier hinted.

Phyllis shushed him.

"You are hating it, Tib," Miss Slattery said.

Tibby Szabo drew down his lip.

"I vill get dronk. On Epple's plonk.''

She saw that his teeth were ever so slightly decalcified. She saw that he was a little, fat black man, whom she had loved, and loved still. From habit. Like biting your nails.

I must get out of it, she said. But you didn't, not out of biting your nails, until you forgot; then it was over.

The dancing had begun, and soon the kissing. The twangling of guitars broke the light into splinters. The slurp of claret stained the jokes. The teddies danced.

The grazier danced the Spanish dances. His elastic-sides were so authentic. Apple fell upon her bottom.

Not everyone, not yet, had discovered Tibby Szabo was a little, fat, black man, with serrated teeth like a shark's. There was a girl called Felicia who came and sat in Tibby's lap. Though he opened his knees and she shot through, it might not have bothered Miss Slattery if Felicia had stayed.

"They say," Phyllis Wimble whispered, "they are all madly queer."

"Don't you know by now," Miss Slattery said, "that everyone is always queer?"

But Phyllis Wimble could turn narky.

"Everyone, we presume, but Tibby Szabo."

Then Miss Slattery laughed and laughed.

"Tibby Szabo," she laughed, "is just about the queerest thing I've met."

"Faht is zet?" Tibby asked.

"Nossing, darling," Miss Slattery answered. "I love you with all my body, and never my soul."

It was all so *mouvementé*, said one of Apple's friends.

The grazier danced. He danced the Spanish dances. He danced bareheaded, and in his Lesbian hat. He danced in his shirt, and later, without.

"They say," whispered Phyllis Wimble, "there are two men locked in the lavatory together. One is a teddy, but they haven't worked out who the other can be."

"Perhaps he is a social-realist," Miss Slattery suggested.

She had a pain.

The brick-red grazier produced a stockwhip, too fresh from the shop, too stiff, but it smelled intoxicatingly of leather.

"Oh," Miss Slattery cried, "stockwhips are never *made*, they were there in the beginning."

As the grazier uncoiled his brand-new whip, the lash fell glisteningly. It flicked a corner of her memory, unrolling a sheet of blazing blue, carpets of dust, cattle rubbing and straining past. She could not have kept it out even if she had wanted to. The electric sun beating on her head. The smell of old, sweaty leather had made her drunker than bulk claret.

"Oh, God, I'm gunna burn up!" Miss Slattery protested.

And took off her top.

She was alarmingly smooth, unscathed. Other skins, she knew, withered in the sun. She remembered the scabs on her dad's knuckles.

She had to get up then.

"Give, George!" she commanded. "You're about the crummiest crack I ever listened to."

Miss Slattery stood with the stockwhip. Her breasts snoozed. Or contem-

437

plated. She could have been awaiting inspiration. So Tibby Szabo noticed, leaning forward to follow to its source the faintest blue, of veins explored on previous expeditions.

Then, suddenly, Miss Slattery cracked, scattering the full room. She filled it with shrieks, disgust, and admiration. The horsehair gadfly stung the air. Miss Slattery cracked an abstract painting off the wall. She cracked a cork out of a bottle.

"Brafo, Petuska!" Tibby Szabo shouted. "Vas you efer in a tseerkoos?"

He was sitting forward.

"Yeah," she said, "a Hungarian one!"

And let the horsehair curl round Tibby's thigh.

He was sitting forward. Tibby Szabo began to sing:

> "Csak egy kislány
> van a világon,
> az is az én
> drága galambo-o-om!"

He was sitting forward with eyes half-closed, clapping and singing.

> "Hooray for love,
> it rots you, . . ."

Miss Slattery sang.

She cracked a cigarette out of the grazier's lips.

> "A jó Isten
> de nagyon szeret,"

sang Tibby Szabo,

> "hogy nékem adta
> a legszebbik-e-e-et!"*

Then everybody was singing everything they had to sing, guitars disintegrating, for none could compete against the syrup from Tibby Szabo's compulsive violin.

* "Only one little girl   The good God
  in the world,   must love me indeed
  and she is   to have given me
  my dear little dove!   the most beautiful one!"

While Miss Slattery cracked. Breasts jumping and frolicking. Her hair was so brittle. Lifted it once again, though, under the tawny sun, hawking dust, drunk on the smell of the tepid canvas water-bags.

Miss Slattery cracked once more, and brought down the sun from out of the sky.

It is not unlikely that the world will end in thunder. From the sound of it, somebody must have overturned *Hypotenuse of Angst*. Professional screamers had begun to scream. The darkness filled with hands.

"Come close, Petuska."

It was Tibby Szabo.

"I vill screen you," he promised, and caressed.

When a Large Person appeared with a candle. She was like a scone.

"These studios," the Large Person announced, "are let for purposes of creative arts, and the exchange of intellectual ideas. I am not accustomed to louts — and worse," here she looked at Miss Slattery's upper half, "wrecking the premises," she said. "As there has never been any suspicion that this is a Bad House, I must ask you all to leave."

So everybody did, for there was the Large Person's husband behind her, looking as though he might mean business. Everybody shoved and poured, there was a singing, a crumbling of music on the stairs. There was a hugging and a kissing in the street. Somebody had lost his pants. It was raining finely.

Tibby Szabo drove off very quickly, in case a lift might be asked for.

"Put on your top, Petuska," he advised. "You vill ketch a colt."

It sounded reasonable. She was bundling elaborately into armholes.

"Waddayaknow!" Miss Slattery said. "We've come away with the grazier's whip!"

"Hef vee?" Tibby Szabo remarked.

So they drove in Tibby's Jag. They were on a spiral.

"I am so tired," Miss Slattery admitted.

And again:

"I am awful tired."

She was staring down at those white rugs in Tibby's flat. The soft, white, serious pile. She was propped on her elbows. Knees apart. Must be looking bloody awful.

"Petuska," he was trying it out, "vill you perhaps do vun more creck of ze whip?"

He could have been addressing a convalescent.

"Oh, but I am tired. I am done," she said.

"Just vun little vun."

Then Miss Slattery got real angry.

"You and this goddam lousy whip! I wish I'd never set eyes on either!"

439

Nor did she bother where she lashed.

"Ach! Oh! Aÿ-yaÿ-yaÿ! Petuska!"

Miss Slattery cracked.

"What are the people gunna say when they hear you holler like that?"

As she cracked, and slashed.

"Aÿ! It is none of ze people's business. *Pouff! Yaÿ-yaÿ-yaÿ-yaÿ!"* Tibby Szabo cried. "Just vun little vun more!"

And when at last she toppled, he covered her very tenderly where she lay.

"Did anyone ever want you to put on boots?"

"What ever for?" asked Phyllis Wimble.

But Miss Slattery found she had fetched the wrong file.

"Ah, dear," she said, resuming. "It's time I thought about a change," she said. "I'm feeling sort of tired."

"Hair looks dead," said Phyllis Wimble. "That is always the danger signal."

"Try a new rinse."

"A nice strawberry."

Miss Slattery, whose habit had been to keep Thursday evening for Tibby Szabo, could not bear to any more. Saturdays she still went, but at night, for the nights were less spiteful than the days.

"Vair vas you, Petuska, Sursday evening?" Tibby Szabo had begun to ask.

"I sat at home and watched the telly."

"Zen I vill install ze telly for here!"

"Ah," she said, "the telly is something that requires the maximum of concentration."

"Are you changing, Petuska?" Tibby asked.

"Everything is changing," Miss Slattery said. "It is an axiom of nature."

She laughed rather short.

"That," she said, "is something I think I learned at school. Same time as Balaton."

It was dreadful, really, for everyone concerned, for Tibby Szabo had begun to ring the Providential. With urgent communications for a friend. Would she envisage Tuesday, Vensday, Friday?

However impersonally she might handle the instrument, that old Huthnance would come in and catch her on the phone. Miss Slattery saw that Huthnance and she had almost reached the point of no return.

"No," she replied. "Not Thursday. Or any other day but what was agreed. Saturday, I said."

She slammed it down.

So Miss Slattery would drag through the moist evenings. In which the scarlet hibiscus had furled. No more trumpets. Her hair hung dank, as she trailed through the acid, yellow light, towards the good address at which her lover lived.

"I am developing a muscle," she caught herself saying, and looked round to see if anyone had heard.

It was the same night that Tibby Szabo cried out from the bottom of the pit: "Vhy em I condemned to soffer?"

Stretched on mink, Miss Slattery lay, idly flicking at her varnished toes. Without looking at the view, she knew the rhinestones of Sydney had never glittered so heartlessly.

"Faht for do you *torture* me?"

"But that is what you wanted," she said.

Flicking. Listless.

"Petuska, I vill gif you *any*sink!"

"Nossing," she said. "I am going," she said.

"*Gowing*? Ven vee are so suited to each ozzer!"

Miss Slattery flicked.

"I am sick," she said, "I am sick of cutting a rug out of your fat Hungarian behind."

The horsehair slithered and glistened between her toes.

"But faht vill you do visout me?"

"I am going to find myself a thin Australian."

Tibby was on his knees again.

"I am gunna get married," Miss Slattery said, "and have a washing-machine."

"*Yaÿ-yaÿ-yaÿ! Petuska!*"

Then Miss Slattery took a look at Tibby's eyes, and re-discovered a suppliant poodle, seen at the window of an empty house, at dusk. She had never been very doggy, though.

"Are you ze Defel perheps?" cried Tibby Szabo.

"We Australians are not all that unnatural," she said.

And hated herself, just a little.

As for Tibby Szabo, he was licking the back of her hand.

"Vee vill make a finenshul arrangement. Pretty substenshul."

"No go!" Miss Slattery said.

But that is precisely what she did. She got up and pitched the grazier's stock-whip out of the window, and when she had put on her clothes, and licked her lips once or twice, and shuffled her hair together — she went.

Five-Twenty

MOST EVENINGS, weather permitting, the Natwicks sat on the front veranda to watch the traffic. During the day the stream flowed, but towards five it began to thicken, it sometimes jammed solid like: the semi-trailers and refrigeration units, the decent old-style sedans, the mini-cars, the bombs, the Holdens and the Holdens. She didn't know most of the names. Royal did, he was a man, though never ever mechanical himself. She liked him to tell her about the vehicles, or listen to him take part in conversation with anyone who stopped at the fence. He could hold his own, on account of he was more educated, and an invalid has time to think.

They used to sit side by side on the tiled veranda, him in his wheelchair she had got him after the artheritis took over, her in the old cane. The old cane chair wasn't hardly presentable any more; she had torn her winter cardy on a nail and laddered several pair of stockings. You hadn't the heart to get rid of it, though. They brought it with them from Sarsaparilla after they sold the business. And now they could sit in comfort to watch the traffic, the big steel insects of nowadays, which put the wind up her at times.

Royal said, "I reckon we're a shingle short to'uv ended up on the Parramatta Road."

"You said we'd still see life," she reminded, "even if we lost the use of our legs."

"But look at the traffic! Worse every year. And air. Rot a man's lungs quicker than the cigarettes. You should'uv headed me off. You who's supposed to be practical!"

"I thought it was what you wanted," she said, keeping it soft; she had never been one to crow.

"Anyway, I already lost the use of me legs."

As if she was to blame for that too. She was so shocked the chair sort of jumped. It made her blood run cold to hear the metal feet screak against the little draught-board tiles.

"Well, I 'aven't!" she protested. "I got me legs, and will be able to get from 'ere to anywhere and bring 'ome the shopping. While I got me strength."

She tried never to upset him by any show of emotion, but now she was so upset herself.

They watched the traffic in the evenings, as the orange light was stacked up in thick slabs, and the neon signs were coming on.

"See that bloke down there in the parti-coloured Holden?"

"Which?" she asked.

"The one level with our own gate."

"The pink and brown?" She couldn't take all that interest tonight, only you must never stop humouring a sick man.

"Yairs. Pink. Fancy a man in a pink car!"

"Dusty pink is fashionable." She knew that for sure.

"But a man!"

"Perhaps his wife chose it. Perhaps he's got a domineering wife."

Royal laughed low. "Looks the sort of coot who might like to be domineered, and if that's what he wants, it's none of our business, is it?"

She laughed to keep him company. They were such mates, everybody said. And it was true. She didn't know what she would do if Royal passed on first.

That evening the traffic had jammed. Some of the drivers began tooting. Some of them stuck their heads out, and yarned to one another. But the man in the pink-and-brown Holden just sat. He didn't look to either side.

Come to think of it, she had noticed him pass before. Yes. Though he wasn't in no way a noticeable man. Yes. She looked at her watch.

"Five-twenty," she said. "I seen that man in the pink-and-brown before. He's pretty regular. Looks like a business executive."

Royal cleared his throat and spat. It didn't make the edge of the veranda. Better not to notice it, because he'd only create if she did. She'd get out that watering-can after she had pushed him inside.

"Business executives!" she heard. "They're afraid people are gunner think they're poor class without they *execute*. In our day nobody was ashamed to *do*. Isn't that about right, eh?" She didn't answer because she knew she wasn't meant to. "Funny sort of head that cove's got. Like it was half squashed. Silly-lookun bloody head!"

"Could have been born with it," she suggested. "Can't help what you're born with. Like your religion."

There was the evening the Chev got crushed, only a young fellow too. Ahhh, it had stuck in her throat, thinking of the wife and kiddies. She ran in, and out again as quick as she could, with a couple of blankets, and the rug that was a present from Hazel. She had grabbed a pillow off their own bed.

She only faintly heard Royal shouting from the wheel-chair.

She arranged the blankets and the pillow on the pavement, under the orange sky. The young fellow was looking pretty sick, kept on turning his head as though he recognized and wanted to tell her something. Then the photographer from the *Mirror* took his picture, said she ought to be in it to add a touch of human interest, but she wouldn't. A priest came, the *Mirror* took his picture, administering what Mrs Dolan said they call Extreme Unkshun. Well, you couldn't poke fun at a person's religion any more than the shape of their head, and Mrs Dolan was a decent neighbour, the whole family, and clean.

When she got back to the veranda, Royal, a big man, had slipped down in his wheel-chair.

He said, or gasped, "Wotcher wanter do that for, Ella? How are we gunner get the blood off?''

She hadn't thought about the blood, when of course she was all smeared with it, and the blankets, and Hazel's good Onkaparinka. Anyway, it was her who would get the blood off.

"You soak it in milk or something," she said. "I'll ask. Don't you worry."

Then she did something. She bent down and kissed Royal on the forehead in front of the whole Parramatta Road. She regretted it at once, because he looked that powerless in his invalid chair, and his forehead felt cold and sweaty.

But you can't undo things that are done.

It was a blessing they could sit on the front veranda. Royal suffered a lot by now. He had his long-standing hernia, which they couldn't have operated on, on account of he was afraid of his heart. And then the artheritis.

"Arthritis."

"All right," she accepted the correction. "Arth-er-itis."

It was all very well for men, they could manage more of the hard words.

"What have we got for tea?" he asked.

"Well," she said, fanning out her hands on the points of her elbows, and smiling, "it's a surprise."

She looked at her watch. It was five-twenty.

"It's a coupler nice little bits of fillet Mr Ballard let me have."

"Wotcher mean let you have? Didn't you pay for them?"

She had to laugh. "Anything I have I pay for!"

"Well? Think we're in the fillet-eating class?"

"It's only a treat, Royal," she said. "I got a chump chop for myself. I like a nice chop."

He stopped complaining, and she was relieved.

"There's that gentleman," she said, "in the Holden."

They watched him pass, as sober as their own habits.

Royal — he had been his mother's little king. Most of his mates called him "Roy". Perhaps only her and Mrs Natwick had stuck to the christened name, they felt it suited.

She often wondered how Royal had ever fancied her: such a big man, with glossy hair, black, and a nose like on someone historical. She would never have said it, but she was proud of Royal's nose. She was proud of the photo he had of the old family home in Kent, the thatch so lovely, and Grannie Natwick sitting in her apron on a rush-bottom chair in front, looking certainly not all that different from Mum, with the aunts gathered round in leggermutton sleeves, all big nosey women like Royal.

She had heard Mum telling Royal's mother, "Ella's a plain little thing, but what's better than cheerful and willing?" She had always been on the mousey

444

side, she supposed, which didn't mean she couldn't chatter with the right person. She heard Mum telling Mrs Natwick, "My Ella can wash and bake against any comers. Clever with her needle too." She had never entered any of the competitions, like they told her she ought to, it would have made her nervous.

It was all the stranger that Royal had ever fancied her.

Once as they sat on the veranda watching the evening traffic, she said, "Remember how you used to ride out in the old days from 'Bugilbar' to Cootramundra?"

"Cootamundra."

"Yes," she said. "Cootramundra." (That's why they'd called the house "Coota" when they moved to the Parramatta Road.)

She had been so dazzled on one occasion by his parti-coloured forehead and his black hair, after he had got down from the saddle, after he had taken off his hat, she had run and fetched a duster, and dusted Royal Natwick's boots. The pair of new elastic-sides was white with dust from the long ride. It only occurred to her as she polished she might be doing something shameful, but when she looked up, it seemed as though Royal Natwick saw nothing peculiar in Ella McWhirter dusting his boots. He might even have expected it. She was so glad she could have cried.

Old Mr Natwick had come out from Kent when a youth, and after working at several uncongenial jobs, and studying at night, had been taken on as book-keeper at "Bugilbar". He was much valued in the end by the owners, and always made use of. The father would have liked his son to follow in his footsteps, and taught him how to keep the books, but Royal wasn't going to hang around any family of purse-proud squatters, telling them the things they wanted to hear. He had ideas of his own for becoming rich and important.

So when he married Ella McWhirter, which nobody could ever understand, not even Ella herself, perhaps only Royal, who never bothered to explain (why should he?) they moved to Juggerawa, and took over the general store. It was in a bad way, and soon was in a worse, because Royal's ideas were above those of his customers.

Fulbrook was the next stage. He found employment as book-keeper on a grazing property outside. She felt so humiliated on account of his humiliation. It didn't matter about herself because she always expected less. She took a job in Fulbrook from the start, at the "Dixie Cafe" in High Street. She worked there several years as waitress, helping out with the scrubbing for the sake of the extra money. She had never hated anything, but got to hate the flies trampling in the sugar and on the necks of the tomato sauce bottles.

At weekends her husband usually came in, and when she wasn't needed in the shop, they lay on the bed in her upstairs room, listening to the corrugated iron and the warping white-washed weatherboard. She would have loved to do some-

445

thing for him, but in his distress he complained about "wet kisses". It surprised her. She had always been afraid he might find her a bit too dry in her show of affection.

Those years at the "Dixie Cafe" certainly dried her up. She got those freckly patches and seams in her skin in spite of the lotions used as directed. Not that it matters so much in anyone born plain. Perhaps her plainness helped her save. There was never a day when she didn't study her savings-book, it became her favourite recreation.

Royal, on the other hand, wasn't the type that dries up, being fleshier, and dark. He even put on weight out at the grazing property, where they soon thought the world of him. When the young ladies were short of a man for tennis the book-keeper was often invited, and to a ball once at the homestead. He was earning good money, and he too saved a bit, though his instincts weren't as mean as hers. For instance, he fancied a choice cigar. In his youth Royal was a natty dresser.

Sometimes the young ladies, if they decided to inspect the latest at Ryan's Emporium, or Mr Philup, if he felt like grogging up with the locals, would drive him in, and as he got out they would look funny at the book-keeper's wife they had heard about, they must have, serving out the plates of frizzled steak and limp chips. Royal always waited to see his employers drive off before coming in.

In spite of the savings, this might have gone on much longer than it did if old Mr Natwick hadn't died. It appeared he had been a very prudent man. He left them a nice little legacy. The evening of the news, Royal was driven in by Mr Philup and they had a few at the Imperial. Afterwards the book-keeper was dropped off, because he proposed to spend the night with his wife and catch the early train to attend his father's funeral.

They lay in the hot little room and discussed the future. She had never felt so hectic. Royal got the idea he would like to develop a grocery business in one of the posh outer suburbs of Sydney. "Interest the monied residents in some of the luxury lines. Appeal to the imagination as well as the stomach."

She was impressed, of course, but not as much as she should have been. She wasn't sure, but perhaps she was short on imagination. Certainly their prospects had made her downright feverish, but for no distinct, sufficient reason.

"And have a baby." She heard her own unnatural voice.

"Eh?"

"We could start a baby." Her voice grew word by word drier.

"There's no reason why we couldn't have a baby. Or two." He laughed. "But starting a new life isn't the time to start a baby." He dug her in the ribs. "And you the practical one!"

She agreed it would be foolish, and presently Royal fell asleep.

What could she do for him? As he lay there breathing she would have loved to stroke his nose she could see faintly in the light from the window. Again unpractical, she would have liked to kiss it. Or bite it suddenly off.

She was so disgusted with herself she got creaking off the bed and walked flat across the boards to the washstand and swallowed a couple of Aspros to put her solidly to sleep.

All their life together she had to try in some way to make amends to Royal, not only for her foolishness, but for some of the thoughts that got into her head. Because she hadn't the imagination, the thoughts couldn't have been her own. They must have been put into her.

It was easier of course in later life, after he had cracked up, what with his hernia, and heart, and the artheritis taking over. Fortunately she was given the strength to help him into the wheel-chair, and later still, to lift, or drag him up on the pillows and over, to rub the bed-sores, and stick the pan under him. But even during the years at Sarsaparilla she could make amends in many little ways, though with him still in his prime, naturally he mustn't know of them. So all her acts were mostly for her own self-gratification.

The store at Sarsaparilla, if it didn't exactly flourish, gave them a decent living. She had her problems, though. Some of the locals just couldn't accept that Royal was a superior man. Perhaps she had been partly to blame, she hardly dared admit it, for showing one or two "friends" the photo of the family home in Kent. She couldn't resist telling the story of one of the aunts, Miss Ethel Natwick, who followed her brother to New South Wales. Ethel was persuaded to accept a situation at Government House, but didn't like it and went back, in spite of the Governor's lady insisting she valued Ethel as a close personal friend. When people began to laugh at Royal on account of his auntie and the family home, as you couldn't help finding out in a place like Sarsaparilla, it was her, she knew, it was her to blame. It hurt her deeply.

Of course Royal could be difficult. Said stockbrokers had no palate and less imagination. Royal said no Australian grocer could make a go of it if it wasn't for flour, granulated sugar, and tomato sauce. Some of the customers turned nasty in retaliation. This was where she could help, and did, because Royal was out on delivery more often than not. It embarrassed her only when some of them took it for granted she was on their side. As if he wasn't her husband. Once or twice she had gone out crying afterwards, amongst the wormy wattles and hens' droppings. Anyone across the gully could have heard her blowing her nose behind the store, but she didn't care. Poor Royal.

There was that Mr Ogburn said, "A selfish, swollen-headed slob who'll chew you up and swallow you down." She wouldn't let herself hear any more of what he had to say. Mr Ogburn had a hare-lip, badly sewn, opening and closing. There was nothing frightened her so much as even a well-disguised hare-lip. She got the palpitations after the scene with Mr Ogburn.

Not that there was anything wrong with her.

She only hadn't had the baby. It was her secret grief on black evenings as she walked slowly looking for the eggs a flighty hen might have hid in the bracken.

Dr Bamforth said, looking at the nib of his fountain pen, "You know, don't you, it's sometimes the man?"

She didn't even want to hear, let alone think about it. In any case she wouldn't tell Royal, because a man's pride could be so easily hurt.

After they had sold out at Sarsaparilla and come to live at what they called "Coota" on the Parramatta Road, it was both easier and more difficult, because if they were not exactly elderly they were getting on. Royal used to potter about in the beginning, while taking care, on account of the hernia and his heart. There was the business of the lawn-mowing, not that you could call it lawn, but it was what she had. She loved her garden. In front certainly there was only the two square of rather sooty grass which she would keep in order with the push-mower. The lawn seemed to get on Royal's nerves until the artheritis took hold of him. He had never liked mowing. He would lean against the veranda post, and shout, "Don't know why we don't do what they've done down the street. Root the stuff out. Put down a green concrete lawn."

"That would be copying," she answered back.

She hoped it didn't sound stubborn. As she pushed the mower she bent her head, and smiled, waiting for him to cool off. The scent of grass and a few clippings flew up through the traffic fumes reminding you of summer.

While Royal shuffled along the veranda and leaned against another post. "Or pebbles. You can buy clean, river pebbles. A few plastic shrubs, and there's the answer."

He only gave up when his trouble forced him into the chair. You couldn't drive yourself up and down a veranda shouting at someone from a wheel-chair without the passers-by thinking you was a nut. So he quietened.

He watched her, though. From under the peak of his cap. Because she felt he might still resent her mowing the lawn, she would try to reassure him as she pushed. "What's wrong, *eh*? While I still have me health, me *strength* — I was always what they call *wiry* — why shouldn't I cut the *grass*?"

She would come and sit beside him, to keep him company in watching the traffic, and invent games to amuse her invalid husband.

"Isn't that the feller we expect?" she might ask. "The one that passes at five-twenty," looking at her watch, "in the old pink-and-brown Holden?"

They enjoyed their snort of amusement all the better because no one else knew the reason for it.

Once when the traffic was particularly dense, and that sort of chemical smell from one of the factories was thickening in the evening air, Royal drew her attention. "Looks like he's got something on his mind."

Could have too. Or it might have been the traffic block. The way he held his hands curved listlessly around the inactive wheel reminded her of possums and monkeys she had seen in cages. She shifted a bit. Her squeaky old chair. She felt uneasy for ever having found the man, not a joke, but half of one.

Royal's chair moved so smoothly on its rubber-tyred wheels it was easy to push him, specially after her practice with the mower. There were ramps where necessary now, to cover steps, and she would sometimes wheel him out to the back, where she grew hollyhock and sunflower against the palings, and a vegetable or two on raised beds.

Royal would sit not looking at the garden from under the peak of his cap.

She never attempted to take him down the shady side, between them and Dolans, because the path was narrow from plants spilling over, and the shade might have lowered his spirits.

She loved her garden.

The shady side was where she kept her staghorn ferns, and fishbones, and the pots of maidenhair. The water lay sparkling on the maidenhair even in the middle of the day. In the blaze of summer the light at either end of the tunnel was like you were looking through a sheet of yellow cellophane, but as the days shortened, the light deepened to a cold, tingling green, which might have made a person nervous who didn't know the tunnel by heart.

Take Mrs Dolan the evening she came in to ask for the loan of a cupful of sugar. "You gave me a shock, Mrs Natwick. What ever are you up to?"

"Looking at the plants," Mrs Natwick answered, whether Mrs Dolan would think it peculiar or not.

It was the season of cinerarias, which she always planted on that side, it was sheltered and cold-green. The wind couldn't bash the big spires and umbrellas of blue and purple. Visiting cats were the only danger, messing and pouncing. She disliked cats for the smell they left, but didn't have the heart to disturb their elastic forms curled at the cineraria roots, exposing their colourless pads, and sometimes pink, swollen teats. Blushing only slightly for it, she would stand and examine the details of the sleeping cats.

If Royal called she could hear his voice through the window. "Where'uv you got to, Ella?"

After he was forced to take to his bed, his voice began to sort of dry up like his body. There were times when it sounded less like a voice than a breath of drowsiness or pain.

"Ella?" he was calling. "I dropped the paper. Where are yer all this time? You know I can't pick up the paper."

She knew. Guilt sent her scuttling to him, deliberately composing her eyes and mouth so as to arrive looking cheerful.

"I was in the garden," she confessed, "looking at the cinerarias."

"The what?" It was a name Royal could never learn.

The room was smelling of sickness and the bottles standing on odd plates.

"It fell," he complained.

She picked up the paper as quick as she could.

"Want to go la-la first?" she asked, because by now he depended on her to raise him and stick the pan under.

But she couldn't distract him from her shortcomings; he was shaking the paper at her. "Haven't you lived with me long enough to know how to treat a newspaper?"

He hit it with his set hand, and certainly the paper looked a mess, like an old white battered brolly.

"Mucked up! You gotter keep the pages *aligned*. A paper's not readable otherwise. Of course you wouldn't understand because you don't read it, without it's to see who's died." He began to cough.

"Like me to bring you some Bovril?" she asked him as tenderly as she knew.

"Bovril's the morning," he coughed.

She knew that, but wanted to do something for him.

After she had rearranged the paper she walked out so carefully it made her go lopsided, out to the front veranda. Nothing would halt the traffic, not sickness, not death even.

She sat with her arms folded, realizing at last how they were aching.

"He hasn't been," she had to call after looking at her watch.

"Who?" she heard the voice rustling back.

"The gentleman in the pink Holden."

She listened to the silence, wondering whether she had done right.

When Royal called back, "Could'uv had a blow-out." Then he laughed. "Could'uv stopped to get grogged up." She heard the frail rustling of the paper. "Or taken an axe to somebody like they do nowadays."

She closed her eyes, whether for Royal, or what she remembered of the man sitting in the Holden.

Although it was cold she continued watching after dark. Might have caught a chill, when she couldn't afford to. She only went inside to make the bread-and-milk Royal fancied of an evening.

She watched most attentively, always at the time, but he didn't pass, and didn't pass.

"Who?"

"The gentleman in the Holden."

"Gone on holiday." Royal sighed, and she knew it was the point where a normal person would have turned over, so she went to turn him.

One morning she said on going in, "Fancy, I had a dream, it was about that man! He was standing on the side path alongside the cinerarias. I know it was him because of his funny-shaped head."

"What happened in the dream?" Royal hadn't opened his eyes yet; she hadn't helped him in with his teeth.

"I dunno," she said, "it was just a dream."

That wasn't strictly truthful, because the Holden gentleman had looked at her, she had seen his eyes. Nothing was spoken, though.

"It was a sort of red and purple dream. That was the cinerarias," she said.

"I don't dream. You don't when you don't sleep. Pills aren't sleep."

She was horrified at her reverberating dream. "Would you like a nice soft-boiled egg?"

"Eggs all have a taste."

"But you gotter eat *something*!"

On another morning she told him — she could have bitten off her tongue — she *was* stupid, *stupid*, "I had a dream."

"What sort of dream?"

"Oh," she said, "a silly one. Not worth telling. I dreamed I dropped an egg on the side path, and it turned into two. Not two. A double-yolker."

She never realized Royal was so much like Mrs Natwick. It was as she raised him on his pillows. Or he had got like that in his sickness. Old men and old women were not unlike.

"Wasn't that a silly one?" she coaxed.

Every evening she sat on the front veranda and watched the traffic as though Royal had been beside her. Looked at her watch. And turned her face away from the steady-flowing stream. The way she bunched her small chest she could have had a sour breath mounting in her throat. Sometimes she had, it was nervousness.

When she went inside she announced, "He didn't pass."

Royal said — he had taken to speaking from behind his eyelids. "Something muster happened to 'im. He didn't go on holiday. He went and died."

"Oh, no! He wasn't of an age!"

At once she saw how stupid she was, and went out to get the bread-and-milk.

She would sit at the bedside, almost crouching against the edge of the mattress, because she wanted Royal to feel she was close, and he seemed to realize, though he mostly kept his eyelids down.

Then one evening she came running, she felt silly, her calves felt silly, her voice, "He's come! At five-twenty! In a new cream Holden!"

Royal said without opening his eyes, "See? I said 'e'd gone on holiday."

More than ever she saw the look of Mrs Natwick.

Now every evening Royal asked, "Has he been, Ella?"

451

Trying not to make it sound irritable or superior, she would answer, "Not yet. It's only five."

Every evening she sat watching, and sometimes would turn proud, arching her back, as she looked down from the veranda. The man was so small and ordinary.

She went in on one occasion, into the more than electric light, lowering her eyelids against the dazzle. "You know, Royal, you could feel prouder of men when they rode horses. As they looked down at yer from under the brim of their hats. Remember that hat you used to wear? Riding in to Cootramundra?"

Royal died quietly that same year before the cinerarias had folded, while the cold westerlies were still blowing; the back page of the *Herald* was full of those who had been carried off. She was left with his hand, already set, in her own. They hadn't spoken, except about whether she had put out the garbage.

Everybody was very kind. She wouldn't have liked to admit it was enjoyable being a widow. She sat around for longer than she had ever sat, and let the dust gather. In the beginning acquaintances and neighbours brought her little presents of food: a billy-can of giblet soup, moulded veal with hard-boiled egg making a pattern in the jelly, cakes so dainty you couldn't taste them. But when she was no longer a novelty they left off coming. She didn't care any more than she cared about the dust. Sometimes she would catch sight of her face in the glass, and was surprised to see herself looking so calm and white.

Of course she was calm. The feeling part of her had been removed. What remained was a slack, discarded eiderdown. Must have been the pills Doctor gave.

Well-meaning people would call to her over the front fence, "Don't you feel lonely, Mrs Natwick?" They spoke with a restrained horror, as though she had been suffering from an incurable disease.

But she called back proud and slow, "I'm under sedation."

"Arrr!" They nodded thoughtfully. "What's 'e given yer?"

She shook her head. "Pills," she called back. "They say they're the ones the actress died of."

The people walked on, impressed.

As the evenings grew longer and heavier she sat later on the front veranda watching the traffic of the Parramatta Road, its flow becoming syrupy and almost benign: big bulbous sedate buses, chrysalis cars still without a life of their own, clinging in line to the back of their host-articulator, trucks loaded for distances, empty loose-sounding jolly lorries. Sometimes women, looking out from the cabins of trucks from beside their men, shared her lack of curiosity. The light was so fluid nobody lasted long enough. You would never have thought boys could kick a person to death, seeing their long soft hair floating behind their sports models.

Every evening she watched the cream Holden pass. And looked at her watch.

It was like Royal was sitting beside her. Once she heard herself, "Thought he was gunner look round tonight, in our direction." How could a person feel lonely?

She was, though. She came face to face with it walking through the wreckage of her garden in the long slow steamy late summer. The Holden didn't pass of course of a Saturday or Sunday. Something, something had tricked her, not the pills, before the pills. She couldn't blame anybody, probably only herself. Everything depended on yourself. Take the garden. It was a shambles. She would have liked to protest, but began to cough from running her head against some powdery mildew. She could only blunder at first, like a cow, or runty starved heifer, on breaking into a garden. She had lost her old wiriness. She shambled, snapping dead stems, uprooting. Along the bleached palings there was a fretwork of hollyhock, the brown fur of rotting sunflower. She rushed at a praying mantis, a big pale one, and deliberately broke its back, and was sorry afterwards for what was done so easy and thoughtless.

As she stood panting in her black, finally yawning, she saw all she had to repair. The thought of the seasons piling up ahead made her feel tired but necessary, and she went in to bathe her face. Royal's denture in a tumbler on top of the medicine cabinet, she ought to move, or give to the Sallies. In the meantime she changed the water. She never forgot it. The teeth looked amazingly alive.

All that autumn, winter, she was continually amazed, at the dust she had let gather in the house, at old photographs, books, clothes. There was a feather she couldn't remember wearing, a scarlet feather, she *can't* have worn, and gloves with little fussy ruffles at the wrists, silver piping, like a snail had laid its trail round the edges. There was, she knew, funny things she had bought at times, and never worn, but she couldn't remember the gloves or the feather. And books. She had collected a few, though never a reader herself. Old people liked to give old books, and you took them so as not to hurt anybody's feelings. *Hubert's Crusade*, for instance. Lovely golden curls. Could have been Royal's father's book. Everybody was a child once. And almost everybody had one. At least if she had had a child she would have known it wasn't a white turnip, more of a praying mantis, which snaps too easy.

In the same box she had put away a coloured picture, *Cities of the Plain*, she couldn't remember seeing it before. The people escaping from the burning cities had committed some sin or other nobody ever thought, let alone talked, about. As they hurried between rocks, through what must have been the "desert places", their faces looked long and wooden. All they had recently experienced could have shocked the expression out of them. She was fascinated by what made her shiver. And the couples with their arms still around one another. Well, if you were damned, better hang on to your sin. She didn't blame them.

She put the box away. Its inlay as well as its content made it something secret and precious.

The autumn was still and golden, the winter vicious only in fits. It was what you could call a good winter. The cold floods of air and more concentrated streams of dark-green light poured along the shady side of the house where her cinerarias had massed. She had never seen such cinerarias: some of the spired ones reached almost as high as her chin, the solid heads of others waited in the tunnel of dark light to club you with their colours, of purple and drenching blue, and what they called "wine". She couldn't believe wine would have made her drunker.

Just as she would sit every evening watching the traffic, evening was the time she liked best to visit the cinerarias, when the icy cold seemed to make the flowers burn their deepest, purest. So it was again evening when her two objects converged: for some blissfully confident reason she hadn't bothered to ask herself whether she had seen the car pass, till here was this figure coming towards her along the tunnel. She knew at once who it was, although she had never seen him on his feet; she had never seen him full-face, but knew from the funny shape of his head as Royal had been the first to notice. He was not at all an impressive man, not much taller than herself, but broad. His footsteps on the brickwork sounded purposeful.

"Will you let me use your phone, please, madam?" he asked in a prepared voice. "I'm having trouble with the Holden."

This was the situation she had always been expecting: somebody asking to use the phone as a way to afterwards murdering you. Now that it might be about to happen she couldn't care.

She said yes. She thought her voice sounded muzzy. Perhaps he would think she was drunk.

She went on looking at him, at his eyes. His nose, like the shape of his head, wasn't up to much, but his eyes, his eyes, she dared to think, were filled with kindness.

"Cold, eh? but clean cold!" He laughed friendly, shuffling on the brick paving because she was keeping him waiting.

Only then she noticed his mouth. He had a hare-lip, there was no mistaking, although it was well sewn. She felt so calm in the circumstances. She would have even liked to touch it.

But said, "Why, yes — the telephone," she said, "it's this way," she said, "it's just off the kitchen — because that's where you spend most of your life. Or in bed," she ended.

She wished she hadn't added that. For the first time since they had been together she felt upset, thinking he might suspect her of wrong intentions.

But he laughed and said, "That's correct! You got something there!" It sounded manly rather than educated.

She realized he was still waiting, and took him to the telephone.

While he was phoning she didn't listen. She never listened when other people were talking on the phone. The sight of her own kitchen surprised her. While his familiar voice went on. It was the voice she had held conversations with.

But he was ugly, real ugly, *deformed*. If it wasn't for the voice, the eyes. She couldn't remember the eyes, but seemed to know about them.

Then she heard him laying the coins beside the phone, extra loud, to show.

He came back into the kitchen smiling and looking. She could smell him now, and he had the smell of a clean man.

She became embarrassed at herself, and took him quickly out.

"Fair bit of garden you got." He stood with his calves curved through his trousers. A cockly little chap, but nice.

"Oh," she said, "this," she said, angrily almost, "is nothing. You oughter see it. There's sunflower and hollyhock all along the palings. I'm famous for me hollyhocks!" She had never boasted in her life. "But not now — it isn't the season. And I let it go. Mr Natwick passed on. You should'uv seen the cassia this autumn. Now it's only sticks, of course. And hibiscus. There's cream, gold, cerise, scarlet — double and single."

She was dressing in them for him, revolving on high heels and changing frilly skirts.

He said, "Gardening's not in my line," turning his head to hide something, perhaps he was ashamed of his hare-lip.

"No," she agreed. "Not everybody's a gardener."

"But like a garden."

"My husband didn't even like it. He didn't have to tell me," she added.

As they moved across the wintry grass, past the empty clothes-line, the man looked at his watch, and said, "I was reckoning on visiting somebody in hospital tonight. Looks like I shan't make it if the N.R.M.A. takes as long as usual."

"Do they?" she said, clearing her throat. "It isn't somebody close, I hope? The sick person?"

Yes he said they was close.

"Nothing serious?" she almost bellowed.

He said it was serious.

Oh she nearly burst out laughing at the bandaged figure they were sitting beside, particularly at the bandaged face. She would have laughed at a brain tumour.

"I'm sorry," she said. "I understand. Mr Natwick was for many years an invalid."

Those teeth in the tumbler on top of the medicine cabinet. Looking at her. Teeth can look, worse than eyes. But she couldn't help it, she meant everything

455

she said, and thought.

At this moment they were pressing inside the dark-green tunnel, her sleeve rubbing his, as the crimson-to-purple light was dying.

"These are the cinerarias," she said.

"The what?" He didn't know, any more than Royal.

As she was about to explain she got switched to another language. Her throat became a long palpitating funnel through which the words she expected to use were poured out in a stream of almost formless agonized sound.

"What is it?" he asked, touching her.

If it had happened to herself she would have felt frightened, it occurred to her, but he didn't seem to be.

"What is it?" he kept repeating in his familiar voice, touching, even holding her.

And for answer, in the new language, she was holding him. They were holding each other, his hard body against her eiderdowny one. As the silence closed round them again, inside the tunnel of light, his face, to which she was very close, seemed to be unlocking, the wound of his mouth, which should have been more horrible, struggling to open. She could see he had recognized her.

She kissed above his mouth. She kissed as though she might never succeed in healing all the wounds they had ever suffered.

How long they stood together she wasn't interested in knowing. Outside them the river of traffic continued to flow between its brick and concrete banks. Even if it overflowed it couldn't have drowned them.

When the man said in his gentlest voice, "Better go out in front. The N.R.M.A. might have come."

"Yes," she agreed. "The N.R.M.A."

So they shuffled, still holding each other, along the narrow path. She imagined how long and wooden their faces must look. She wouldn't look at him now, though, just as she wouldn't look back at the still faintly smouldering joys they had experienced together in the past.

When they came out, apart, and into the night, there was the N.R.M.A., his pointed ruby of a light burning on top of the cabin.

"When will you come?" she asked.

"Tomorrow."

"Tomorrow. You'll stay to tea."

He couldn't stay.

"I'll make you a *pot* of tea?"

But he didn't drink it.

"Coffee, then?"

He said, "I like a nice cup of coffee."

Going down the path he didn't look back, or opening the gate. She would not let herself think of reasons or possibilities, she would not think, but stood planted in the path, swayed slightly by the motion of the night.

Mrs Dolan said, "You bring the saucepan to the boil. You got that?"

"Yeeehs." Mrs Natwick had never been a dab at coffee.

"Then you throw in some cold water. That's what sends the gravel to the bottom." This morning Mrs Dolan had to laugh at her own jokes.

"That's the part that frightens me," Mrs Natwick admitted.

"Well, you just do it, and see," said Mrs Dolan; she was too busy.

After she had bought the coffee Mrs Natwick stayed in the city to muck around. If she had stayed at home her nerves might have wound themselves tighter, waiting for evening to come. Though mucking around only irritated in the end. She had never been an idle woman. So she stopped at the cosmetics as though she didn't have to decide, this was her purpose, and said to the young lady lounging behind one of the counters, "I'm thinking of investing in a lipstick, dear. Can you please advise me?"

As a concession to the girl she tried to make it a laughing matter, but the young person was bored, she didn't bat a silver eyelid. "Elderly ladies," she said, "go for the brighter stuff."

Mrs Natwick ("my little Ella") had never felt so meek. Mum must be turning in her grave.

"This is a favourite." With a flick of her long fingers the girl exposed the weapon. It looked too slippery-pointed, crimson-purple, out of its golden sheath.

Mrs Natwick's knees were shaking. "Isn't it a bit noticeable?" she asked, again trying to make it a joke.

But the white-haired girl gave a serious laugh. "What's wrong with noticeable?"

As Mrs Natwick tried it out on the back of her hand the way she had seen others do, the girl was jogging from foot to foot behind the counter. She was humming between her teeth, behind her white-smeared lips, probably thinking about a lover. Mrs Natwick blushed. What if she couldn't learn to get the tip of her lipstick back inside its sheath?

She might have gone quickly away without another word if the young lady hadn't been so professional and bored. Still humming, she brought out a little pack of rouge.

"Never saw myself with mauve cheeks!" It was at least dry, and easy to handle.

"It's what they wear."

Mrs Natwick didn't dare refuse. She watched the long fingers with their silver nails doing up the parcel. The fingers looked as though they might resent touching anything but cosmetics; a lover was probably beneath contempt.

The girl gave her the change, and she went away without counting it.

*　　*　　*

She wasn't quiet, though, not a bit, booming and clanging in front of the toilet mirror. She tried to make a thin line, but her mouth exploded into a purple flower. She dabbed the dry-feeling pad on either cheek, and thick, mauve-scented shadows fell. She could hear and feel her heart behaving like a squeezed, rubber ball as she stood looking. Then she got at the lipstick again, still unsheathed. Her mouth was becoming enormous, so thick with grease she could hardly close her own lips underneath. A visible dew was gathering round the purple shadows on her cheeks.

She began to retch like, but dry, and rub, over the basin, scrubbing with the nailbrush. More than likely some would stay behind in the pores and be seen. Though you didn't have to see, to see.

There were Royal's teeth in the tumbler on top of the medicine cabinet. Ought to hide the teeth. What if somebody wanted to use the toilet? She must move the teeth. But didn't. In the present circumstances she couldn't have raised her arms that high.

Around five she made the coffee, throwing in the cold water at the end with a gesture copied from Mrs Dolan. If the gravel hadn't sunk to the bottom he wouldn't notice the first time, provided the coffee was hot. She could warm up the made coffee in a jiffy.

As she sat on the veranda waiting, the cane chair shifted and squealed under her. If it hadn't been for her weight it might have run away across the tiles, like one of those old planchette boards, writing the answers to questions.

There was an accident this evening down at the intersection. A head-on collision. Bodies were carried out of the crumpled cars, and she remembered a past occasion when she had run with blankets, and Hazel's Onkaparinka, and a pillow from their own bed. She had been so grateful to the victim. She could not give him enough, or receive enough of the warm blood. She had come back, she remembered, sprinkled.

This evening she had to save herself up. Kept on looking at her watch. The old cane chair squealing, ready to write the answers if she let it. Was he hurt? Was he killed, then? Was he — what?

Mrs Dolan it was, sticking her head over the palings. "Don't like the accidents, Mrs Natwick. It's the blood. The blood turns me up."

Mrs Natwick averted her face. Though unmoved by present blood. If only the squealing chair would stop trying to buck her off.

"Did your friend enjoy the coffee?" Mrs Dolan shouted; nothing nasty in her: Mrs Dolan was sincere.

"Hasn't been yet," Mrs Natwick mumbled from glancing at her watch. "Got held up."

"It's the traffic. The traffic at this time of evenun."

"Always on the dot before."

"Working back. Or made a mistake over the day."

Could you make a mistake? Mrs Natwick contemplated. Tomorrow had always meant tomorrow.

"Or he could'uv," Mrs Dolan shouted, but didn't say it. "I better go inside," she said instead. "They'll be wonderun where I am."

Down at the intersection the bodies were lying wrapped in someone else's blankets, looking like the grey parcels of mice cats sometimes vomit up.

It was long past five-twenty, not all that long really, but drawing in. The sky was heaped with cold fire. Her city was burning.

She got up finally, and the chair escaped with a last squeal, writing its answer on the tiles.

No, it wasn't lust, not if the Royal God Almighty with bared teeth should strike her down. Or yes, though, it was. She was lusting after the expression of eyes she could hardly remember for seeing so briefly.

In the effort to see, she drove her memory wildly, while her body stumbled around and around the paths of the burning city there was now no point in escaping. You would shrivel up in time along with the polyanthers and out-of-season hibiscus. All the randy mouths would be stopped sooner or later with black.

The cinerarias seemed to have grown so luxuriant she had to force her way past them, down the narrow brick path. When she heard the latch click, and saw him coming towards her.

"Why," she screamed laughing though it sounded angry, she *was*, "I'd given you up, you know! It's long after five-twenty!"

As she pushed fiercely towards him, past the cinerarias, snapping one or two of those which were most heavily loaded, she realized he couldn't have known that she set her watch, her life, by his constant behaviour. He wouldn't have dawdled so.

"What is it?" she called at last, in exasperation at the distance which continued separating them.

He was far too slow, treading the slippery moss of her too shaded path. While she floundered on. She couldn't reach the expression of his eyes.

He said, and she could hardly recognize the faded voice, "There's something — I been feeling off colour most of the day." His mis-shapen head was certainly lolling as he advanced.

"Tell me!" She heard her voice commanding, like that of a man, or a mother, when she had practised to be a lover; she could still smell the smell of rouge. "Won't you tell me — *dearest*?" It was thin and unconvincing now. (As a girl she had once got a letter from her cousin Kath Salter, who she hardly knew: *Dearest Ella . . .*)

Oh dear. She had reached him. And was given all strength — that of the lover she had aimed at being.

Straddling the path, unequally matched — he couldn't compete against her strength — she spoke with an acquired, a deafening softness, as the inclining cinerarias snapped.

"You will tell me what is wrong — dear, dear." She breathed with trumpets.

He hung his head. "It's all right. It's the pain — here — in my arm — no, the shoulder."

"Ohhhhh!" She ground her face into his shoulder forgetting it wasn't *her* pain.

Then she remembered, and looked into his eyes and said, "We'll save you. You'll see."

It was she who needed saving. She knew she was trying to enter by his eyes. To drown in them rather than be left.

Because, in spite of her will to hold him, he was slipping from her, down amongst the cinerarias, which were snapping off one by one around them.

A cat shot out. At one time she had been so poor in spirit she had wished she was a cat.

"It's all right," either voice was saying.

Lying amongst the smashed plants, he was smiling at her dreadfully, not his mouth, she no longer bothered about that lip, but with his eyes.

"More air!" she cried. "What you need is air!" hacking at one or two cinerarias which remained erect.

Their sap was stifling, their bristling columns callous.

"Oh! Oh!" she panted. "Oh God! Dear love!" comforting with hands and hair and words.

Words.

While all he could say was, "It's all right."

Or not that at last. He folded his lips into a white seam. His eyes were swimming out of reach.

"Eh? Dear — dearest — darl — darlig — darling love — *love* — LOVE?" All the new words still stiff in her mouth, that she had heard so far only from the mouths of actors.

The words were too strong she could see. She was losing him. The traffic was hanging together only by charred silences.

She flung herself and covered his body, trying to force kisses — no, breath, into his mouth, she had heard about it.

She had seen turkeys, feathers sawing against each other's feathers, rising afterwards like new noisy silk.

She knelt up, and the wing-tips of her hair still dabbled limply in his cheeks. "Eh? Ohh luff!" She could hardly breathe it.

She hadn't had time to ask his name, before she must have killed him by loving too deep, and too adulterously.

James
McAuley

Terra Australis

Voyage within you, on the fabled ocean,
And you will find that Southern Continent,
Quiros' vision — his hidalgo heart
And mythical Australia, where reside
All things in their imagined counterpart.

It is your land of similes: the wattle
Scatters its pollen on the doubting heart;
The flowers are wide-awake; the air gives ease.
There you come home; the magpies call you Jack
And whistle like larrikins at you from the trees.

There too the angophora preaches on the hillsides
With the gestures of Moses; and the white cockatoo,
Perched on his limbs, screams with demoniac pain;
And who shall say on what errand the insolent emu
Walks between morning and night on the edge of the plain?

But northward in valleys of the fiery Goat
Where the sun like a centaur vertically shoots
His raging arrows with unerring aim,
Stand the ecstatic solitary pyres
Of unknown lovers, featureless with flame.

Mating Swans

A pair of black swans on the lake
Twine their necks in amorous play.
The cob turns in a swirling wake,
Treading the maze of love's delay
Till she receives him, sinking low;
Then both their urgent necks lift high
United in a strident cry
Forced from love's exultant throe.
Parting as excitement ebbs,
They fuss their plumes with busy nebs,
Shake them smooth, and gently glide
On the water side by side.

They crease the angle of their wake
Along a liquid depth of sky;
White clouds inverted in the lake
Quiver as they paddle by
Towards a reed-fringed island, where
Green willows arch their springing shoots
And a frog croaks beneath the roots,
And shags hold synod, beaks in air.
Soon the swan will heap her nest,
Drawing reeds against her breast,
Whilst the watchful cob near by
Forbids the world with bright red eye.

Merry-Go-Round

Bright-coloured, mirror-plated, strung with lights,
With swan-shaped cars and prancing wooden horses,
The silent waiting merry-go-round invites
A swarm of eager riders for its courses.

It moves: a painted miniature cosmos, turning
With planetary music blaring loud.
The riders lean intent, lips parted, faces burning;
Brief smiles float out towards the watching crowd.

On their brass poles the horses rise and fall
In undulant flight; the children ride through dreams.
How faery-bright to them, how magical,
The crude and gaudy mechanism seems!

Almost I see the marvel that they see,
And hear like them the music of the spheres;
They smile out of the enchanted whirl to me.
The lights and colours suddenly dim with tears.

But now their turning world is slowing, slowing;
Horses and music stop: how brief the ride!
New-comers clamber on as these are going
Reluctantly to join the crowd outside.

To the Holy Spirit

Leaving your fragrant rest on the summit of morning calm,
Descend, Bird of Paradise, from the high mountain;
And, plumed with glowing iris along each curving wire,
Visit in time our regions of eucalypt and palm.

Dance, prophetic bird, in rippling spectrums of fire,
Ray forth your incandescent ritual like a fountain;
Let your drab earthly mate that watches in morning calm
Unseen, be filled with the nuptial splendours of your desire.

Engender upon our souls your sacred rhythm: inspire
The trembling breath of the flute, the exultant cosmic psalm,
The dance that breaks into flower beneath the storm-voiced mountain;
Array in your dazzling intricate plumage the swaying choir.

Secret Song

None but your ear could trace
My spirit's inmost tone;
Meanings that words efface
Were caught by you alone.

None but your thought could find
In that dark destined lot
To which I was confined
The password I forgot.

None but your voice could touch
So gently on my pain
As not to rouse too much
What might not rest again.

Pietà

A year ago you came
Early into the light.
You lived a day and night,
Then died; no-one to blame.

Once only, with one hand,
Your mother in farewell
Touched you. I cannot tell,
I cannot understand

A thing so dark and deep,
So physical a loss:
One touch, and that was all

She had of you to keep.
Clean wounds, but terrible,
Are those made with the Cross.

St John's Park, New Town

Often I walk alone
Where bronze-green oaks embower
John Lee Archer's tower
Of solid Georgian stone.

Tradition is held there,
Such as a land can own
That hasn't much of one.
I care — but do I care?

Not if it means to turn
Regretful from the raw
Instant and its vow.

The past is not my law:
Queer, comical, or stern,
Our privilege is now.

Holiday

Sunlight runs like fluid gold in the veins,
A soft hilarity upon hair and skin.
    A bird's momentary shadow stains
        The stone paths we walk in.

It is good not to do what we should do,
But something good we needn't do — like spin
    Straw into gold, or living into
        Surprises, as this thin

Voltage of pale sunshine may incite.
For loving is a game where both can win,
    And freedom to do nothing right
        Is the flower of discipline.

The Convict and the Lady

An incident in St George's Church, Battery Point

Voluntaries of Clarke and Boyce
    Flow temperately sweet
With Gamba, Flute, and Clarabel,
And pedal Bourdon trampled well
    By shapely kid-skinned feet.

An apparition from the tower
    Suspends the diapason. —
Will she scream? No, courage wins,
And in that empty church begins
    An interesting liaison.

"Lady, I am a fugitive
    That's taken refuge here.
Up into the tower I crept,
Two days and nights I've waked and slept,
    But hunger masters fear.

"Now fetch me food, or fetch the law,
    For I am at your mercy.
Though forfeited in youthful spleen,
My birth and station were not mean,
    My name is Eustace Percy."

So every day she brings her lunch,
    And practises the organ.
She finds him breeches, coat and vest,
And takes word to The Sailor's Rest,
    To a man named Harry Morgan.

One Sunday, as the lady plays
    "Recessional in A",
A stranger joins the genteel throng
That files out after Evensong;
    Unmarked, he slips away.

In darkness a small boat rows out
    Into the estuary.
The brig looms up upon the tide,
A shadow clambers up the side —
    And Eustace Percy's free!

So ends the tale? No, three years passed;
    From Hull a letter came:
"I thrive in my new way of life . . . ."
The lady sailed to be his wife,
    And shared a borrowed name.

Organist, for that lady's sake,
    Select your stops and play
This postlude that I chose expressly,
By Samuel Sebastian Wesley,
    "Recessional in A".

Wistaria

Does that wistaria vine still break in flower
Like grape-clusters transformed to lilac light
For bees to hover in? It had a power,
Then, to absorb all feelings into sight.

And the mute aching sweetness of its scent
Stored up the quotient of long afternoons
Where time stretched forward, empty of event,
Drifting with bells, pagodas, pale balloons —

Shapes that changed back to flowers at a touch.
The soul must feed on something for its dreams,
In those brick suburbs, and there wasn't much:
It can make do with little, so it seems.

Its formal home had crossed flags at the back
And reverent doubt up front. In equipoise
Between the brass cross and the Union Jack,
It could still quiver to the cheerful noise

That called upon all things to render praise.
Of all things, I liked best that tough old vine
Roping our side fence, offering my days
Clusters of hope that stirred the sense like wine.

Credo

That each thing is a word
Requiring us to speak it:
From the ant to the quasar,
From clouds to ocean floor —

The meaning not ours, but found
In the mind deeply submissive
To the grammar of existence,
The syntax of the real;

So that alien is changed
To human, thing into thinking:
For the world's bare tokens
We pay golden coin,

Stamped with the king's image;
And poems are prophecy
Of a new heaven and earth,
A rumour of resurrection.

Late Winter

The pallid cuckoo
Sent up in frail
Microtones
His tiny scale

On the cold air.
What joy I found
Mounting that tiny
Stair of sound.

One Tuesday in Summer

That sultry afternoon the world went strange.
Under a violet and leaden bruise
The air was filled with sinister yellow light;
Trees, houses, grass took on unnatural hues.

Thunder rolled near. The intensity grew and grew
Like doom itself with lightnings on its face.
And Mr Pitt, the grocer's order-man,
Who made his call on Tuesdays at our place,

Said to my mother, looking at the sky,
"You'd think the ending of the world had come."
A leathern little man, with bicycle-clips
Around his ankles, doing our weekly sum,

He too looked strange in that uncanny light;
As in the Bible ordinary men
Turn out to be angelic messengers,
Pronouncing the Lord's judgments why and when.

I watched the scurry of the small black ants
That sensed the storm. What Mr Pitt had said
I didn't quite believe, or disbelieve;
But still the words had got into my head,

For nothing less seemed worthy of the scene.
The darkening imminence hung on and on,
Till suddenly, with lightning-stroke and rain,
Apocalypse exploded, and was gone.

By nightfall things had their familiar look.
But I had seen the world stand in dismay
Under the aspect of another meaning
That rain or time would hardly wash away.

Because

My father and my mother never quarrelled.
They were united in a kind of love
As daily as the *Sydney Morning Herald*,
Rather than like the eagle or the dove.

I never saw them casually touch,
Or show a moment's joy in one another.
Why should this matter to me now so much?
I think it bore more hardly on my mother,

Who had more generous feeling to express.
My father had dammed up his Irish blood
Against all drinking praying fecklessness,
And stiffened into stone and creaking wood.

His lips would make a switching sound, as though
Spontaneous impulse must be kept at bay.
That it was mainly weakness I see now,
But then my feelings curled back in dismay.

Small things can pit the memory like a cyst:
Having seen other fathers greet their sons,
I put my childish face up to be kissed
After an absence. The rebuff still stuns

My blood. The poor man's curt embarrassment
At such a delicate proffer of affection
Cut like a saw. But home the lesson went:
My tenderness thenceforth escaped detection.

My mother sang *Because*, and *Annie Laurie,*
White Wings, and other songs; her voice was sweet.
I never gave enough, and I am sorry;
But we were all closed in the same defeat.

People do what they can; they were good people,
They cared for us and loved us. Once they stood
Tall in my childhood as the school, the steeple.
How can I judge without ingratitude?

Judgment is simply trying to reject
A part of what we are because it hurts.
The living cannot call the dead collect:
They won't accept the charge, and it reverts.

It's my own judgment day that I draw near,
Descending in the past, without a clue,
Down to that central deadness: the despair
Older than any hope I ever knew.

Numbers and Makes

The house we lived in faced the western line.
I used to sit and write the number down
Of every locomotive as it passed:
From the humdrum all-stations-into-town,

To the great thunderers that shook the house.
And passengers would wave back from the train.
I would watch out for when the signals moved
To stop or slow or all clear, and then strain

To catch the oncoming noise around the bend.
Or sometimes for variety I'd perch
Where I could note the make of every car
That passed along the street. Pure research,

Disinterested — but why, and into what?
There was no question then, no answer now.
Why change the memory into metaphors
That solitary child would disavow?

Tabletalk

In tabletalk my father used to tell
Of the escaped nun kidnapped by a priest;
Or innocent girls in the confessional,
Closeted in the dark with some gross beast.

By contrast, Anglican restraint was good:
It kept religion in its proper place. —
What all this talk was for, I understood
Only long after; but it left a trace.

In an unguarded moment once, I drew
Deserved rebuke for letting on I had
A plan of reading the whole Bible through:
He thought this a quick way of going mad.

On relatives my parents were agreed:
Too much association doesn't do,
And doubly so with the bog-Irish breed —
They're likely to want something out of you.

On friendship too the doctrine was as cold:
They're only making use of you you'll find;
Prudence consists in learning to withhold
The natural impulse of the sharing mind.

What is the wisdom that a child needs most?
Ours was distrust, a coating behind the eye
We took in daily with the mutton roast,
The corned-beef salad, and the shepherd's pie.

St John's Park

The mountain is streaked white, the air is cold.
Under a pure blue sky the players begin.
Thickly-clotted prunus lines the way in,
And wattles put on helmets of heavy gold.

A dark-green gum bursts out in crimson flowers.
Old people slowly rot along the wall.
The young ones hardly notice them at all.
Both live in the same picture-book of hours.

Four-turreted a square tower balks the sky,
Casting a shadow; an organ softly plays.
The afternoon wears out in a gold daze.
On ragged wings, uttering its carking cry

A raven scavenges; a flock of gulls
Flies from the tip. The last teams leave the park.
The old have crept inside to meet the dark.
Loss is what nothing alters or annuls.

At nightfall glaring traffic rushes by
Filling the air with reek and the scream of brakes.
Faint stars prick out a sign. And Vega wakes
Liquid and trembling on the northern sky.

In the Huon Valley

Propped boughs are heavy with apples,
Springtime quite forgotten.
Pears ripen yellow. The wasp
Knows where windfalls lie rotten.

Juices grow rich with sun.
These autumn days are still:
The glassy river reflects
Elm-gold up the hill,

And big white plumes of rushes.
Life is full of returns;
It isn't true that one never
Profits, never learns:

Something is gathered in,
Worth the lifting and stacking;
Apples roll through the graders,
The sheds are noisy with packing.

Wet Day

Rain sweeps in as the gale begins to blow,
The water is glaucous-green and mauve and grey.
A pelican takes refuge on the bay;
Snow-white and black it rides the complex flow.

A child stands in a yellow mackintosh.
Gulls lift away and circle round about.
Cans, bottles, and junk appear as the tide runs out.
Wind cannot sweep away nor water wash

The dreck of our vulgarity. I think
The world has never been redeemed; at least
The marks it bears are mostly of the Beast —
The broken trust, the litter, and the stink.

Keep the Season

Keep the season: let the hive
Rob the day to pay the dark;
Pollen-scented thieves deprive
Leatherwood and ironbark,
Then in telltale dance expound
Where the sweetness can be found.

Keep the season: birds repeat
In the plainchant we have lost
Melismatic turns so sweet
As to hide what love can cost:
Let their Latin fill the air
With devotion, with despair.

Keep the season: let the heart
Work its mystery one more time,
Fabricating, sick with art,
Virtue crazed and stained like crime.
If we knew enough to give
We might find a way to live.

At Rushy Lagoon

Wet mirrors covering soft peat.
Swag-bellied graceful mares in foal.
Red-umber bulls on plashing feet
With mild white face and curly poll.

Crutching time; each heavy ewe
Is trimmed and slides off down the chute.
The mountains are cut out in blue.
An opalescent sky is mute.

Ducks loiter. Children play before tea.
In the home paddock a lone goose
Follows the cows for company.
It is a world of sense and use.

Winter Drive

Fallow fields, dark pewter sky,
Steely light on the wet plain,
Evening falls in freezing rain
With a promise and a lie.

Promise in the leaden sky,
In the leaden fields' bleak shine,
In the slate vats full of wine,
In the knowledge that we die.

But the lie is in the soul,
And it rots the world we have
Till there's nothing left to save.

Dying world and deadened sky,
Traffic roars beyond control.
What is left to make us try?

Saturday Morning

Dark swamping rain, then morning shine;
The silver puddles in the path
Shatter where starlings take a bath.
A sheet drags loosely from the line.

Gulls toss at random on each gust,
A raven heavily flies low.
The lesser hills are crowned with snow.
Another day to take on trust

After the tempest of the night;
Boys' voices from the Home next door
Ring out like chimes, and every chore

Seems blest in ordinary light:
Firewood is cut, and sodden leaves
Are scooped in handfuls from blocked eaves.

In Northern Tasmania

Soft sodden fields. The new lambs cry,
And shorn ewes huddle from the cold.
Wattles are faintly tinged with gold.
A raven flies off silently.

Bare hawthorn thickets pearled with rain
Attract the thornbill and the wren.
Timber-trucks pass now and then,
And cows are moving in the lane.

At dusk I look out through old elms
Where mud-pools at the gatepost shine.
A way of life is in decline,

And only those who lived it know
What it is time overwhelms,
Which they must gradually let go.

Music Late at Night

Black gashes in white bark. The gate
Is clouded with spicy prunus flowers.
The moon sails cold through the small hours.
The helpless heart says, hold and wait.

Wait. The lighted empty street
Waits for the start of a new day,
When cars move, dogs and children play.
But now the rigid silence is complete.

Again that soundless music: a taut string,
Burdened unbearably with grief
That smiles acceptance of despair,

Throbs on the very threshold of spring
In the burst flower, the folded leaf:
Puzzling poor flesh to live and care.

Morning Voluntary

Morning comes with milk and bread.
Wind-blown puddles seem to flow.
Clouds have a brown look of snow.
Cat comes limping from the shed.

The white birch with arms outspread,
Having changed its wealth for gold,
Drifts it down into the mould.
Stalky vines glow darker red.

News that no one wants to know
Comes in with the milk and bread.
Turn the music loud instead,
Finish waking up and go.

Flat strokes dinned out overhead
Dropping through the red and gold
Tell the tale that must be told.
Friday's child is full of dread.

Very little can be said.
Cold inconstant breezes blow.
Starlings comment in a row.
Spots of black invade the red.

Parish Church

Bonewhite the newborn flesh, the crucified,
The risen body; bonewhite the crowding faces.
Green, crimson, yellow, blue the robes are dyed,
The wings and armour, the skies and heavenly places.

We used to sing at Easter in the choir
With trumpet and harmonium and drums,
Feeling within our hearts new-kindled fire.
Now I'm the only one that ever comes.

I bring with me my griefs, my sins, my death,
And sink in silence as I try to pray.
Though in this calm no impulse stirs my breath,
At least there's nothing that I would unsay.

Bush Scene

Harsh, dry, abrasive, spiky, rough,
Untidy, tattered, irregular:
Beauty is not a word you'd choose
For what's most characteristic here.
Although the bush has many things
Of perfect beauty — butterflies,
The graceful spinebill, tiger-orchids —
By no stretch is it a *locus amoenus*
In which imagination finds
Man's paradisal garden or park.
Less easy attractions hold the mind.
Of all these varied eucalypts
Choose one — this one; and let the eye
Explore its rangy airy structure:
How long-stemmed leafy parasols make
A balance of asymmetries,
Sustained once only by one tree.
Three yellow-tailed black cockatoos
(*funereus funereus*!)
Screech harshly from the breeze-swept boughs.

Shirley
Hazzard

Woollahra Road

IDA WAS supposed to be having her nap, but when she heard a horse and cart coming down the street she got off the bed and climbed on the window seat to look out. The milkman came in the morning, and it was too early in the afternoon for the baker; a cart at this hour could only mean a hawker — and sure enough, it was a man selling clothes props. The decrepit cart was laden with saplings of eucalyptus, roughly stripped and forked at one end.

"Props for fourpence." The horse dawdled down the road, pausing at each gate. "Props for fourpence." Nothing moved in the street, not even a dog. The day was hot and very dry. The prim gardens, the lank gum trees were deaf, motionless. "Props for fourpence." The cry was growing fainter.

The child, bored, went back to fetch a paint book and her doll, Rosie, from the crumpled pink coverlet. Returning to the window, she took up a crayon and did a little more work on a house she had been drawing. She added a plume of smoke to the chimney, because, although she could not remember ever having seen a smoking chimney, her picture books were full of them. Here in Australia, it seemed to have been summer all her life — breathless, burning days of drought. The pictures of smoking chimneys were like the snow scenes that arrived on cards from England each year during the Christmas heat wave — brief representations of that other, authoritative world where seasons were reversed (it was implied, correctly), and where children wore gaiters and mufflers and lived indoors.

The front garden, which the window overlooked, was on the shady side of the house, but even there the soft turf had died in the drought and been replaced by crisp, resistant buffalo grass, which also grew on the more exposed sides of the house. The steps were bordered with pink and blue hydrangeas, and with beds of fuchsia and daphne. Palm trees stood on the lawn. At the end of the short drive were red hibiscus and trees of wattle and frangipani. At the side, a wall covered with wilted Dorothy Perkins roses separated this house from the Armstrongs'. Sometimes the Armstrong boys, Rex and Leslie, came to play. Rex was eleven and enormous, and quickly got bored with Ida because she was so little. He wore grey knickerbockers, and a blazer with a crest, and a straw boater circled by a broad, striped ribbon. The Armstrongs had kept Rex in a good school — ''in spite of everything''. The Armstrongs had lost all their money.

It was 1935, and Ida was four years old.

She would have liked to go into the garden, but her mother would be annoyed if she didn't sleep, and in any case the back of the house was more amusing. The back garden was huge, and had beds of flowers and vegetables and an orchard. A swing had been built in the orchard, and if you were swung high enough you could touch the mandarin trees by extending your feet. Beyond the orchard was a field of high grass forbidden to children because of snakes. The snakes occasionally came into the garden and had to be killed with a heavy stick that was kept in the garage for the purpose. The grass of the field was cut down from time to time by Alfie, the man who did the garden, and lost cricket balls would turn up then, or an old kite, or singed rocket butts left over from Empire Night. The grass was never burned off now, because of the danger of fire.

Even the orchard and the garden had their perils. There were bees in the grove of buddleia. In the mornings, kookaburras perched on the lowest branches of the trees, looking for lizards or worms, and would burst out laughing right over your head. And there was a grey goanna, like a short, thick snake, harmless but horrible, that came to the kitchen door to be fed by the maid, Marge, with raw eggs.

The perils of the back garden were so attractive that Ida turned her back on the window and slid down from the wooden seat. Taking Rosie up by one china arm, she made her way out of the room. The hallway was dark — blinds were drawn and doors closed at this time of day — and she descended the stairs carefully, grasping the rods of the banister with her free hand. From the foot of the steps, she went through to the back of the house, where a screen door opened from her father's study on to a glassed-in veranda.

It was hot on the veranda, but there sat her mother, in a blue dress, sewing. Her mother, who was dark and beautiful and very loving, had strong, impatient opinions, and a quick temper that flared without warning and was felt through the house. Ida was both afraid to be out of her sight and afraid of making her angry, and she creaked the screen door open and looked cautiously around it.

But her mother just smiled and let her come and sit on the polished floor beside her and play with the coloured silks and reels of cotton in the quilted box. Ida lined them up in their varying sizes and then in their different shades, and when she tired of that she simply sat leaning against her mother's leg, rubbing with one finger the round button on the high-heeled shoe. The sun burned on them through the glass; her mother came here to sew because of the light, but she hated the heat, Ida knew. She couldn't breathe, she said, until the southerly started to blow in the evening — the cool south wind that reached Sydney from the sea. She couldn't bear to see the garden wither in the drought. One evening, she went out and watered the lawn, although that was prohibited because of the water shortage, and a passerby, seeing her with the hose, had shouted that he would report her to the City Council. Her mother threw down the hose in a fury, and came inside and said she was sick of the drought and the depression. When Marge told her it would get cooler soon, in May, she just shook her head and said she was homesick. On the study wall there was a photograph of a girl in a fur coat standing in snow, like the Christmas cards.

Jock, the Airedale, who was nosing about in the field, suddenly began to bark and came running up through the orchard. The abrupt activity shook the trees, or so it seemed, and sharpened the light. The shoe button shifted out from under Ida's finger as her mother rose to look through the glass of the veranda.

A woman had come round the corner of the house and was walking very slowly towards the back door. She was dressed in black and carried a large, square hessian bag that flapped, almost empty, against her thigh. Her slow, slow walk carried her past the flowers and the vegetables and the barking dog, but she didn't look about her. By her face and her figure she was not old, but her walk was old. Her feet moved painfully on the smooth flagstone path. The uneven hem of her dress reached, in some places, almost to her ankles. She wore a round hat of black felt, crammed down on her head.

The kitchen door opened as she reached it, and Marge looked out. The dog slipped inside, still barking in little short puffs. The woman spoke, not accentuating her words with any movement, clasping the thick loops of the bag against her hip. Marge — short, plump, and fair — came out on to the step and closed the door behind her because of the flies. The voices came indistinctly through the hot glass of the veranda. In a moment, Marge opened the door again and both women disappeared into the house.

Ida and her mother had moved away from the windows; they heard Marge's step before they could sit down again. Marge appeared on the veranda, her face creased and uneasy. Ida knew, before she spoke, that her voice would be lowered. It was so low, in fact, that the child could scarcely hear.

"Walking all day," she said, "poor soul . . . this heat . . . she's looking for work" and ". . . children . . ."

Ida's mother stuck the needle into the sewing in her hand and put it down on the chair. Her face, too, was troubled. She went inside, through the study and into the hall, with Marge and Ida following, and down the corridor to the kitchen.

The woman was standing by the kitchen table, still holding her bag. She looked austerely at the group in the doorway. The skin of her face and arms was brown and dry, but she had young features and, under the battered hat, limp, dark hair. She didn't speak, but sat at the table when she was asked, and drank a glass of lemonade straight down without stopping. When she had done that, she seemed to sag in her chair; she propped her elbow on the table and her brow on her hand, and closed her eyes.

At the sink, the two women were slicing and spreading, and Marge had brought a jug of milk from the ice chest. Ida stretched her own elbow on to the table's edge, staring and wishing that the woman in black had not come. Her arrival had turned everyone silent and queer, and she did not look at Ida or speak to her, as women usually did, but sat there, almost lifeless, with the brim of her ugly hat lowered over her hand. After a moment, the child drew away and sat down on a box of groceries that had been delivered that day from Anthony Hordern's. Beside the groceries, Alfie had placed a shined pair of her father's shoes, and, putting Rosie down, she picked up one shoe and began to play with the laces. The heavy shoe slipped between her knees and distended the floral lap of her dress, but she pretended to be intent on it, hoping that when she looked up the woman would be preparing to leave.

Instead, her mother was putting plates on the table and a glass of milk, and the bowl of fruit from the dining room. No one paid any attention to Ida, even though she had dirtied her dress with the shoe, which she now tumbled back on to the floor. The woman began to eat from a plate of cold meat, with sharp motions of her fork and knife. She showed no signs of going away. Marge was making the strong tea, dark and bitter even when it had milk in it, that they had every afternoon, and a cup and saucer had been set on the table. Ida saw with relief that her mother's tea tray had also been laid — the tray with willow-pattern china and a plate of Arnott's biscuits that was carried to the back veranda every afternoon.

When the tea was ready, her mother filled the cup on the table and her own cup on the tray. In an undertone, she asked Marge to fetch some tinned food from the basement. Then she picked up the tray herself and went out of the kitchen so quickly that Ida, who was afraid of being left with the woman at the table, jumped up and scuttled out after her.

The dog, stretched out on a patch of uncarpeted floor in the study, scrambled to his feet as they passed through, and pattered on to the veranda. He and Ida were allowed one biscuit each from the tea tray — which always meant one more. Ida took up her position by her mother's chair, wondering if the ritual would restore their afternoon. But her mother was not thinking of her; she was frowning over the dishes on the little cane table at her side. When Ida looked at her, she handed her a biscuit absent-mindedly, and broke one in half for Jock, and sighed.

The mother and child might have been sheltering there, they were so still, when the kitchen door clanged at last and the slow, flat steps sounded on the path. The steps grew fainter, until they could not be heard at all, and Ida thought that her mother would smile now and give her the second biscuit. Even Marge was relieved, it seemed, singing in the kitchen a song she would not ordinarily have chosen: "K-K-K-Katy." She sang this only when she was unnerved, because it was disrespectful; Kate was the name of Ida's mother.

". . . the only g-g-g-girl that I adore," Marge sang.

Ida looked warily at her mother, who smiled at last — almost with complicity — and reached toward the plate.

The singing suddenly broke off. "Oh!" said Marge. "Oh, Madam!"

As her mother started up, Ida had once more the impression that the light changed. There was barely time to reach the doorway before Marge appeared there.

"Oh, Madam, please come!" she was saying. "That woman . . ." and they all hurried after her into the house.

The kitchen was orderly, the table cleared, instead of the scene of carnage Ida expected. You wouldn't have known the woman had been there. But where the shoes had lain, and the doll, there was nothing at all — just the shiny green speckles of the linoleum.

"Rosie!" Ida howled in rage and horror. "Rosie!" Rosie, at that moment, was shuddering along Woollahra Road in a hessian bag, jostled by a pair of shoes. Appalled, the child flung herself round to be comforted, and as she did so it occurred to her that now her mother would get really, terribly angry — even worse than over the business of the hose, angrier than Ida herself.

But her mother seated herself at the table, where the strange woman had sat, and lowered her brow on her propped hand. She did not utter a word.

The Picnic

IT WAS like Nettie, Clem thought, to wear a dress like that to a picnic and to spill something on it. His wife, May, was wearing shorts and a plaid shirt, and here was Nettie in a dress that showed her white arms and shoulders — and, as she bent over the wine stain, her bosom; a dress with a green design of grapes and vine leaves. He could tell, too, that she had been to the hairdresser yesterday, or even this morning before setting out to visit them. She hadn't changed at all. Unrealistic, that was the word for Nettie. . . . But the word, suggesting laughter and extravagance, unexpectedly gave him pleasure. Feeling as though Nettie herself had cheated him of his judgment, he turned away from her and glanced down the hillside to where May was playing catch with Ivor, their youngest boy.

If May had left them alone deliberately, as he assumed she had — and he honored that generosity in her — she was mistaken in thinking they had anything to say to one another. They had been sitting for some minutes in complete silence, Nettie repacking the remains of the lunch into the picnic basket or, since the accident with the wine, fiddling with her dress. But what could two people talk about after ten years (for it must be getting on to that)? Nettie, though quite chatty throughout lunch, certainly hadn't said much since. Perhaps she expected him to mention all that business; it would fit in with her sentimental ideas. Naturally, he had no intention of doing anything of the kind — why bring up something that happened at least ten years ago and made all three of them miserable enough, God knows, at the time? Yes, that would be Nettie all over, wanting to be told that he had often thought about her, had never forgotten her, never would — although whole months passed sometimes when Nettie never entered his head, and he was sure it must be the same way for her; at least, he presumed so. Even then, he would remember her only because someone else — May, perhaps — spoke of her.

In fact, it was because someone else brought her to his attention that the thing had come about in the first place. He had not, in the beginning, thought her attractive — a young cousin of May's who came to the house for weekends in the summer. He had scarcely noticed her until a casual visitor, the wife of one of his partners, spoke about her. A beautiful woman, she had called her — the phrase struck him all the more because he or May would have said, at most, a pretty girl. And Nettie, that day, had been dressed in a crumpled yellow cotton, he remembered — not at her best at all. Later, he had reflected that his whole life had been jeopardized because someone thoughtlessly said: "She is beautiful."

Now Nettie looked up at him, drawing her hair away from her face with the back of her hand. Still they did not speak, and to make the silence more natural by seeming at his ease Clem stretched on his elbow among the ferns. Nettie released the loop of hair and poured a little water from a thermos onto the mark on her dress. Her earrings swung; her dress shifted along one shoulder. Her head lowered intently — he supposed that she had become short-sighted and refused to wear glasses.

He could hardly recall how it had developed, what had first been said between them, whether either of them resisted the idea. His memories of Nettie were like a pile of snapshots never arranged according to date. He could see her quite clearly, though, sitting in a garden chair, and in a car, and, of all things, riding a bicycle; and facing him across a table — in a restaurant, he thought — looking profoundly sad and enjoying herself hugely.

If, he told himself, I were to say now that I've thought of her (just because it would please her — and they would probably never meet again), she might simply get emotional. Not having thought of it for years, she might seize the opportunity to have a good cry. Or perhaps she doesn't really want to discuss the past; perhaps she's as uncomfortable as I. . . . All the same, she looked quite composed. He might almost have said a little satirical, as though she found his life quite dull and could rejoice that, after all, she had not shared it. (He saw himself, for an instant, with what he imagined to be her eyes. What a pity she had come just now — he had worked hard last winter, and he thought it had told on him.)

It was true, of course, that he had responsibilities, couldn't be rushing about the world pleasing himself, as she could. But no man, he assured himself irritably, could be entirely satisfied with what had happened to him. There must always be the things one had chosen not to do. One couldn't explore every possibility — one didn't have a thousand years. In the end, what was important? One's experience, one's ideas, what one read; some taste, understanding. He had his three sons, his work, his friends, this house. There was Matt, his eldest boy, who was so promising. (Then he recalled that during lunch today he had spoken sharply to Matt over something or other, and Nettie had laughed. She had made a flippant remark about impatience; that he hadn't changed at all, was that it? Some such silly, proprietary thing — which he had answered, briefly, with dignity. He knew himself to be extremely patient.)

Yes, Nettie could be quite tiresome, he remembered — almost with relief, having feared, for a moment, his own sentimentality. She made excessive demands on people; her talk was full of exaggerations. She had no sense of proportion, none whatever — and wasn't that exactly the thing one looked for in a woman? And she took a positive pride in condoning certain kinds of conduct, because they demonstrated weaknesses similar to her own. She was not fastidious, as May was.·

That was it, of course. He had in his marriage the thing they would never have managed together, Nettie and he — a sort of perseverance, a persistent understanding. Where would Nettie have found strength for the unremitting concessions of daily life? She was precipitated from delight to lamentation without logical sequence, as though life were too short; she must cram everything in and perhaps sort it out later. (He rather imagined, from the look of things, that the sorting process had been postponed indefinitely.) For her, all experience was dramatic, every love eternal. Whereas he could only look on a love affair, now, as a displacement, not just of his habits — though that, too — but of his intelligence. Of the mind itself. Being in love was, like pain, an indignity, a reducing thing. So nearly did it seem in retrospect a form of insanity, the odd thing to him was that it should be considered normal.

Not that it wasn't exciting in its own way, Nettie's ardor, her very irresponsibility. It was what had fascinated him at the time, no doubt. And she was easily amused — though that was one of her drawbacks; she laughed at men, and naturally they felt it. Even when she had been, so to speak, in love with him, he had sometimes felt she had laughed at him, too.

In all events, his marriage had survived Nettie's attractions, whatever they were. It was not easy, of course. In contrast to Nettie, May assumed too many burdens. Where Nettie was impetuous and inconsiderate, May was scrupulous and methodical. He was often concerned about May. She worried, almost with passion (he surprised himself with the word), over human untidiness, civic affairs, the international situation. He was willing to bet that the international situation never crossed Nettie's mind. May had a horror of disorder — "Let's get organized," she would say, faced with a picnic, a dinner party; faced with life itself. If his marriage lacked romance, which would scarcely be astonishing after twenty years, it was more securely established on respect and affection. There were times, he knew, when May still needed him intensely, but their relations were so carefully balanced that he was finding it more and more difficult to detect the moment of appeal.

He felt a sudden hatred for Nettie, and for this silence of hers that prejudiced one's affections and one's principles. She tried — he could feel it; it was to salve her own pride — to make him consider himself fettered, diminished, a shore from which the wave of life receded. And what had *she* achieved, after all, that she should question the purpose of his existence? He didn't know much about her life these past few years — which alone showed there couldn't be much to learn. A brief, impossible marriage, a lot of trips, and some flighty jobs. What did she have to show for all this time — without children, no longer young, sitting there preoccupied with a stain on her dress? She couldn't suggest that he was to blame for the turn her life had taken — she wasn't all *that* unjust. She had suffered at the time, no doubt, but it was so long ago. They couldn't begin now to accuse or vindicate one another. That was why it was much better not to open the subject at all, actually. He glanced severely at her, restraining her recriminations. But she had lost her mocking, judicial air. She was still looking down, though less attentively. Her hands were folded over her knee.

Well, she *was* beautiful; he would have noticed it even if it had never been pointed out to him. . . . All at once he wanted to say "I have often thought of you" (for it was true, he realized now; he thought of her every day). Abruptly, he looked away. At the foot of the hill, May had stopped playing with the children and was sitting on a rock. It is my own decision, he reminded himself, that Nettie isn't mine, that I haven't seen her in all these years. And the knowledge, though not completely gratifying, gave him a sense of integrity and self-denial, so that when he looked at her again it was without desire, and he told himself, I have grown.

He has aged, Nettie thought. Just now, looking into his face — which was, curiously, more familiar to her than anyone else's — she had found nothing to stir her. One might say that he was faded, as one would say it of a woman. He would soon be fifty. He had a fretful, touchy air about him. During lunch, when she had laughed at his impatience, he had replied primly (here in her mind she pulled a long, solemn, comic face): "I have my faults, I suppose, like everyone else." And like everyone else, she noted, he was willing to admit the general probability so long as no specific instance was brought to his attention. He made little announcements about himself, too, protesting his tolerance, his sincerity. "I am a sensitive person," he had declared, absolutely out of the blue (something, anyway, that no truly sensitive person would say). He was so cautious — anyone would think he had a thousand years to live and didn't need to invite experience. And while, of course, any marriage must involve compromise (and who, indeed, would know that better than she?), that was no reason for Clem and May to behave toward one another like a couple of . . . civil servants.

She could acknowledge his intelligence. And he had always been a very competent person. Wrecked on a desert island, for instance (one of her favorite criteria), he would have known what to do. But life demanded more, after all, than the ability to build a fire without matches, or recognize the breadfruit tree on sight. And one could hardly choose to be wrecked simply in order to have an opportunity for demonstrating such accomplishments.

Strange that he should have aged like this in so short a time — it would be precisely eight years in June since they parted. It was still a thing she couldn't bring herself to think of, the sort of thing people had in mind when they said, not quite laughing, that they wouldn't want their youth over again. Oddly enough, it was the beginning, not the end, that didn't bear thinking about. One weekend, they had stopped at a bar, in the country, on the way to this house. It was summer, and their drinks came with long plastic sticks in them. Clem had picked up one of the sticks and traced the outline of her fingers, lying flat on the

Formica tabletop. They had not said anything at all, then, but she had known simply because he did that. Even now, the thought of his drawing that ridiculous plastic stick around her fingers was inexpressibly touching.

Naturally, she didn't imagine poor old Clem had planned an affair in advance, but even at the time she had felt he was ready for something of the kind — that she was the first person he happened to notice. For the fact was that they were not really suited to one another, which he would have discovered if he had ever tried to understand her properly. He had no idea of what she was like, none whatever. To this day, she was sure, he thought her trivial, almost frivolous. (And she was actually an acutely sensitive person.) No wonder they found nothing to say to one another now.

It *was* a strain, however, their being alone like this. And how like May to have arranged it this way, how ostentatiously forbearing. Magnanimous, Clem would have called it (solemn again), but May had a way, Nettie felt, of being magnanimous, as it were, at one's expense. Still, what did it matter? Since they had invited her, after she had run into May in a shop one afternoon, she could hardly have refused to come. In an hour or two it would be over; she need never come again.

It did matter. It wouldn't be over, really. Her life was associated with Clem's, however little he might mean to her, now, and she must always be different because she had known him. She wasn't saying that he was responsible for the pattern of her life — she wasn't that unjust. It was, rather, that he cropped up, uninvited, in her thoughts almost every day. She found herself wondering over and over again what he would think of things that happened to her, or wanting to tell him a story that would amuse him. And surely that is the sense, she thought, in which one might say that love is eternal. She was pleased when people spoke well of him in her hearing — and yet resentful, because she had no part, now, in his good qualities. And when she heard small accusations against him, she wondered whether she should contest them. But, for all she knew, they might be justified. That was the trouble with experience; it taught you that most people were capable of anything, so that loyalty was never quite on firm ground — or, rather, became a matter of pardoning offenses instead of denying their existence.

She sympathized with his attitude. It was tempting to confine oneself to what one could cope with. And one couldn't cope with love. (In her experience, at any rate, it had always got out of hand.) But, after all, it was the only state in which one could consider oneself normal; which engaged all one's capacities, rather than just those developed by necessity — or shipwreck. One never realized how much was lacking until one fell in love again, because love — like pain, actually — couldn't be properly remembered or conveyed.

How sad it was. Looking into his face just now, finding nothing of interest, she had been so pierced by sadness that tears filled her eyes and she had to bend over the stain on her dress to hide her face. It was absurd that they should face each other this way — antagonistically, in silence — simply because they had once been so close. She would have done anything for him. Even though she no longer cared for him, saw his weakness quite clearly, still she would do anything for him. She cared for him, now, less than for any man she knew, and yet she would have done anything. . . . It *was* a pity about her dress, though — wine was absolutely the worst thing; it would never come out.

Upright on her rock, May gave a short, exhausted sigh. She closed her eyes for a moment, to clear them, and Ivor called out to her that she must watch him, watch the game. She looked back at him without smiling. On either side, her palms were pressed hard against the stone.

Nothing in Excess

"THE AIM of the Organization," Mr Bekkus dictated, leaning back in his chair and casting up his eyes to the perforations of the sound-proof ceiling; "The *aim* of the Organization," he repeated with emphasis, as though he were directing a firing-squad — and then, "the *long-range* aim," narrowing his eyes to this more distant target, "is to fully utilize the resources of the staff and hopefully by the end of the fiscal year to have laid stress —"

Mr Bekkus frequently misused the word "hopefully". He also made a point of saying "locate" instead of "find", "utilize" instead of "use", and never lost an opportunity to indicate or communicate; and would slip in a "basically" when he felt unsure of his ground.

"— to have laid greater stress upon the capacities of certain members of the staff at present in junior positions. Since this bears heavily" — Mr Bekkus now leant forward and rested his elbows firmly on his frayed blue blotter — "on the nature of our future work force, attention is drawn to the Director-General's directive set out in (give the document symbol here, Germaine), asking that Personnel Officers communicate the names of staff members having — what was the wording there?" He reached for a mimeographed paper in his tray.

"Imagination," Germaine supplied.

"— imagination and abilities which could be utilized in more responsible posts." Mr Bekkus stopped again. "Where's Swoboda?"

"He went to deposit your pay-cheque, Mr Bekkus."

"Well, when he comes in tell him I need the figures he's been preparing. Better leave a space at the end, then, for numbers of vacant posts. New paragraph. Candidates should be recommended solely on the basis of outstanding personal attributes, bearing in mind the basic qualifications of an international civil servant as set forth in Part II (that's roman, Germaine) of the Staff Regulations with due regard to education, years of service, age, and administrative ability. Read that back. . . . All right. We'll set up the breakdown when Swoboda comes across with the figures. Just bang that out, then — copies all round." Mr Bekkus was always saying "Bang this out" or "Dash that off" in a way that somehow minimized Germaine's role and suggested that her job was not only unexacting but even jolly.

"Yes, Mr Bekkus." Germaine had closed her book and was searching for her extra pencil among the papers on the desk.

"You see how it is, Germaine," said Mr Bekkus, again leaning back in the tiny office as if he owned it all. "The Director-General is loosening things up, wants people who have ideas, individuality, not the run-of-the-mill civil servants we've been getting round here." His gesture was apparently directed towards the outer office, which Germaine shared with Swoboda, the clerk. "Not just

491

people who fit in with the requirements. And he's prepared to *relax* the requirements in order to get them."

Germaine wrinkled her forehead. "But you did say." She turned up her notes again.

"What did I say?" asked Mr Bekkus, turning faintly hostile.

"Here. Where it says about due regard."

"Ah — the necessary qualifications. My dear girl, we have to talk in terms of suitable candidates. You can't take on just anybody. You wouldn't suggest that we promote people merely to be kind to them?" Since Germaine looked for a moment as if she might conceivably make such a suggestion, he added belligerently, "Would you?"

"Oh — no." And, having found her pencil under the Daily List of Official Documents, she added, "Here it is."

"Why, these are the elementary qualifications in any organization today." Holding up one hand, he enumerated them on his outstretched fingers. "University education" — Mr Bekkus would have been the last to minimize the importance of this in view of the years it had taken him to wrest his own degree in business administration from a reluctant provincial college. "Administrative ability. Output. Responsibility. And leadership potential." Having come to the end of his fingers, he appeared to dismiss the possibility of additional requirements; he had in some way contrived to make them all sound like the same thing.

"I'll leave a blank then," said Germaine. "At the end of the page." She tucked her pencil in the flap of her book and left the room.

Stupid little thing, Mr Bekkus thought indulgently — even, perhaps, companionably. Germaine at any rate need not disturb herself about the new directive: she was lucky to be in the Organization at all. This was the way Mr Bekkus felt about any number of his colleagues.

"Yes, come in, Swoboda. Good. Sit down, will you, and we'll go over these. I've drafted a memo for the Section Chief to sign."

Swoboda pulled up a chair to the corner of the desk. Swoboda was in his late thirties, slender, Slavic, with a nervous manner but quiet eyes and still hands. Having emerged from Europe after the war as a displaced person, Swoboda had no national standing and had been hired as a clerk by the Organization in its earliest days. As a local recruit he had a lower salary, fewer privileges, and a less interesting occupation than the internationally recruited members of the staff, but in 1947 he had counted himself fortunate to get a job at all. This sense of good fortune had sustained him for some time; it is possible, however, that after more than twenty years at approximately the same rank it was at last beginning to desert him.

Bekkus wanted to be fair. Swoboda made him uneasy, but Bekkus would have admitted that Swoboda could turn in good work under proper supervision. Mr

492

Bekkus flattered himself (as he correctly expressed it) that he had supervised Swoboda pretty thoroughly during the time he had had him in his office — had organized him, in fact, for the maximum potential. Still, Swoboda made him uneasy, for there was something withdrawn about him, something that could not be brought out under proper supervision or even at the Christmas party. Bekkus would have said that Swoboda did not fully communicate.

But Bekkus wanted to be fair. Swoboda was a conscientious staff member, and the calculations he now laid on the corner of the desk represented a great deal of disagreeable work — work which Bekkus freely, though silently, admitted he would not have cared to do himself.

Bekkus lifted the first page. "All right. And did you break down the turnover?"

"Here, sir. The number of posts vacated each year in various grades."

Bekkus glanced down a list headed Resignations and Retirement. "Good God, is that all? Is this the total? How can we fit new people in if hardly anyone leaves?"

"You're looking at the sub-total. If you'll allow me." Swoboda turned the page to another heading: Deaths and Dismissals.

"That's more like it," said Bekkus with relief. "This means that we can move about fifty people up each year from the Subsidiary into the Specialized grades." (The staff was divided into these two categories, and there had been little advancement from the Subsidiary to the Specialized. Those few who had in fact managed to get promoted from the lower category were viewed by their new colleagues much as an emancipated slave must have been regarded in ancient Rome by those born free.)

"The trouble, of course," went on Bekkus, "is to find capable people on the existing staff. You know what the plan is, Swoboda. The D.-G. wants us to comb the Organization, to comb it thoroughly" — Bekkus made a gesture of grooming some immense shaggy animal — "for staff members of real ability in both categories who've been passed over, keep an eye open for initiative, that kind of thing. These people — these staff members, that is — have resources which have not been fully utilized, and which *can* be utilized, Swoboda. . . ." Mr Bekkus paused, for Swoboda was looking at him with more interest and feeling than usual, then pulled himself together and added, "within the existing framework." The feeling and interest passed from Swoboda's expression and left no trace.

Bekkus handed back the tables. "If you'll get Germaine to stick this in at the foot of the memo, I think we're all set. And then bring me the file on Wyatt, will you? That's A. Wyatt, in the Translation Section. I have to take it to the Board. It's a case for compulsory retirement."

"Got one," Algie Wyatt underlined a phrase on the page before him.

"What?" asked Lidia Korabetski, looking up from the passage she was translating.

"Contradiction in terms." Algie was collecting contradictions in terms: to a nucleus of "military intelligence" and "competent authorities" he had added such discoveries as the soul of efficiency, easy virtue, enlightened self-interest, Bankers Trust, and Christian Scientist.

"What?" Lidia asked again.

"*Cultural mission*," replied Algie, turning the page and looking encouraged, as if he studied the document solely for such rewards as this.

Lidia and Algie were translators at the Organization. That is to say that they sat all day — with an hour off for lunch and breaks for tea — at their desks translating Organization documents out of one of the five official languages and into another. Lidia, who had been brought up in France of Russian and English parentage, translated into French from English and Russian; Algie, who was British and had lived much abroad, translated into English from French and Spanish. They made written translations only, the greater drama of the oral interpretation of debates being reserved for the Organization's simultaneous interpreters. The documents Algie and Lidia translated contained the records of meetings, the recommendations of councils, the reports of committees, the minutes of working groups, and were not all noted for economy or felicity of phrase. However, both Algie and Lidia were resourceful with words and sought to convey the purport of these documents in a faithful and unpretentious manner.

In the several years during which Lidia and Algie had shared an office at the Organization, it had often been remarked that they made an odd pair. This is frequently said of two people whose personalities are ideally complementary, as was the case in this instance. It was also commonly agreed that there was no romance between them — as is often said where there is nothing but romance, pure romance, romance only, with no distracting facts of any kind.

When Lidia first came to share his office, Algie was about fifty-five years old. He was an immense man, of great height and bulky body, whose scarlet face and slightly bloodshot blue eyes proclaimed him something of a drinker. His health having suffered in the exercise of a great capacity for life, he shifted himself about with a heaving, shambling walk and was breathless after the least exertion. When he entered the office in the morning he would stand for some seconds over his desk, apparently exhausted by the efforts, physical and mental, involved in his having arrived there. He would then let himself down, first bulging outwards like a gutted building, then folding in the middle before collapsing into his grey Organization chair. For a while he would sit there, speechless and crimson-faced and heaving like a gong-tormented sea.

Although education and upbringing had prepared him for everything except the necessity of earning his own living, this was by no means Algie's first job.

During the thirties he had worked for the Foreign Office in the Balkans, but resigned in order to go to Spain as a correspondent during the Civil War. He spent most of the Second World War as an intelligence officer with the British Army in North Africa and during this time produced a creditable study on Roman remains in Libya and a highly useful Arabic phrase-book for British soldiers. After the war, his private income having dwindled to almost nothing, he entered the Organization in a dramatic escape from a possible career in the world of commerce.

It was not known how Algie came to apply to the Organization; still less how the Organization came to admit him. (It was said that his dossier had become confused with that of an eligible Malayan named Wai-lat, whose application had been unaccountably rejected.) Once in, Algie did the work required of him, overcoming a natural indolence that would have crushed other men. But he and the Organization were incompatible, and should never have been mated.

The Organization had bred, out of a staff recruited from its hundred member nations, a peculiarly anonymous variety of public official, of recognizable aspect and manner. It is a type to be seen to this very day, anxiously carrying a full briefcase or fumbling for a *laissez-passer* in airports throughout the world. In tribute to the levelling powers of Organization life, it may be said that a staff member wearing a sari or *kente* was as recognizable as one in a dark suit, and that the face below the fez was as nervously, as conscientiously Organizational as that beneath the Borsalino. The nature — what Mr Bekkus would have called the "aim" — of the Organization was such as to attract people of character; having attracted them, it found it could not afford them, that there was no room for personalities, and that its hope for survival lay, like that of all organizations, in the subordination of individual gifts to general procedures. No new country, no new language or way of life, no marriage or involvement in war could have so effectively altered and unified the way in which these people presented themselves to the world. It was this process of subordination that was to be seen going on beneath the homburg or turban. And it was Algie's inability to submit to this process that had delivered his dossier into the hands of Mr Bekkus at the Terminations Board.

To Algie it seemed that he was constantly being asked to take leave of those senses of humour, proportion, and the ridiculous that he had carefully nurtured and refined throughout his life. He could not get used to giving, with a straight face, a continual account of himself; nor could he regard as valid a system of judging a person's usefulness by the extent of his passion for detail. He found himself in a world that required laborious explanation of matters whose very meaning, in his view, depended on their being tacitly understood. His idiosyncrasy, his unpunctuality, his persistence in crediting his superiors with precisely that intuition they lacked and envied, were almost as unwelcome at the Organization as they would have been in the commercial world. He was, in short, an exception: that very thing for which organizations make so little allowance.

Sometimes as Algie sat there in the mornings getting back his breath, Lidia would tell him where she had been the previous evening, what she had been reading or listening to, some detail that would fill the gap since they had left the office the night before. When she did not provide these clues, it usually meant that she had been seeing a lover. She would never have mentioned such a thing to Algie, because of the romance between them.

Like many of the women who worked at the Organization, Lidia was unmarried. Unlike them, she remained so by her own choice. Years before, she had been married to an official of the Organization who had died on his way to a regional meeting of the Global Health Commission in La Paz. (His car overturned on a mountain road, and it was thought that he, like many of the delegates to the Commission, had been affected by the altitude.) Lidia had loved this husband. For some time after his death she kept to herself, and, even when this ceased to be the case, showed no inclination to remarry. She was admired by her male colleagues and much in demand as a companion, being fair-haired, slender, and not given to discussing her work out of office hours.

"Mustn't forget," Algie now said. "Got an appointment at two-thirty. Chap called Bekkus in Personnel."

Lidia gave an absent-minded groan. "Bekkus. Dreary man."

"A bit boring." This was the strongest criticism Algie had ever been known to make of any of his colleagues.

"Boring isn't the word," said Lidia, although it was. She became more attentive. "Isn't he on the Appointments and Terminations Board?"

"What's that?"

"Committee for improving our calibre."

Algie quoted:

> "Improvement too, the idol of the age,
> Is fed with many a victim."

There was nothing Algie enjoyed more than the apt quotation, whether delivered by himself or another. It gave him a momentary sensation that the world had come right; that some instant of perfect harmony had been achieved by two minds meeting, possibly across centuries. His own sources, fed by fifty years of wide and joyous reading, were in this respect inexhaustible. He had an unfashionable affection, too, for those poets whom he regarded as his contemporaries — Belloc, Chesterton, de la Mare — and would occasionally look up from his work (the reader will have gathered that looking up from his work was one of Algie's most pronounced mannerisms) to announce that "Don John of Austria is gone by Alcalar," or to ask "Do you remember an Inn, Miranda?"

From all of which it will readily be seen why Algie's file was in the hands of

Mr Bekkus and why Algie was not considered suitable for continued employment at the Organization. It may also be seen, however, that Algie's resources were of the kind never yet fully utilized by organization or mankind.

"Yes, here it is." Lidia had unearthed a printed list from a yellowing stack of papers on the heating equipment beside her. "R. Bekkus. Appointments and Terminations Board."

"Well, I've *been* appointed," Algie remarked, pushing his work away completely and preparing to rise to his feet, "so perhaps it's the other thing." He pressed his hands on the desk, heaved himself up and presently shambled off into the corridor.

Lidia went on with her work, and for fifteen minutes there was silence in the office she shared with Algie. It was a room typical of offices throughout the Organization — grey-walled, like that of Mr Bekkus, and floored with rubber tiles of a darker grey. Panels of fluorescent lighting were let into the white soundproofing that covered the ceiling. A wide low window-sill was formed by the metal covers of the radiators, and along this ledge at various intervals were stacked small sheaves of papers — the lower ones yellowing, the upper ones filmed with the grit that found its way through the aluminium window frames. (In each office the heating could be adjusted to some extent, so that in all the rooms of the Organization its international character was manifest in temperatures that ranged from nostalgic approximations of the North Sea to torrid renderings of conditions along the Zambesi.) Algie's and Lidia's desks were pushed together, facing one another, and each had a grey chair upholstered in dark blue. Blue blotters were centred on the desks and surrounded by trays of papers, black desk-sets, stapling machines, and dishes of paper clips — and, in Lidia's case, a philodendron in a cracked ceramic *cache-pot*. On each desk there was also a telephone and a small engagement pad on a metal fixture. There was a typewriter in one corner of the room, and a bookcase — into whose upper shelves dictionaries and bound documents had been crammed — stood with its back to the wall. On the lowest shelf of this bookcase were a pair of galoshes, a watering can, an unwashed glass vase, a Wedgwood cup and saucer, three cafeteria spoons, and a single black glove.

On one wall, a calendar — the gift of a Japanese travel concern — was turned to the appropriate month (this was not always the case in Organization offices), displaying a colourful plate which bore, to Algie's delight, the legend "Gorgeous bunch of blooming peonies".

From the windows, which were vast and clean, one looked on to a wide river and to its industrial banks beyond. The presence of the river was refreshing, although it carried almost continuously the water traffic — coal and railway barges, tugs, tankers, and cargo vessels — of the great city in which the Organization was laid. Oceans and rivers with their simple and traditional associations

497

of purification and continuity are excellent things to have outside office windows, and in this case helped in some measure to express that much misrepresented, highly commendable and largely unachieved thing — the aim of the Organization.

"Some bad news, I'm afraid." Tong put his head round Lidia Korabetski's door — this was literally true, since Tong's small neat head and long neck were all of him that showed. Tong was beaming. "Some bad news, yes." Not naturally malicious, he had developed rapidly since entering bureaucracy.

Lidia, lifting her head, could not help asking, "What is it?"

"Wyatt at lunch?" Tong nodded towards Algie's empty desk.

"He's been back from lunch for ages," said Lidia defensively. Lunch at the Organization was officially one hour, and Algie was often overdue.

"They're not renewing his contract."

"What contract?"

"His Permanent Contract, of course." Permanence, at the Organization, was viewed in blocks of five years, and a Permanent Contract was subject to quinquennial review. "The Terminations Board decided against renewing. They're going to let him retire early instead."

"But he doesn't want to retire early. How unfair."

"Another sort of place would have fired him."

"And *another* sort of place would have promoted him."

"Look — I like him too — everyone likes him — but there's a limit." Limits were often proudly cited at the Organization.

Lidia took up her pencil again. "He's a good translator."

"Well — that's an opinion I never went along with. We worked together once, you know — on the Preliminary Survey of Intolerance. I had to correct him repeatedly."

Lidia raised her eyebrows, but merely asked, "Do you get full pension if you're retired before time?"

"Wouldn't be a bit surprised if he ends up better off than we do."

"Oh come."

"Well, at least they're not firing him. They're being decent. That's one thing you can say for the Organization. They're decent about this sort of thing. They wouldn't fire him."

"He'd get more money if they did." (Certain indemnities were involved in the rupture of Permanence.) Lidia put her head back down to her work. "I've got to get on with this."

Tong, passing Algie coming from the elevators, raised his hand in cordial greeting. "All O.K. with you, I hope, Wyatt?" (Tong was a man who could reverse himself in this way.)

"Splendid," grunted Algie. (Algie was a man who could grunt such a word.)

He went slowly along the corridor to the office he shared with Lidia.

An odd pair, Tong thought. He still had not told the news about Algie to his friend Pike in Inland Waterways on the floor below. Rather than wait for the elevator, he opened a dangerously heavy door marked "Sortie de Secours" and ran down the emergency stairs.

"Tong was here," Lidia said.

"Saw him in the corridor." Algie let himself into his chair. "Tong," he mused. "The very word is like a bell."

Lidia had no way of telling whether Algie had been informed that he was to be retired early. She would have liked to make him some show of solidarity but could only offer him a peppermint, which he refused.

"You free for lunch tomorrow?" she asked — Algie's telegraphic manner of communication having rubbed off on her to some extent.

"Tomorrow — what's tomorrow?" Algie turned several pages of his desk calendar. "Sorry, no. Lunching with Jaspersen. Could change it, perhaps?"

"No, no," said Lidia hastily, for Jaspersen was the one friend of Algie's who held an influential position in the Organization. "Some other day."

"Better make it soon," remarked Algie — from which Lidia realized that he knew his fate.

They went on with their work in silence for some moments. Then Algie let out a snort of laughter. "Listen to this. Chap here got it in a nutshell: *In the year under review, assistance was rendered to sixty differing countries.*"

Olaf Jaspersen was a year younger than Algie Wyatt and had been at Cambridge with him. People found this hard to believe, for Jaspersen was lean and fleet, his eye was clear, his features youthful. He wore dark, well-cut clothes during the week, and tweeds on Saturday mornings — which he invariably spent at the office. He had joined the Organization shortly after Algie. From the first he had been given important responsibilities, which he handled with efficiency and charm. He now held one of the most senior posts in the Organization and had established a reputation for common sense, justice, and rather more style than was usual. Things seemed to go right with Jaspersen. His career was prospering, his wife was beautiful, his children intelligent; he had even come into a small inheritance lately.

But something had happened to Olaf Jaspersen in recent years. He had fallen in love.

He had fallen in love with the Organization. Like someone who for a long time enjoys the friendship of a beautiful woman but boasts that he would not dream of having an affair with her, he had been conquered all the more completely in the end. During his early years on the staff, he had maintained his outside interests, his social pleasures — the books he read for nothing but enjoyment, the conversations he had that bore no apparent relation to his Organization duties. This state of affairs had flagged, diminished, then altogether ceased to be the case. He was still an able man, but his concept of ability had been coloured by Organization requirements; he found it harder to believe in the existence of abilities that did not directly contribute to the aim of the Organization. He was still, on occasion, gay — but his wit now sprang exclusively from Organization sources and could only be enjoyed by those in the Organizational know (of whom, fortunately for this purpose, his acquaintances had come to be principally composed). He had joined the staff because he believed sincerely, even passionately, in the importance of the Organization; that importance had latterly become indistinguishable from his own. He held, no doubt correctly, that the dissolution of the Organization would be calamitous for the human race; but one felt that the survival of the human race, should the Organization fail, would be regarded by him as a piece of downright impertinence.

Algie liked Olaf Jaspersen. He admired his many good qualities, including those gifts of energy and application which had not been bestowed upon himself. Algie's youthful memories of a lighter, livelier Jaspersen contributed to the place of the present Jaspersen in his affections. Jaspersen, in turn, had recollections of an Algie full of fun and promise, and regretted that the fun had increased in inverse ratio to the promise.

If his loyalty to Algie was in part due to Algie's never having rivalled him professionally, this was a common human weakness and need not be held against him. Jaspersen was genuinely grieved when he learned that Algie was to be retired before time, and genuinely wished to assist him. He therefore came to their lunch appointment prepared to give good advice.

The staff of the Organization took their meals in either of two places: a large and noisy cafeteria where they stood in line, or a large and noisy dining-room where they could — at additional cost — be served. The food, which was plain and good, was substantially the same in both places, although it may be said that in the dining-room the plates were slightly lighter and the forks slightly heavier. It was to the dining-room that Olaf Jaspersen took Algie for lunch this day.

Jaspersen, a man of too much taste to adopt the line of "Well now, what's this I hear?", found it difficult to raise with Algie the delicate question of enforced resignation. In Jaspersen's view, expulsion from the Organization was a very serious matter — more serious, one might even have said, than it was to Algie himself. When Algie and he were settled with their Scotches and had ordered their respective portions of codfish cakes and chicken à la king, he bent towards Algie. "A bad development," he said. "Can't tell you how sorry."

"Ah well," said Algie, "not to worry." He gave Jaspersen an appreciative nod, and went on with his drink, which he had already gone on with quite a bit.

"Rolls?" asked the waitress, wheeling up a portable oven.

"Er — one of those," Jaspersen said.

Putting it on his plate, she identified it with the words, "Corn muffin."

"Mistake," said Algie. "Nothing but crumbs."

"Look here, Algie, I know these fellows — on the Board, I mean. Not bad chaps — not villainous, nothing like that — but slow. Not overloaded with ideas. Only understand what's put in front of 'em. Got to be played their way or they can't grasp, you know."

"Ah well," said Algie again, briskly setting down his glass as if to herald a change of subject.

"Let me get you another one of those. My point is — in order to handle these chaps, you've got to get inside their minds. Talk their language." He fished a pamphlet out of his pocket. "I brought this for you. It's the Procedure of Appeal." He began to hand it across the table, but at that moment the waitress came up with their lunch.

"Codfish cakes?"

"Here," said Algie, making room. He took the pamphlet from Jaspersen and laid it on the table beside his plate. His second drink arrived, and Jaspersen ordered half a bottle of white wine.

"The Board," Jaspersen went on, spearing a cube of chicken, "is not the ultimate authority. That Bekkus is just a glorified clerk."

"Point is," Algie observed, "he *has* been glorified."

"I've been thinking about your case," said Jaspersen, "and I don't see how you could lose an appeal. I honestly don't. But get moving on it immediately — you don't have a moment to waste."

"What year is this?" inquired Algie, turning the bottle round. "Not at all bad." When he had demolished the first codfish cake, he said, "It's good of you, Olaf. But I'm not going to appeal."

Jaspersen looked less surprised than might have been expected. "Think it over," was all he said.

"No," Algie said. "Really. Better this way."

After a pause, Jaspersen went on kindly. "You have, of course, exactly the sort of qualities the Organization can't cope with. With the Organization it has to be — moderation in all things. I sometimes think we should put up in the main lobby that inscription the Greeks used in their temple: 'Nothing in Excess'." Jaspersen was pleased to have hit on this reconciliation of Algie's virtues with those of the Organization, for Algie was generally a pushover for the Greeks.

Algie finished another codfish cake and drank his wine, but when he replied Jaspersen was startled by the energy in his voice.

"Nothing in excess," Algie repeated. "But one has to understand the meaning of excess. Why should it be taken, as it seems to be these days, to refer simply to self-indulgence, or violence — or enjoyment? Wasn't it intended, don't you

501

think, to refer to all excesses — excess of pettiness, of timorousness, of officiousness, of sententiousness, of censoriousness? Excess of stinginess or rancour? Excess of bores?'' Algie went back to his vegetables for a while, and Jaspersen was again surprised when he continued. ''At the other end of that temple, there was a second inscription — 'Know Thyself'. Didn't mean — d'you think — that we should be mesmerized by every pettifogging detail of our composition. Meant we should understand ourselves in order to be free.'' Algie laid down his knife and fork and pushed away his plate. He handed back to Jaspersen the Procedure of Appeal. ''No thanks old boy, really. Fact is, I'm not suited to it here, and from that point of view these chaps are right. You tell me to get inside their minds — but if I did that I might never find my way out again.''

''But Algie, what about your pension? Think of the risk, at your age.''

''I do get something, you know — a reduced pension, or a lump sum. And then — for someone like me, the real risk is to stay.''

After that, they talked of other things. But Jaspersen felt disturbed and sad, and his sadness was greater than he could reasonably account for.

Lidia was coming down in the elevator when Millicent Bass got in. Lidia, on her way to the cafeteria, was pressed between a saintly Indian from Political Settlements (a department high on Algie's list of contradictions in terms) and Swoboda from Personnel, who greeted her in Russian. Behind her were two young Africans, speaking French and dressed in Italian suits, a genial roly-poly Iranian, and a Paraguayan called Martinez-MacIntosh with a ginger moustache. In front of her was a young girl from the Filing Room who stood in silence with her head bowed. Her pale hair, inefficiently swept upwards, was secured by a plastic clip, so that Lidia had a close view of her slender, somewhat pathetic neck and the topmost ridges of her spinal column. The zipper of her orange wool-jersey dress had been incompletely closed, and the single hook above it was undone. Lidia was toying with the idea of drawing this to the girl's attention when the elevator doors opened at the sixteenth floor to admit Millicent Bass.

Miss Bass was a large lady with a certain presence. One felt that she was about to say ''This way please'' — an impression that was fortified, when the elevator doors disclosed her, by the fact that she was standing, upright and expectant, with a document in her hand. She got in, raking the car as she did so with a hostile stare. Her mouth was firmly set, as if to keep back warmer words than those she habitually spoke, and her protuberant eyes were slightly belligerent, as if repressing tears.

Lidia knew her well, having once worked on a report for which Miss Bass was responsible. This was a Report on the Horizontal Coordination of Community Programmes, for Miss Bass was a member of the Department of Social and Anthropological Questions.

"Hello Millicent."

"Haven't seen you for a while, Lidia." Miss Bass squeezed in next to the girl in orange and, as far as she was able to do so, looked Lidia up and down. "You're far too thin," she announced. (She had the unreflective drawl of her profession, a voice loud yet exhausted.)

When the elevator disgorged them at the cafeteria, Miss Bass completed her scrutiny of Lidia. "You spend too much money on clothes."

Lidia was pondering the interesting fact that these two remarks, when reversed ("You are far too fat" and "You should spend more money on clothes"), are socially impermissible, when Millicent took her off guard by suggesting they lunch together. Rather than betray herself by that fractional hesitation which bespeaks dismay, she accepted heartily. Oh God how ghastly, she said to herself, dropping a selection of forks, knives, and spoons loudly on to a tray.

As they pushed their trays along, Millicent Bass inquired, "How much does a dress like that cost?" When Lidia was silent, she went on handsomely, "You don't have to tell me if you don't want to."

I know that, thought Lidia. It's being *asked* that annoys me.

"This all right for you?" Millicent asked her as they seated themselves near the windows. Lidia nodded, looking around and seeing Bekkus deep in conversation with a colleague at the adjacent table. They transferred their dishes from the tray and placed their handbags on a spare chair. Millicent also had her document, much annotated about the margins, which she pushed to the vacant side of the table. "I was going to run through that," she said regretfully. She unfolded a paper napkin in her lap and passed Lidia the salt. "Those codfish cakes look good."

Lidia began her lunch, and they exchanged casual remarks in high voices across the cafeteria din. (While talking with Miss Bass of things one did not particularly care about, one had the sensation of constantly attempting to allay her suspicions of one's true ideas and quite different interests.) Miss Bass then spoke in some detail of a new report she was working on, a survey of drainage in Polynesia. Conditions were distressing. There was much to be done. She gave examples.

"Poor things," Lidia murmured, stoically finishing her meal.

"It's no use saying 'poor things', Lidia." Miss Bass often took it on herself to dictate the responses of others. "Sentiment doesn't help. What's needed is know-how."

Lidia was silent, believing that even drains cannot supplant human feeling.

"The trouble with you, Lidia, is that you respond emotionally, not pragmatically. It's a device to retain the sense of patronage. Unconscious, of course. You don't think of people like these as your *brothers*." Miss Bass was one of those who find it easy and even gratifying to direct fraternal feelings towards large numbers

503

of people living at great distances. Her own brother — who was shiftless and sometimes tried to borrow money from her — she had not seen for over a year. "You don't relate to them as individuals." In Miss Bass's mouth the very word "individuals" denoted legions.

Lidia, casting about for a diversion, was softened to see that Mr Bekkus had brought out photographs of what appeared to be a small child and was showing them to his companion.

"Who *is* that man?" Millicent asked. "I've seen him around for years."

"Bekkus, from Personnel." Lidia lowered her voice. "He's on the Appointments and Terminations Board."

"My baby verbalizes," Bekkus was saying to his colleague. "Just learning to verbalize."

"Speaking of which," Millicent went on, "I hear you're losing your friend."

Lidia hesitated, then dug her spoon into her *crème caramel*. "You mean Algie."

"Well, there's a limit after all," Miss Bass said, sensing resistance.

"I'll miss him."

Miss Bass was not to be repulsed. "He is impossible."

Lidia laughed. "When people say that about Algie, it always reminds me of Bakunin."

"One of the new translators?" asked Miss Bass, running through the names of the Russian Section in her mind.

"No, no. I mean the Russian revolutionary."

"He's a friend of Algie's?" Millicent inquired — sharply, for politics were forbidden to the Organization staff, and a direct affiliation with them was one of the few infallible means of obtaining summary dismissal.

"He died a century ago."

"What's he got to do with Algie?" Miss Bass was still suspicious.

"Oh — he was a big untidy man, and he once said — when someone told him he was impossible — 'I shall continue to be impossible so long as those who are now possible remain possible.' "

Millicent was not amused. "The Organization cannot afford Algie Wyatt."

"He's a luxury," Lidia admitted.

"Pleasure-loving," said Miss Bass, as if this were something unnatural.

"Yes," Lidia agreed.

"And always trying to be clever."

"That's right," said Lidia.

"I'd prefer a more serious attitude," said Miss Bass. And it was true; she actually would.

Lidia held her spoon poised for a moment and said seriously, "Millicent, please don't go on about Algie. I don't like it."

Millicent's only idea of dignity was standing on it, and she did this for some minutes. Soon, however, she forgot what had been said and inquired about the terms of Algie's retirement.

"I really don't know anything about it." Lidia dropped her crumpled napkin on her plate.

"He has a choice, I believe — a reduced pension or a lump sum. That's the arrangement for enforced resignation."

"I don't *know*," said Lidia. "Shall we go?"

When they left the cafeteria, they walked along together to the elevators.

"Now I hope you won't think me hard," Miss Bass was beginning, when the elevator arrived — fortunately, perhaps, for her aspiration.

Algie was sitting at his desk when Lidia entered the office. They smiled at each other, and when she was seated at her desk, Lidia asked, "Did you have a nice time with Jaspersen?"

"Splendid," grunted Algie, going on with his work. He added, for once without looking up, "Wanted me to appeal my case. Shan't do it, though."

"Perhaps you ought to think about it?"

Algie shook his head, still writing. A little later he murmured aloud, "Never more, Miranda. Never more."

"Algie," Lidia said, putting down her pencil. "What do you think you'll do, then? Take a reduced pension?"

Now Algie did look up, but kept his pencil in his hand. "No. No. Take my lump sum and look for a small house somewhere along the Mediterranean. In the south of Spain, perhaps. Málaga, or Torremolinos. Good climate, some things still fairly cheap."

"Do you know anyone there?"

"Someone sure to turn up." He went on with his work for a moment. "Only thing is — it's very dangerous to die in Spain."

"How do you mean?"

"Law insists you be buried within twenty-four hours. Doctors not allowed to open your veins. If you should happen still to be alive, you wake up and find yourself in your coffin. When my time comes, I'm going down to Gibraltar and die in safety. Very dangerous to die in Spain."

"But what if one's really dead?"

Algie looked solemn. "That's a risk you have to take."

Algie died the following year at Torremolinos. He died very suddenly, of a stroke, and had no time to reach safety in Gibraltar. An obituary paragraph of some length appeared in the London *Times*, and a brief notice in the Organization's staff gazette, which misspelt his name. For so large a man, he left few material traces in the world. The slim remnants of his lump sum went to a sixteen-year-old nephew. His book on Roman remains in Libya is being reissued by an English publisher with private means.

Just about the time of Algie's death, Lidia became engaged to a handsome Scotsman in the Political Settlements Department. Although they have since been married, Lidia has kept her job and now shares her office with a Luxembourgeois who seldom looks up from his work and confesses to having no memory for verse. No one mourned the death of Algie more than Olaf Jaspersen, who remarked that he felt as if he had lost a part of himself. Jaspersen has recently attended important conferences abroad, and has taken to coming in to the office on Sundays. Millicent Bass is being sent to Africa, and regards this as a challenge; her arrival there is being accepted in the same spirit.

Swoboda has been put forward for a promotion, but has been warned that there may be some delay. Mr Bekkus has received *his* promotion, though over some objections. He is still combing the Organization, with little success, for unutilized sources of ability and imagination. He continues to dictate letters in his characteristic style, and his baby is now verbalizing fluently along much the same lines.

Algie's last letter to Lidia was written only a few days before he died, but reached her some weeks later, as he had neglected to mark it '*Correo Aéreo*'. In this letter he reported the discovery of several new contradictions in terms and mentioned, among other things, that Piero della Francesca died on the same day that Columbus discovered America, and that there is in Mexico a rat poison called The Last Supper. Such information is hard to come by these days; now that Algie was gone, Lidia could not readily think of another source.

David
Campbell

Harry Pearce

I sat beside the red stock route
And chewed a blade of bitter grass
And saw in mirage on the plain
A bullock wagon pass.
Old Harry Pearce was with his team.
"The flies are bad," I said to him.

The leaders felt his whip. It did
Me good to hear old Harry swear,
And in the heat of noon it seemed
His bullocks walked on air.
Suspended in the amber sky
They hauled the wool to Gundagai.

He walked in Time across the plain,
An old man walking in the air;
For years he wandered in my brain,
And now he lodges here.
And he may drive his cattle still
When Time with us has had his will.

Men in Green

There were fifteen men in green,
Each with a tommy-gun,
Who leapt into my plane at dawn;
We rose to meet the sun.

Our course lay to the east. We climbed
Into the break of day,
Until the jungle far beneath
Like a giant fossil lay.

We climbed towards the distant range
Where two white paws of cloud
Clutched at the shoulders of the pass.
The green men laughed aloud.

They did not fear the ape-like cloud
That climbed the mountain crest
And rode the currents of the air
And hid the pass in mist.

They did not fear the summer's sun
In whose hot centre lie
A hundred hissing cannon shells
For the unwatchful eye.

And when at Dobadura we
Set down, each turned to raise
His thumb towards the open sky
In mockery and praise.

But fifteen men in jungle green
Rose from the kunai grass
To come aboard, and my green men
In silence watched them pass:
It seemed they looked upon themselves
In a prophetic glass.

There were some leaned on a stick
And some on stretchers lay,
But few walked on their own two feet
In the early green of day.

They had not feared the ape-like cloud
That climbed the mountain crest;
They had not feared the summer's sun
With bullets for their breast.

Their eyes were bright, their looks were dull,
Their skin had turned to clay.
Nature had met them in the night
And stalked them in the day.

And I think still of men in green
On the Soputa track
With fifteen spitting tommy-guns
To keep a jungle back.

Windy Gap

As I was going through Windy Gap
A hawk and a cloud hung over the map.

The land lay bare and the wind blew loud
And the hawk cried out from the heart of the cloud,

"Before I fold my wings in sleep
I'll pick the bones of your travelling sheep,

"For the leaves blow back and the wintry sun
Shows the tree's white skeleton."

A magpie sat in the tree's high top
Singing a song on Windy Gap

That streamed far down to the plain below
Like a shaft of light from a high window.

From the bending tree he sang aloud,
And the sun shone out of the heart of the cloud

And it seemed to me as we travelled through
That my sheep were the notes that trumpet blew.

And so I sing this song of praise
For travelling sheep and blowing days.

Snow-gums

Moonlight and snow and snow-gums:
After much living turn, return
To the soul's climate, to cold forms
Wind cuts in ice and stone.

There stand like Socrates
Barefoot through the winter's night;
Burn in snowbound silences
As the trees hold the moonlight.

The powdered bloom along the bough
Wavers like a candle's breath;
Where snow falls softly into snow
Iris and rivers have their birth.

Night Sowing

O gentle, gentle land
Where the green ear shall grow,
Now you are edged with light:
The moon has crisped the fallow,
The furrows run with night.

This is the season's hour:
While couples are in bed,
I sow the paddocks late,
Scatter like sparks the seed
And see the dark ignite.

O gentle land, I sow
The heart's living grain.
Stars draw their harrows over,
Dews send their melting rain:
I meet you as a lover.

Song for the Cattle

Down the red stock route
Hock-deep in mirage
Rode the three black drovers
Singing to the cattle.

And with them a young woman,
Perhaps some squatter's daughter
From homestead or township,
Who turned her horse easily.

To my mind she was as beautiful
As the barmaid in Brewarrina
Who works at the Royal. Men
Ride all day to see her.

Fine-boned as a brigalow
Yet ample as a granary,
She has teeth good for laughing
Or biting an apple.

I'm thinking of quitting
My mountain selection,
The milking at morning
And the lonely axe-echoes;

Of swapping my slab hut
For a rolled-up blanket
And heading north-westward
For a life in the saddle —

For the big mobs trailing
Down the empty stock routes,
A horned moon at evening
And songs round the campfire.

Yes, I'll soon be drinking
At the Royal in Brewarrina
And ambling through mirage
With the squatter's daughter.

Town Planning

The plover cries in air
For the town has grown
And hatched its brick cottages
Amongst the stone.

Where young lambs danced
By grave-faced sheep,
Five hundred pretty housewives
Wake and sleep.

Nine months later,
And not one day more,
There's a new baby-carriage
By each front door.

Five hundred children
And the nappies to dry —
The housewives gossip,
Grow old and die.

Overhead the plover,
Like the moon apart,
Tells his lonely knowledge
Of the human heart.

We Took the Storms to Bed

We took the storms to bed at night
When first we loved. A spark
Sprang outward from our loins to light
Like genesis the dark.

On other things our minds were bent,
We did not hear the Word,
But locked like Sarah in her tent
The listening belly heard.

And though we wept, she laughed aloud
And fattened on her mirth:
As strange as creatures from a cloud
Our children walk the earth.

Mothers and Daughters

The cruel girls we loved
Are over forty,
Their subtle daughters
Have stolen their beauty;

And with a blue stare
Of cool surprise,
They mock their anxious mothers
With their mothers' eyes.

The Boongary

In the night, they say, the boongary can be heard walking in the trees
Carl Sofus Lumholtz

On Monday night I went to bed,
A snow-gum sprang from my sleeping head
By the banks of the Grubberdedrack.

On Tuesday night it grew so tall
Birds nested there and made their call
By the banks of the Grubberdedrack.

On Wednesday night an axeman came,
He said, I'll ringbark your snow-gum
By the banks of the Grubberdedrack.

On Thursday night the axe did crack
And turned on him like a tiger snake
By the banks of the Grubberdedrack.

On Friday night the white sun shone
At midnight in my green snow-gum
By the banks of the Grubberdedrack.

On Saturday night in my branching hair
Grey thrushes filled with song the air
By the banks of the Grubberdedrack.

On Sunday night while I lay at ease
The boongary walked within the trees
By the banks of the Grubberdedrack.

513

Droving

Down the red stock route, my tall son
Droves with his girl the white-faced steers
From the high country, as we would years
Ago beneath a daylight moon.
But now these two must bring them down
Between the snow-gums and the briars
Hung with their thousand golden tears,
To camp beside the creek at noon.
And finding them so sure and young,
The flower-fat mob their only care,
The days I thought beyond recall
Are ringed about with magpie song;
And it seems in spite of death and war
Time's not so desperate after all.

Windy Nights

Naked in snowdrifts, we've made love,
In city parks, at the front gate,
And thought no deeper truth to prove
Than this, that lovers cannot wait.
What if the whole world disapprove,
Though it should be a crowded street?
See how instinctive lovers move
To get their clothes off when they meet.
O what do lovers love the best,
Upstairs naked or downstairs dressed?
Windy nights and hot desire
Or an old book and a steady fire?
Ask your mistress. Should she pause,
She has a lover out of doors.

from *Works and Days*

MERINOS

Sheep! You can keep them! What cynic godhead made them?
Or did they think themselves through the sheep-pad paths
Of evolution? A little wool to warm savages,
And nibbling at tuber peelings around the hearths.

Sheep! Move a mob one way, it elects the other;
Cross a creek, sheep stamp the pebbles and ring around,
And when they do start leaping, follow the current
Downstream to a cliff-face. Half a dozen drowned!

Sheep! They're not dumb, they know every trick in the book:
Bale up, go down, dig in, at the cry of ''Sheep!''
Ask the penner-up. Ask Paterson: merinos,
He wrote, made our men sardonic or they would weep!

LOAFING

It's good to take a day off late in spring,
To let the reins hang easy and sheepdogs trot
At heel in the mare's shadow through cushioning clover
When instead of the cry of crows, high larks are singing.

They climb the light from nests where hen-quail herd
Their speckled young. Ducks act a broken wing,
Splashing downstream through pools to set trout darting
In slippery flotillas at the tail end of runs.

Red cattle graze or spellbound gaze from willows,
But bulls are busy. They paw up loam and bawl
Among the yellow daisies, locking horns for heifers.
An idle day is good in the spring or fall.

The Australian Dream

The doorbell buzzed. It was past three o'clock.
The steeple-of-Saint-Andrew's weathercock
Cried silently to darkness, and my head
Was bronze with claret as I rolled from bed
To ricochet from furniture. Light! Light
Blinded the stairs, the hatstand sprang upright,
I fumbled with the lock, and on the porch
Stood the Royal Family with a wavering torch.

"We hope," the Queen said, "we do not intrude.
The pubs were full, most of our subjects rude.
We came before our time. It seems the Queen's
Command brings only, 'Tell the dead marines!'
We've come to you." I must admit I'd half
Expected just this visit. With a laugh
That put them at their ease, I bowed my head.
"Your Majesty is most welcome here," I said.
"My home is yours. There is a little bed
Downstairs, a boiler-room, might suit the Duke."
He thanked me gravely for it and he took
Himself off with a wave. "Then the Queen Mother?
She'd best bed down with you. There is no other
But my wide bed. I'll curl up in a chair."
The Queen looked thoughtful. She brushed out her hair
And folded up *The Garter* on a pouf.
"Distress was the first commoner, and as proof
That queens bow to the times," she said, "we three
Shall share the double bed. Please follow me."

I waited for the ladies to undress —
A sense of fitness, even in distress,
Is always with me. They tucked away
Their state robes in the lowboy; gold crowns lay
Upon the bedside tables; ropes of pearls
Lassoed the plastic lampshade; their soft curls
Were spread out on the pillows and they smiled.
"Hop in," said the Queen Mother. In I piled
Between them to lie like a stick of wood.
I couldn't find a thing to say. My blood
Beat, but like rollers at the ebb of tide.
"I hope your Majesties sleep well," I lied.
A hand touched mine and the Queen said, "I am
Most grateful to you, Jock. Please call me Ma'am."

Starting from Central Station

FROM *STARTING FROM CENTRAL STATION*

A moon hangs in the air,
Its hands at ten past ten:
My father leaps alive
And I shrink to his son.

My father strides ahead
And stops to have a word
With men in caps who laugh.
He slips them a reward.

The trolley rolls behind
With boxes stacked like bricks:
Smoke and a whistle blow
And I am fifty-six.

Houses move through the parks,
Streets run with greens and reds:
Night conjures up the same
Old promises and dreads.

The train is on its way
And daylight gets to work,
Puts father in a box
And shoves him in the dark.

The Tourist Trade

Where once the ghostly swagman,
As curlews haunt a swamp,
Cried, "Who'll come waltz Matilda?"
They've built a tourist camp.

Cod flap among detergents,
Refusing lemonade
And sing with tenor voices,
God bless the tourist trade!

The wallabies are busy
Hopping from His to Hers
And stuff their Fowler toilets
Brimful with Bathurst burrs;

Then stand with young in pouches
To see the tourists pass
Like Swan Lake ballerinas
With thistles up their arse.

At dusk the last koala
Hands out an ice grenade
To Mum & Dad & Kevin
To spread the tourist trade.

Sandstone Country

FROM *LETTERS TO A FRIEND*

FOR DOUGLAS STEWART

Walking alone these hunchback animal hills
    And finding already in May
The red-wine spring cups of the native fuchsia
Breaking from stone, I think of you, old friend.

And although times and your regard have changed
    Since first you spelled their spiked
Belled living hieroglyphics to awake
Imagination, delight and they remain.

Heaths' frosts are here, dwarf apple; wattles unclench
    Hard yellow fists to dust
Quick mating honeyeaters — those needle-sharp birds
That plucked, to round a song, your daughter's hair.

By Cowan Creek that was where other hair,
    The waterfall rocklily,
Froze in cascades; and there it was we paused
Stilled by three lyrebirds' tumbling mimicry.

Well, it's your country. If you made it mine
    So that it keens to eye and ear
And sticks change into water-dragons, here
Cart-rut shell and scribbly-gum write "*yours*".

Glenrowan

FROM KELLY COUNTRY

They've burnt the grass beneath the pepper-trees
Where Mrs Jones' hotel
Once flared between the railway and the hill.
A roadsign says *Police*.

Under the trees there is a dump for cars:
Their wry pathetic shells
Stripped and forgotten, rust among old bottles,
Victims of other wars.

Behind stand two new churches. As the hard
Dawn tips the steepled hills,
On time the *Spirit* yells upon its rails,
Passing the scrapper's yard.

Two Views

For Lesueur aboard *Le Géographe* the scene
Was a kind of paradise. The swans are black
Pothooks butting haloes on a lake
Stippled and swept by wildfowl. On tender green
Banks, like picnickers beside the Seine,
In female poses kangaroos look back
At naked hunters fishing in a bark
Canoe the sacred waters in the sun.

Augustus Earle, in hell, thirty years on,
Depicts *A Native Family of New South Wales
Sitting down on an English Settler's Farm*.
The fallen king has rum to keep him warm
And Brisbane's jacket. On the veranda rails
The farmer straddles, pointing. Is that a gun?

Trawlers

Sun orchids and wild iris as violet-blue
As the wine-dark sea; and a death below, the ocean
Unfolds silk petals on rock — bolts thrown on
Aphrodite's table. But death is cloaked, is true,
On this eminence. Close sleepless eyes and you
Are in the old nightmare. In imagination
Gloucester stood here beside Poor Tom, his son,
And threw himself down to find, as most men do,
That he must put up with blindness and dishonour.
Rounding the lighthouse come the trawlers sailing
To their rusty haven. In baskets, flowers of the sea
Are stacked in quicksilver tiers for gutting, scaling;
And the John Dory at this silver hour
Still bear Christ's thumb-marks, his blessing at Galilee.

Bellbirds

Bell-miners ring like axemen in the green timber:
Chink ching and a water tree
Sways on its dappled bole, one hundred feet
Of waterfall, and falls; and the long reach
Rocks in pockets of light in the shocked silence
Of water tinkling over stone. *Ching chink!*

The axes redouble their labour, falling like rain;
Lopping the branches, chopping the bole
Into lengths for the waiting jinker. And the bells
Ring out *ching chink* from the harness of the horses
As the forests melt away. In snowing sawmills
You can hear the thawing of the water. *Ching!*

Chink chink! Ching ching! To the song of tiny hammers
Houses go up in the clearing. Men squint down beams;
The beams arch over like ribs, barring the stars
That chime at night in the lonely tree by the window;
And two bell-miners cock their heads in their cage,
Rusty green birds that sometimes sing *ching chink*.

from *The Man in the Honeysuckle*

LIZARD AND STONE

A bronze lizard
Is wrapped around a river stone

The lizard is half awake
The stone has not yet woken

Each preserves an outward stillness

Within the stone
A dance of atoms
Warms the basking lizard

The warmth of the lizard
Quickens the atoms

About the stone and lizard
Where they lie like lovers
The cosmos dances.

MOSQUITOES

Mosquitoes are blood relations
They doze on the white ceiling
Like the children upstairs
While we wake below

We are their livelihood
They wish us no harm
Stealing through windows
With their fine instruments
And teething drone
There they say you hardly felt it

And they work like surgeons
While we stir in sleep
Tapping veins adjusting
The flow   dim
Figures at work   murmuring
Creatures of the subconscious
Extinct cloaked vampires

Spirits hooked on blood
Live scarlet drops
Hanging like fruit bats
From the ceiling — our babies
Our own flesh and blood
Loving us and jealous
Mmmmmm they cry at dusk
They are helpless without us.

SCRIBBLY-GUMS

1

White parchment trees
Recording
The brief lives of insects

An automatic writing
Telling all and nothing

2

The freedom of setting out
And careless inland wanderings

The indecisive
Changes of course
And cramped return
To a dry waterhole

3

Following no footsteps
I walked through a world
Of my own creation

Miraculously a birth
We lay together
I placed a rifle
Across my chest in death

Following no footsteps
I walked through a world
Of my own creation.

Snake

The tiger snake moves
Like slow lightning. Like
A yard of creek water
It flows over rocks
Carving the grass.

Where have you gone,
Long fellow, cold brother,
Like a lopped limb or
Truth that we shy from
Leaving a cast skin?

Snakes are like a line
Of poetry: a chill
Wind in the noon,
A slalom in the spine
Setting ears back, hair on end.

''Some people will not live
With a snake in the house.''
Mice make off. Look
Under your chair; worse
Take down a book:

A line like an icicle!

The Tiger Snake.

Tree in a Landscape

FROM *SONGS OF A BUSH HATTER*

It came as a complete surprise
After long noons of waiting
The tree seemed to grow of its own volition

Its roots split the rock
Its leaves wove lean shadows
No one believed that I had made it

I put a starling in a hollow
In another a scarlet parrot
Birds woke in the boughs
Insects scribbled their brief histories

The tree stripped its bark
Lives blew about me
I lay down in its shade
A small part of the landscape
That entranced I created.

Crab

FROM *SONGS OF CHANCE*

The crab sidled out
From its hiding place
Beneath my shoulder-blade

Fending with one enlarged claw
It scuttled sideways
And settled in an outcropping elbow

It left tiptoe tracks
In the hard sands of the ulna
Pain broke on the white beach

The crab has reached my hand
In the dreck at the high-tide line
Look what I have found.

The Wimmera

FROM WITH A BLUE DOG

Steel lines melt
Into the rim of the horizon
Where plain and sky are welded
And at intervals shimmer
Along the tracks like bins
The silver temples of Ceres
In whose shadow tractors crawl
Over the floor of the plain
As mortal as men
Before the vast seasons
Brown green and blond
That move as slow as
Fairweather cumulus
Over tin towns and temporary homes
And the sky fits
The walls of the horizon
Like a silver lid.

The Return of Jason

I am an old man,
I have wandered a long time
Changing under the changing moon.
I did not guess I would end
On the seashore without a friend
But I am content.

I know the ways of the wind.
It blows this way and that way
In the changeable mind
Until the will snaps like a hinge.
One time fortune made me cringe.
Reeds are wise, reeds bend.

I am no longer proud.
I have returned as often in dream
To the point from which I set out.
In the ship's shade I smile;
After all, it was worth while.
Like the oar, the oarsman is bent.

Young men laugh at death,
Love is their golden fleece.
Old men go back to the earth.
They return what they have taken
To grass-root and bracken.
What is there to lament?

Here by the *Argo*'s prow,
The Branch of Dodona
Nods to me now:
Men and boughs break;
Praise life while you walk and wake;
It is only lent.

Elizabeth
Harrower

The Beautiful Climate

THE SHAWS went down to the cottage on Scotland Island every week-end for two years. Hector Shaw bought the place from some hotel-keeper he knew, never having so much as hinted at his intention till the contract was signed. Then he announced to his wife and daughter the name of a certain house, his ownership of it, its location, and the fact that they would all go down every Friday night to put it in order.

It was about an hour's drive from Sydney. At the Church Point wharf they would park the car, lock it up, and wait for the ferry to take them across to the island.

Five or six families made a living locally, tinkering with boats and fishing, but most of the houses round about were week-enders, like the Shaws' place. Usually these cottages were sold complete with a strip of waterfront and a jetty. In the Shaws' case the jetty was a long spindly affair of grey wooden palings on rickety stilts, with a perpendicular ladder that had to be climbed getting in and out of the boat. Some of the others were handsome constructions equipped with special flags and lights to summon the ferry-man when it was time to return to civilisation.

As Mr. Shaw had foretold, they were constantly occupied putting the house in order, but now and then he would buy some green prawns, collect the lines from the spare-bedroom cupboard, and take his family into the middle of the bay to fish. While he made it obligatory to assume that this was a treat, he performed every action with his customary air of silent, smouldering violence, as if to punish misdemeanours, alarming his wife and daughter greatly.

Mrs. Shaw put on her big straw sun-hat, tied it solemnly under her chin, and went behind him down the seventy rough rock steps from the house. She said nothing. The glare from the water gave her migraine. Since a day years before when she was a schoolgirl learning to swim, and had almost drowned, she had had a horror of deep water. Her husband knew it. He was a difficult man, for what reason no one had been able to discover, least of all Hector Shaw himself.

Del followed her mother down the steep bushy track, not speaking, her nerves

Russell Drysdale *Landscape with Figures* 1972
Oil on canvas 76 × 127 cm
Robert Holmes à Court Collection

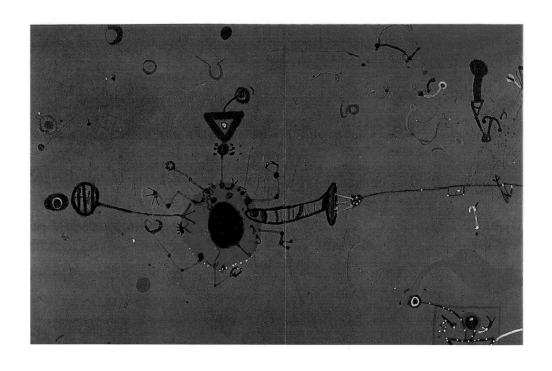

John Olsen *Salute to Slessor's Five Bells* 1972–73 (section of mural)
Acrylics on marine ply 21 × 3 m (approx)
Sydney Opera House Trust

raw, her soundless protests battering the air about her. She did not *want* to go, nor, of course, could she want to stay when her absence would be used against her mother.

They were not free. Either the hostage, or the one over whom a hostage was held, they seemed destined to play for ever if they meant to preserve the peace. And peace had to be preserved. Everything had always been subordinated to this task. As a child, Del had been taught that happiness was nothing but the absence of unpleasantness. For all she knew, it was true. Unpleasantness, she knew, could be extremely disagreeable. She knew that what was irrational had to be borne, and she knew she and her mother longed for peace and quiet — since she had been told so so often. But still she did not want to go.

Yet that they should not accompany her father was unthinkable. That they should all three be clamped together was, in a way, the whole purpose of the thing. Though Del and her mother were aware that he might one day sink the boat deliberately. It wasn't *likely*, because he was terrified of death, whereas his wife would welcome oblivion, and his daughter had a stony capacity for endurance (so regarding death, at least, they had the upper hand): but it was *possible*. Just as he might crash the car some day on purpose if all three were secure together in it.

"Why do we *do* it?" Del asked her mother relentlessly. "You'd think we were mental defectives the way we troop behind him and do what we're told just to save any trouble. And it never does. Nothing we do makes sure of anything. When I go out to work every day it's as if I'm out on parole. You'd think we were hypnotised."

Her mother sighed and failed to look up, and continued to butter the scones.

"*You're* his wife, so maybe you think you have to do it, but I don't. I'm eighteen."

However, till quite recently she had been a good deal younger, and most accustomed to being used in the cause of peace. Now her acquiescence gnawed at and baffled her, but though she made isolated stands, in essence she always did submit. Her few rebellions were carefully gauged to remain within the permitted limits, the complaints of a prisoner-of-war to the camp-commandant.

This constant nagging from the girl exhausted Mrs. Shaw. Exasperation penetrated even her alarming headaches. She asked desperately, "What would you do if you *didn't* come? You're too nervous to stay in town by yourself. And if you did, what would you do?"

"*Here*. I have to come *here*, but why do we have to go in the boat?" On a lower note, Del muttered, "I wish I worked at the kindergarten seven days a week. I dread the night and week-ends."

She could *think* a thing like that, but never say it without a deep feeling of shame. Something about her situation made her feel not only, passively, abused, but actively, surprisingly, guilty.

All her analysis notwithstanding, the fishing expeditions took place whenever the man of the family signified his desire for some sport. Stationed in the dead centre of the glittering bay, within sight of their empty house, they sat in the open boat, grasping cork rollers, feeling minute and interesting tugs on their lines from time to time, losing bait and catching three-inch fish.

Low hills densely covered with thin gums and scrub sloped down on all sides to the rocky shore. They formed silent walls of a dark subdued green, without shine. Occasional painted roofs showed through. Small boats puttered past and disappeared.

As the inevitable pain began to saturate Mrs. Shaw's head, she turned gradually paler. She leaned against the side of the boat with her eyes closed, her hands obediently clasping the fishing-line she had been told to hold.

The dazzle of the heavy summer sun sucked up colour till the scene looked black. Her light skin began to burn. The straw sun-hat was like a neat little oven in which her hair, her head and all its contents, were being cooked.

Without expression, head lowered, Del looked at her hands, fingernails, legs, at the composition of the cork round which her line was rolled. She glanced sometimes at her mother, and sometimes, by accident, she caught sight of her father's bare feet or his arm flinging out a newly-baited line, or angling some small silver fish off the hook and throwing it back, and her eyes sheered away.

The wooden interior of the boat was dry and burning. The three fishers were seared, beaten down by the sun. The bait smelled. The water lapped and twinkled blackly but could not be approached: sharks abounded in the bay.

The cottage was fairly dilapidated. The walls needed painting inside and out, and parts of the veranda at the front and both sides had to be re-floored. In the bedrooms, sitting-room and kitchen, most of the furniture was old and crudely-made. They burned the worst of it, replacing it with new stuff, and what was worth salvaging Mrs. Shaw and Del gradually scrubbed, sanded and painted.

Mr. Shaw did carpentering jobs, and cleared the ground nearby of some of the thick growth of eucalyptus gums that had made the rooms dark. He installed a generating plant, too, so that they could have electric light instead of relying on kerosene lamps at night.

Now and then his mood changed inexplicably, for reasons so unconnected with events that no study and perpetuation of these external circumstances could ensure a similar result again. Nevertheless, knowing it could not last, believing it might, Mrs. Shaw and Del responded shyly, then enthusiastically, but always with respect and circumspection, as if a friendly lion had come to tea.

These hours or days of amazing good humour were passed, as it were, a few feet off the ground, in an atmosphere of slightly hysterical gaiety. They sang, pumping water to the tanks; they joked at either end of the saw, cutting logs for winter fires; they ran, jumped, slithered, and laughed till they had to lean against the trees for support. They reminded each other of all the incidents of other days like these, at other times when his nature was in eclipse.

"We'll fix up a nice shark-proof pool for ourselves," he said. "We own the water-frontage. It's crazy not to be able to cool off when we come down. If you can't have a dip here, surrounded by water, what's the sense? We'd be better to stay home and go to the beach, this weather."

"Three cheers!" Del said. "When do we start?"

The seasons changed. When the nights grew colder, Mr. Shaw built huge log-fires in the sitting-room. If his mood permitted, these fires were the cause of his being teased, and he liked very much to be teased.

Charmed by his own idiosyncrasy, he would pile the wood higher and higher, so that the walls and ceiling shone and flickered with the flames, and the whole room crackled like a furnace on the point of explosion. Faces scorching, they would rush to throw open the windows, then they'd fling open the doors, dying for air. Soon the chairs nearest the fire would begin to smoke and then everyone would leap outside to the dark veranda, crimson and choking. Mr. Shaw laughed and coughed till he was hoarse, wiping his eyes.

For the first few months, visitors were non-existent, but one night on the ferry the Shaws struck up a friendship with some people called Rivers, who had just bought a cottage next door. They came round one Saturday night to play poker and have supper, and in no time weekly visits to each other's house were established as routine. Grace and Jack Rivers were relaxed and entertaining company. Their easy good-nature fascinated the Shaws, who looked forward to these meetings seriously, as if the Rivers were a sort of rest-cure ordered by a specialist, from which they might pick up some health.

"It was too good to last," Mrs. Shaw said later. "People are so funny."

The Rivers' son, Martin, completed his army training and went down to stay on the island for a month before returning to his marine-engineering course at a technical college in town. He and Del met sometimes and talked, but she had not gone sailing with him when he asked her, nor was she tempted to walk across the island to visit his friends who had a pool.

"Why not?" he asked.

"Oh, well . . ." She looked down at the dusty garden from the veranda where they stood. "I have to paint those chairs this afternoon."

"*Have* to?" Martin had a young, open, slightly-freckled face.

Del looked at him, feeling old, not knowing how to explain how complicated it would be to extricate herself from the house, and her mother and father. He would never understand the drama, the astonishment, that would accompany her statement to them. Even if, eventually, they said, "Go, go!" recovering from their shock, her own joylessness and fatigue were so clear to her in anticipation that she had no desire even to test her strength in the matter.

But one Saturday night over a game of cards, Martin asked her parents if he might take her the next night to a party across the bay. A friend of his, Noel Stacey, had a birthday to celebrate.

Del looked at him with mild surprise. He had asked her. She had refused.

Her father laughed a lot at this request as though it were very funny, or silly, or misguided, or simply impossible. It turned out that it *was* impossible. They had to get back to Sydney early on Sunday night.

If they *did* have to, it was unprecedented, and news to Del. But she looked at her father with no surprise at all.

Martin said, "Well, it'll be a good party," and gave her a quizzical grin. But his mother turned quite pink, and his father cleared his throat gruffly several times. The game broke up a little earlier than usual, and, as it happened, was the last one they ever had together.

Not knowing that it was to be so, however, Mrs. Shaw was pleased that the matter had been dealt with so kindly and firmly. "What a funny boy!" she said later, a little coyly, to Del.

"Is he?" she said indifferently.

"One of the new generation," said Mr. Shaw, shaking his head and eyeing her with caution.

"Oh?" she said, and went to bed.

"She didn't really want to go to that party at all," her mother said.

"No, but we won't have him over again, do you think? He's got his own friends. Let him stick to them. There's no need for this. These fellows who've been in army camps — I know what they're like."

"She hardly looked at him. She didn't care." Mrs. Shaw collected the six pale-blue cups, saucers and plates on the wooden tray, together with the remnants of supper.

With his back to the fire, hands clasped behind him, Mr. Shaw brooded. "He had a nerve though, when you come to think of it. I mean — he's a complete stranger."

Mrs. Shaw sighed anxiously, and her eyes went from one side of the room to the other. "I'm sure she didn't like him. She doesn't take much interest in boys. You're the only one."

Mr. Shaw laughed reluctantly, looking down at his shoes.

As more and more of the property was duly painted and repaired, the Shaws tended to stop work earlier in the day, perhaps with the unspoken intention of making the remaining tasks last longer. Anyway, the pressure was off, and Mrs. Shaw knitted sweaters, and her husband played patience, while Del was invariably glued to some book or other.

No one in the district could remember the original owner-builder of their cottage, or what he was like. But whether it was this first man, or a later owner, *someone* had left a surprisingly good library behind. It seemed likely that the builder had lived and died there, and that his collection had simply been passed on with the property from buyer to buyer, over the years.

Books seemed peculiarly irrelevant on this remote hillside smelling of damp earth and wood-smoke and gums. The island had an ancient, prehistoric, undiscovered air. The alphabet had yet to be invented.

However, the books *had* been transported here by someone, and Del was pleased to find them, particularly the many leather-bound volumes of verse. Normally, in an effort to find out why people were so peculiar, she read nothing but psychology. Even after she knew psychologists did not know, she kept reading it from force of habit, in the hope that she might come across a formula for survival directed specifically at her: *Del Shaw, follow these instructions to the letter!* . . . Poetry was a change.

She lay in a deck-chair on the deserted side-veranda and read in the mellow three o'clock, four o'clock, sunshine. There was, eternally, the smell of grass and burning bush, and the homely noise of dishes floating up from someone's kitchen along the path of yellow earth, hidden by trees. And she hated the chair, the mould-spotted book, the sun, the smells, the sounds, her supine self.

And they came on a land where it was always afternoon.

"It's like us, exactly like us and this place," she said to her mother, fiercely brushing her long brown hair in front of the dressing-table's wavy mirror. "Always afternoon. Everyone lolling about. Nobody *doing* anything."

"My goodness!" Her mother stripped the sheets off the bed to take home to the laundry. "I thought we'd all been active enough this week-end to please anyone. And I don't see much afternoon about Monday morning."

"Active! That isn't what I mean. Anyway, I don't mean here or this week-end. I mean everyone, everywhere, all the time. Ambling round till they die." Oh, but that wasn't what she meant, either.

Mrs. Shaw's headache look appeared. "It's off to the doctor with you tonight, Miss!"

Del set her teeth together. When her mother had left the room with her arms full of linen, still darting sharp glances at her daughter, Del closed her eyes and raised her face to the ceiling.

Let me *die*.

The words seemed to be ground from her voiceless body, to be ground, powdered stone, from her heart.

She breathed very slowly; she slowly righted her head, carefully balancing its weight on her neck. Then she pulled on her suede jacket, lifted her bag, and clattered down the uneven stone steps to the jetty. It always swayed when anyone set foot on it.

When the cottage had been so patched and cleaned that, short of a great expenditure of capital, no further improvement was possible, Hector Shaw ceased to find any purpose in his visits to it. True, there was still the pool to be tackled, but the summer had gone by without any very active persuasion, any pleading, any teasing, from his wife and daughter. And if *they* were indifferent, far be it from him. . . .

Then there was another thing. Not that it had any connexion with the place, with being on Scotland Island, but it had the side-effect of making the island seem less — safe, salubrious, desirable. Jack Rivers died from a heart-attack one Sunday morning. Only fifty-five he was, and a healthier-looking fellow, you couldn't have wished to meet.

Since the night young Martin Rivers had ruined their poker parties, they had seen very little of Jack and Grace. Sometimes on the ferry they had bumped into each other, and when they had the Shaws, at least, were sorry that it had all worked out so badly. Jack and Grace were good company. It was hard not to feel bitter about the boy having spoiled their nice neighbourly friendship so soon before his father died. Perhaps if Jack had spent more time playing poker and less doing whatever he did do after the Saturdays stopped. . . .

On a mild mid-winter night, a few weeks after Jack Rivers's funeral, the Shaw family sat by the fire. Del was gazing along her corduroy slacks into the flames, away from her book. Her parents were silent over a game of cards.

Mr. Shaw took a handful of cashew nuts from a glass dish at his side and started to chew. Then leaning back in his chair, his eyes still fixed on his cards, he said, "By the way, the place's up for sale."

His wife stared at him. "What place?"

"*This* place." He gave her his sour, patient look. "It's been on Dalgety's books for three weeks."

"What for?" Del asked, conveying by the gentleness of her tone, her total absence of criticism. It was dangerous to question him, but then it was dangerous not to, too.

"Well, there isn't much to do round here now. And old Jack's popped off —" (He hadn't meant to say that!) Crunching the cashew nuts, he slid down in his chair expansively, every supra-casual movement premeditated as though he were playing *Hamlet* at Stratford.

The women breathed deeply, not with regret, merely accepting this new fact in their lives. Mrs. Shaw said, "Oh! . . ." and Del nodded her comprehension. Changing their positions imperceptibly, they prepared to take up their occupations again in the most natural and least offensive ways they could conceive. There was enormous potential danger in any radical change of this sort.

"Ye-es," said Mr. Shaw, drawing the small word out to an extraordinary length. "Dalgety's telling them all to come any Saturday or Sunday afternoon." Still he gazed at his handful of cards, then he laid them face down on the table, and with a thumb, thoughtfully rubbed the salt from the cashews into the palm of his other hand. It crumbled onto his knees, and he dusted it down to the rug, seeming agreeably occupied in its distribution.

"Ye-es," he said again, while his wife and daughter gazed at him painfully. "When and if anyone takes the place, I think we'd better use the cash to go for a trip overseas. What do you say? See the Old Country. . . . Even the boat trip's pretty good, they tell me. You go right round the coast here (that takes about a week), then up to Colombo, Bombay, Aden, through the Suez, then up through the Mediterranean, through the Straits of Messina, past some volcano, and past Gibraltar to Marseilles, then London."

There was a silence.

Mr. Shaw turned away from the table and his game, and looked straight into his wife's grey eyes — a thing he rarely did. Strangers were all right, he could look at them, but with relations, old acquaintances, his spirit, unconscious, was ashamed and uneasy.

"Go away?" his wife repeated, turning a dreadful colour.

He said, "Life's short. I've earned a holiday. Most of my typists've been abroad. We'll have a year. We'll need a year. *If* someone turns up on the ferry one day and *wants* the place, that is. There's a bit of a slump in real estate just now, but I guess we'll be okay."

And they looked at each other, the three of them, with unfamiliar awe. They were about to leave this dull pretty city where they were all so hard to live with, and go to places they had read about, where the world was, where things happened, where the photographs of famous people came from, where history was, and snow in cities, and works of art, and splendour . . .

Poetry and patience were discarded from that night, while everyone did extra jobs about the cottage to add to its attractiveness and value. Mrs. Shaw and Del planted tea-trees and hibiscus bushes covered with flowers of palest apricot, and pink streaked with red. Mr. Shaw cemented the open space under the house (it was propped up on columns on its steep hillside) and the area underneath was like a large extra room, shady and cool. They put some long bamboo chairs down there, fitted with cushions.

Most week-end afternoons, jobs notwithstanding, Del went to the side-veranda to lean over the railing out of sight and watch the ferry go from jetty to jetty and return to Church Point. She watched and willed, but no one ever came to see the house.

It was summer again, and the heatwave broke records. Soon it was six months since the night they had talked about the trip.

Always the island was the same. It was scented, self-sufficient; the earth was warm underfoot, and the air warm to breathe. The hillside sat there, quietly, rustling quietly, a smug curving hillside that had existed for a long time. The water was blue and sparkled with meaningless beauty. Smoke stood in the sunny sky above the bush here and there across the bay, where other week-end visitors were cooking chops, or making coffee on fuel stoves.

Del watched the ferries and bargained with fate, denying herself small pleasures, which was very easy for her to do. She waited. Ferries came and went round the point, but never called at their place.

They lost heart. In the end it would have been impossible even to mention the trip. But they all grieved with a secret enduring grief as if at the death of the one person they had loved. Indeed, they grieved for their own deaths. Each so unknown and un-understood, who else could feel the right regret? From being eaten by the hillside, from eating one another, there had been the chance of a reprieve. Now it was evidently cancelled, and in the meantime irretrievable admissions had been made. . . .

At the kindergarten one Tuesday afternoon Miss Lewis, who was in charge, called Del to the telephone. She sat down, leaning her forehead on her hand before lifting the receiver.

"Hullo?"

"Del, your father's sold the cottage to a pilot. Somebody Barnes. He's bought the tickets. We've just been in to get our cabins. We're leaving in two months."

"What? . . . A pilot?"

"Yes. We're going on the *Arcadia* on the 28th of November. The cabins are lovely. Ours has got a porthole. We'll have to go shopping, and get injections and passports —"

"We're *going*?"

"Of course we are, you funny girl! We'll tell you all about it when you get home tonight. I've started making lists."

They were going. She was going away. Out in the world she would escape from them. There would be room to run, outside this prison.

"So we're off," her mother said.

Del leaned sideways against the wall, looking out at the eternal afternoon, shining with all its homey peace and glory. "Oh, that's good," she said. "That's good."

J. R.
Rowland

Revisiting New England

Bare bones. Cold dazzling streams.
Skies remote and white as miracles.
Delicate distances. Leaflessness. Black pines.
Granite-cobbled hills. Beams

Of light silent from heights.
This setting without colour is the sacred
Cathedral of my childhood, before all
Names, assertions, schemes, reversals, slights

Or knowledge of elsewhere; before damage
Or coalescence of the complex substance
That now comprises self. No compromise
Adulterates its purity; its image

Lives beneath papers, cables, interviews,
Meetings, parties, greetings, airport waitings,
Official negotiations and frustrations
In various cities, inconstant as the news

And insubstantial, that evaporate to bring
Me back to this earliest landscape of late winter
Distant, silent, permanent: vocal only
Through the cuckoo's seven notes of spring.

from *At Noosa*

All day the house blooms like a sail
　With air and light
Trembles at anchor on its gaptoothed piles
In a seawind soft as talc that touches and again touches
　Like a sweet mother. Spade and pail
Trip us by open doors, pennies and shells
Scatter on ledges and on windowsills

With combs, my thongs, your lipstick, safetypins.
　Sand in the shower
Salty towels on the veranda rail
The worn mirror's bloodshot brown eye
　Shows us each evening darker skins
Eyes clearer, bleaching hair. Sunstruck we lie
At ease or swim or climb the rocks or play

At sandcastles on the dazzling field
　Of empty beach
Plump as the children's faces, that grow warm
And smooth and simple to the touch as sand.
　At dark the children yield
Willingly to sleep, as the sea sound
Builds over the house a temple, round

Columns and low roof, that rise
　Close by our windows, where
The folding surf renews its hiss and crumple
Vague white on white in darkness, till the moon
　Swelling towards fullness like the days
Restores the distance, floods the sky with milk
The sea with diamond flashes, breathing silk

Scents in our faces. As we find each other
   A child laughs in sleep
And still we have uncounted days, our view
Ends in no cliff, the beach is ours,
   Morning fulfils the stars' pledge of fair weather.
All true; yet items in the full account
Are sandflies, washing-up, mosquitoes, rent

Three days' rain, and something like a quarrel.
   Lara and Zhivago
Had no children, nor is laundry mentioned
By Lawrence in a similar situation
   With Frieda in the cottage at Thirroul:
It makes a certain difference to the tone.
Exaltation needs to be alone

And art selects; but if we take the whole
   Seldom we shall
Do better, or be better as ourselves.
Be thankful then the mosquitoes were so few
   The time so radiant, that if we did fail
Our failures served to toughen the alloy,
As stars give sense to night, or night to day.

Eric C.
Rolls

The Ballad of the Old Captain

Here's a map of the world, I say —
Of the universe it may be —
And I sit down with compass and pen,
Ruler, dividers — I'm at it again —
To find out where I'm going.

I chart us clear of the boiling seas
And of many a good ship's peril
At the edge of the world where sailors' knees
Crumple beneath their loads of sin
For fear of life hereafter;

And hope to berth in the Isles of Spice
For a cargo of sandalwood,
Cinnamon, nutmeg, everything good
To the nose of a skipper offended for years
At freights of hide and skin.

I sign on a crew awash with beer,
As good as any other,
But I reckon without my lolly legs
That fumble me down to the wrong long pier
Where a strange ship droops at her moorings.

I flipperty-flop on a rolling bridge
Like a dumpling in a stew;
A garrulous compass shows me the way
And the cross-eyed son of a drunk Malay
Hangs to a wheel askew.

We founder, of course, by berg or rock:
I don't go down with the ship:
I swim about for thirteen days
Then wash at last on a barren land
Like any piece of wreck.

There is never a sign of fruit or flesh
And certainly none of Friday;
On a puddle of water and bony fish
My life is thin as a drunkard's wish
And my soul near shrunk away.

I am saved in time and put to bed
Like a piece of crinkled leather.
While parsons nourish my soul again,
Physicians and surgeons, all eminent men,
Restitch its case together.

Sister Comfort on hand in the wings
Counsels an easy life
So I sit for a time in a rocking chair
While my head tick-tock to my pendulum arms
Moves counter-clockwise nowhere;

Till I find an old chart, and compass, and pen —
Weigh anchor, you lubbers! I'm at it again!

Bruce
Beaver

Angels' Weather

Watching Rushcutters' bright bayful of masts and coloured keels,
Half-sensing Dufy's muse walking on that gull, sail
And cobalt sky reflecting surface,
I open my senses to the gift of it and hear
The yacht club telecommunication paging
A Mr Fairweather over the water;
Watch gulls wheeling one after the other
After another with sustenance in its beak.
Frantic as white sharks they thresh the blue waters of the air.
Perched on a dory a shag replete
Flaps dry and stretches out its black umbrella wings.
On the mud-flat's rank solarium
A few grounded parent birds are teaching their young
To walk tip-web-toe,
Heads pointed up at the sun-mote
Swarms of gnat-fry,
Fishing the citron-scented shallows of noon.

Passing are pattern-stockinged girls
With old dogs and strollers full of family.
Prim seated or grass floored the sun imbibers,
Some still hung from last night's
Vinegary round of dark: the White Lady presiding
Somewhere near the tolling two o'clock till,
Honing her crescent. Now only
The grass poking its tongues out at our fears;
The coral trees' crimson beaks of bloom pecking the blue
Above the doughy park's arena of tiger-striped
And cougar-charcoaled athletes
A murmuration of applause for no one in particular
From the immense and yellow foliaged
Fig leafing through the wind;
Spectator of the sportive weather.

Olympiads of effort are stored, restored
Within that echo-memory of clapping leaf.
Now we are all sun lovers, steaming in tweeds and combinations.
Be it upon our own heads
This blessed incontinent surrendering
To the open-handed noon broadcasting silence
And the bright winged seeds of peace which find their nest
In an evening of visionary trees.

Letter xxix

FROM LETTERS TO LIVE POETS

Two houses on from here someone is burning off.
Woodsmoke redolent of other summers.
Salt air and woodsmoke.
Faint and thin at first the recollections
but always there waiting to be remembered.
At weekend's early morning
the families of relatives
to North Harbour's bay and little beaches:
coarse shell-sanded cloths
of gold interspersed with porous
rocks oyster decorated,
bright water weed-webbed.

The mud flat of Forty Baskets
grey blue with circular soldier crabs
round grey eyeballs rolling in mud lids,
massing and rustling, sinking at a footstep.
The suspension bridge quivering
above the insignificant waterfall.
A small boy could lose his way
along the meandering sand track
surrounded by a bitter fragrance, wafts
of wild bush blossom clumped under eucalypts,
the bark scribbled with spirit writing,
the trunks thick enough to hide
the bay's bright water.

The heated air unfolding
sachets of herb smells.
The clip and whirr of beetles,
the dizzy ringing of cicadas
high above the family group
ranged upon a small beach
of coarse clean sand,
white and gold spread between
a jade tide and grey hollowed rocks.

The hierarchy of the children
already emulating adults.
The men and boys wading for oysters,
toes feeling through old, thin canvas shoes
the bladed lip, the corrugated shell.
The women and girls preparing
a large meal of multicoloured
salads. Hot faces and cool
cotton print floral dresses,
some in woollen one-piece bathing suits.
Rattle of knives, rustle of paper plates,
sing-song of popular tunes.
The soft salt smell of sliced
cucumber, fresh bread's warm
fragrance, tang of pickled onions,
wafts of cool cologne.
Noses savouring, eyes eating in,
mouths awash with expectation.

The magic ritual of the fire-making
between smoke-blackened rocks,
with aromatic twigs and leaves.
The billy sizzling, bubbling at the boil.
Tap the tin sides, so,
pour and breathe a benison
of salt air, fresh leaves,
sweet smoky tea among
the lively company of peers and elders.

After, with handkerchiefs knotted
on sun-touched heads, the breathless
games of chase or crouched upon
the musty leaves, hiding, twigs prickling.
Earth smell predominating.
A giant ant an inch from the nose
rolling boulder grains of sand.
Then down to the shore in the afternoon's
heat, leaping from rocks into clear
water, the cool embrace of it.

All day the *genius loci* of the sun,
the chiming of cicadas.

Towards the red-gold and grey
evening hazy with last fires,
the fathers rowing back, crunching
aground with a catch of next to nothing
but tales; their sunburnt *bonhomie*
and a smell of green prawns.
The slight chill and the inner glow
of the ceremonial hour. The songs
and promises of constancy —
Where has it gone?
Nowhere I can't recall
with the help of a little woodsmoke
sifting through evening air.

from *Odes and Days*

Day 25

The green within the green of grass
resolved into a bird of green and red.
Another and another came to peck
and amble underneath the walnut,
always so many feet away from it.
And there, upon the walnut's bole,
the black and white and ebon
beak of magpie tensed as if
for flight — yet pausing, ruffling
a few feathers, gimlet eye intent
on the smaller, gayer coloured
fellows who seemed not to notice
the black and white brigade of one.
I looked away for several minutes.
Then I looked again and things
were much the same. And in this way
the trio and the sentry stayed
the same for maybe half an hour.
Why? Lorenz would know. Maybe
any birdwatcher could have told me.
There seemed to me to be a meeting
of something like four minds and one
was cannier and jealous of its scope.

DAY 46

It is that hour of the early evening
when the time-pressed clerks
and the shop-girls drift wanly
homeward, another day worn off
their lives by an egregious friction
of wasted hours rubbed together
in a time-clock's steely bowels.
But the day itself has been so
fair, and is now; so bright
and laced by exquisite breezes
I imagine the people running
through the effervescent shallows
or lazing on the wide, glowing
sands, or trailing fingers in
cool wavelets, the hair blown
back, the eyes filled with blue
vistas and the golden light
of the sun coins spun through
the deep air, or sitting on shaded
balconies that face the fading
east or aspiring west, both satisfying
the dreamed of well-being only the
habitually exploited can imagine.

R. H.
Morrison

Memento

Tack on the canvas, stretch it, then with charcoal
Block in what will end as grey sky streaked with blue.
In the middle foreground: the open shed, tools,
The man at the forge, the broken buggy, bars
Of iron; to his left, old hames, straps discarded
But kept. Much sun and rain have bleached the shed's hewn
Slabs of mountain ash since eighteen eighty-two;
Was this built under the pines by that farmer's
Father, or did the trees grow up green round it,
Then lower their boughs? Into the foreground go
The border collie and three hens. The design
Must paint the smell of super, the anvil's sound:
Children, not knowing, will ask, begging to be told,
"What does 'farm' mean?" and "What were draught-horses like?"

Timber Town

Here life's all in the making. Everything's new:
That semi-trailer loaded with cases there,
The petrol-serving roadhouse girl in blue,
Fresh as the tang of resin in the air.

Must you poetically think of these pines
As forest giants? It won't be long before
The new sawmill, with decrescendo whines,
Must deal with them; they represent someone's floor.

The Australian workers are new, both New and Old,
Like their houses of wood or Mount Gambier stone.
They drink wine rather warm, and beer very cold,
And even office-boys have cars of their own.

Everything here's so fresh that years and years
Must pass before a ghost would haunt these streets,
This bank or Post Office still unwet by tears,
These homes where on Saturdays everyone meets.

It's strange then that one person driving through,
And stopping here for tea and a hot pie,
Perversely sees it as no longer new
But marked by time after generations die,

And foretells the ancient pines forgotten there,
Inevitable graves and monuments,
And the sharp tang of resin in the air,
The most poignant of all nostalgic scents.

Kath
Walker

Tree Grave

When our lost one left us
For the Shadow Land,
In bark we bound him,
A weeping band,
And we bore him, wailing
Our wild death croon
To his lonely tree-grave
By the Long Lagoon.

Our wandering fires
Are now far away,
But our thoughts are turning
By night and day
Where he lies for ever
Under the white moon,
By the lit waters
Of the still lagoon.

His hunts are over
And the songs he made;
Poor lonely fellow,
He will be afraid
When the night winds whisper
Their ghostly tune
In the haunted swamp-oaks
By the Long Lagoon.

The Child Wife

They gave me to an old man,
Joyless and old,
Life's smile of promise
So soon to frown.
Inside his gunya
My childhood over,
I must sit for ever,
And the tears fall down.

It was love I longed for,
Young love like mine,
It was Dunwa wanted me,
The gay and brown.
Oh, old laws that tether me!
Oh, long years awaiting me!
And the grief comes over me,
And the tears fall down.

Happy the small birds
Mating and nesting,
Shrilling their gladness
No grief may drown.
But an old man's gunya
Is my life for ever,
And I think of Dunwa,
And the tears fall down.

Ballad of the Totems

My father was Noonuccal man and kept old tribal way,
His totem was the Carpet Snake, whom none must ever slay;
But mother was of Peewee clan, and loudly she expressed
The daring view that carpet snakes were nothing but a pest.

Now one lived right inside with us in full immunity,
For no one dared to interfere with father's stern decree:
A mighty fellow ten feet long, and as we lay in bed
We kids could watch him round a beam not far above our head.

Only the dog was scared of him, we'd hear its whines and growls,
But mother fiercely hated him because he took her fowls.
You should have heard her diatribes that flowed in angry torrents
With words you never see in print, except in D. H. Lawrence.

"I kill that robber," she would scream, fierce as a spotted cat;
"You see that bulge inside of him? My speckly hen make that!"
But father's loud and strict command made even mother quake;
I think he'd sooner kill a man than kill a carpet snake.

That reptile was a greedy-guts, and as each bulge digested
He'd come down on the hunt at night as appetite suggested.
We heard his stealthy slithering sound across the earthen floor,
While the dog gave a startled yelp and bolted out the door.

Then over in the chicken-yard hysterical fowls gave tongue,
Loud frantic squawks accompanied by the barking of the mung,
Until at last the racket passed, and then to solve the riddle,
Next morning he was back up there with a new bulge in his middle.

When father died we wailed and cried, our grief was deep and sore,
And strange to say from that sad day the snake was seen no more.
The wise old men explained to us: "It was his tribal brother,
And that is why it done a guy" — but some looked hard at mother.

She seemed to have a secret smile, her eyes were smug and wary,
She looked as innocent as the cat that ate the pet canary.
We never knew, but anyhow (to end this tragic rhyme)
I think we all had snake for tea one day about that time.

Understand, Old One

Understand, old one,
I mean no desecration
Staring here with the learned ones
At your opened grave.
Now after hundreds of years gone
The men of science coming with spade and knowledge
Peer and probe, handle the yellow bones,
To them specimens, to me
More. Deeply moved am I.

Understand, old one,
I mean no lack of reverence.
It is with love
I think of you so long ago laid here
With tears and wailing.
Strongly I feel your presence very near
Haunting the old spot, watching
As we disturb your bones. Poor ghost,
I know, I know you will understand.

What if you came back now
To our new world, the city roaring
There on the old peaceful camping place
Of your red fires along the quiet water,
How you would wonder
At towering stone gunyas high in air
Immense, incredible;
Planes in the sky over, swarms of cars
Like things frantic in flight.
What if you came at night upon these miles
Of clustered neon lights of all colours
Like Christian newly come to his Heaven or Hell
And your own people gone?
Old one of the long ago,
So many generations lie between us
But cannot estrange. Your duty to your race
Was with the simple past, mine
Lies in the present and the coming days.

Note: This came after I had visited an old native burial ground not
far from Brisbane, where University people were excavating bones
and had invited me along. I wrote it down at once while
impressions were still fresh.

Colin
Thiele

Silent Sam

In Hobson's pub against the hill
where Time is drunk and malt has mouldered,
the bar-top, thick and heavy-shouldered,

sweeps hugely to its corner niche;
and there, like Socrates the thinker,
stands little Sam, the silent drinker.

His knurled and knotty fingers curl
like grain-whorled wood around his schooner;
and sometimes late and sometimes sooner

the strangers nudge and nod and ask
how any man, spared hex or illness,
contrives to say so much with stillness.

The glyptic secrets of his days
are etched across his face's leather
like carved and panelled western weather.

So far diminutive, and yet
his stance bestrides the raucous rumble,
the busy bar-room's rough and tumble,

where barrel barmen in their sleeves
half-soused with sliding foam, or mopping
beery counter-slicks and slopping,

never cease to watch his eye;
and waitresses, though rankly idle,
buck their buttocks, mince and sidle,

in ecstasy at every glance.
Perceptive visitors in wonder
leave their waiting drinks to ponder

earnestly the legend's roots,
and study women's hints that hover
round their silent midnight lover,

or gauge the terse laconic praise
of men in attitudes of meekness
who, tyrannized by malt and weakness,

stand like horses at their stalls,
and judge superlative or shoddy
the attributes of every body.

For men are men of many parts
and most, albeit embraced as brothers,
are small in some and big in others.

Nor does Hobson's pub disguise
that men or women quick of nature
know each other's shape and stature

and, like shoppers, judge and choose;
for few things spread a reputation
like a client's approbation.

Though Sam be inarticulate
his legend builds on beery leisure
and the warm coquettish pleasure

of the darkness where his way,
if reticent without denying,
yet proves greatly satisfying.

Small wonder that, accepting truth,
the marvelling district ranks him thinker
and drinks to Sam the silent drinker.

Murray Mouth

So this is where it ends at last!

Half a continent poured out
through the long tide-swept sand —
the snouts of bars,
the crunch of wet shells shining,
and at night the swinging stars!

No guard of honour from great old trees,
no bustle of ships or wharves,
no city lights, no high bluffs or banks,
not even a nation's thanks.

Only the long low beaches on and on,
and in the white sandhills a gap, a smoothness lying,
and a channel, a rip,
a strange wild stir . . .

Who would wish it other?

Alone, unmarred, the spirit of the land
it springs from slips to rest.
Sardonic old saunterer, here at last
is death and burial in the line of surf —
free as the south wind edged with agate,
no ships or sewers, smoke or smear of oil,
no lumber, roadways or tilled soil . . .
only a great old river at its end,
silently, unrecognised by light or bell,
swept under the wild hooves of the South
and blessed only by the ponderous pelican's farewell.

Rosemary
Dobson

A Fine Thing

To be a scarecrow
To lean all day in a bright field
With a hat full
Of bird's song
And a heart of gold straw;
With a sly wink for the farmer's daughter,
When no one sees, and small excursions;
Returning after
To a guiltless pose of indolence.

A fine thing
To be a figurehead
With a noble brow
On a ship's prow
And a look to the end of the world;
With the sad sounds of wind and water
And only a stir of air for thinking;
The timber cutting
The green waves, and the foam flashing.

To be a snowman
Lost all day in deep thought,
With a head full
Of snowflakes
And no troubles at all,
With an old pipe and six buttons,
And sometimes children in woollen gaiters;
But mostly lonely,
A simple fellow, with no troubles at all.

Country Morning

I heard the cock at morning crow
Among the bright-bunched parsley-leaves
And with my curious, wilful eye
Saw the bird of paradise,
Marvellous creature that can yet
In fury and in flame beget
Itself upon its own decay.

I heard in darkness as I lay
The horses' hoofbeats on the hill
And saw the coursers of the sun
Trampling into beaten gold
The patient labours of the frost.
Then wheeled, that fiery, fuming host,
And leapt the world from height to height.

The farmer's wife began her day
With yawns and sighs and sleepy cries
And though I knew she went to milk
My inward eye saw otherwise.
Oh strange — the rattle of the pail
Was Phoebus shaking out his mail
Who puts such glittering armour on.

Cock Crow

Wanting to be myself, alone,
Between the lit house and the town
I took the road, and at the bridge
Turned back and walked the way I'd come.

Three times I took that lonely stretch,
Three times the dark trees closed me round,
The night absolved me of my bonds;
Only my footsteps held the ground.

My mother and my daughter slept,
One life behind and one before,
And I that stood between denied
Their needs in shutting-to the door.

And walking up and down the road
Knew myself, separate and alone,
Cut off from human cries, from pain,
And love that grows about the bone.

Too brief illusion! Thrice for me
I heard the cock crow on the hill
And turned the handle of the door
Thinking I knew his meaning well.

Child of Our Time

The world is yours, and you must take
Your making, breaking, shaping way:
That instant when the cord was cut
Ended my brief imperial sway.

Mine only was the being shaped
In darkness and in solitude
Moving upon the tides of dream,
Unknown yet known beatitude.

All that is done. Now every step
You take is further still from me
Along your destined path to death,
Light, darkness or eternity.

Child of an age beyond my dreams,
My comprehension, watch, or care,
Where do you go who may set foot
Upon some distant, radiant star?

All women who since time began
Have trembled for an eager child
Feared dangers fixed and bounded by
The narrow circuit of the world.

I see the wounded moon, I fear
The travelling star, the mushroom cloud,
Beneath the perilous universe
For you, for you, my head is bowed.

Country Press

Under the dusty print of hobnailed boot,
Strewn on the floor the papers still assert
In ornamental gothic, swash italics
And bands of printer's flowers (traditional)
Mixed in a riot of typographic fancy,
This is the *Western Star*, the Farmer's Guide,
The Voice of Progress for the Nyngle District.
Page-proofs of double-spread with running headlines
Paper the walls, and sets of cigarette-cards
Where pouter-bosomed showgirls still display
The charms that dazzled in the nineteen hundreds.
Through gaping slats
Latticed with sun the ivy tendrils fall
Twining the disused platen thrust away
Under a pall of dust in nineteen-twenty.
Draw up a chair, sit down. Just shift the galleys.
You say you have a notice? There's no one dies
But what we know about it. Births, deaths and marriages,
Council reports, wool prices, river-heights,
The itinerant poem and the classified ads —
They all come homewards to the *Western Star*.
Joe's our type-setter. Meet Joe Burrell. Joe's
A promising lad — and Joe, near forty-seven,
Peers from a tennis-shade and, smiling vaguely,
Completes the headline for the Baptist Social.
The dance, the smoke-oh, and the children's picnic
Down by the river-flats beneath the willows —
They all come homewards and Joe sets them all,
Between the morning and the mid-day schooner.
Oh, *Western Star* that bringest all to fold,
The yarding sales, the champion shorthorn bull,
And Williams' pain-relieving liniment,
When I shall die
Set me up close against my fellow-men,
Cheer that cold column headed "Deaths" with flowers,
Or mix me up with Births and Marriages;
Surround the tragic statement of my death
With euchre-drives and good-times-had-by-all
That, with these warm concomitants of life
Jostled and cheered, in lower-case italics
I shall go homewards in the *Western Star*.

Brett Whiteley *Big Orange (Sunset)* 1974
Oil on wood 244 × 305.5 cm
Art Gallery of New South Wales

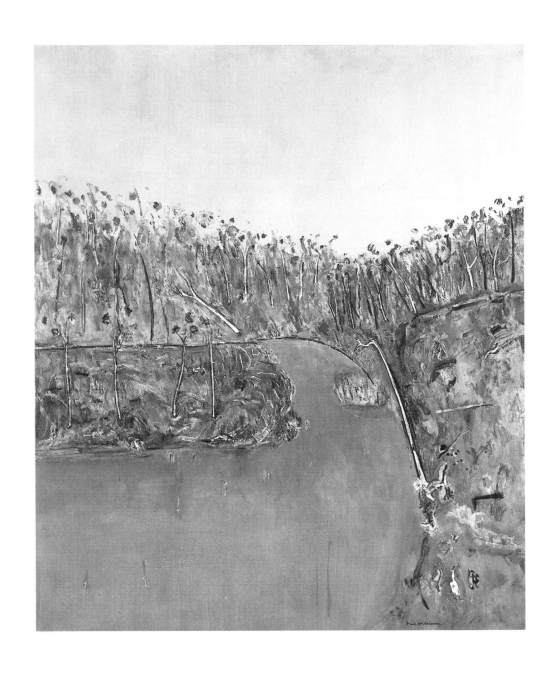

Fred Williams *Landscape with Goose* 1974
Oil on canvas 183.5 × 152.7 cm
Australian National Gallery

Landscape in Italy

Were there, then, roses in the grass?
And saints with holy feet who trod
The mountain paths on pilgrimage
With rapt face looking up to God?

Was there a bird on every tree
Beyond the city's walls and towers
And angels stepping gently by
Over the field-embroidering flowers?

Was there, far off, a ship at sea
With storm-tossed sailors bent in prayer,
And did, above the violent clouds,
Saint Nicholas, to save, appear?

Landscapes, once seen, in memory
Waver and tremble to a dream.
How lay the contours of the hills
We viewed that day, where ran the stream?

But Art, more durable than thought
Between event and memory
Has interposed her coloured chart
To show in perpetuity

That but five steps from where we lay
Drowsing upon the short-cropped grass
Lightly, with all her springtime flowers,
Did Botticelli's Flora pass.

Ghost Town: New England

The grass is bleached by summer sun
The dry pods rustle underfoot,
On quartz-bright rocks the lichens creep
Like frail anemones betrayed
Still trembling towards an unknown sea.
Up the steep shoulder of the hill
The wind goes scattering seeds of light.

Here at the edge the mind goes on,
The eyes go on, though steps must stop
At plunging scarps where dizzily
The plumes of haze shroud and unshroud
Knife-edge and scree; and down and down
Still sight must drop, be cut and grazed,
To find at last the dry creek-bed.

This is no landscape for the eye
Cupped by a hand to shield the mind
From earth's most naked cruelty.
Who looks the longest must take on
The fierceness of the eagle-hawk,
His hungry thought, his still intent,
His burnished, undeflected eye.

How fared they then who built and lived
Beneath the shoulder of the hill,
Who planted with their hopeful hands
The oak, the fruit, the sheltering hedge,
The store, the church, the bakery
Where still the letters are discerned
That here for man is meal, his bread.

The houses lean against the wind,
Their eyes are scarfed with sheets of tin.
I heard in all that stillness once
The cracked complaining of the bell.
A door that shut on nothing scraped,
And with a turning, sick unease
I saw a child's discarded shoe.

Was it on such a summer's day
They gathered from the bakery,
The store, the church, and beckoned on
By the compulsion of the fall,
Plunged to those knife-edged silences?
His mind, as mine, will veer away
Who lacks the hawk's unwavering eye.

Folding the Sheets

FROM *DAILY LIVING*

You and I will fold the sheets
Advancing towards each other
From Burma, from Lapland,

From India where the sheets have been washed in the river
And pounded upon stones:
Together we will match the corners.

From China where women on either side of the river
Have washed their pale cloth in the White Stone Shallows
"Under the shining moon".

We meet as though in the formal steps of a dance
To fold the sheets together, put them to air
In wind, in sun over bushes, or by the fire.

We stretch and pull from one side and then the other —
Your turn. Now mine.
We fold them and put them away until they are needed.

A wish for all people when they lie down in bed —
Smooth linen, cool cotton, the fragrance and stir of herbs
And the faint but perceptible scent of sweet clear water.

The Stone Circles

". . . I was wonderfully surprized at the sight of those vast stones . . ."
John Aubrey, Monumenta Britannica *c. 1663*

Long Meg dances, and her dancing daughters
Join together to make a ring,
Tread the maze and pace the pathway.
Clap hands together and let's all sing:

"Long Meg and her twenty-nine daughters,
The Twelve Apostles and the Rollright Stones,
The Devil's Quoits and the Ring of Brodgar,
Avebury, Stonehenge and Ballynoe."

They lunge and prop at the summer solstice,
Pound the earth of the dancing-floor.
Cumbersome steps for Cumbrian circles;
Sarsen petticoats sweep the moor.

Sarsen caps of Tertiary sandstone,
Gowns of limestone and dolerite —
Any old thing to outface the weather
Dancing blind on Midsummer Night.

Dancing giants skip and stagger,
Set to partners, shake the ground,
Give, receive, and exclude in circles:
God's in the middle and the dance goes round.

Clap hands together and let's all sing:

"Stripple Stones and the Top of Riley,
Kirkslight Rig and Drizzelcombe,
The Three Kings and the Merry Maidens,
Bogton Mill and Cauldside Burn."

Aeons pass here, and the Hawkesbury sandstone
Sinks to a bare brown burning plain,
Seas subside and cities vanish,
Ash and cinders fall like rain.

Weathered menhirs stand in circles
Plotting movements for the dance,
Megaliths of pitted concrete
Plan a serpentine advance.

Giant squared-off single structures
Take their partners, make a ring.
Where's the ghost of old John Aubrey?
Clap hands together and let's all sing:

"National Mutual, Royal Insurance,
Centrepoint and T & G,
Caltex, Philips, Hilton, Esso,
QANTAS, ANSETT, M L C."

Kevin
Gilbert

Where Nomads Tread

A sun scorched sea
that aeons ago
was home of leviathans
now
burnt sand
where nomads tread
unkis't by soothing rain
or snow
encarnadined by desert glow
the profound awe-filled
spaces teach
the nobler truths
that minds can reach
past sombre silence gold.

Desmond
O'Grady

Life, Debts and Miracles of F. X. Horgan

SHORTLY AFTER he had turned fifty, Father Francis Xavier Horgan began hearing the voices. Although he had been practising heroic asceticism, he suspected they were not angelic in origin for the first, which came during his end-of-Mass prayers for the conversion of Russia, was "Go Pretty Boy for the Welter."

Horgan shook his head, as if to dislodge a flea from his ear, and caught up with the congregation asking God to do something about the Bolsheviks. He knew that Pretty Boy, a sluggish starter, did not stand a dog's chance. Pretty Boy romped home at fifteens.

As he went about his duties in the following days, FX contemplated the fact that if he had punted $400 on Pretty Boy, he would have wiped out the parish debt. Must have been a tip from the best source, he concluded.

A short time before, he had become parish priest in one of Perth's outlying suburbs. He had resolved to justify the trust of the bishop who had accepted him after his addiction to racing had made him a blacksheep in Melbourne archdiocese.

Fellow curates in Melbourne had not appreciated Horgan's disappearance on Saturday afternoons when confession lines were longest. At times he would hear some confessions before going walkabout, other times he would not even front. Challenged, he pleaded claustrophobia in the confessional. This did not placate hard-pressed colleagues who could hardly advise impatient penitents to seek Horgan at Flemington, Caulfield or Moonee Valley racecourses where his friends plunged after hearing his lightning-quick calculations.

His own punting was neither heavy nor profitable. As his was a pure passion, this did not discourage him. His father, a successful businessman, had been a keen punter but even before he took young Francis Xavier to the racetracks, the boy knew all about the sport of kings from long hours spent over *The Sporting Globe*.

His passion continued unabated through his seminary years. As a young curate, he had plans to form a syndicate with lay friends to buy a racehorse.

Nothing came of it but, on his free days, FX liked visiting stud farms just as he would happily attend midweek city meetings and country races without laying a bet.

But it was betting which finally cruelled his pitch in Melbourne. He was shunted from one parish to another until the archbishop told him he would have to hear confessions Saturday afternoons or else. Dammit, you have a Race Mass every year before the Cup, FX would like to have protested, but was abashed by the melancholy authority of the man who was archbishop at that time. FX spent his Saturdays nailed to the confessional but began to bet heavily, and unsuccessfully, with backlane starting-price bookies. As the backlanes were thick with parishioners, word circulated.

The archdiocese had its share of boozy priests and womanisers but FX was a worse headache.

"Father Horgan seems to lack even normal foresight," said the archbishop in his pleasing brogue when told of FX's losses. "What sort of spiritual guide can he be?"

To tell the truth, Father Francis Xavier Horgan brought to mind a form guide more readily than a spiritual guide. Powerfully built, he had the face of a race-track clocker. His cheeks were glazed as if winddried. His parched lips seemed stuck together: he did not open his mouth readily and apparently it hurt him to smile. His face was wooden, except for one eye whose drooping lid made it look shrewd, but he talked as intensely as an evangelical preacher, although FX's message usually concerned what was going in the handicap the following Saturday.

FX's dog collar sat uneasily on a neck which should have been open to the sun. His black clerical hat perched jauntily at the back of his head. He was serious enough about being a priest but on Saturday his heart beat in time with horses' hooves. He should have been chaplain at Flemington racecourse.

Only someone as trusting as the auxiliary of Perth, a crony since seminary days, would have given him another chance after Melbourne. The surprises of grace are infinite, the more venerable said, when they learned FX was a new man who spurned the temptations of the racetrack: that was his heroic asceticism. Take a swab, his former curates said when word of FX's new life reached Melbourne. The auxiliary of Perth died young but convinced that he had done at least one good deed. FX's parish priest soon followed in his wake. FX was a spiritual orphan with a flock of 3,000 and a parish debt of $6,000. It was then that he began to receive messages.

They were perfectly clear but rare, whereas the debt grew steadily. He was unsure whether to regard them as temptation or inspiration.

He knew Whitenose would win the Three-Year-Old Stakes as he was leaving

St. Jude's, redolent with incense, following Benediction. After a struggle with himself, he decided not to plunge but confided in Clarrie Hickey who made a packet on the heavily built bay.

"Straight from the horse's mouth, I'd say, Frank," said Hickey, jumping out of his skin at the possibilities. "Don't worry, I'll weigh in Sunday morning," which was a not-altogether convincing promise of a large contribution to Sunday's collection.

Hickey was a spruce, sharp little man who could have been a jockey. He ran a bakery but also shared FX's passion for horses. He owned one, Inkling, a fine-boned grey which had performed well on country tracks without being placed in the city.

Hickey frequently suggested that FX have a flutter. He redoubled his efforts after Whitenose's victory but, with a clenching of the will, FX stood firm. Each Saturday afternoon he was advising sinners that backsliding could only be avoided if they shunned occasions of sin. The first slip, he told them, was fatal.

His virtuous restraint, however, did nothing to diminish the parish debt which depressed him and his parishioners each time he mentioned it. He found himself thinking that his father, with his inventive business instinct, would have found an answer.

After a talk to the confirmation class at the local school, he knew that Soldiering On was the hope for the Derby but he did not pass word on to Hickey. It was a lonely, pointless victory for him when Soldiering On came home at 7–2. At those prices, he would need to have invested heavily to cancel the debt. He regretted he had not punted on Whitenose.

FX now found the debt at the bottom of every cup of weak presbytery tea. He felt an old man as he walked the parish streets asking dully how he could shift its brute weight. The collections each Sunday were pathetic antidotes, the parishioners were clerks and working-class people at full stretch to clothe, feed and educate their children. FX wanted them to have a flash of excitement in their lives, he regretted harping on the debt.

As he led a class of twelve-year-old boys in the Stations of the Cross, he knew the remedy: Golgotha in the Maiden Plate. The meeting was at Kalgoorlie which confirmed his feeling that he had the inside running. As Kalgoorlie was over three hundred miles from Perth, he would be out of range of indiscreet eyes.

FX emptied the parish kitty. Golgotha's odds had lengthened to 25s by the time he plunged. It led all the way only to be pipped on the post. At the verdict, FX felt his heart stop pumping. Pins and needles stabbed his left arm. But he revived reluctantly, repeating Golgotha like an incantation. He had to borrow his train fare home from a strapper.

He confessed to Clarrie. "It was an each way tip," said Clarrie, grinning craftily, probably piqued that FX had tried to make a killing on the quiet.

Alongside the snowballing parish debt, there was now another secret one. FX dreaded being caught with his hand in the kitty. Don't I get any credit for the temptations I withstood, he asked? Or had he been ignoring inspiration? "Never look a gift horse . . ." came to mind.

Clarrie advised him Inkling was a goer for the next country meeting. "I timed him to do two furlongs in 23 the other morning." Clarrie's eyes glistened greedily. Inkling did show signs, but he was a little too light-on to FX's expert eye.

He attended the meeting. Inkling flew home but finished a length from the third placegetter. FX was glad he had kept his hands in his pockets.

He would wait for infused knowledge. He became assiduous, sitting backbreaking hours in the confessional, walking his shoes thin on home visits, preparing the parish school children for the sacraments. But illumination loitered. And the more zealous FX became, the more he feared exposure as a fraud.

Anxiety must have made him go along with Clarrie's suggestion. Clarrie supplied the money, FX flew to Melbourne to acquire from Australia's most eminent batterymaker his masterpiece. It was to make Inkling a sure winner at Kalgoorlie. The battery burnt in FX's palm as if it were a particle of hell. If it had been a packet of contraceptives, he would not have been more ashamed.

Unwittingly, the archbishop almost wrecked plans by asking FX to christen his nephew's child on the race day. The answer was hiring a plane which would reach Kalgoorlie in ample time for FX to install the battery. FX regretted having to put a swiftie over the archbishop who, he imagined, would fall off his episcopal throne if he could see one of his parish priests being piloted to Kalgoorlie.

When his plane was within half an hour of Kalgoorlie, it was slashed by rain, cuffed by wind. The pilot, Atkinson, a small-featured young man who had taxied endlessly around the tarmac as if uncertain how to take off, said he would turn back to avoid a storm moving up from the Bight.

FX had placed sufficient money in Perth for Inkling's defeat to land him on a criminal charge. The advancing black clouds were his idea of the wrath of God.

His own wrath seemed capable of driving the plane straight through the boiling cloud-wall. Then the plane began bucking: when it dropped in an air pocket, FX cracked his head. FX's prayers for survival became more vehement than his orders to fly on.

Atkinson tried to skirt the storm. Although it hammered further north, the flight remained uncomfortably pneumatic until the engine cut. Throat dry, voice hoarse, FX sat silent as the plane glided to land beside a deserted football oval.

Faintly he asked if the engine could be fixed. He suspected there was nothing wrong with it, that Atkinson had landed because he was disgruntled but the pilot's face was chalky with fear.

Atkinson pottered with the engine as if it were his Saturday afternoon hobby.

FX could see Inkling at the tail of the field, weighed down by the money he was carrying to the bookmakers.

FX climbed down, hating the aloof gums in the distance. The soggy ground reminded him that Inkling would be ill-at-ease on a wet track. FX felt the surge of straining horses, saw the iridescent flash of jockeys' silks. He was marooned. Even if he could have hitched a ride, it was too late to reach Kalgoorlie in time.

FX, hands in his pockets, chill wind putting a higher glaze on his cheeks, wondered if the traitorous plane could be a means of escape. But where? Come down halfway across the Nullarbor? He asked Atkinson how much juice was left.

"Just enough to get us back to Perth." Atkinson's forehead was corrugated. "Burnt it up on that buckin' joyride."

FX climbed back to his seat and slumped forward, feeling like a motherless child such a long way from home.

He saw himself as a boy pushing a bicycle, whose chain had broken, up an endless hill in Bourke Road, invoking Divine aid. He could not remember the outcome, only the intensity of his plea. Or again, while a seminarian, clambering over a rocky ledge in the Grampians. Loose stones had shifted under his feet, rolling, then bouncing on their echoing way. He was afraid to go either backwards or forwards. An engine had begun thumping in the distance and it was some seconds before he realized it was his blood. Skin sentient with fear, he had flashed an SOS to Christ. But he had a direct line then.

What is the good of a God, he asked, if he doesn't help when most needed? Rescue me from this situation, he bargained, and I'll steer clear of racecourse perdition in future. He saw the useless battery in his left hand as the germ of corruption and closed his eyes to shut out the world.

Atkinson, still tinkering, invited him to turn on the plane's radio for the race. FX had not thought of that possibility. By the time it was tuned, Inkling and the other twelve competitors were taking their position in the starting stalls.

The race caller, whose measured rhythm would accelerate with the horses, described the favourite, Buckley's Chance, as well placed from the start. He ran through the field before he mentioned Inkling as hemmed in by the last bunch of horses.

FX crouched over the crackling set, his ruddy cheeks an intenser ruby, his shrewd eye vacant, as if hearing a life sentence. The caller had Buckley's Chance making light work of the heavy track but, as they came to the home turn, it faded while Andrea Doria and Inkling moved up strongly.

FX's hopes were ignited by the caller's excited litany. Inkling forced his way through on the inside as they settled for the run to the judges, sweeping past Buckley's Chance and with half a length on Andrea Doria. FX turned up the volume as the caller's hysteria peaked:

"But Black'nTan - is - coming - home - stoutly - on - the - outside - here -

he - comes - look - at - him - go - making - up - ground - like - an - express - train.''

FX could see him, huge, black as sin.

''Inkling's - fighting - on - gamely - in - the - run - to - the - post - Buckley's Chance - and Andrea Doria - dropping - back - through - a - bunched - field - Cracko'Dawn - moving - up - the - whip's - on - Black'nTan - got - his - head - in - front - on - the - line - but - I'll - leave - that - one - to - the - camera.''

I've backed it all up, FX told Christ quietly but with his fists clenched. He was a big man. Come good now, he begged but would like to have threatened. Dried saliva lined the corner of his mouth. Just open the judge's eyes to Inkling's win, that's all — if You're really there. What's the good of stony silence when I'm tearing my guts out? Christ, come off Your highhorse.

Atkinson was asking if Horgan had backed Inkling each way but he had not heard. He concentrated on the caller's voice, now subdued: ''Inkling it is: I thought Black 'n Tan had got up in the last stride but there's the judges' verdict after closely examining the print: Inkling, Black 'n Tan and Crack o' Dawn, which came from nowhere, third.''

''Alleluia!'' FX shouted, throwing his arms wide and remembering the battery crushed in his palm. Palm Saturday, he thought, seeing his triumphal entry to Perth as a solvent parish priest.

His first impulse was to throw the battery away. His second was to give it to Clarrie but that would be to abet sharp practice. He decided to sell it back to its maker who, after all, otherwise would only make another.

All right, he told himself, when Atkinson finally took him aloft, so it wasn't a miracle, just a great run by Inkling. But he'd honour his word all the same: Do a decent turn to Horgan and he'll return the compliment.

He was as good as his word, or better. He acquired a new buoyancy. He convinced people they could lick temptation. He reduced his contacts with Clarrie and kept away from racetracks. Only at the end of the year did he announce that the parish debt had been cancelled and he did not hint how. It was unprecedented. Throughout the archdiocese, his managerial ability and strong character were admired. It was rumoured that he ran five miles before breakfast each morning. He did not mind hearing all the confessions on Saturday afternoons.

When the city's biggest parish needed a new parish priest, FX was the natural choice. He was given a warm welcome and a fresh-faced assistant who was still looking for the answers in theological reviews. The parish debt, which had topped $130,000, seemed to have a life of its own. Insiders tipped FX as the next auxiliary bishop.

After many years on the outer, FX appreciated the trust in him. He soon realized that a miracle was necessary to cancel the debt. However he battled against it with orthodox methods. He became irascible, grey, lined by worry. Smiling seemed to have become even more painful. He inaugurated a third collection at each Mass but it was like milking a dry cow. Frustrated by the lack of response, he would berate latecomers and those who loitered at the back of the church.

"Come on — there's room up front," he would thunder. "No good hiding behind the paper stand — or the baptismal font." Like driven sheep, they would edge forward looking for an early pew. "No need to be ashamed when you're about the service of the Lord," he would insist, getting a charge from such harangues.

He had settled for the long haul. Fellow parish priests now accepted him as one of their own, even if he was bad news for their whisky reserves.

The archbishop was always encouraging although, FX suspected, disappointed by his inability to dint the debt. One plunge, FX used to think when he reached the bottom of his Johnny Walker, could be sufficient to topple that debt. But he had turned his back on all that.

Besides, even though messages still came occasionally, he could not unscramble them. Maybe the signals were weaker. Or too much religious static blunted reception.

The Apostleship of Prayer intention for October was China. FX took it as a pointer to Fu Manchu in the three-mile event. Long March came from a long way back to win.

Something was coming through as he was leading the rosary after evening devotions. A furtive additional sign of the cross scotched the distraction. He recalled it only when Simple Simon squeezed home in the weight-for-age.

He was ashamed when, at a crowded 11 o'clock Mass on the Fifth Sunday after the Melbourne Cup, what should have been "Dominus Vobiscum" involuntarily came out as "Dob it on Tony's Cone." He remembered it when the weight-for-age the following Saturday was won by Ice-cream King.

Leafing through the *Australasian Catholic Record* in the presbytery after first Friday Mass, he knew that Herman Utix was the answer for him. But as he had never heard of it, he ignored the hint. Of course it was a winner, running away from Key Rigamarole with The Good News a poor third.

Psalm 22 leapt off the page as he was reading his breviary:

The Lord is my shepherd,

I shall not want;

He leads me by pastures green . . .

But Green Pastures was so short that an enormous outlay would have been needed to match the debt. Green Pastures won only on a protest. However, in the last race, a rank outsider, Lord Shepherd, came home. The doubles quote was 50 to 1, a gift to anyone who would trust his intuition. FX had to recognize the message had gone right past him.

His clerical hat was fixed squarely on his head, his dog collar no longer chafed. Horses for courses, he reminded himself, trusting he was on the right track. This life was losing its flavour, which reassured him he was on a sure thing for the next. Only when he heard a race broadcast did he doubt that he could stick it out to the finishing post.

But most Saturday afternoons, when the race-caller's muezzin cries riveted true believers, Father Francis Xavier Horgan was hiding in the confessional. A transistor as compact as a battery lay silent in his lap except in the rare pauses between penitents who appreciated his speed and his dry-lipped assertion that they could always make a new start.

Gwen

Harwood

Triste, Triste

In the space between love and sleep
when heart mourns in its prison
eyes against shoulder keep
their blood-black curtains tight.
Body rolls back like a stone, and risen
spirit walks to Easter light;

away from its tomb of bone,
away from the guardian tents
of eyesight, walking alone
to unbearable light with angelic
gestures. The fallen instruments
of its passion lie in the relic

darkness of sleep and love.
And heart from its prison cries
to the spirit walking above:
"I was with you in agony.
Remember your promise of paradise,"
and hammers and hammers, "Remember me."

So the loved other is held
for mortal comfort, and taken,
and the spirit's light dispelled
as it falls from its dream to the deep
to harrow heart's prison so heart may waken
to peace in the paradise of sleep.

In Brisbane

By the old bridge in flaring sunlight
a ghost is waiting, with my face
of twenty years ago, to show me
the paths I never can retrace.

Here as of old upon the river
float light's beguiling images.
Over a quilt of blue the branches
bend with domestic tenderness.

Here, to my blood's exalted rhythm,
silly with love I'd pace for hours
sifting the piecemeal revelations
of life and time through falling flowers.

Intemperate ghost, who longed to hazard
the pure space of experience,
to bid unheard-of constellations
form from their joyful elements:

these trees that cannot hold their blossom,
the public handsomeness of stone
remain. Your grand abstractions shimmered
like light on water, and are gone.

My ghost, my self, most intimate stranger
standing beneath these lyric trees
with your one wineglassful of morning
snatched from the rushing galaxies,

bright-haired and satin-lipped you offer
the youth I shall not taste again.
I know, I bear to know your future
unlooked-for love, undreamed-of pain.

With your untempered spirit shatter
the glass of time that keeps apart
what was and is.
            Through fractured sunlight
I see a less-than-shadow pass

to light again. A cloud of blossom
drifts on the water's changing face
from the blue trees unfolding summer
above my head in sunlit space.

Springtime, Oyster Cove

TO THE MEMORY OF JAMES MCAULEY

Springtime returns, old love thought lost
and found by chance. The hillside lapses
from its strict tones of cold to sweetness.
Wildflowers illuminate their names:
white iris, scorpion everlasting,
lilac bells, speedwell, waxflower, musk.
Seabirds possess their field of blue,
songbirds their bowl of milky sky.
Sapphire, turquoise, pastoral
viridian on the hills of Bruny.
Everything's occupied with life,
thrusting, relentless, fountaining
with sap and hope.
                        You dreamed about
a world where all is possible, all
creatures teach wisdom to their young.
The serpent of the intellect,
redeemed, coils in majestic truth.
Children of men outname old Adam
in peaceful cities.
                        The sun sinks
ancient and great.
                        Set down the wine
among the living. Evening falls
in saffron, lilac, melting silver.
Death's soft tongue breaks your bones, in darkness
returns you to the earth you loved,
its changing lights more beautiful,
to those who mourn you, for your song.

Estuary

TO REX HOBCROFT

Wind crosshatches shallow water.
Paddocks rest in the sea's arm.
Swamphens race through spiky grass.
A wire fence leans, a crazy stave
with sticks for barlines, wind for song.
Over us, interweaving light
with air and substance, ride the gulls.

Words in our undemanding speech
hover and blend with things observed.
Syllables flow in the tide's pulse.
My earliest memory turns in air:
Eclipse. Cocks crow, as if at sunset;
Grandmother, holding a smoked glass,
says to me, *"Look. Remember this."*

Over the goldbrown sand my children
run in the wind. The sky's immense
with spring's new radiance. Far from here,
lying close to the final darkness,
a great-grandmother lives and suffers,
still praising life: another morning
on earth, cockcrow and changing light.

Over the skeleton of thought
mind builds a skin of human texture.
The eye's part of another eye
that guides it through the maze of light.
A line becomes a firm horizon.
All's as it was in the beginning.
Obscuring symbols melt away.

"Remember this." I will remember
this quiet in which the questioning mind
allows reality to enter
its gateway as a friend, unchallenged,
to rest as a friend may, without speaking;
light falling like a benediction
on moments that renew the world.

New Music

To Larry Sitsky

Who can grasp for the first time
these notes hurled into empty space?
Suddenly a tormenting nerve
affronts the fellowship of cells.
Who can tell for the first time
if it is love or pain he feels,
violence or tenderness that calls
plain objects by outrageous names

and strikes new sound from the old names?
At the service of a human vision,
not symbols, but strange presences
defining a transparent void,
these notes beckon the mind to move
out of the smiling context of
what's known; and what can guide it is
neither wisdom nor power, but love.

Who but a fool would enter these
regions of being with no name?
Secure among their towering junk
the wise and powerful congregate
fitting old shapes to old ideas,
rocked by their classical harmonies
in living sleep. The beggars' stumps
bang on the stones. Nothing will change.

Unless, wakeful with questioning,
some mind beats on necessity,
and being unanswered learns to bear
emptiness like a wound that no
word but its own can mend; and finds
a new imperative to summon
a world out of unmeasured darkness
pierced by a brilliant nerve of sound.

Dust to Dust

I dream I stand once more
in Ann Street by the old
fire station. The palms
like feather dusters move
idly in stifling air.
The sky's dusted with gold.
A footfall; someone comes;
I cannot speak for love.

We walk in silence past
All Saints'. The dead do rise,
do live, do walk and wear
their flesh. Your exile's done.
So, so, resume our last
rejoicing kiss. Your eyes
flecked with my image stare
in wonder through my own.

Round us air turns to flame.
Ashes rain from the sky.
A firebell clangs and clangs
insanely as I wake
to absence with your name
shaping my lips. I lie
losing the dream that hangs
fading in air. I shake

the last of night away.
These bright motes that define
morning inside my room
hold not one grain of you.
Another sunstruck day
whose moving dust-motes shine
remote from any dream
cannot restore, renew

our laughter that hot night
when by All Saints' we talked
in the brief time we had.
During *Magnificat*
an urchin stopped to write
on the church wall. He chalked
his message: GOD IS MAD.
I say amen to that.

Iris

Three years with our three sons you worked to build her,
    named for the rainbow, late and lively child
whom the sea fondles. A fresh breeze has filled her.
    Tension and buoyant ease are reconciled

as she puts off the heavy yoke of land
    and takes the wind's light burden in her sails.
Ship-shape; an even keel: we understand
    old clichés truly — sixty pounds of nails

gripping her ribs, six hundredweight of lead
    flourishing water's frail cascading lace.
Age after age the same, still tenanted
    with earth's first creatures, water bears no trace

of time or history on its shining skin.
    Far from the shore where small crabs trim the rotten
scraps from a city's fringes, we begin
    (husband and wife so long we have forgotten

all singularity), our day of rest
    above that element where none sit hand
in hand, salt glitter tossed from crest to crest
    lights nothing of those gulfs where none can stand

upright; here nothing smiles; pity's unknown.
    A crippled gull I found helplessly dying
used its last life to stab me to the bone.
    Some old, lost self strikes from time's shallows, crying

"Beyond habit, household, children, I am I.
    Who knows my original estate, my name?
Give me my atmosphere, or let me die."
    — Give me your hand. The same pure wind, the same

light-cradling sea shall comfort us, who have
    built our ark faithfully. In fugitive
rainbows of spray she lifts, wave after wave,
    her promise: those the waters bear shall live.

An Old Graveyard

I

Tasmania: the first skies of spring,
  earth's windy hollows charged with light.
It would be comforting to sing
  old parables of winter's flight

as water blazes and clouds burn
  like angels challenging the sun;
but memory and grief return
  raging from underground, to one

loved through all seasons, whose farewell
  was absolute: flower after flower
spring's airy syllables foretell
  the resurrection of that hour.

II

Pulled by the magnet of the sky
  stone's held aloft by earth and air;
voices of praise and mourning lie
  long dead, but song is everywhere:

earth's mindless song, to which she nurses
  the restless hungering of her own
small creatures, while soft air rehearses
  time's litany with ruined stone.

III

Time present and time past
  no more beguiling
we shall be given at last
  to earth's confiding,
then earth and time will strip
  bones from their hiding;
take eye, and cheek, and lip;
  and leave us smiling.

September Snow, Hobart

To Vivian Smith

Snow in the streets, snow on suburban homes,
settling on hyacinth-hearted slicks of oil,
on dwarfs in primary colours, hunchback gnomes;
snow in the city, piling ermine on
King Edward's mantle, covering Sir John
Franklin's heroic seagull-favoured head;
snow fluttering on the winter-bitten soil
of council gardens, resting where the dead

rest under lawn, glossing the when and where
of early names on headstones piled among
bushes and creepers. Colour thaws from air
and earth. Whiteness is all. In their strict hives
of glass and concrete, workers take their lives
briefly into their hands. An old clerk leaning
from a window holds a snowflake on his tongue,
and smiles as if some unsuspected meaning

suspended time and reason, so he might
skip down the corridors with young elated
girls to the freshness of that pastoral white.
How the heart sleeps, how long! But it shall waken
as earth is changed, the town's old habit shaken
by the snow's miracle. Ah, to be young:
and for one living moment, recreated,
he stands with morning melting on his tongue.

Suburban Sonnet

She practises a fugue, though it can matter
to no one now if she plays well or not.
Beside her on the floor two children chatter,
then scream and fight. She hushes them. A pot
boils over. As she rushes to the stove
too late, a wave of nausea overpowers
subject and counter-subject. Zest and love
drain out with soapy water as she scours
the crusted milk. Her veins ache. Once she played
for Rubinstein, who yawned. The children caper
round a sprung mousetrap where a mouse lies dead.
When the soft corpse won't move they seem afraid.
She comforts them; and wraps it in a paper
featuring: *Tasty dishes from stale bread*.

David's Harp

Saturday morning. I rehearse
the Sunday hymns, fortissimo,
in the cool twilight of the church,
adding new stops at every verse.
Someone creaks the west door. I know
I am the object of his search,
gazed at, as though from far away.
He must be thirty, if a day.

I turn my seventeen-year-old
profile a trifle heavenwards,
and hastily reduce the sound,
accommodating to his bold
descant on *David's Harp*. The Lord's
house might as well be Circe's ground.
  "With thee all night I mean to stay,
  and wrestle till the break of day."

"With thee all night." So Wesley wrote,
though not with secular intent.
What flourishes that tune will bear!
My tenor wreathes it note by note
in rich Handelian ornament.
Faint burnt-out incense on the air
offends his Presbyterian nose.
He sneezes, stares across the rows

of empty pews between us; still
singing, walks to the organ; stands
beside me; puts his arms around
my waist and squeezes me until
I gasp, then gently lifts my hands
to his, and kisses me. He's sound
of wind. His kiss is long. We share
at last a common need for air.

"Give me one kiss, my bonny lass!"
Vain as a cat, I frown and toss
my head. He watches Brisbane's hot
sunshine, strained through Victorian glass,
lacquer a Station of the Cross.
He scowls and thunders: "Thou shalt not
make any graven images."
But as he bends his head to kiss

the image of his hope, the door
moves with its useful warning creak.
He steps aside. I start to play.
He fills his lungs, and sings once more,
   "Speak to me now, in blessings speak."
A death-pale curate come to pray
kneels, and is forced to find his Lord
through a loud F sharp major chord.

Where's that bright man who loved me, when
there was not much to love? He died
soon after. The undying flow
of music bears him close again,
handsome and young, while I am tried
in time's harsh fires. Dear man, I know
your worth, being now less ignorant of
the nature and the names of love.

Mother Who Gave Me Life

Mother who gave me life
I think of women bearing
women. Forgive me the wisdom
I would not learn from you.

It is not for my children I walk
on earth in the light of the living.
It is for you, for the wild
daughters becoming women,

anguish of seasons burning
backward in time to those other
bodies, your mother, and hers
and beyond, speech growing stranger

on thresholds of ice, rock, fire,
bones changing, heads inclining
to monkey bosom, lemur breast,
guileless milk of the word.

I prayed you would live to see
Halley's Comet a second time.
The Sister said, When she died
she was folding a little towel.

You left the world so, having lived
nearly thirty thousand days:
a fabric of marvels folded
down to a little space.

At our last meeting I closed
the ward door of heavy glass
between us, and saw your face
crumple, fine threadbare linen

worn, still good to the last,
then, somehow, smooth to a smile
so I should not see your tears.
Anguish: remembered hours:

a lamp on embroidered linen,
my supper set out, your voice
calling me in as darkness
falls on my father's house.

In the Middle of Life

Hopeless in middle age to soften
those hearts long petrified by hate,
or melt from features loved so often
in friendship's warmth, their desolate
mantle of self-sustaining spite.
We see ourselves, in callous light,

stripped of the vanity that conjured
for everyone an emperor's suit.
Who can drink flattery uninjured,
or banquet on illusion's fruit?
Unwelcome nourishment, but real,
is truth's unpalatable meal.

We need our enemies to teach us
what friends in kindness never show.
Where magnanimity can't reach us
the darts of hatred lodge and glow,
lighting our follies and pretensions,
our self-esteem's absurd dimensions.

Think of a still-life painter toiling
to keep the bloom of life intact,
fish, fruit and blossom slowly spoiling
while his brush holds the flowers erect,
the fruit unwrinkled, and the flesh
sea-lustred on the stinking fish.

All that can perish falls apart.
The labours of self-love can cease.
But in that gallery of the heart
where memory hangs each masterpiece
of things unalterably past,
the wisdom and the pain will last.

Death Has No Features of His Own

Death has no features of his own.
He'll take a young eye bathed in brightness
and the raging cheekbones of a raddled queen.
Misery's cured by his appalling taste.
His house is without issue. He appears
garlanded with lovebirds, hearts and flowers.
Anything, everything.
                   He'll wear my face and yours.
Not as we were, thank God. As we shall be
when we let go of the world, late ripe fruit falling.
What we are is beyond him utterly.

Thea
Astley

A Man Who is Tired of Swiper's Creek is Tired of Life

IF YOU were to ask me what makes us different up here — or what makes it different, for that matter — perhaps I could say it's because the place is ruled by the Gang of One.

This is the place where anything screwball is normal and often where what is normal is horrible. Life in the Golden Circle. Chuck the facts together and you get a freak collage landscape where politicians, goodness gracious, my goodness, believe in apartheid; where bomb squads can spend up to an hour defusing a case of mangoes; where we have our own Rapetown, one of whose local thugs is accepted resignedly and affectionately as Virge the Ripper.

"It's quite simple," one of the local aldermen said in his defence. "A woman's place is in the home. There is nothing finer," he said, "than a feminine woman and a mother."

That's telling 'em! Well, buster, here's to that and here's to the man who said, "When a man is tired of Swiper's Creek he is tired of life."

There's always been a lot of sad poetry about the place; and the distances that separate us, I mean the physical distances, are like the verse-breaks in a ballad; and once, once we believed the ballad might never end but go on accumulating its chapters of epic while the refrain, the almost unwordable quality that mortises us together, retained its singular soul. How express the tears of search?

Years ago, balking at the potency of the place, I once tried the New World, the US of A, groping after a Dvorak myth I thought might purge this, erase the Swiper's Creeks of the mind: but Dvorak had been eight decades away from the hamburger ritz and plastic pizazz that threatened with its deep-freeze camouflage to choke me. The transplant did not take.

It wasn't simply the potency of this place I was jibbing at; it was something else as well. I was trying to cut myself off from the home town, the old folks at — my slugabout harmless dad and my desperately fading still with-it mama. Long-time gone now — if time goes, that is, rather than us. I'm inclined to think the only moving is done by us. And another trouble with the New World is it's not easy to get in for any length of absorbing purpose. Not like here where it's gumming up with southerners, people who weren't born here and didn't grow up here but have hopped in for their chop.

Yes. It's a kind of carpet-bagger's paradise.

Which is not the explanation for my presence. As I said before, I like it here; and in the middle of the animal bayings of exploiters I still hear the dying music of this sad poetry.

As a business-man I'm a failure, for the place isn't really working. How do you estimate the profits from an average two guests a week in a town off the beaten track? For most of this year, I suppose, I've been subtracting the interest level of my customers from the deficit and striking some sort of balance; but it really just won't do.

Last week the interest dividends were particularly thin. There was this big meaty upright woman and her silent wacker of a mate, and the only juice I extracted was the fact that Mrs Wacker measured plane distances by noggins. "It's two beers from Brissy to Townsville," she announced heartily, "and then one more to the Top." She was given to those underplay phrases so dear to our myth: "After the blow," she'd say, referring to our worst cyclone in years; or "Bit of a dry" when she meant no rain in eight.

Or I could tell you about the sandy ex-academic (genuine) who came through last month from crocodile country, stayed a week, and pleaded to work out his board by helping round the place. He had half an ear chewed off, and whether this was the result of his labours before or after his new life I never cared to ask. Middle-ageing, he was only just recovering from his bitterness, and told me one morning as we were frying up the jack-fruit for breakfast that he'd tried real estate (the second oldest profession!) for a while, run a soft-drink factory, organised rackety bus tours, and worked as a bar-hand. Now he's beached in an iron shack up the coast where his books moulder and he spends his days reading and fishing.

"What made you give it up?" I ask. "The soft cop, I mean."

"Soft?"

"Well, sorry," I say. "Suitable-soft. A university job sounds easier than pulling pints or flogging mangrove acreages."

"I left," he tells me, whipping the jack-fruit over with his spatula as if he's been at it for years, "the morning one of my colleagues said, 'This student has an expression problem. And not only that, he has an inability-to-read-the-textbooks-attend-classes-and-submit-essays problem. I do think we should take this into consideration and give him his pass!' "

"And did they?"

"Of course. I was developing an ulcer. Oh, my God, don't let's talk about it. That's the first time in three years I've even mentioned it. Getting away. That's the thing. Getting away. What about you?"

He must see there's nothing for me to get away from and, resentful of irony, I tell him this; but he serves me my breakfast with style and there is no irony, I swear, despite our oddly reversed roles and the empty units.

"Change," he says, his mouth full. "Change." He's gobbling away like a pudgy old hen and blinks now and again over the tops of his horn-rims. "Why don't you shoot up to my place for a bit? I won't apologise, dear chap, for the shackery of it, but I'll be away for a while down south — if only to prove by contrast, of course, that this is the best of all possible worlds. You like fishing?"

Yes, I say. I like fishing. A kind of poetry, too, fishing. And I think along these lines for a little and feel I'd like to write it down some time. If fishing is the poetry of living then maybe the real difference between prose and poetry is that with prose you have to go out to the margins. You take my symbol, of course!

Mac heads south in his camper-van, leaving me with the key to his padlocked humpy and instructions on borrowing a semi-ute he's left back of a pub; and I close shop for a week on the customers I'm never going to have and trundle my inertia north.

So here I am, nudging the equator, and it's so long Crusader Rabbit and the Mutant Lobe from Outer Space!

This place should be irritable and brimming with the befuddled phrasings of its history; but it's a ghost hulk now, swinging lightly on its river moorings, its ports slitted against sun. The main street with its dying pubs, its dying stores, stretches out against the muscle tug of river; and the sad poetry takes over, not for what's left but for what isn't.

In the hot open spaces of the town there's no populace of ghosts; no trace of the trepang fishers, the cedar cutters, the miners, the thousands of yellow men or scraps of half-starved curfewed blacks, the publicans, card-sharpers, pick-pockets, prostitutes, the milky newchums. Yet as the days go by I discover they're all here, all back again in reduced numbers in a town that has budded and swelled and ripened and is now withering on the twig of the blue river; and suddenly I'm sickened with the pointlessness of our passion for growing, begetting, dying — and not a thing to show for it. Once this town panted under a miasma bubbling with gold-light; but it's a waste now, howling for time. Time doesn't move; we do, foot-slogging towards the old three score and ten till the boots split open and there's not even a footprint left of those others who've been beaten by the static character of the world. Time wins out. The place stands still; and if it waits long enough, just blinking now and again in the humid weather, the landscape becomes what it once was.

What's left? Some white-painted rails beside the river, but the mangroves are moving in on them and the northern headland that amusedly watched Cook fothering his ship stares unchanged at the now-empty convent, the joss house, the wizened houses, the two placid monuments quiet in the heart of their stone with that one violent moment of their history. I close my eyes for a second, inept sentimentalist, and across blue water the masts of unhurried ships move continually into light. I open them and there's only a natty launch with a crew-cut dumping a slop-bucket into the tides and a sun-hatted frump holding a line.

The hot roadway holds only me and one other, an old and hobbling parody of myself, left leg bent out at a grotesque right-angle from the hip, for whom each step is a terrible problem in geometry; and as we approach, meet, our silent eyes establish kinship.

Who needs Crusader Rabbit? The Mutant Lobe? There's a story in one of the islands east of here that the spirits of dead natives walk north along the final atoll of the group to their final country, and if you walk that way yourself and meet one of the spirits returning from that taking-off point, death will claim you in the year. Perhaps this, although it's mainland, is simply a reduplication of the ultimate launching-pad of the dream.

Under lamp-light Mac's house takes on meaning.

It's two miles out of town on a south-facing beach cut off from the main road by a tidal lagoon and a creek with lasciviously warm shallows. (I found it easily enough. The barman at the second pub drew a map on the back of his hand between drinks.) Books clutter the place so fully there's barely room for the camp stretcher and the rough sink he has rigged up to the water-tank. I take my tea onto the sand-strip beyond the house into sea-chant and watch the place come alive under its mango-trees and frangipani. Two hundred yards away down the beach there's a twinned kerosene glow from a pup tent where a couple of campers are staying. Not your regular campers — the dusk-cries of kids and straying pups and smell of fried steaks — but a whiskered drop-out I passed on the way in, striding the track in his own darkness, and a girl whom I waded past in the creek. She was standing thigh-deep, her skirts hoicked up, dangling a turnip-shaped net in the slack water, lifting the net dreamily, inspecting and lowering it again. When I spoke she barely raised her head for the space of her half-smile.

Along the beach I can hear their voices blown in ragged word-strips from light to ear. Oh, the lighted houses! The comfort, the mystery of the lighted houses!

I fall asleep drugged by the scent of mangoes.

Have you noticed how houses have their especial qualities of happiness or anger or sheer nothing at all? Mac's house, despite its temporary nature, is filled with the absent man: I find him in scribbled memos on old calendars, on the heart pills he's forgotten to take with him, the wafer of sandsoap dried out on the kitchen window-sill. I understand what made him scribble "A pox on erudition!" along the shelf where some of his books are stacked, and I track his droppings throughout the morning with delight, right to the page he's ripped from Plato's *Republic* and tacked to the canvas walls of his dunny.

I lean in on his abandoned contentment and suck it in with the thick fleshy smell of the mangoes and the vanishing scent of limes.

Evening.

Just as I settle into a nine o'clock lassitude, thumbing my way along Mac's shelves, the Pup-tents appear at my shadowy door bearing a half-flagon of poisonous red to sweeten the intrusion and discover themselves to me as Carl and Rosebud.

Conversationally it's the same old stuff that I've heard — oh, I've heard before — along the Mango waterways, and I turf them at last into the dark again and listen to the ripe fruit explode on the tin roof.

Day three like they're out of coffee man and I buy them off with a quickpack and flee from them across the creek to the parked ute and drive into town which is, I notice, filled with old folk. You want a list? In the first pub I discover an eighty-year-old joker from the Outer Hebrides who has lived the last five years there in a caravan crammed with the ghosts of relatives he'll never see again; two ageing characters from Minneapolis who are trying to run a carriers' business and sell exhausted pot-plants as a side-line; a middle-aged lady from Perth who conducts gospel sessions; a retired chicken-farmer from Sydney; a rubber-planter from New Guinea.

Beached. The lot of them. Sea-wrack.

And the town is plugged with mangoes. I've never seen so many. They split beneath my foot. They stain my ankle. Their hot yellow perfume dogs me. I see boxes piled with them sitting unclaimed on fence-posts, outside shop doorways, on pub verandas. Even when I drive down to the wharf in the afternoon for a spot of fishing with the characters from Minneapolis, there are two cartons of them rotting in the sun. And as darkness sifts in from the sea the stench of them challenges the salt-breath of the river-mouth.

The pot-planters know what's what! We've been together three hours of idle quietness on the splintered boards of the wharf and they have enough subtlety to invite me to share their catch — not this evening but the next. I like that. Enough is enough is enough of people. But when I reach Mac's shack the Pup-tents are back again as I fry up my catch, and what can I do but share? Mind you, it's not the fish I begrudge; it's the washings of silence and sea-tune that are being fractured so that I indicate early in the piece my lewd and elderly preference for solitariness. Carl's fingers have been scratching the spines of Mac's books. He wants to borrow a couple. I explain they're not mine, but he's oblivious to the protocol that goes with possession.

"Jesus, man!" he protests. "You've got to be kidding!"

Morning four I discover a couple of blanks on the shelves and realise the floppy screen of Rosebud's caftan has its uses. Down the beach the limp smoke from the Pup-tents' breakfast fire scrawls its indifference as I wonder whether or not to limp my accusations across the beach and confront them amid the incoherent scrub. Wise, I try town instead, hang about the front, the pubs, until it's time to meet my Minneapolis mates.

At six the pub verandas are filling up with the seedy, the old, the sun-blasted discards of the tropics; and here we are, the lot of us, gulping our beers and pushing the conversation across flat decades of memory while the wavering atmospherics of the place suggest another drink and another. Somewhere behind the bar a radio is crackling with pop, but no one is listening; and I notice the fourth time the barman comes over to take our order that there are still faint traces of the map he drew for me on the back of his age-spotted hand.

My Minneapolis pot-planters are just suggesting we go back to their place for that promised meal when I notice across the room that the Pup-tents have come in. Out of place they look with their young bodies and faces in this crowd of old-timers hunched over their drinks. They're sucking nicely at something harmless in long glasses and they're not talking much, merely staring, spaced-out, around the room at the rest of us. I even forget them for a while as we finish off our last drinks, sitting passive and sluggish under the punching light of the bare globes and deadened with smoke; so that it comes with the shock of explosion when Rosebud suddenly springs from her chair, strides across the room and kicks a litter-bin to the floor with a crash. "Filth!" she yells. "Filth! Rotten and old and filth!"

The bar goes silent. No one moves. Even the barman is frozen in action with one hand poised to take a bottle from the shelf behind him. Shoving between tables, the girl kicks a smoking stand over and there's a ripping clatter as it screeches its metallic way across concrete. Carl's face bears the smallest of smiles. Then she whacks a third bin to the ground at the feet of the elderly watchers whose faces are blank before her violence and screams again, "Dying! Old! Rotten! Dying!" and lurches her rage into the street.

When I get back to the shack the Pup-tents are gone and I suppose now they are lugging their packs in search of Eden, still walking into late and later summer.

I'm leaving today. This place is too close to the bone, the me, the ultimate me of me.

I've padlocked Mac's shack and with exaggerated and farewelling care I park his old ute square onto the back fence of the pub while I take one last monochrome snapshot of the town with my good-bye eyes, finding the lens isn't blurred this time as I haul myself onto the makeshift bus that runs out to the air-strip. The driver is a thin courteous socialist fanatic not given to many words, except to tell me he's pulling out of the job in two years and he can't wait for retirement. Where? I ask. And he says here.

We pick up mail and we pull in at the bakery to take up a crate of bread for the plane which will unload it along with its cartons of Courvoisier and toilet paper on one of the tourist islands of the blest south of here; and as I give him a hand I crack my elbow so sharply on the metal edges of the van I'm aware of mortality. Aware. All the way out on the empty road, aware: the lagoon is still under a clotting of water-lilies; the road-house near it advertising steak-night fries and reef-bakes is unpeopled; beside the abandoned brick-works an old cement-mixer is covering itself with vines. When the van drops me off at the waiting-shed there's no one in sight but an old codger dragging a hose along the garden-strip and plunging the nozzle for a brief transfusion into the struggling roots of allamanda and hibiscus.

For ten minutes the sky stays empty and then the little plane appears, miles down the coast but swelling each second till it's dipping, circling, and swinging in for its run down the strip.

The bus goes out to meet it.

At first the plane appears empty, but after a while I see the pilot helping down an old woman, very tiny, very frail. From this distance I see his arm directing her to the shed and slowly, step after tiny step, she shuffles towards me carrying her bulging grandma bag; and I wonder, as I watch her cover painfully that hundred-yard stretch, if it seems like ten miles. After she has struggled to the gate off the tarmac, I see that despite the morning heat she's wearing an old blue cardigan and clutching a straggling afterthought bunch of flowers someone has given her. It's a very tiny bunch. I help her onto the seat. There's no one around. The pilot. The bus driver. The fat old codger running the hose. Me.

She has a pressed and diffident face that's trying to be brave alone at the top of the lost end of the world.

"Is anyone meeting you?" I ask. No one out there seems to care. We really are in limbo.

She's deaf and I try again.

"It's not too hot," she says and gives a timid bit of a smile, tugging her old cardigan round her.

I repeat my question.

"Can't stand the cold. My daughter, she's gone to Goulburn. It's too cold for me. I love the heat."

"Do you?" I have to shout it again. "Do you?"

"Oh, yes. Can't bear that cold."

I gaze all round me at the empty circle in the scrub. The pilot. The bus driver helping unstack the plane. The old codger. And behind us, beyond this last hoop of reality, the untranslatable idiom of trees and emptiness.

I say more loudly, "Isn't anyone meeting you?"

She flashes me an old tired look. "I'm going to the hospital."

"Hospital?"

"It's a place for old people like. Well, I'm old, aren't I?" she asks defiantly.

On your own! I marvel. Dumped?

"Where's your family then?"

She catches the last words.

"Oh, it was a big one. Six I had. Four boys and two girls. The boys, they're married, all of them, and I got eight grandchildren."

She nods and in reflex one brittle hand feels for the scraggy flowers that are all that's left of them up here. "Eight!" Smiling and nodding to herself.

"And your girls?"

"They give me these. The littlest one did."

"But your daughters? Your girls? What about them?"

"Oh, they're married, too. They're down south. It's too cold for me that place."

"I suppose you know it up here, then?" I say.

"What's that?"

"I say I suppose you know it up here. Have you been here before?"

"Not here. My daughter was here though. She lived here. She says it's not too cold. She fixed it all for me. Said the heat would do me good."

"Did she?"

"Yes. She says when she went to Goulburn, 'Mum, you won't like it. It's freezing,' she said. 'I know just the place for you. You won't need your woollies there, eh?'"

The old lady looked across the tarmac into heat glitter that crackled with southern frost and mumbled a little to herself, but I couldn't catch much of it.

"You must have been pretty busy with six," I say. "Kept you working."

"What's that?"

"I said six must have kept you busy."

She nodded. "Oh, yes. I was always busy. I used to say I never had the right to be tired." She gave her little smile again. "I got the right now, eh?"

"You've got the right."

The bus driver and the pilot were both waving and calling me across to the plane for take-off. It's pretty informal here. That's why I like it.

And then the moment gathered itself into a point. Somehow I couldn't bear to leave her like this in stranger country — but what could I do, what could I say? She sat there tugging her cardigan round her vanishing body and hugging her big dilly bag that looked like her only luggage, that and the little bunch of garden flowers.

"I've got to go now," I say. "I hope you had a nice trip up."

She doesn't hear, but she sees me get up and she sees the pilot walking over to the safety fence calling me, and she is wobbling to her feet again.

"He didn't fly too high," she says.

I can't bear it.

I tell her again I have to go and she still doesn't hear and there's the smallest touch on my arm when I make to leave, as if something has alighted there no stronger than a breath; and I turn without looking round and limp across the grass past the old bloke with his hose, through the gate, and out into the heat of the air-strip.

But when I'm settled in the plane and look back through the window I see she is coming after me. Slowly. Half-way across the tarmac — and she doesn't really know where to go or what is happening to her. The bus driver is making waving signs from his van, shooing her away and I roar at him through glass "Let her get on the bloody bus here, will you? Please!" I'm crying. "Please!"

But he must be a rules man, for he keeps on waving her off; and finally the pilot goes over to her and takes one delicate arm and points her back.

Returned to Mango, the collective inexorable corrupting motions of the world press in on me and the little journey I had made, supposed to promise change, has become part of the pressure.

I ache like a tooth and I'm not sure whether the ache starts in the heart or the head.

Reply, reply, my questing self demands in unravelling sessions with Fixer (still morose), Willy Fourcorners (folk simples), 'Notes' Galipo (financial plasters), with Brain and Bosie. Brain throbs with crazy advice.

"Migrate. Get yourself a little raft and drift — preferably north. Say you're a refugee from fascism. Deep-seated ineradicable fascism."

Turn on. Tune in. Drop out. But it's the last piece of that philosophic hogwash I reject. I — want — to tune — *in*.

"Easy," Tripp says. (Remember Doc. Tripp? Maxie?) "The problem for most people is they see themselves as total animal — all excitability and want. They forget the other half, the half that accepts its biological mortality. Spirit. Soul, if you like."

"You sound like Rassini."

"Not him! He's a professional. You have to come to amateurs for the nitty-gritty."

I inspect Tripp's face, a haphazard collection of good-natured wrinkles, defined by too much sun. He's shed his last guard along with his practice and his teeth and lives alone in a flash forgotten house on the inlet which his third wife had stuffed with unsuitable furniture and appalling paintings by the artist son of his first marriage. When visitors make social noises asking who did them, he tells them someone broke in.

He walks me down the sloping lawn to the landing where his latest and final

597

wife, fitted out for ghost horizons, swings lightly on the ruminating tide, aching for the sea.

"Are you looking for oblivion?" he asks. "Or a place in memory? Well, you won't get that," he says. "It's such a tawdry thing."

"Being remembered?"

"Being remembered."

Reeftown is concealed by mangroves. There's no trace at all of Mango skulking in purple hills.

We sit on the rocking deck of his boat and Tripp cartoons, briefly, skilfully, his plans for this year, next year, some time, never. He tells me he'll be leaving next month and sailing north and east, light and easy, and suggests I join him.

"It's not rejection ache you've got. It's acceptance. The bloody ache to accept yourself. The soul part." He gives me a sly grin. "That's what they mean by the islands of the blest!"

Birth, marriage, death, re-birth. They're the only neat endings, traditional culminations for living — for books, even — and what bogus back-watering punctuation they are! Living is serial, an unending accretion of alternatives.

As the afternoon sun gutters, I promise I'll join him.

But will I?

David
Malouf

This Day under My Hand

FOR JILL AND LANCE PHILLIPS

Well it was never mine,
not really. My father bought it
in my name to save
the tax in '45:
streaked weatherboard, no view
to speak of, only the sand
-hills of Moreton Island,
humpbacked and white like whales.

My sister will stock its rooms
with cedar and brass,
her kids leave sandprints of
their sneakers on its floors,
small arms spread to conjure
again from moonlit shallows
the old rock-cod they hooked
at dawn out on the reef.

Sandcrabs throw their claws
in a copper pot, hiss
red, their agonies
sealed off under a lid.
At nine the Scrabble board,
small words interlocking
down and across that fill
an evening, square by square.

599

Storm-lanterns. Tigermoths
at the wirescreen door. Slow fan
of the light at Cowan Cowan.
The cold Pacific banging,
an open gate. Australia
hitched like a watertank
to the back verandah, all night
tugging at our sleep.

A world away. I let it
go, my hold
on a continent: sheerwater
gulls, the sundrenched crevice
where lobsters crawl. Under
the shadow of my hand,
night fills the house, climbs into
its cupboards, its beds.

In one of them a child
is dreaming: sea fog
trickles from a fist.
It seeps through hoop-pine branches
and a jetty's planks still warm from
the sun, rolls under
a barbed-wire fence, flows into
his mouth. Midnight comes on.

He sleeps. Morning approaches
the far side of his head.
There are dreams we cannot keep
at a distance: salt, gull's cry —
each lost thing shines and thrashes
alive in the net.
From a dark bay hissing
like crabs, red tropic suns.

Glasshouse Mountains

FOR JUDITH

Seen always across
a bay called Deception
— abandoned pier, bait kiosk,
the prawnfleet swinging
at anchor with the moon —
five gables of glass.

No one casts the stone,
or could over that sunlit
stone's throw of water,
to shatter them. On clear days
they stand far off, move close
under cover of rain.

At night safe in our beds
we dream of them: brows
of giants frown up
from the bay's depths, our pebbles
skip leagues of bright water
to snap at their heads.

So close, so close! We push
off for their further shore.
Our arms grow stronger
for rowing. Like lodestones
they draw us. The shadows
strike out from our flesh.

The grey sandpiper dips
through matchwood spars, sea-lice,
keen flakes of moonlight, scatter
and burn. The bay dries
to white salt on our fingers,
to black on our lips.

O giants unkilled who walk
tonight the moonlit water
-lanes of my sleep.
In the bay a small boy's throwing
arm weighed down
with stones, five mountain peaks.

Off the Map

All night headlamps dazzle
the leaves. Truck drivers
throbbing on pills
climb out of the sleep

of farm towns prim
behind moonlit lace, bronze Anzacs
nodding, leaden-headed,
at ease between wars,

and out into a dream
of apple-orchards, paddocks
tumbling with mice,
bridges that slog the air

— black piers, bright water — silos
moonstruck, pointing nowhere,
like saints practising stillness
in the ripple of grain.

They thunder across country
like the daredevil boys
of the 'Fifties who flourished
a pistol in banks,

and rode off into headlines
and hills or into legends
that hang grey-ghostly over
campfires in the rain.

Now kids, bare-footed, wade
in the warm hatched tyre-marks
of country dust, the print
of monsters; cattle stare.

All night through the upland
spaces of our skull
in low gear shifting skyward
they climb towards dawn.

A lit butt glows, a beercan
clatters. Strung out
on the hills, new streets that shine
in the eyes of farmboys, cities

alive only at nightfall
that span a continent.
Nameless. Not to be found
by day on any map.

An Ordinary Evening at Hamilton

The garden shifts indoors, the house lets fall
its lamp light, opens
windows in the earth,

and the small stars of the grass, the night insects,
                    needlepoint
a jungle more dense
than any tapestry, where Saturn burns, a snow owl's nest,
                    and melons feed

their crystal with hot sugars of the moon. The Pacific
breaks at our table,
each grain

of salt a splinter of its light at midday, deserts
flare on the lizard's tongue. Familiar rooms
glow, rise through the dark — exotic islands; this house

a strange anatomy
of parts, so many neighbours in a thicket:
hair, eyetooth, thumb.

Decade's End

Stocktaking: what have I put
away out of these seven
fat years to be used
against the seven lean?

Postcards of travel: slow
Rhine barges towing
cathedrals through fog,
toward dawn the Aegean

breaking dolphin-backed
with islands, and twice
in a cool decade love
that wrings us dry wrung me

dry. I survived
as we all did Cuba's
nine day hiss and splutter.
Like straw men caught

with a matchbox in the wind
we kindled at a spark, we
were dry sticks and newsprint
pouring out smuts,

and I dreamed of the hornets' nest
my father burned, black
ear-wax dripped, the wingless
stumbling from Troy.

We burn, but so slowly,
consuming our fats,
that we barely feel it. Candles
trembling, swaying,

feeding the body's flame,
we glow, we fade; not all
of us even in seven
years can be renewed.

But the light at least is something
to read by, till we learn
to do without it, growing
accustomed to the dark.

Jack
Davis

Camped in the Bush

Wind in the hair
Of a sleeping child
And the tree-tops wavering,
The starlight mild.

The moon's first peep
On the sand-plain rise,
And the fox in the shadows
With flashing eyes.

Over the campfire
The bat cries shrill
And a ''semi'' snarls
On the Ten Mile Hill.

And the lonely whistle
Of the train at night,
Where my kingdom melted
In the city's light.

Warru

Fast asleep on the wooden bench,
Arms bent under the weary head,
There in the dusk and the back-street stench
He lay with the look of the dead.

I looked at him, then back through the years,
Then knew what I had to remember —
A young man, straight as wattle spears,
And a kangaroo hunt in September.

We caught the scent of the 'roos on the rise
Where the gums grew on the Moore;
They leaped away in loud surprise,
But Warru was fast and as sure.

He threw me the fire-stick, oh what a thrill!
With a leap he sprang to a run.
He met the doe on the top of the hill,
And he looked like a king in the sun.

The wattle spear flashed in the evening light,
The kangaroo fell at his feet.
How I danced and I yelled with all my might
As I thought of the warm red meat.

We camped that night on a bed of reeds
With a million stars a-gleaming.
He told me tales of Noong-ah* deeds
When the world first woke from dreaming.

He sang me a song, I clapped my hands,
He fashioned a needle of bone.
He drew designs in the river sands,
He sharpened his spear on a stone.

I will let you dream — dream on, old friend —
Of a boy and a woman in September,
Of hills and stars and the river's bend —
Alas, that is all to remember.

*Noong-ah — Aboriginal tribe of the south-west of
Western Australia.

Aboriginal Reserve

The long low sweeping ground,
The horizon black in starlight
And somewhere now the sound
Of a child's cry in the night.

They stir a fire that is dying,
The sparks fly upward blending
With night and a people crying.
O where, O where is the ending?

The mind forgets tomorrow,
Eyes grow dull with the years,
Afraid of the heights of sorrow
And to fathom the depths of fears.

Death of a Snake

Six foot dugite of ebony sheen,
Gliding through granite where he can't be seen.

But the magpies shout "Look out!" And squawking:
"Boy, beware of where you're walking!"

He's moving faster, find a waddy!
Leaping breathless, crush that body.

Twisting, turning, belly yellow,
Now he's dead, a harmless fellow.

As meat to eat he's highly rated,
But alas, I'm too sophisticated.

Now find a place for him to rest,
So fling him on the bull-ants' nest.

Vivian
Smith

For My Daughter

Made from nothing: bud and rose,
kisses, water, mystery:
you who grew inside our need
run, in your discovery,

out of the garden's folded light,
out of the green, the fountain's spray,
past the shrubs, the dew-lit ferns,
out to the noise, the street, the day:

and stand, in your astonishment,
beneath the hanging heavy limes
(O my child, O my darling daughter,
summer was full of wars and crimes)

to see the foal, the clown, the doll,
the circus and procession band
march up the street and march away . . .
And so you turn and take my hand.

Still Life

This still life is still life after all.
These massed hydrangeas standing near the wall
as big as cushions puffed up on a chair
loll their heads like pink clowns in the air
who just perform and do not need to know.
They bloom with blue like heaped up mountain snow.

These flowers bring such fullness to the room
they stand like resurrections from the tomb.
Now at season's end with tarnished golds
the year rots like a mirror which still holds
blue and silver merging with the frame.
These are colours with a flower's name.

We sit and watch their clouds of pink, their sheen,
the way they look both savage and serene
drawing the light and holding it at bay:
a storm inside a storm that has been stilled
with something finished, something unfulfilled.

Tasmania

Water colour country. Here the hills
rot like rugs beneath enormous skies
and all day long the shadows of the clouds
stain the paddocks with their running dyes.

In the small valleys and along the coast,
the land untamed between the scattered farms,
deconsecrated churches lose their paint
and failing pubs their fading coats of arms.

Beyond the beach the pine trees creak and moan,
in the long valley poplars in a row,
the hills breathing like a horse's flank
with grasses combed and clean of the last snow.

Early Arrival: Sydney

Red cockatoo crests caught on coral-trees:
my Sydney emblems. Dragging the land in view
our ship hauls glass and concrete to its side
as gulls fly up and snatch and scream and glide
away on a sea smeared with a trace of blue.

The neons flicker and the skyline wakes.
The orange suburbs float through miles of calm;
a pastel-coloured terrace shades its slope.
While five gulls fight for nothing on a rope,
the breeze picks out a single listless palm.

The city's like a room far undersea
with locked arcades where shadow-waves subside.
Grey windows bend great cloud-shapes as they pass.
Beyond these tiles, tunnels, iron, glass,
the flat waters of green inlets ride
where all the folded yachts are chained away.

But here the huge hotels still sway in space
with the exactness of a foreign place.

Late April: Hobart

Turning from the mirror full of leaves
that draws the autumn garden through the room
I note that brown's the colour of decay,
but in the garden how it just achieves
a sense of balance between rot and bloom
where old chrysanthemums lean all one way

as if an angle meant avoiding change.
Thick with its burden of excess and loss
this time of year depresses and elates:
all points of stillness hover out of range;
wind strips the season to its sticks and dross
and days to a blue scratched out of southern slates.

This autumn garden is decay of gold,
a waste of mildew, fading reds that glow
as in bare boughs the brown and gold respond.
Each day the corners lengthen shades of cold
and silver rain gives way to mountain snow
and black and sour grows the lily pond.

Gone are the statements of the summer dawn
when love grew more abundant with excess;
sustained by filth, fertility survives.
Fulfilment needs its time to be withdrawn
in its own silence, much like holiness.
In time each shifting harmony arrives.

And now it's this dark brevity of gold
with so much withering as colours glow
as if the frugal with the fecund mates.
The sunlight dazzles with its April cold
and through the red the brown begins to show.
Beneath it all such final bareness waits.

At an Exhibition of Historical Paintings, Hobart

The sadness in the human visage stares
out of these frames, out of these distant eyes;
the static bodies painted without love
that only lack of talent could disguise.

Those bland receding hills are too remote
where the quaint natives squat with awkward calm.
One carries a kangaroo like a worn toy,
his axe alert with emphasized alarm.

Those nearer woollen hills are now all streets;
even the water in the harbour's changed.
Much is alike and yet a slight precise
disparity seems intended and arranged —

as in that late pink terrace's facade.
How neat the houses look. How clean each brick.
One cannot say they look much older now,
but somehow more themselves, less accurate.

And see the pride in this expansive view:
churches, houses, farms, a prison tower;
a grand gesture like wide-open arms
showing the artist's trust, his clumsy power.

And this much later vision, grander still:
the main street sedate carriages unroll
towards the tentative, uncertain mountain:
a flow of lines the artist can't control —

the foreground nearly breaks out of its frame
the streets end so abruptly in the water . . .
But how some themes return. A whaling ship.
The last natives. Here that silent slaughter

is really not prefigured or avoided.
One merely sees a profile, a full face,
a body sitting stiffly in a chair:
the soon-forgotten absence of a race . . .

Album pieces: bowls of brown glazed fruit . . .
I'm drawn back yet again to those few studies
of native women whose long floral dresses
made them first aware of their own bodies.

History has made artists of all these
painters who lack energy and feature.
But how some gazes cling. Around the hall
the pathos of the past, the human creature.

The Restorers

I read in today's paper how the scrub
is getting help from its new band of friends:
regeneration of depleted park,

forest will recover lost growth;
the Big Scrub logged away by '99
now furnished with a thousand tiny trees.

And suddenly the names all come alive,
wildings planted out in the thin rain,
white cedar, cheesewood, yellow wood, black bean

lifting their leaves from earth's torn tapestry.
And I remember nuns before the war
with needles into lace restoring threads

bringing back to life a lost design.

Morris
Lurie

A King of the Road

You CAN lead a horse to water, but you can't make my father buy a car. Master psychologists have tried. For example, my mother. "Abe, let's buy a car," she says. "I don't need it," my father says. "What for?" And he takes down our perfectly all right toaster from its shelf and gets busy on it with the small screwdriver which he always carries, and at such moments, when he's fixing, no one talks to him.

We move forward a month. Picture a spring night, a star-crammed sky, a black Pontiac stopping at our front gate. My father gets out first, then my mother. My mother tells Uncle Sam for the twentieth time to thank Tzila for the wonderful supper, really, she shouldn't have gone to all that trouble, and then, catching up with my father, who already has his key in the front door lock, she says, "See how it is when you have a car? Right to the door." "A nice lift," my father says.

How long does the water-on-stone treatment take? I lie in my bed and listen to it happening, drip, drip, at the other end of the passage, in my parents' bed. A month, two? Time doesn't mean anything. Occasionally I hear a loud "No!" and from its violence I know that things are about to happen.

And they do. One Sunday morning, when I have stewed in my bed past the point of pleasure, I get up and my father is not at home. "Where's dad?" I ask my mother. For every Sunday for as long as I can remember, my father has been out in the garden, either mowing a lawn or pulling up weeds or just standing and thinking about one of those two. "Don't bother me, can't you see I'm busy," my mother says. She has taken out all the cutlery and is lining the drawers with new white paper, a thing which she does only for *pesach*, or if someone spills something in a drawer, but never at any other time. No answer. I make a breakfast. An hour later my father comes in, looking flushed. "Well?" my mother asks. "I don't need a car!" my father says. "What for?" The driving lessons have begun.

The next Sunday I am awake at seven, dressed in five minutes, sitting on my bed and then standing up and then sitting down again, a thousand times, waiting for my father to go out and begin his lesson. I hear a car toot. My father is in the kitchen, drinking tea, and I hear the cup fall from his hands, with an enormous sound, as though every piece of china in our kitchen has been broken, and then I hear him moving quickly down the passage, fumbling with the front door, the door slamming, and then my father's steps running down the path. I am out, also running, but quietly, and from the front room window, concealed behind the drawn blind, I see everything.

There is a short, bald man sitting at the wheel of a large green car. He sees my father. He slides over on the seat, leans over and opens the door, and my father gets in. They talk for a long time, the man pointing, my father nodding. Then the car starts. My father's face is a study of concentration and terror. He looks at the bald man. The man points to something. My father does something with his hands, then puts them both on the wheel, high up, and I see — or feel — how white his knuckles are. Then the car begins to move.

It shoots forward, stops, bounces, seems to come back, then forward again, up into the air, over to one side, and I hide my face. And when next I look, the street in front of our house is empty.

I run outside, forgetting all caution, all stealth. And I am just in time. The green car is at the very end of our street, where it meets the main road, and it's not moving. I watch it, and it seems to stand there for ever, hours, while my heart waits too. Then suddenly it is gone, as though wires have jerked it round the corner, and I breathe out.

I don't bother to wait around to see my father drive back. Everyone has difficulties at the beginning, I rationalize, it's only natural, after all. But something has died inside me. When he comes back from his lesson I am mowing the lawn and frightened to look him in the eye. I mow like a madman, front *and* back, and then I start on the weeds, and the only thing that stops me finishing them is my mother calling me in to lunch. Never again do I go out to see the lesson begin, not once.

Once again time has no meaning. Months pass, one after another, and it is as though my father has always gone for driving lessons on a Sunday morning, I can't remember a time when he didn't. And when my Uncle Sam drops around and says to my father, "So, you're taking the lessons, uh?" and slaps my father on the shoulder, I leave the room.

Naturally, it's me who brings in the letter with the picture-window envelope and my father's name typed inside. "Ah," says my father, getting his toaster-fixing hands to it as though it was the last *latke* in the world, while I feign indifference. But at the dinner table I am spared nothing. The talk is all of licences, only of licences, and this licence, my father's, is held up and waved and shown and finally my father lets it out of his hand for just a few seconds and lets me hold it. "Nu, scholar," he says, "can you read it?" and snatches it away before I have even had a chance to focus. "You know how long it took Max Lazarus to get this, this piece of paper? Nu? Ten months! Ha! And about his wife I'm not even going to mention." While my mother, the master psychologist, serves the soup and says not a word.

Now the talking in bed starts again, the soft voices in the dark, the whispers, and then the loud "No!" while I lie in bed and strain for details. But this time there is no secrecy.

My father announces, the next night, that he is going to buy a car, he has decided, even the colour he knows. Blue, in two shades, the lighter one on the top, like the Finkelsteins have. Well, not exactly like the Finkelsteins have, theirs is the old model, already out of date. "Tomorrow I put down my name," he says, looking already a good three feet taller than he actually is. "Eight months," he says to me. "For such a car, you have to wait eight months. Don't worry, I'll get it in six."

Once again I lose track of the time, but as the months creep past, and speed, and lunge forward, and relentlessly advance, I keep surprising my father, sitting all alone in the front room with the light off, his licence held in both hands, his eyes riveted to it. "Oh, I'm sorry," I say, having switched on the light, "I didn't know you were . . . I wanted to hear something on the radio." "I don't want the radio!" my father shouts, and stands up and lunges out of the room, putting the licence away quickly inside his wallet, pushing the wallet down deep inside his trouser pocket, then standing in the passage, not knowing where to go.

This happens again and again, maybe four times. As the time for the car's arrival draws near, my father grows more and more quiet. To speak to him is at your own risk. Even my mother, that master psychologist, can't draw near. "Abe, maybe you should have a few more lessons, to brush up," she says. "You know, to get the feel." "No!" my father shouts, and it is only his iron will that keeps him from taking out his licence at the table and staring at it.

Then one night, a Thursday, the phone rings. My mother answers. I hear her talking for a half minute, and then she says, "Just a minute, I'll get him," and then she calls out, "Abe, for you! The car!"

My father scrambles to his feet and his face is flushed and ashen at the same time. He holds the telephone receiver as I saw him holding the wheel of the green car for his second lesson. "Hello?" he says, in a voice I have never heard him use before. "Tomorrow? All right. I'll — yes . . ." and the phone falls from his fingers.

"Tomorrow," he says to my mother, who is standing a foot away, about six inches from me.

"Well, ring up Sam and tell him to go with you," my mother says.

"I don't need Sam," my father says. "I can drive."

"The city traffic, Abe," my mother says, and my father says, "You call him."

My mother dials, and gets, of course, Aunt Tzila, who is always first to the phone. "Tzila?" she says, "the car has arrived. What? Yes, we just heard, now on the telephone, they rang us up, it's ready." "Nu?" says my father, suddenly impatient. "C'mon, let me speak." And he takes the receiver out of my mother's hand while she is in the middle of a word, explaining that it is a two shades of blue car, like the Finkelsteins', but, naturally, a new model —

"Tzila?" my father says. "Thank you, thank you. Naah, I'm not excited, what's a car? It's a machine, that's all. Yes, a blue, two shades, that's what I ordered. Blue is a good colour, you don't have to wash it so much. Ha ha, yeah . . . Listen, is Sam there?"

There is a pause for some seconds while Aunt Tzila calls out to Sam that he's wanted on the phone, it's the car, it's arrived, a blue one, two shades.

"Hello, Sam," my father says. "Listen . . . yeah, tomorrow. Listen, Sam, maybe it would be a good idea if . . . ah! There? In the showroom? Four o'clock. Come a bit earlier, so we can . . . Four o'clock? Nu, good. What? Just a minute, I'll put her back on, she's standing right here. Four o'clock, all right?"

And he gives the phone back to my mother, so she can speak some more with Aunt Tzila, and then, unable to employ his iron will a second longer, he plunges his hand into his pocket, draws out the wallet, with loving care unfolds the licence from its place inside, and studies it, really studies it, until he looks up and sees me watching him. "You haven't got any lessons?" he shouts at me, and I flee to the sanity of my room.

Four o'clock the following afternoon I am already standing outside our house, waiting. And so is everyone else in our street. Somehow the word has spread. All the street is in their gardens, or standing and talking, looking nonchalant, but I know what they're waiting to see. Even Mr Pinter, who hasn't spoken to my father in four years, after some difference of opinion which time has long obliterated, is there.

Only my mother won't come outside. "I'll come, I'll come," she says to me, but she stays inside.

It is half past four. The street is still empty of the car. Now, if anything, there are more people than ever, and their nonchalance has gone. For all their talking and occasionally laughing, I can feel an electric tension in the street. In just a few minutes, a second, one beat of my heart . . .

And then the car appears.

We see it turning slowly into the street, two shades of blue, my father at the wheel. It makes an elaborate turn, and then pauses, and begins again. The street is quiet.

"Mum!" I call out, but she is already there, by my side.

"*He's* driving," my mother says. "Why isn't Sam driving?"

But it is my father at the wheel. Sam is sitting next to him, a separate shape.

"Mum, don't worry," I say, or shout, or something, running out into the street, then back on to the nature strip, then out into the street again.

The car comes closer. It is moving as quietly as a stream of oil, as slowly as a dream. Now it is close enough for me to see my father's face. It is like a tomato, the sun, beaming, shining, bursting, and his smile is enormous. I have never seen my father look so radiant, like a king on the field of battle when the enemy has fled.

My father smiles to everyone, on both sides of the street, as he drives his brand-new car. He smiles to Mr Pinter, who shrinks, to the two ladies at number twelve, to the Obers, the Winters, to all. And then I see Uncle Sam lean over and say something to him and point at something inside the car and my father looks down for a second and does something with his hand and then looks up again, his face serious now for a second, though still bright red, and then the smile comes back, and now he is almost at our house and beginning to turn — our gates are open, the garage yawns wide — and his smile is still enormous and in this fashion my father drives into our fence.

"Oh!" gasps my mother, inside her throat.

The car shakes, shudders, stops. A door flies open. My Uncle Sam is out. "Nothing, nothing," he says, and he is running to the front of the car, bending to see what has happened, looking up at my mother, then back to the front of the car, then at my father, who hasn't moved. He sits, his hands still on the wheel, the colour draining out of him, like a stone.

"My God!" says my mother, a hand to her heart.

"Don't worry, don't worry," Uncle Sam says, and he runs around behind the car and comes up and opens the door on my father's side.

"I'll fix it," he says. Like a stone, my father gets out.

Now, expertly, in a flurry of gears, looking at no one and at everyone, craning his neck to see behind him, sitting up straight, moving like a machine, he shoots the car back, corrects its angle, and whips it up our drive and into the garage.

I run to see what has happened. My mother is a step behind me. My father stands on the nature strip, not moving.

Uncle Sam is out of the car, the keys in his hand. He has a kind of smile on his face. "Ah, it's —" he starts to say, but we push past him and rush to the front of the car and stare at it.

There is a dent in the front bumper about the size of a pea.

"My God!" says my mother, again and again, over and over, shaking from side to side, as the old Mrs Fisher does on Yom Kippur, totally immersed in her prayers.

Uncle Sam stands with the keys in his hand and doesn't know what to do. He begins to say something, "Ah, believe me, *my* first car, you should have seen how —"

He stops. No one is listening to him. My father has come up the drive and is standing next to him, looking at the car but not going around to see the front of it.

"The fence is all right," he says.

Finally my mother is persuaded to come inside, what's the point of standing here? "I'll have a cup of tea," Uncle Sam says, smacking his hands together, smiling, but no one is fooled. I am sent to close the front gates.

My mother makes the tea and Uncle Sam tells us all, at least three times, how it was with his first car, why, this is nothing, not even an accident. And my father drinks his tea and doesn't say a word. Nor does my mother. Both my parents are deep inside themselves.

When Uncle Sam has gone — "Don't worry, Abe," patting my father on the arm — my mother suddenly comes alive. "Go in your room. It's enough for one day," she says to me, and she closes the kitchen door and — but I'm not sure about this — locks it.

Then I hear their voices, now loud, now soft, and then my mother opens the door and goes to the telephone, closing another door so I can't hear what she's saying, and then when she has finished there she calls me to come out.

We eat in total silence, not a word. When we are drinking our tea, my father says, "I'm selling the car," and then picks up his cup and ends the matter with a loud sip of his tea.

The next morning, before eight, two men come and take away the car. I watch them signing papers, and then they hand my father a cheque, and he puts it inside his wallet and shakes their hands and goes out with them to the garage, but that part I don't watch. Who wants to see a brand-new car, two shades of blue, being driven away at eight o'clock on a sad Saturday morning? No one.

By Sunday, my father is already boasting of his fine sense of business. Because there is a waiting list, it seems, and so many people desirous of possessing this model, these people are willing to pay quite a certain amount more than the car actually costs, for the privilege of immediate possession.

"Don't worry about me," my father says. "I know how to make a good business. Who needs a car anyhow? What for? You have to wash it, oil it, insure it, what for? What's wrong with the bus? Here, take a look at this cheque, you ever seen such a figure? Uh, scholar?"

And my mother, the master psychologist, smiles and says, "I'll ring up Tzila. Maybe Sam will take us, we'll go to the beach."

Bruce
Dawe

The Not-so-good Earth

For a while there we had 25-inch Chinese peasant families
famishing in comfort on the 25-inch screen
and even Uncle Billy whose eyesight's going fast
by hunching up real close to the convex glass
could just about make them out — the riot scene
in the capital city for example
he saw that better than anything, using the contrast knob
to bring them up dark — all those screaming faces
and bodies going under the horses' hooves — he did a terrific job
on that bit, not so successful though
on the quieter parts where they're just starving away
digging for roots in the not-so-good earth
cooking up a mess of old clay
and coming out with all those Confucian analects
to everybody's considerable satisfaction
(if I remember rightly Grandmother dies
with naturally a suspenseful break in the action
for a full symphony orchestra plug for Craven A
neat as a whistle probably damn glad
to be quit of the whole gang with their marvellous patience.)
We never did find out how it finished up . . . Dad
at this stage tripped over the main lead in the dark
hauling the whole set down smack on its inscrutable face,
wiping out in a blue flash and curlicue of smoke
600 million Chinese without a trace . . .

Homecoming

All day, day after day, they're bringing them home,
they're picking them up, those they can find, and bringing them
home,
they're bringing them in, piled on the hulls of Grants, in trucks, in
convoys,
they're zipping them up in green plastic bags,
they're tagging them now in Saigon, in the mortuary coolness
they're giving them names, they're rolling them out of
the deep-freeze lockers — on the tarmac at Tan Son Nhut
the noble jets are whining like hounds,
they are bringing them home
— curly-heads, kinky-hairs, crew-cuts, balding non-coms
— they're high, now, high and higher, over the land, the steaming
chow mein
their shadows are tracing the blue curve of the Pacific
with sorrowful quick fingers, heading south, heading east,
home, home, home — and the coasts swing upward, the old
ridiculous curvatures
of earth, the knuckled hills, the mangrove-swamps, the desert
emptiness . . .
in their sterile housing they tilt towards these like skiers
— taxiing in, on the long runways, the howl of their homecoming
rises
surrounding them like their last moments (the mash, the splendour)
then fading at length as they move
on to small towns where dogs in the frozen sunset
raise muzzles in mute salute,
and on to cities in whose wide web of suburbs
telegrams tremble like leaves from a wintering tree
and the spider grief swings in his bitter geometry
— they're bringing them home, now, too late, too early.

Life-cycle

FOR BIG JIM PHELAN

When children are born in Victoria
they are wrapped in the club-colours, laid in beribboned cots,
having already begun a lifetime's barracking.

Carn, they cry, Carn . . . feebly at first
while parents playfully tussle with them
for possession of a rusk: Ah, he's a little Tiger! (And they are . . .)

Hoisted shoulder-high at their first League game
they are like innocent monsters who have been years swimming
towards the daylight's roaring empyrean

Until, now, hearts shrapnelled with rapture,
they break surface and are forever lost,
their minds rippling out like streamers

In the pure flood of sound, they are scarfed with light, a voice
like the voice of God booms from the stands
Ooohh you bludger and the covenant is sealed.

Hot pies and potato-crisps they will eat,
they will forswear the Demons, cling to the Saints
and behold their team going up the ladder into Heaven,

And the tides of life will be the tides of the home-team's fortunes
— the reckless proposal after the one-point win,
the wedding and honeymoon after the grand-final . . .

They will not grow old as those from more northern States grow old,
for them it will always be three-quarter-time
with the scores level and the wind advantage in the final term,

That passion persisting, like a race-memory, through the welter of seasons,
enabling old-timers by boundary-fences to dream of resurgent lions
and centaur-figures from the past to replenish continually the present,

So that mythology may be perpetually renewed
and Chicken Smallhorn return like the maize-god
in a thousand shapes, the dancers changing

But the dance forever the same — the elderly still
loyally crying Carn . . . Carn . . . (if feebly) unto the very end,
having seen in the six-foot recruit from Eaglehawk their hope of salvation.

Definition of Loving

Thank you for love, no matter what its outcome,
that leads us to the window in the dark,
that adds another otherness to others,
that holds out stars as if they were first diamonds
found in a mine that had been long closed down,
that hands out suns and makes us ask each morning:
What else do we need, picnickers in time?
Thank you for love that does not hang on answers,
that says, "Enough's enough, to love is plenty . . ."
— by such signs do we know the world exists,
amo ergo sum, thank you for that.
The miles, the years, the lives that lie between
— they always lay there, and they always will,
but look, the loved one spans that dizzy distance
by the act of being, and we lovers turn
our faces steadily *thou*-wards as a field
of sunflowers like a tracking station turns,
charting its meaning by the westering sun.

Homo Suburbiensis

For Craig McGregor

One constant in a world of variables
— a man alone in the evening in his patch of vegetables,
and all the things he takes down with him there

Where the easement runs along the back fence and the air
smells of tomato-vines, and the hoarse rasping tendrils
of pumpkin flourish clumsy whips and their foliage sprawls

Over the compost-box, poising rampant upon
the palings . . .
           He stands there, lost in a green
confusion, smelling the smoke of somebody's rubbish

Burning, hearing vaguely the clatter of a dish
in a sink that could be his, hearing a dog, a kid,
a far whisper of traffic, and offering up instead

Not much but as much as any man can offer
— time, pain, love, hate, age, war, death, laughter, fever.

Drifters

One day soon he'll tell her it's time to start packing,
and the kids will yell "Truly?" and get wildly excited for no reason,
and the brown kelpie pup will start dashing out, tripping
                                                    everyone up,
and she'll go out to the vegetable-patch and pick all the green
                                        tomatoes from the vines,
and notice how the oldest girl is close to tears because she was
                                                    happy here,
and how the youngest girl is beaming because she wasn't.
And the first thing she'll put on the trailer will be the bottling-set
                            she never unpacked from Grovedale,
and when the loaded ute bumps down the drive past the blackberry-
                            canes with their last shrivelled fruit,
she won't even ask why they're leaving this time, or where
                                            they're heading for
— she'll only remember how, when they came here,
she held out her hands bright with berries,
the first of the season, and said:
"Make a wish, Tom, make a wish."

Murray
Bail

Paradise

BREAKING INTO light, this long silver bus. It comes rumbling from its concrete pen. Grunting away. It reaches North Terrace by stopping and yawning; its full length swings.

Yawns left, climbs past Rosella, hesitates at Maid 'n Magpie, take the left, roads are empty, petrol stations are empty, car yards are empty, shops are empty, hold her steady, chassis doesn't pitch then, there are couples behind curtains, there's a dog, watch him, man on a bike, shiftworker in a coat probably. Now the road's stirring, milkman turns a corner, leaves the road open, driver taps the steering wheel rim, enormous view of life in the morning, foot taps contented by it.

The bus had PARADISE printed on the front, sides and back. It was a long run to the suburb. At the outer reaches it specialized in young married women with prams; and Merv Hector had to smile. From his position in the driving seat he could see the new generation hair-dos, skirts, worried eyebrows. Gentle, slow-eyed Hector waited for them, was happy to be of service. When one of them waved between stops he would stop the great silver machine every time. His conductors were quick to see they were riding with a soft heart. Straightforward characters, they were quick to assert themselves. "Be an angel, Merv. Stop at the shops there for some smokes." They also went to him when sick of things.

This time his conductor was Ron. His voice, tightly pitched. "Getting up at this hour really makes me wonder. We're not carrying a soul. Look, it really makes me sick."

Merv shook his head. Through the pure windscreen the road was alive ahead of him. Below his feet the bus was really travelling. It made you feel alive.

"There's the people we get on the way back," Merv said.

He made a long sentence of it, as he did when contented, and heard Ron's breath come out dissatisfied.

"There's too bloody many then. We should have two here serving then. All the school kids; they never have to pay properly. What time is it?"

They were entering Paradise. As usual Hector waited to be thrilled by it, he

626

stared and was ready, but a disappointment spread like the morning shadows. Streets were golden but it seemed more like a finishing sunset than the beginning of a day. When he stopped the bus it seemed to be further away — Paradise did. New tiles pointing in the sky spoilt the purity. But Paradise could be close by. It felt close by. The air light, bright; he was at the edge of something. Hector's stubborn fifty-four-year-old eyesight produced these messages for his heart but he was required to turn the bus, and he turned the bus around.

"Hell, we're going to really get hot and crowded."

It was Ron running his finger around his collar.

"She'll be right," said Hector.

"Hang on a sec. Let us out at the shop. You want some chewy?"

Stopped. Merv Hector was mild cheese from Norwood. At the M.T.T. he was considered slow and forgetful. But he was dependable enough, and voiced no objections to the long early morning runs. His moon wife was stupefied by his sincerity. He was older. Their garden grew weeds. His watch was inaccurate, and he stumbled near the garden. "Dear?" he sometimes said to Enid and faded out. The distance to Paradise, with the great screen framing all kinds of life, gave him this gentle advice: move, slow down, stop, let them get on, move, see, Paradise. The world was beautiful. It was plainly visible.

Now Ron said something again.

"Look at all the bloody kids. Just what I need. Alright! Move down the back!"

The bus grew squatter and fatter with the weight of everybody. Ron battled through, and the air was hot and human. They were now channelled by houses near the city, yet it was confusing.

A green bread van turned while Merv wondered. The shape was smacked by the metal at Merv's feet and the whole green turned over and over like a dying insect, a round pole came zooming forward, Hector's world entered it and splintered. Glass splattered. A crying uniform over Hector's shoulder cracked the windscreen.

There was the crash, Hector remembered. And the memory of Paradise persisted. If there was a beautiful place he could watch for like that.

He was wrinkling and gave a twitch.

He found other work.

"Morning."

"Morning. Six, thanks."

"Six, and?"

"Eight."

"Right there."

"Two for me."

"Back a bit, sir. Up we go."

Inside a driver's uniform again. They hold their breaths and stare at lights blinking. 4, 5, feel the altitude moving below the toes, 6, blink, blink, 7, 8, turn the lever, doors further up: whrrp! abrupt stop, men breathe into ears, business face veins, Windsor knots left-right-centre. Right this little lift will help, reach the top, an essential task in the latest glass architecture.

I'll go to Heaven.

Merv Hector settled on his stool in the lift. Shuffling and throat-clearing squashed the space into a noise box. Like the run to Paradise, he was at the entrance with a mild face, helping them: they stepped out at certain vertical intervals, sped down horizontal tunnels for special meetings. These repetitions gave him the most gentle pleasure. He was in the centre of activity and happily assisting. His placid role in giving this regular service, regular service, settled his features.

In the mornings a lemon-headed man unlocked the building and the lifts.

"How are you today?"

"What are you this early for?" the caretaker answered.

"Well," Hector began.

The caretaker cut him off. "If the others come here late, you've got to get here at this hour."

"It's a good building you've got," Hector suggested, in all seriousness.

"What's good about it? You don't have to live in it."

And Hector had to take some keys to him one morning right up to the eight-eenth floor. He was touched by the high silence. Outside the wind scratched at the glass. Inside currents of cold air tugged at his sleeve like the mysterious breathing of a giant snowman. It was some height, near the clouds. God. Hector marvelled. His veins, his eyes seemed to be swelling. Was this pleasure? It must be nearer to heaven, or Paradise, up there.

"What's your trouble?"

The caretaker came up behind.

"Give us the keys, and scoot. They're buzzing you."

Merv ran back to the lift.

"Is it alright if I bring my lunch on the roof?" he called out.

"Christ Almighty!" the watchman said.

Why, the roof was high. It was peaceful. He could watch noises made by the street-people below. And clouds closed in; could almost touch me. And someone had placed pot plants along the edge, and wind trembled their green. Did the lonely caretaker put them there? The slow question gently surrounded him with pleasure, and near the clouds he chewed on Enid's sandwiches.

The lift was always crowded. He kept going up down, up down, all day. Now he preferred going up to down. Going down it was back to the street, hot and old. So he kept going up, and late one morning kept going, kept going, and wondering, crashed into the ceiling. Roof hit roof — or there were springs to stop him. But it was enough to jump him off the stool, and the caretaker arrived.

"No one's ever done that before, you bloody fool."

"Strike," said Hector.

He was dazed.

Merv Hector continued. His hour on the roof was something to look forward to. I'm very near it, he said in the silence. Full of pretty, dazed visions he slept past two, and was immediately fired by the caretaker.

"Even if you come here early," said the caretaker, signalling up and down with his arm. "Useless, useless."

Hair on Hector's head looked electrocuted. It was fifty-four-year-old stuff flaking and greying: always looked as if he had left a speedboat. He wore brown eye-glasses. Sometimes he touched his lips with his fingers vibrating, exactly as though they played a mouth organ.

Home with Enid she carried on a bit.

But she noticed something. He had been weeding the garden. One finger was cut by a buried piece of china — a broken pre-war saucer of some description — and self-pity moved him to silence. He seemed to dry up. More or less alone, he shaved vaguely. He didn't say much.

He was not his cheery self, she said.

"Why don't you get another job, dear? We can settle down after."

Hector agreed.

"You sit there," the young man pointed. "The phone goes, write down what they say. Just sit here. The Bureau rings about every half hour. Arrange the switches like so. You can make any words they tell you. At the moment it's RAIN DEVELOPING."

Hector looked through the tiny window, looked across the wall of the building and there, in enormous lights, were the words RAIN DEVELOPING.

"If we had an automatic system," the young man said, "you wouldn't have to mess around with all these switches. But it's easy enough."

"Yes," admitted Hector absently.

So this is how the weather lights work, he thought.

This is what I do.

The room was tiny, concrete: enough to depress anybody. It was high in the dead part of the building, ignored by the air-conditioning. A plastic ashtray sat on the small table.

The black phone gave a sudden ring. A voice told him to change the message to RAIN. "Right, then," said Hector. He fiddled with switches, concentrating, then turned them on. Through the window he saw the sudden change in the message and automatically wondered what the people below thought. Would they believe in that? Would they notice his sign? How many would be caught without coats, umbrellas, rudimentary shelter?

But there was no rain — not a drop. Standing at the window he became concerned. Merv looked at his message. He looked down at the people-shapes moving casually. Then, miraculously it seemed, rain began hitting and splashing. His sign shined in triumph; and the thought that his warning had saved people flooded him with specific pleasure. It was good, and he clenched himself. He looked up then at the clouds. They seemed to be pressing down on his room, around his life, down his mouth, showering his vision with rain. God, he wondered.

Down on the street depressed figures ran from point to point. The shining traffic remained queued, steam rose, and three silver buses waited bumper to bumper. It recalled certain mornings behind the steering wheel, the giant screen wipers scanned repetitiously like radar, squish-a-squish. Now he stared through the glass window, up at the clouds, up into the heart of the rain. He felt settled, sure, safe, glad to be there; he thought of home, the maroon chair, and his Enid.

Nothing's the matter, he said. I'm fine, he wanted everyone to know. On the panel he moved across and switched the message to FINE.

The huge bright lights said FINE as the rain kept splashing down. Altogether, Merv Hector marvelled at every single thing. He stared at his sign. It was true. He loved the clouds. It was another world, and he was there. The phone began to ring.

Les A.
Murray

Sydney and the Bush

When Sydney and the Bush first met
there was no open ground
and men and girls, in chains and not,
all made an urgent sound.

Then convicts bled and warders bred,
the bush went back and back,
the men of Fire and of Earth
became White men and Black.

When Sydney ordered lavish books
and warmed her feet with coal
the bush came skylarking to town
and gave poor folk a soul.

Then bushmen sank and factories rose
and warders set the tone —
the Bush, in quarter-acre blocks,
helped families hold their own.

When Sydney and the Bush meet now
there is antipathy
and fashionable suburbs float
at night, far out to sea.

When Sydney rules without the Bush
she is a warders' shop
with heavy dancing overhead,
the music will not stop

and when the drummers want a laugh
Australians are sent up.
When Sydney and the Bush meet now
there is no common ground.

An Absolutely Ordinary Rainbow

The word goes round Repins,
the murmur goes round Lorenzinis,
at Tattersalls, men look up from sheets of numbers,
the Stock Exchange scribblers forget the chalk in their hands
and men with bread in their pockets leave the Greek Club:
There's a fellow crying in Martin Place. They can't stop him.

The traffic in George Street is banked up for half a mile
and drained of motion. The crowds are edgy with talk
and more crowds come hurrying. Many run in the back streets
which minutes ago were busy main streets, pointing:
There's a fellow weeping down there. No one can stop him.

The man we surround, the man no one approaches
simply weeps, and does not cover it, weeps
not like a child, not like the wind, like a man
and does not declaim it, nor beat his breast, nor even
sob very loudly — yet the dignity of his weeping

holds us back from his space, the hollow he makes about him
in the midday light, in his pentagram of sorrow,
and uniforms back in the crowd who tried to seize him
stare out at him, and feel, with amazement, their minds
longing for tears as children for a rainbow.

Some will say, in the years to come, a halo
or force stood around him. There is no such thing.
Some will say they were shocked and would have stopped him
but they will not have been there. The fiercest manhood,
the toughest reserve, the slickest wit amongst us

trembles with silence, and burns with unexpected
judgements of peace. Some in the concourse scream
who thought themselves happy. Only the smallest children
and such as look out of Paradise come near him
and sit at his feet, with dogs and dusty pigeons.

Ridiculous, says a man near me, and stops
his mouth with his hands, as if it uttered vomit —
and I see a woman, shining, stretch her hand
and shake as she receives the gift of weeping;
as many as follow her also receive it

and many weep for sheer acceptance, and more
refuse to weep for fear of all acceptance,
but the weeping man, like the earth, requires nothing,
the man who weeps ignores us, and cries out
of his writhen face and ordinary body

not words, but grief, not messages, but sorrow
hard as the earth, sheer, present as the sea —
and when he stops, he simply walks between us
mopping his face with the dignity of one
man who has wept, and now has finished weeping.

Evading believers, he hurries off down Pitt Street.

The Ballad of Jimmy Governor

H.M. Prison, Darlinghurst, 18th January 1901

You can send for my breakfast now, Governor.
The colt from Black Velvet's awake
and the ladies all down from the country
are gathered outside for my sake.

Soon be all finished, the running.
No tracks of mine lead out of here.
Today, I take that big step
on the bottom rung of the air
and be in Heaven for dinner.
Might be the first jimbera there.

The Old People don't go to Heaven,
good thing. My mother might meet
that stockman feller my father
and him cut her dead in the street.
Mother, today I'll be dancing
your way and his way on numb feet.

But a man's not a rag to wipe snot on,
I got that much into their heads,
them hard white sunbonnet ladies
that turned up their short lips and said
my wife had a slut's eye for colour.
I got that into their head

and the cow-cockies' kids plant up chimneys
they got horse soldiers out with the Law
after Joe and lame Jack and tan Jimmy —
but who learnt us how to make war
on women, old men, babies?
It ain't all one way any more.

The papers, they call us bushrangers:
That would be our style, I daresay,
bushrangers on foot with our axes.
It sweetens the truth, anyway.
They don't like us killing their women.
Their women kill us every day.

And the squatters are peeing their moleskins,
that's more than a calf in the wheat,
it's Jimmy the fencer, running
along the top rail in the night,
it's the Breelong mob crossing the ranges
with rabbitskins soft on their feet.

But now Jack in his Empire brickyard
has already give back his shoes
and entered the cleanliness kingdom,
the Commonwealth drums through the walls
and I'm weary of news.

I'm sorry, old Jack, I discharged you,
you might have enjoyed running free
of plonk and wet cornbags and colour
with us pair of outlaws. But see,
you can't trust even half a whitefeller.
You died of White Lady through me.

They tried me once running, once standing:
one time ought to do for the drop.
It's more trial than you got, I hear, Joe,
your tommyhawk's chipped her last chop.
I hope you don't mind I got lazy
when the leaks in my back made me stop.

If any gin stands in my print
I'll give her womb sorrow and dread,
if a buck finds our shape in the tussocks
I'll whiten the hair in his head,
but a man's not a rag to wipe boots on
and I got that wrote up, bright red,

where even fine ladies can read it
who never look at the ground
for a man that ain't fit to breed from
may make a terrible bound
before the knacker's knife gets him.
Good night to you, father. Sleep sound.

Fetch in my breakfast, Governor,
I have my journey to make
and the ladies all down from the country
are howling outside for my sake.

Jimbera: half-caste Aboriginal
White Lady: methylated spirits and powdered milk. A
fringe cocktail, definitely, but not yet obsolete.

The House of Four-X

Something over ten thousand
beer bottles went to build
a house, once, in Queensland.

Something over ten thousand
mullions of glitter and gloom
fixed and cemented

and every one of them drained
as a point of honour
by the solitary owner.

Picture, in midsummer shade,
the static yet ripple-cool sheen
of ten thousand leadlights.

Picture, when lamps burned inside,
a shadowy, manifold bee
in his shrine of light-cells,

vast, torpid and festive at once
singing Christmas jinks and hooray!
in the heart of Queensland,

so that when he went courting at last
and brought home a bride for his house
(picture that darkly)

there must have been almost excess
even for those tropic parts
of fullness, of wholeness,

Pharaoh and Israel at sport,
bricks heaped to dry in the sun,
straw by the paddockful.

And I hope it survives yet, their priesthood,
it would be drear loss to us all,
not only Queensland,

considering chill glass houses now
which bewilder many
and have nourished no one,

if jealous time and the world
had shattered those honeydew grilles
and the wind grown jagged,

and there were no strong sons to shout
through sleepouts of radiance and chink,
bearing high dozens.

LES A. MURRAY

Flowering Eucalypt in Autumn

That slim creek out of the sky
the dried-blood western gum tree
is all stir in its high reaches:

its strung haze-blue foliage is dancing
points down in breezy mobs, swapping
pace and place in an all-over sway

retarded en masse by crimson blossom.
Bees still at work up there tack
around their exploded furry likeness

and the lawn underneath's a napped rug
of eyelash drift, of blooms flared
like a sneeze in a redhaired nostril,

minute urns, pinch-sized rockets
knocked down by winds, by night-creaking
fig-squirting bats, or the daily

parrot gang with green pocketknife wings.
Bristling food for tough delicate
raucous life, each flower comes

as a spray in its own turned vase,
a taut starburst, honeyed model
of the tree's fragrance crisping in your head.

When the Japanese plum tree
was shedding in spring, we speculated
there among the drizzling petals

what kind of exquisitely precious
artistic bloom might be gendered
in a pure ethereal compost

of petals potted as they fell.
From unpetalled gum-debris
we know what is grown continually,

a tower of fabulous swish tatters,
a map hoisted upright, a crusted
riverbed with up-country show towns.

The Buladelah-Taree Holiday Song Cycle

1

The people are eating dinner in that country north of Legge's Lake;
behind flywire and venetians, in the dimmed cool, town people eat Lunch.
Plying knives and forks with a peek-in sound, with a tuck-in sound
they are thinking about relatives and inventory, they are talking about customers
    and visitors.
In the country of memorial iron, on the creek-facing hills there,
they are thinking about bean plants, and rings of tank water, of growing a
    pumpkin by Christmas;
rolling a cigarette, they say thoughtfully Yes, and their companion nods,
    considering.
Fresh sheets have been spread and tucked tight, childhood rooms have been
    seen to,
for this is the season when children return with their children
to the place of Bingham's Ghost, of the Old Timber Wharf, of the Big Flood
    That Time,
the country of the rationalized farms, of the day-and-night farms, and of the Pitt
    Street farms,
of the Shire Engineer and many other rumours, of the tractor crankcase furred
    with chaff,
the places of sitting down near ferns, the snake-fear places, the cattle-crossing-
    long-ago places.

2

It is the season of the Long Narrow City; it has crossed the Myall, it has entered
    the North Coast,
that big stunning snake; it is looped through the hills, burning all night there.
Hitching and flying on the downgrades, processionally balancing on the climbs,
it echoes in O'Sullivan's Gap, in the tight coats of the flooded-gum trees;
the tops of palms exclaim at it unmoved, there near Wootton.
Glowing all night behind the hills, with a north-shifting glare, burning behind
    the hills;
through Coolongolook, through Wang Wauk, across the Wallamba,
the booming tarred pipe of the holiday slows and spurts again; Nabiac chokes
    in glassy wind,
the forests on Kiwarric dwindle in cheap light; Tuncurry and Forster swell like
    cooking oil.
The waiting is buffed, in timber villages off the highway, the waiting is buffeted:
the fumes of fun hanging above ferns; crime flashes in strange windscreens, in
    the time of the Holiday.
Parasites weave quickly through the long gut that paddocks shine into;
powerful makes surging and pouncing: the police, collecting Revenue.

The heavy gut winds over the Manning, filling northward, digesting the towns,
   feeding the towns;
they all become the narrow city, they join it;
girls walking close to murder discard, with excitement, their names.
Crossing Australia of the sports, the narrow city, bringing home the children.

3

It is good to come out after driving and walk on bare grass;
walking out, looking all around, relearning that country.
Looking out for snakes, and looking out for rabbits as well;
going into the shade of myrtles to try their cupped climate, swinging by one hand
   around them,
in that country of the Holiday . . .
stepping behind trees to the dam, as if you had a gun,
to that place of the Wood Duck,
to that place of the Wood Duck's Nest,
proving you can still do it; looking at the duck who hasn't seen you,
the mother duck who'd run Catch Me (broken wing) I'm Fatter (broken wing),
   having hissed to her children.

4

The birds saw us wandering along.
Rosellas swept up crying out *we think we think*; they settled farther along;
knapping seeds off the grass, under dead trees where their eggs were, walking
   around on their fingers,
flying on into the grass.
The heron lifted up his head and elbows; the magpie stepped aside a bit,
angling his chopsticks into pasture, turning things over in his head.
At the place of the Plough Handles, of the Apple Trees Bending Over, and of
   the Cattlecamp,
there the vealers are feeding; they are loosely at work, facing everywhere.
They are always out there, and the forest is always on the hills;
around the sun are turning the wedgetail eagle and her mate, that dour
   brushhook-faced family:
they settled on Deer's Hill away back when the sky was opened,
in the bull-oak trees way up there, the place of fur tufted in the grass, the place
   of bone-turds.

5

The Fathers and the Great-Grandfathers, they are out in the paddocks all the
   time, they live out there,
at the place of the Rail Fence, of the Furrows Under Grass, at the place of the
   Slab Chimney.
We tell them that clearing is complete, an outdated attitude, all over;
we preach without a sacrifice, and are ignored; flowering bushes grow dull to our
   eyes.

We begin to go up on the ridge, talking together, looking at the kino-coloured ants,
at the yard-wide sore of their nest, that kibbled peak, and the workers heaving
    vast stalks up there,
the brisk compact workers; jointed soldiers pour out then, tense with acid;
    several probe the mouth of a lost gin bottle:
Innuendo, we exclaim, *literal minds!* and go on up the ridge, announced by finches;
passing the place of the Dingo Trap, and that farm hand it caught, and the place
    of the Cowbails,
we come to the road and watch heifers,
little unjoined devons, their teats hidden in fur, and the cousin with his loose-
    slung stockwhip driving them.
We talk with him about rivers and the lakes; his polished horse is stepping
    nervously,
printing neat omegas in the gravel, flexing its skin to shake off flies;
his big sidestepping horse that has kept its stones; it recedes gradually, bearing
    him;
we murmur *stone-horse* and *devilry* to the grinners under grass.

6

Barbecue smoke is rising at Legge's Camp; it is steaming into the midday air,
all around the lake shore, at the Broadwater, it is going up among the paperbark
    trees,
a heat-shimmer of sauces, rising from tripods and flat steel, at that place of the
    Cone-shells,
at that place of the Seagrass, and the tiny segmented things swarming in it, and
    of the Pelican.
Dogs are running around disjointedly; water escapes from their mouths,
confused emotions from their eyes; humans snarl at them Gwanout and
    Hereboy, not varying their tone much;
the impoverished dog people, suddenly sitting down to nuzzle themselves;
    toddlers side with them:
toddlers, running away purposefully at random, among cars, into big drownie-
    water (come back, Cheryl-Ann!).
They rise up as charioteers, leaning back on the tow-bar; all their attributes
    bulge at once;
swapping swash shoulder-wings for the white-sheeted shoes that bear them,
they are skidding over the flat glitter, stiff with grace, for once not travelling to
    arrive.
From the high dunes over there, the rough blue distance, at length they come
    back behind the boats,
and behind the boats' noise, cartwheeling, or sitting down, into the lake's warm
    chair;
they wade ashore and eat with the families, putting off that uprightness, that
    assertion,

eating with the families who love equipment, and the freedom from equipment,
  with the fathers who love driving, and lighting a fire between stones.

7

Shapes of children were moving in the standing corn, in the child-labour
  districts;
coloured flashes of children, between the green and parching stalks, appearing
  and disappearing.
Some places, they are working, racking off each cob like a lever, tossing it on
  the heaps;
other places, they are children of child-age, there playing jungle:
in the tiger-striped shade, they are firing hoehandle machine guns, taking cover
  behind fat pumpkins;
in other cases, it is Sunday and they are lovers.
They rise and walk together in the sibilance, finding single rows irksome, hating
  speech now,
or, full of speech, they swap files and follow defiles, disappearing and appearing;
near the rain-grey barns, and the children building cattleyards beside them;
the standing corn, gnawed by pouched and rodent mice; generations are moving
  among it,
the parrot-hacked, medicine-tasseled corn, ascending all the creek flats, the wire-
  fenced alluvials,
going up in patches through the hills, towards the Steep Country.

8

Forests and State Forests, all down off the steeper country; mosquitoes are always
  living in there:
they float about like dust motes and sink down, at the places of the Stinging Tree,
and of the Staghorn Fern; the males feed on plant-stem fluid, absorbing that
  watery ichor;
the females meter the air, feeling for the warm-blooded smell, needing blood for
  their eggs.
They find the dingo in his sleeping-place, they find his underbelly and his anus;
they find the possum's face, they drift up the ponderous pleats of the fig tree,
  way up into its rigging,
the high camp of the fruit bats; they feed on the membranes and ears of bats;
  tired wings cuff air at them;
their eggs burning inside them, they alight on the muzzles of cattle,
the half-wild bush cattle, there at the place of the Sleeper Dump, at the place
  of the Tallowwoods.
The males move about among growth tips; ingesting solutions, they crouch
  intently;
the females sing, needing blood to breed their young; their singing is in the scrub
  country;
their tune comes to the name-bearing humans, who dance to it and irritably grin
  at it.

9

The warriors are cutting timber with brash chainsaws; they are trimming
  hardwood pit-props and loading them;
Is that an order? they hoot at the peremptory lorry driver, who laughs; he is also
  a warrior.
They are driving long-nosed tractors, slashing pasture in the dinnertime sun;
they are fitting tappets and valves, the warriors, or giving finish to a surfboard.
Addressed on the beach by a pale man, they watch waves break and are reserved,
  refusing pleasantry;
they joke only with fellow warriors, chaffing about try-ons and the police, not
  slighting women.
Making Timber a word of power, Con-rod a word of power, Sense a word of
  power, the Regs. a word of power,
they know belt-fed from spring-fed; they speak of being *stiff*, and being *history*;
the warriors who have killed, and the warriors who eschewed killing,
the solemn, the drily spoken, the life peerage of endurance; drinking water from
  a tap,
they watch boys who think hard work a test, and boys who think it is not a test.

10

Now the ibis are flying in, hovering down on the wetlands,
on those swampy paddocks around Darawank, curving down in ragged dozens,
on the riverside flats along the Wang Wauk, on the Boolambayte pasture flats,
and away towards the sea, on the sand moors, at the place of the Jabiru Crane.
leaning out of their wings, they step down; they take out their implement at once,
out of its straw wrapping, and start work; they dab grasshopper and ground-
  cricket
with nonexistence . . . spiking the ground and puncturing it . . . they swallow
  down the outcry of a frog;
they discover titbits kept for them under cowmanure lids, small slow things.
Pronging the earth, they make little socket noises, their thoughtfulness jolting
  down-and-up suddenly;
there at Bunyah, along Firefly Creek, and up through Germany,
the ibis are all at work again, thin-necked ageing men towards evening; they are
  solemnly all back
at Minimbah, and on the Manning, in the rye-and-clover irrigation fields;
city storemen and accounts clerks point them out to their wives,
remembering things about themselves, and about the ibis.

11

Abandoned fruit trees, moss-tufted, spotted with dim lichen paints; the fruit trees
  of the Grandmothers,
they stand along the creekbanks, in the old home paddocks, where the houses were;

they are reached through bramble-grown front gates, they creak at dawn behind
    burnt skillions,
at Belbora, at Bucca Wauka, away in at Burrell Creek,
at Telararee of the gold-sluices.
The trees are split and rotten-elbowed; they bear the old-fashioned summer
    fruits,
the annual bygones: china pear, quince, persimmon;
the fruit has the taste of former lives, of sawdust and parlour song, the tang of
    Manners;
children bite it, recklessly,
at what will become for them the place of the Slab Wall, and of the Coal Oil
    Lamp,
the place of moss-grit and swallows' nests, the place of the Crockery.

12

Now the sun is an applegreen blindness through the swells, a white blast on the
    sea-face, flaking and shoaling;
now it is burning off the mist; it is emptying the density of trees, it is spreading
    upriver,
hovering above the casuarina needles, there at Old Bar and Manning Point;
flooding the island farms, it abolishes the milkers' munching breath
as they walk towards the cowyards; it stings a bucket here, a teatcup there.
Morning steps into the world by ever more southerly gates; shadows weaken
    their north skew
on Middle Brother, on Cape Hawke, on the dune scrub toward Seal Rocks;
steadily the heat is coming on, the butter-water time, the clothes-sticking time;
grass covers itself with straw; abandoned things are thronged with spirits;
everywhere wood is still with strain; birds hiding down the creek galleries, and
    in the cockspur canes;
the cicada is hanging up her sheets; she takes wing off her music-sheets.
Cars pass with a rational zoom, panning quickly towards Wingham,
through the thronged and glittering, the shale-topped ridges, and the
    cattlecamps,
towards Wingham for the cricket, the ball knocked hard in front of smoked-glass
    ranges, and for the drinking.
In the time of heat, the time of flies around the mouth, the time of the west
    veranda,
looking at that umbrage along the ranges, on the New England side;
clouds begin assembling vaguely, a hot soiled heaviness on the sky, away there
    towards Gloucester;
a swelling up of clouds, growing there above Mount George, and above
    Tipperary;
far away and hot with light; sometimes a storm takes root there, and fills the
    heavens rapidly;

darkening, boiling up and swaying on its stalks, pulling this way and that,
   blowing round by Krambach;
coming white on Bulby, it drenches down on the paddocks, and on the wire
   fences;
the paddocks are full of ghosts, and people in cornbag hoods approaching;
lights are lit in the house; the storm veers mightily on its stem, above the roof;
   the hills uphold it;
the stony hills guide its dissolution; gullies opening and crumbling down,
   wrenching tussocks and rolling them;
the storm carries a greenish-grey bag; perhaps it will find hail and send it down,
   starring cars, flattening tomatoes,
in the time of the Washaways, of the dead trunks braiding water, and of the
   Hailstone Yarns.

13

The stars of the holiday step out all over the sky.
People look up at them, out of their caravan doors and their campsites;
people look up from the farms, before going back; they gaze at their year's worth
   of stars.
The Cross hangs head-downward, out there over Markwell;
it turns upon the Still Place, the pivot of the Seasons, with one shoulder rising:
"Now I'm beginning to rise, with my Pointers and my Load . . ."
hanging eastwards, it shines on the sawmills and the lakes, on the glasses of the
   Old People.
Looking at the Cross, the galaxy is over our left shoulder, slung up highest in
   the east;
there the Dog is following the Hunter; the Dog Star pulsing there above Forster;
   it shines down on the Bikies,
and on the boat-hire sheds, there at the place of the Oyster; the place of the
   Shark's Eggs and her Hide;
the Pleiades are pinned up high on the darkness, away back above the Manning;
they are shining on the Two Blackbutt Trees, on the rotted river wharves, and
   on the towns;
standing there, above the water and the lucerne flats, at the place of the Families;
their light sprinkles down on Taree of the Lebanese shops, it mingles with the
   streetlights and their glare.
People recover the starlight, hitching north,
travelling north beyond the seasons, into that country of the Communes, and of
   the Banana:
the Flying Horse, the Rescued Girl, and the Bull, burning steadily above that
   country.
Now the New Moon is low down in the west, that remote direction of the
   Cattlemen,

and of the Saleyards, the place of steep clouds, and of the Rodeo;
the New Moon who has poured out her rain, the moon of the Planting-times.
People go outside and look at the stars, and at the melon-rind moon,
the Scorpion going down into the mountains, over there towards Waukivory,
     sinking into the tree-line,
in the time of the Rockmelons, and of the Holiday . . .
the Cross is rising on his elbow, above the glow of the horizon;
carrying a small star in his pocket, he reclines there brilliantly,
above the Alum Mountain, and the lakes threaded on the Myall River, and
     above the Holiday.

Acknowledgements

Poems and Stories

Thanks are extended to the respective publishers and copyright holders for granting permission to include the works listed below. While every effort has been made to trace all copyright holders, in some cases this has proved impossible. The publisher would be pleased to hear from anyone who should be included here.

THEA ASTLEY *A Man Who is Tired of Swiper's Creek is Tired of Life* from *Hunting the Wild Pineapple and Other Related Stories*, Nelson, Melbourne, 1979, reprinted by Penguin Books, 1981: courtesy of Thomas Nelson Australia.

MURRAY BAIL *Paradise* from *Contemporary Portraits and Other Stories*, University of Queensland Press, 1975: courtesy of University of Queensland Press.

MARJORIE BARNARD *The Persimmon Tree* from *The Persimmon Tree and Other Stories*, Clarendon Publishing Company, 1943: courtesy of Curtis Brown (Aust.) Pty Ltd Sydney.

BRUCE BEAVER "Angels' Weather", "Letter XXIX", "Day 25", "Day 46" from *Selected Poems*, Angus & Robertson, 1979: courtesy of Angus & Robertson Publishers.

JOHN BLIGHT "The Island", "Sea Beasts" from *A Beachcomber's Diary*, 1963; "Footprints", "A Fisherman's Cottage", "Shells and Skulls" from *My Beachcombing Days*, 1968. Both published by Angus & Robertson: courtesy of Angus & Robertson Publishers.

VINCENT BUCKLEY "Market Day": courtesy of Vincent Buckley. "Day with its Dry Persistence", from "Stroke", "Election Speech", "No New Thing", "A Summer Like This" from *Selected Poems*, Angus & Robertson, 1981: courtesy of Vincent Buckley and Angus & Robertson Publishers.

DAVID CAMPBELL "Harry Pearce", "Men in Green", "Windy Gap", "Snow-gums", "Night Sowing", "Song for the Cattle", "We Took the Storms to Bed", "Town Planning", "Mothers and Daughters", "The Boongary", "Droving", "Windy Nights", "Merinos", "Loafing", "The Australian Dream", "Starting from Central Station", "The Tourist Trade", "Sandstone Country", "Glenrowan", "Bellbirds", "Snake", "The Return of Jason" from *Selected Poems*, 1978; "Two Views", "Trawlers" from *Words with a Black Orpington*, 1978; "Lizard and Stone", "Mosquitoes", "Scribbly-Gums", "Tree in a Landscape", "Crab", "The Wimmera" from *The Man in the Honey-*

suckle, 1979. All published by Angus & Robertson: courtesy of Angus & Robertson Publishers.

GAVIN CASEY *Talking Ground*, *When Jim was Different* from *Short Shift Saturday*, Angus & Robertson, 1973: courtesy of Angus & Robertson Publishers.

ROBERT CLARK "On Growing Old" from *Segments of the Bowl*, Cheshire, 1967; "The Dogman" from *The Dogman and Other Poems*, Cheshire, 1962. Both poems courtesy of Robert Clark.

PETER COWAN *The Island* from *The Empty Street: Stories*, Angus & Robertson, 1965: courtesy of Angus & Robertson Publishers.

JACK DAVIS "Camped in the Bush", "Warru", "Aboriginal Reserve", "Death of a Snake" from *The First-Born and Other Poems*, Angus & Robertson, 1970: courtesy of J. M. Dent.

FRANK DALBY DAVISON *The Road to Yesterday* from *The Road to Yesterday: Collected Stories*, Angus & Robertson, 1968: courtesy of Angus & Robertson Publishers.

BRUCE DAWE "The Not-so-good Earth", "Homecoming", "Life-cycle", "Definition of Loving", "Homo Suburbiensis", "Drifters" from *Sometimes Gladness: Collected Poems 1954-1982*, Longman Cheshire, 1983: courtesy of Longman Cheshire.

JAMES DEVANEY "The Willows" from *Poems*, Angus & Robertson, 1950: courtesy of Angus & Robertson Publishers.

ROSEMARY DOBSON "A Fine Thing", "Country Morning", "Cock Crow", "Child of Our Time", "Country Press", "Landscape in Italy", "Ghost Town: New England" from *Selected Poems*, Angus & Robertson, 1973: courtesy of Angus & Robertson Publishers. "Folding the Sheets", "The Stone Circles" from *The Three Fates and Other Poems*, Hale & Iremonger, 1984: courtesy of Hale & Iremonger.

MARY DURACK "Red Jack" from *Australian Bush Ballads*, Angus & Robertson, 1955: courtesy of Curtis Brown (Aust.) Pty Ltd Sydney.

GEOFFREY DUTTON "The Island Day" from *Findings and Keepings: Selected Poems 1939-1969*, Australian Letters, 1970; "Winter Sunlight" from *New Poems to 1972*, Australian Letters, 1972. Both poems courtesy of Curtis Brown (Aust.) Pty Ltd Sydney.

MARY FINNIN "Of Bacchus, in the Marsh", "Rain in Glenrowan" from *The Shield of Place*, Angus & Robertson, 1957; "A Farmer's Dirge" from *Off Shears (1958-1978)*, Hawthorn Press, 1979. All by courtesy of Mary Finnin.

ROBERT D. FITZGERALD "Edge", "Song in Autumn", "Bog and Candle", "Macquarie Place", "Quayside Meditation", "As Between Neighbours . . .", "The Wind at Your Door", "Beginnings" from *Forty Years' Poems*, 1965; "Society", "Shared Ground" from *Product: Later Verses*, 1977. Both published by Angus & Robertson: courtesy of Angus & Robertson Publishers.

KEVIN GILBERT "Where Nomads Tread": courtesy of Kevin Gilbert.

FRANK HARDY *The Great Australian Larrikin* from *The Yarns of Billy Borker*, A. H. & A. W. Reed, 1965, reprinted by Angus & Robertson, 1977: courtesy of Angus & Robertson Publishers.

W. E. "BILL" HARNEY "West of Alice" from *Australian Verse from 1805: A Continuum*, Rigby, 1976: courtesy of Ruth Lockwood.

ELIZABETH HARROWER *The Beautiful Climate* from *Modern Australian Writing*, Fontana, 1966: courtesy of Elizabeth Harrower.

WILLIAM HART-SMITH "Columbus Goes West" from *Columbus Goes West*, Jindyworobak, 1943; "The Ship's Cat" from *Australian Poetry 1947*, Angus & Robertson, 1948. Both poems courtesy of Angus & Robertson Publishers.

GWEN HARWOOD "Triste, Triste", "In Brisbane", "Estuary", "New Music", "Dust to Dust", "Iris", "An Old Graveyard", "September Snow, Hobart", "Suburban Sonnet", "David's Harp", "In the Middle of Life" from *Selected Poems*, 1975; "Death Has No Features of His Own", "Springtime, Oyster Cove", "Mother Who Gave Me Life" from *The Lion's Bride*, 1981. Both published by Angus & Robertson: courtesy of Angus & Robertson Publishers.

SHIRLEY HAZZARD *Woollahra Road* from *Australian Writing Today*, Penguin, 1968; *The Picnic* from *Cliffs of Fall*, Playboy Paperbacks, 1981; *Nothing in Excess* from *People in Glass Houses*, Penguin, 1970. All courtesy of Shirley Hazzard.

DOROTHY HEWETT "In Midland where the Trains Go By", "Country Idyll", "Once I Rode with Clancy . . .", "Who Goes round my House by Night?", "Bagman's Ballad", "Last Summer" from *Windmill Country*, Overland, 1968: courtesy of Overland Press.

A. D. HOPE "Australia", "The Death of the Bird", "The Brides", "The Return of Persephone", "Meditation on a Bone", "The Walker", "Agony Column", "Ode on the Death of Pius the Twelfth", "Moschus Moschiferus", " 'With Thee Conversing . . .' ", "The Lamp" from *Collected Poems 1930-1970*, 1970; "Patch and Mend", "A Windy Afternoon", "Winterreise", "Hay Fever", "Country Places", "Spätlese" from *A Late Picking: Poems 1965-1974*, 1975; "The Waters", "Beyond Khancoban", "Aubade", "Hills" from *Antechinus: Poems 1975-1980*, 1981. All published by Angus & Robertson: courtesy of Angus & Robertson Publishers.

W. FLEXMORE HUDSON "Mallee in October", "Nostalgia" from *The Jindyworobaks: Portable Australian Authors*, University of Queensland Press, 1979.

REX INGAMELLS "Slight Autobiography", "Garrakeen", "The Tourist Dump" from *The Jindyworobaks: Portable Australian Authors*, University of Queensland Press, 1979.

"BRIAN JAMES" (JOHN TIERNEY) *The Bunyip of Barney's Elbow* from *The Bunyip of Barney's Elbow*, Angus & Robertson, 1956; *Doolan's Devotions, Joe and Sandy, Bungally* from *Cookabundy Bridge and Other Stories*, Angus & Robertson, 1946. All courtesy of the Estate of the late John Lawrence Tierney.

EVE LANGLEY "Australia" from *A Book of Australian Verse*, Oxford University Press, 1968.

GEOFFREY LEHMANN "Pear Days in Queensland", "The Telescope at Siding Springs", "A Girl Reading a Book in a Country Village" from *Selected Poems*, Angus & Robertson, 1976: courtesy of Angus & Robertson Publishers.

MORRIS LURIE *A King of the Road* from *Outrageous Behaviour: The Best of Morris Lurie*, Penguin, 1984: courtesy of Morris Lurie and Penguin Books Australia Limited.

JAMES MCAULEY "Terra Australis", "Mating Swans", "Merry-Go-Round", "To the Holy Spirit", "Secret Song", "Pietà", "St John's Park, New Town", "Holiday", "The Convict and the Lady", "Wistaria", "Credo", "Late Winter", "One Tuesday in Summer", "Because", "Numbers and Makes", "Tabletalk", "St John's Park", "In the Huon Valley", "Wet Day", "Keep the Season", "At Rushy Lagoon" from *Collected Poems 1936-1970*, Angus & Robertson, 1971: courtesy of Angus & Robertson Publishers. "Winter Drive", "Morning Voluntary", "Saturday Morning", "In Northern Tasmania", "Music Late at Night", from *Time Given: Poems 1970-1976*, Brindabella Press, 1976, reprinted from *Music Late at Night: Poems 1970-73*, Angus & Robertson: courtesy of Angus & Robertson Publishers. "Parish Church" from *Time Given: Poems 1970-1976*, Brindabella Press, 1976: courtesy of Norma McAuley. "Bush Scene" from *A World of Its Own*, ANU Press, 1977: courtesy of Curtis Brown (Aust.) Pty Ltd Sydney.

RONALD MCCUAIG "The Steam Tram", "Au Tombeau de Mon Père" from *The Ballad of Bloodthirsty Bessie and Other Poems*, Angus & Robertson, 1961: courtesy of Angus & Robertson Publishers.

NAN MCDONALD "Wet Summer: Botanic Gardens" from *Selected Poems*, Angus & Robertson, 1969: courtesy of Angus & Robertson Publishers.

KENNETH MACKENZIE "My Friend...", "Drought" from *The Poems of Kenneth Mackenzie*, Angus & Robertson, 1972: courtesy of Angus & Robertson Publishers.

DAVID MALOUF "This Day under My Hand", "Glasshouse Mountains" from *Bicycle*, 1970; "Off the Map", "An Ordinary Evening at Hamilton" from *Neighbours in a Thicket*, 1974. Both published by University of Queensland Press: courtesy of University of Queensland Press. "Decade's End" from *Selected Poems*, Angus & Robertson, 1981: courtesy of Angus & Robertson Publishers.

JOHN MANIFOLD "The Tomb of Lt. John Learmonth, A.I.F.", "The Bunyip and the Whistling Kettle", "Stringybark Creek", "The Map", "Outer Suburbs", "Bogong Jack and the Trooper", "The Stranger" from *Collected Verse*, University of Queensland Press, 1978: courtesy of University of Queensland Press.

ALAN MARSHALL *Wild Red Horses*, *Singing to God* from *Wild Red Horses*, Thomas Nelson, 1976: courtesy of Curtis Brown (Aust.) Pty Ltd Sydney.

DAVID MARTIN "Bush Christmas", "The Other Map", "A Supplication in the Bush", "A Girl Rode into Goulburn" from *Poems 1938-1958*, Edwards & Shaw, 1958: courtesy of David Martin.

JOHN MORRISON *The Incense-burner*, *Morning Glory*, *Dog-box* from *North Wind*, Penguin, 1982: courtesy of John Morrison and Penguin Books Australia Limited.

R. H. MORRISON "Memento", "Timber Town" from *Opus 4*, Hawthorn Press, 1971: courtesy of R. H. Morrison.

IAN MUDIE "Street Vision", "Galah", "The Crab or the Tree", "The Blue Crane" from *The Jindyworobaks: Portable Australian Authors*, University of Queensland Press, 1979: courtesy of Mrs R. Mudie.

LES A. MURRAY "Sydney and the Bush", "An Absolutely Ordinary Rainbow", "The Ballad of Jimmy Governor", "The House of Four-X" from *Selected Poems: The Vernacular*

Republic, 1976; "Flowering Eucalypt in Autumn" from *The People's Otherworld*, 1983; "The Buladelah-Taree Holiday Song Cycle" from *Ethnic Radio*, 1977. All published by Angus & Robertson: courtesy of Angus & Robertson Publishers.

DESMOND O'GRADY *Life, Debts and Miracles of F.X. Horgan* from *Valid for all Countries*, University of Queensland Press, 1979: courtesy of Desmondy O'Grady.

HAL PORTER *At the Galahad, Fiend and Friend, Country Town* from *A Bachelor's Children: Short Stories*, 1962; *Party Forty-two and Mrs Brewer* from *The Cats of Venice*, 1965; *Brett* from *Fredo Fuss Love Life: Short Stories*, 1974; "Mountain Farm", "Cocky Farmer" from *Elijah's Ravens: Poems*, 1968. All published by Angus & Robertson: courtesy of Angus & Robertson Publishers. *The Clairvoyant Goat* from *The Clairvoyant Goat and Other Stories*, 1981; "In an Australian Country Graveyard", "Behind that Sun-splashed Tourist Poster" from *In an Australian Country Graveyard and Other Poems*, 1974. Both published by Nelson: courtesy of Thomas Nelson Australia.

PETER PORTER "Phar Lap in the Melbourne Museum" from *Collected Poems*, Oxford University Press, 1983, © Peter Porter: courtesy of Oxford University Press.

ELIZABETH RIDDELL "Carnival in the Park", "Suburban Song" from *Forbears*, Angus & Robertson, 1961: courtesy of Angus & Robertson Publishers.

ROLAND ROBINSON "Waratah", "Ma-poor-am", "Altjeringa", "Bees" from *Deep Well*, Edwards & Shaw, 1962: courtesy of Roland Robinson.

ERIC C. ROLLS "The Ballad of the Old Captain" from *Sheaf Tosser and Other Poems*, Angus & Robertson, 1967: courtesy of Angus & Robertson Publishers.

J. R. ROWLAND from "At Noosa" from *The Feast of Ancestors: Poems*, Angus & Robertson, 1965: courtesy of Angus & Robertson Publishers. "Revisiting New England" from *Times and Places: Poems of Locality*, Brindabella Press, 1975: courtesy of J. R. Rowland.

E. O. SCHLUNKE *The Enthusiastic Prisoner, The Man Who Liked Music* from *The Man in the Silo and Other Stories*, 1955; *First Flight, The Garden of Dreams* from *The Village Hampden: Stories*, 1958. Both published by Angus & Robertson: courtesy of Angus & Robertson Publishers.

R. A. SIMPSON "The Departure of Governor Macquarie", "Bystander: Anzac Day", "Discoveries" from *Selected Poems*, University of Queensland Press, 1981: courtesy of University of Queensland Press.

KENNETH SLESSOR "Five Visions of Captain Cook", "Nuremberg", "Waters", "Crow Country", "Talbingo", "Wild Grapes", "Country Towns", "Winter Dawn", "City Nightfall", "The Night-ride", from "The Old Play", "The Knife", "North Country", "South Country", "Last Trams", "William Street", "Five Bells", "Beach Burial" from *Selected Poems*, Angus & Robertson, 1975: courtesy of Angus & Robertson Publishers.

VIVIAN SMITH "For My Daughter", "Still Life", "Tasmania", "Early Arrival: Sydney", "Late April: Hobart", "At an Exhibition of Historical Paintings, Hobart", "The Restorers" from *Tide Country*, Angus & Robertson, 1982: courtesy of Angus & Robertson Publishers.

DOUGLAS STEWART "Nodding Greenhood", "Terra Australis", "Mosquito Orchid", "The Snow-gum", "The Fierce Country", "Marree", "The Humorists", "Ruins", "Place Names", "Night Camp", "The Branding Fire", "The Silkworms", "The Blacktracker's Story", "B Flat", "Arthur Stace", "For Kenneth Slessor", "Cave Painting" from *Selected Poems*, Angus & Robertson, 1973: courtesy of Angus & Robertson Publishers.

DAL STIVENS *Warrigal* from *Selected Stories 1936-1968*, Angus & Robertson, 1969: courtesy of Curtis Brown (Aust.) Pty Ltd Sydney.

RANDOLPH STOW "The Ghost at Anlaby", "The Land's Meaning", "Dust", "The Singing Bones", "Landscapes" from *Selected Poems: A Counterfeit Silence*, Angus & Robertson, 1969: courtesy of Richard Scott Simon Ltd London.

COLIN THIELE "Silent Sam", "Murray Mouth" from *Selected Verse*, Rigby, 1970: courtesy of Rigby Publishers.

JOHN THOMPSON "Married Quarrel" from *Thirty Poems*, Edwards & Shaw, 1954: courtesy of Mrs Patricia Thompson.

KATH WALKER "Tree Grave", "The Child Wife", "Ballad of the Totems", "Understand, Old One" from *My People: A Kath Walker Collection*, Jacaranda Press, 1970: courtesy of Jacaranda Wiley.

CHRIS WALLACE-CRABBE "Melbourne", "Terra Australis", "December" from *Selected Poems*, Angus & Robertson, 1973: courtesy of Angus & Robertson Publishers.

JUDAH WATEN *Neighbours* from *Alien Son*, Angus & Robertson, 1952: courtesy of Angus & Robertson Publishers.

FRANCIS WEBB "Cap and Bells", from "Disaster Bay", "Bells of St Peter Mancroft", "For My Grandfather", "End of the Picnic", "A Tip for Saturday", "Five Days Old" from *Collected Poems*, Angus & Robertson, 1977: courtesy of Angus & Robertson Publishers.

PATRICK WHITE *Miss Slattery and Her Demon Lover* from *The Burnt Ones*, Penguin, 1968; *Five-Twenty* from *The Cockatoos: Shorter Novels and Short Stories*, Penguin, 1978. Both stories courtesy of Curtis Brown (Aust.) Pty Ltd Sydney.

JUDITH WRIGHT "Bora Ring", "Bullocky", "South of My Days", "Woman to Man", "The Cycads", "Request to a Year", "At Cooloola", "The Old Prison", "Gum Trees Stripping", "Train Journey", "Wonga Vine", "Night Herons", "The Graves at Mill Point", "A Document", "The Forest" from *Collected Poems 1942-1970*, 1971; "Counting in Sevens" from *Fourth Quarter and Other Poems*, 1976. Both published by Angus & Robertson: courtesy of Angus & Robertson Publishers.

Plates

CHARLES BLACKMAN *Suite of Paintings* 1960, oil and enamel on masonite 121.5 × 183 cm, A. R. Ragless bequest fund 1969, Art Gallery of South Australia.

ARTHUR BOYD *The Mining Town* 1946–47, oil, tempera on composition board 82.7 × 109.2 cm, Australian National Gallery.

ARTHUR BOYD *Wimmera Landscape* c.1960–63, tempera on hardboard 91.3 × 121.3 cm, presented by Godfrey Phillips International Pty Ltd 1968, National Gallery of Victoria.

MERRIC BOYD *Storm* 1948, crayon, conté and wash on paper 27.6 × 37.5 cm, Caltex acquisition 1971, Ballarat Fine Art Gallery, Ballarat City Council.

JOHN BRACK *Collins Street, 5pm* 1955, oil on canvas 114.6 × 162.9 cm, purchased 1956, National Gallery of Victoria.

JOHNNY BULU BULUN *Magpie, Geese and Water Lilies at the Waterhole*, bark painting, Collection Northern Territory Museum of Arts and Sciences.

NOEL COUNIHAN *Pub Talk* 1962, oil on composition board 91.5 × 137.2 cm, Queensland Art Gallery.

RAY CROOKE *Sunrise, Albion Hotel, Normanton* 1962, oil over tempera on composition board 76.5 × 121.7 cm, Queensland Art Gallery.

ROY DE MAISTRE *Carol Singers* 1943, oil on board 94 × 73.8 cm, gift of Patrick White 1974, Art Gallery of New South Wales.

BOB DICKERSON *The Tired Man* c.1956, synthetic enamel on hardboard 137.1 × 153.7 cm, purchased 1957, National Gallery of Victoria.

WILLIAM DOBELL *Billy Boy* 1943, oil on cardboard on hardboard 70.2 × 53.4 cm, Australian War Memorial (30245).

RUSSELL DRYSDALE *Moody's Pub* 1941, oil on wood panel 50.8 × 61.6 cm, purchased 1942, National Gallery of Victoria.

RUSSELL DRYSDALE *Landscape with Figures*, c.1972, oil on canvas 76 × 127 cm, Robert Holmes à Court Collection.

IAN FAIRWEATHER *Alligator Creek, Cairns* 1939, oil and gouache on cardboard 50.2 × 51.2 cm, private collection Melbourne.

LEONARD FRENCH *Autumn in the Garden* 1960, duco, enamel, gold leaf on hessian, mounted on composition board (masonite) 138.2 × 122.5 cm, Queensland Art Gallery.

DONALD FRIEND *Explorers Surprising a Rare Bird* 1963, acrylic with gold leaf on masonite 44 × 32 cm, Leslie Walford Collection.

SALI HERMAN *Reconstruction* 1950, oil on canvas 40.5 × 60.5 cm, South Australian Government Grant 1952, Art Gallery of South Australia.

FRANK HODGKINSON *Paperbark Swamp, Arnhem Land* 1978, gouache on wove paper 55.7 × 75.7 cm, Queensland Art Gallery.

ROBERT JUNIPER *Green Mount Hill* 1969, oil on canvas 150 × 167 cm, National Australia Bank Collection of Modern Art in the Seventies.

ALBERT NAMATJIRA *The Ghost Gum* c.1949, watercolour 36.4 × 26.2 cm, purchased 1950, Bendigo Art Gallery.

SIDNEY NOLAN *Glenrowan* 1947, from the Ned Kelly paintings 1946–47, enamel on composition board 90.4 × 121.2 cm, gift of Sunday Reed 1977, Australian National Gallery.

JOHN OLSEN *Salute to Slessor's Five Bells* 1972–73 (section of mural), acrylics on marine ply 21 × 3 m (approx), commissioned by Sir William Dobell Foundation especially for its site, northern foyer, Sydney Opera House, Concert Hall.

DESIDERIUS ORBAN *South Coast Timberland* 1948, pastel on paper 50.2 × 65.1 cm, purchased 1952, Art Gallery of New South Wales.

JOHN PERCEVAL *Tugboat in a Boat* 1956, synthetic enamel and tempera on hardboard 121.9 × 73.7 cm, purchased 1956, National Gallery of Victoria.

JOHN PERCEVAL *Two Gums — Homage to Buvelot* 1960, oil on board 107.5 × 83.2 cm, purchased 1960, gift of A.N.Z. Bank, Ballarat Fine Art Gallery, Ballarat City Council.

MARGARET PRESTON *Drought — Mirage Country* 1946, monotype on thin laid oriental paper 30.5 × 40.6 cm (comp.), Queensland Art Gallery.

CLIFTON PUGH *Territorial Imperative* 1979, oil on hardboard 90 × 120.7 cm, National Australia Bank Collection of Modern Art in the Seventies.

LLOYD REES *The Silent Bush* 1939, oil on canvas 62 × 77.5 cm, Morgan Thomas bequest fund 1939, Art Gallery of South Australia.

LLOYD REES *Sydney Harbour — Lane Cove River* 1978–79, oil on canvas mounted on board 73 × 87.5 cm, National Australia Bank Collection of Modern Art in the Seventies.

JEFFREY SMART *Cahill Expressway* 1962, oil on plywood 81.2 × 111.7 cm, purchased 1963, National Gallery of Victoria.

JACK CARINGTON SMITH *Foreshore, Simpson's Bay, Bruni Island* 1954, watercolour 28.6 × 38.2 cm, photographer Robert Irison, The University of Melbourne Art Collection.

GRACE COSSINGTON SMITH *The Bridge in Curve* 1930, tempera on composition board 83.8 × 111.8 cm, presented by the National Gallery Society of Victoria 1967, National Gallery of Victoria.

DAVID STRACHAN *Landscape, Hill End* 1961, oil on canvas 65.5 × 81.3 cm, purchased 1962, Art Gallery of New South Wales.

ERIC THAKE *The Week¹y Train Departs, the Dog Goes Back to Sleep* 1971, oil on canvas 60 × 34.5 cm, National Australia Bank Collection of Modern Art in the Seventies.

ALBERT TUCKER *Gippsland Explorer* 1963, oil on composition board 121.4 × 154 cm, Queensland Art Gallery.

ROLAND WAKELIN *Black Mountain, Canberra* 1944, oil on cardboard panel 59.5 × 68.5 cm, purchased 1946, National Gallery of Victoria.

BRETT WHITELEY *Big Orange (Sunset)* 1974, oil on wood 244 × 305.5 cm, gift of Patrick White 1975, Art Gallery of New South Wales.

FRED WILLIAMS *The Half Round Pond* c.1959, oil on composition board 103.2 × 72 cm, Australian National Gallery.

FRED WILLIAMS *Landscape with Goose* 1974, oil on canvas 183.5 × 152.7 cm, Australian National Gallery.

W. BLAMIRE YOUNG *Shadows of a Great City* c.1930, watercolour on paper 45 × 64 cm, gift of the Friends of the S. H. Ervin Gallery 1983, S. H. Ervin Gallery.

Black and White Illustrations

p.2 illust. by Raymond Lindsay, *Trio*, A Book of Poems by Kenneth Slessor, Harley Mathews and Colin Simpson, the Sunnybrook Press 1931: Rare Books, Fisher Library, Univ. of Sydney; p.7 illust. by Norman Lindsay, *Cuckooz Contrey* by Kenneth Slessor, Frank C. Johnson 1932; Curtis Brown (Aust.) Pty Limited; p.16 illust. by Douglas Annand, *The Home Annual* 1 Oct. 1936: Mitchell Library, State Library of NSW; pp.20 & 23 illust. by Norman Lindsay, *Five Bells: Poems by Kenneth Slessor*, Frank C. Johnson 1939: Curtis Brown (Aust.) Pty Limited; p.24 illust. by Russell Drysdale, *The Australian Soldier: A Portrait by John Hetherington*, F. H. Johnston Publishing Company: Fisher Library, Univ. of Sydney; p.82 illust. by Noel Counihan, *The Complete Stories of Alan Marshall*, published by Nelson in association with Lloyd O'Neil 1976: Fisher Library, Univ. of Sydney; p.96 illust. by Margaret Horder, *Songs for all Seasons: 100 Poems for Young People* chosen by Rosemary Dobson, Angus & Robertson Publishers 1964: Fisher Library, Univ. of Sydney; p.135 illust. by Annette Macarthur-Onslow, *Birds: Poems by Judith Wright*, Angus & Robertston Publishers 1967: Fisher Library, Univ. of Sydney; p.187 illust. by staff artist, *Silence into Song: An Anthology of Australian Verse* compiled by Clifford O'Brien, Rigby Limited 1968: Fisher Library, Univ. of Sydney; p.201 illust. by Frank P. Mahony, *Commonwealth Annual*: Rare Books, Fisher Library, Univ. of Sydney, pp.225, 237 & 242 illust. by Arthur Boyd, *The Drifting Continent and Other Poems* by A. D. Hope, Brindabella Press 1979: Rare Books, Fisher Library, Univ. of Sydney; p.263 illust. by Unk White, *Bulletin* 17 Sept 1952: Fisher Library, Univ. of Sydney; p.275 illust. by Unk White, *Bulletin* 26 Oct. 1955: Fisher Library, Univ. of Sydney; pp.276 & 279 illust. by Norman Lindsay, *Sun Orchids And Other Poems* by Douglas Stewart, Angus & Robertson Publishers 1952: Curtis Brown (Aust.) Pty Limited; pp.281, 283 & 284 illust. by Norman Lindsay, *Bulletin* 22 Oct. 1952: Curtis Brown (Aust.) Pty Limited; p.372 illust. by Unk White, *Bulletin* 30 Dec. 1959: Fisher Library, Univ. of Sydney; pp.386 & 387 illust. by Hal Porter, *In an Australian Country Graveyard*, Thomas Nelson (Australia) 1974: Fisher Library, Univ. of Sydney; p.424 illust. by Claire Simpson, *A Beachcomber's Diary* by John Blight, Angus & Robertson Publishers 1963: Fisher Library, Univ. of Sydney; p.462 illust. by Patricia Giles, *A World of Its Own: Poems by James McAuley*, Australian National University Press 1977: Fisher Library, Univ. of Sydney; p.468 illust. by Margaret Horder, *Songs For All Seasons: 100 Poems for Young People* chosen by Rosemary Dobson, Angus & Robertson Publishers 1964: Fisher Library, Univ. of Sydney; p.479 illust. by Patricia Giles, *A World of Its Own: Poems by James McAuley*, Australian National University Press 1977: Fisher Library, Univ. of Sydney; p.517 illust. by William Huff-Johnston, *Starting From Central Station: A sequence of Poems by David Campbell*, Brindabella Press, Canberra 1973: Rare Books, Fisher Library, Univ. of Sydney; p.524 illust. by staff artist, *The Swagman's Note Book*, United Press 1943: Rare Books, Fisher Library, Univ. of Sydney; pp.550, 551 & 552 illust. by Mollie Horseman, *My People: A Kath Walker Collection*, Jacaranda Press 1970: Fisher Library, Univ. of Sydney; p.621 & 622 illust. by Brian Dean, *Times And Seasons: An Introduction to Bruce Dawe*, Cheshire Publishing, Melbourne 1974: Fisher Library, Univ. of Sydney.

Indexes

Index of Authors

Index of Artists

Index of Plates

Index of Titles

Index of First Lines of Poems